Mathematics for a Modern World

Book 3, Third Edition

Authors
E.G. Carli
K.E. Newton
J.S. Telfer

General Editor
John J. Del Grande

 EDUCATIONAL PUBLISHING COMPANY
A DIVISION OF CANADA PUBLISHING CORPORATION
TORONTO ONTARIO CANADA

Written, printed, and bound in Canada

ISBN 0-7715-3623-2

    3 4 5 BP 89 88 87

Metric Office has granted use of the National Symbol
for Metric Conversion.

Photo Credits: Canadian National Railways: pp. 44, 131,
426; Canapress: p. 20; Glenbow Photograph (Calgary,
Alberta): p. 397; IBM Corporation: p. 87; Gail Kenney:
37, 263, 273; Miller Services: pp. 1, 6, 19, 23, 42, 69,
80, 81, 157, 193, 205, 258, 278, 301, 308, 310, 354,
379; NFB Phototheque ONF: pp. 225 (photo by
Thomas Kitchin), 293 (photo by Chris Lund, 1965),
321 (photo by N. Hallendy, 1965), 333 (photo by
George Hunter, 1978), 343 (photo by H. Taylor, 1963),
367 (photo by Pierre Gaudard, 1965); Government of
British Columbia: p. 113; Transport Canada: p. 100.

Portions of the TD1 form, T4 slips, and the Ontario
tax return form in Units 9 and 10 are reproduced by
permission of the Department of National Revenue
and Taxation.

Cover Photograph: Photograph reproduced by
permission of Hans Blohm/Masterfile.

Design: Many Pens Design

Illustration: Loris Lesynski

Technical: Acorn Technical Art

Typesetting: Trigraph Inc.

Consultants

Kenneth L. Banks
Dr. L.B. MacNaughton High School
Moncton, New Brunswick

Donald Frewing
Edward Milne Secondary School
Sooke, British Columbia

Corinne McCabe
Spruce Grove Composite High School
County of Parkland
Spruce Grove, Alberta

ii

Contents

Introduction

Mathematics for a Modern World, Third Edition, has been completely rewritten to suit the changing needs of students, while reflecting the latest thinking of mathematics educators. Significant new material, a new format, and a new overall design have been incorporated with the best features of the previous edition.

The open page format makes the text easy to read.

Short sections give a gradual topic development for better acquisition and retention of material.

Relevant applications are presented throughout the text.

Exercise pages contain a variety of questions for topic reinforcement and application of concepts.

The general organization of the book makes it easy to use and provides a focus for the work being presented.

Text Organization

- The text is divided into 21 units
- The units are grouped into three main parts, each one including topics in Number Applications, Algebra, and Geometry
- A summary of the key points is presented at the end of each main part
- Cumulative review questions are given at the end of each summary
- Special feature pages—including computers, consumer awareness, and mathematics applications pages—are distributed throughout the text
- Side trips provide thought-provoking puzzles or problems
- Activities are included, where appropriate, to provide concrete experience with geometric shapes
- Projects related to the unit topic extend the learning experience to sources outside the text

Unit Organization

- Each unit has several topics
- Each topic is presented in a short section, with several examples provided
- The symbol $\boxed{\$}$ indicates a section that teaches you skills to become an informed consumer
- The symbol $\boxed{?}$ indicates a section that illustrates technological applications
- Main concepts or rules are shown in boxes
- Color is used to highlight main ideas
- Italics are used to show emphasis
- Mathematical terms are shown in boldface type when they are first used
- Exercises directly related to the topic are provided for each section
- Type A exercise questions can be answered orally and discussed in class
- Type B exercise questions provide written reinforcement of material taught
- Answers to B exercises are given at the back of the text

Unit 1

Math Skills You Need

Taking Off ⓢ

Mathematics is all around you. Taking a flight across Canada presents many problems that mathematics can help you to solve. Here is a schedule of Air Canada flights leaving Vancouver for Halifax.

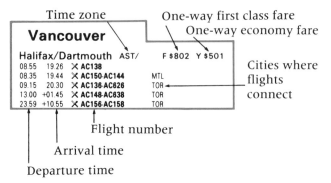

If you were travelling across Canada, you would need to know the time in different time zones. The map shows the time zones of Canada.

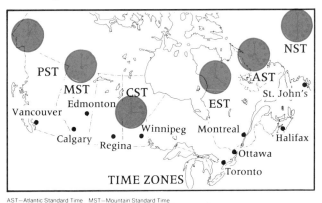

TIME ZONES

AST—Atlantic Standard Time   MST—Mountain Standard Time
CST—Central Standard Time   NST—Newfoundland Standard Time
EST—Eastern Standard Time   PST—Pacific Standard Time

If it is 19:15 in Toronto, find the time in Vancouver.

The clock faces on the map indicate that it is 3 h earlier in Vancouver. Subtract 3 h from Toronto time to find the time in Vancouver.

Vancouver time = 19:15 − 03:00
$$= 16:15$$

The Vancouver time is 16:15.

Here is a partial listing of flights leaving Ottawa for various Canadian cities.

Ottawa/Hull					
	St. John's, Nfld/T.-N. NST/		F $358 Y $224		
	08.15 13.33 ✕ AC616·AC158	HFX			
	09.50 15.45 ✕ AC742·AC743	MTL			
	09.50 15.45 ✕ AC480·AC606	MTL			
	17.00 22.18 ✕ AC138·AC144	HFX			
Vancouver PST/ F $656 Y $410	Regina/Moose Jaw CST/		F $446 Y $279		
09.00 12.08 ✕ AC113	18.30 22.22 ✕ AC153				
10.00 16.18 ✕ AC167	06.20 11.52 ✕ AC441·AC107	TOR			
19.25 21.33 ✕ AC139	07.30 11.52 ✕ AC189·AC107	TOR			
07.30 11.25 ✕ AC189·AC105	TOR	07.30 11.52 ✕ AC189·AC107	TOR		
12.30 16.40 ✕ AC453·AC147	TOR	07.30 12.05 ✕ AC189·AC107	TOR		
15.15 19.45 ✕ AC179·AC247	WPG	10.00 17.45 ✕ AC167·AC293	WPG		
16.30 20.25 ✕ AC461·AC149	TOR				
17.15 21.40 ✕ AC655·AC151	TOR	Winnipeg CST/		F $363 Y $227	
	07.30 10.36 ✕ AC189				
Halifax/Dartmouth AST/ F $248 Y $155	07.55 11.10 ✕ AC161				
08.15 10.43 ✕ AC616	10.00 13.48 ✕ AC167				
12.35 16.09 ✕ AC174	15.15 16.55 ✕ AC179				
17.00 19.26 ✕ AC138	18.20 20.06 ✕ AC181				
17.50 21.45 ✕ AC160	06.20 10.38 ✕ AC441·AC189	TOR			
	17.15 21.18 ✕ AC655·AC197	TOR			
Calgary/Banff MST/ F $550 Y $344	18.30 22.23 ✕ AC153·AC199	TOR			
09.00 11.12 ✕ AC113	18.30 +00.11 ✕ AC153·AC199	TOR			
10.00 15.26 ✕ AC167					
15.15 18.25 ✕ AC179	Zürich GMT+1/TU+1				
12.30 16.35 ✕ AC453·AC121	TOR	18.30 +09.20 ✕ HF306·AC878	MTL	4.5	
16.30 20.10 ✕ AC461·AC145	TOR	18.30 +09.30 HF306·SR135	MTL	2.6.7	
17.15 21.45 ✕ AC655·AC141	TOR	18.30 +10.20 ✕ HF306·AC878	MTL	4.5	29.03
17.30 21.42 ✕ AC463·AC141	TOR	18.30 +10.30 HF306·SR135	MTL	1.2.6.7	24.03

You can use the time zones and airline flight times to find the time in the air for a given flight.

Find the flying time for flight AC179 that leaves Ottawa for Calgary at 15:15.

Arrival time in Calgary is in Mountain Standard Time (MST), while departure time from Ottawa is in Eastern Standard Time (EST). Express the arrival time in EST.

Since Ottawa is further east, *add* 2 h to 18:25. The arrival time is 20:25 (EST).

Subtract to find the flight time.
$$20:25 − 15:15 = 5:10$$

Flight AC179 takes 5 h 10 min to travel from Ottawa to Calgary.

2

Exercise

A 1. Given the following times, find the time in Montreal.

(a) 06:15 in Winnipeg, Manitoba
(b) 17:20 in Sydney, Nova Scotia
(c) 01:10 in Calgary, Alberta
(d) 23:50 in St. John's, Newfoundland

B Use the schedules on page 2 to answer Questions 2 to 4.

2. Find the time needed for a flight from Ottawa to each of the following cities.

(a) flight AC113 to Vancouver
(b) flight AC160 to Halifax
(c) flight AC616 to St. John's
(d) flight AC113 to Calgary

3. A flight is booked between Ottawa and Regina.

(a) How much would you save by buying a one-way economy ticket instead of a one-way first class ticket?

(b) The price of a round-trip ticket is 25% less than 2 one-way tickets. Find how much you would save by buying an economy round-trip ticket instead of 2 one-way economy tickets.

(c) Children between 2 and 11 travel for half the normal fare. Find the total fare for 2 children, aged 9 and 12, if one-way first class tickets are being bought.

(d) Find the total flying time for AC153.

(e) Find the total flying time for AC441.

(f) What is the reason for the difference in your answers to parts (d) and (e)?

4. Flight AC179 from Ottawa to Vancouver touches down in Winnipeg. Below is the schedule of flights departing Winnipeg for Vancouver.

Winnipeg	Vancouver PST/		F $392 Y $245
	08.10	09.57 ✕ AC289	
	11.40	13.31 ✕ AC183	
	14.25	16.18 ✕ AC167	
	14.50	15.50 ✕ AC245	
	16.35	19.18 ✕ AC217	
	18.45	19.45 ✕ AC247	
	07.05	09.18 ✕ AC251-AC203	CAL
	17.10	19.28 ✕ AC833-AC231	EDM

(a) Using the previous schedules, find the total flying time from Ottawa to Winnipeg for flight AC179.

(b) In Winnipeg you must board the next plane for Vancouver. What is the flight number for the next plane?

(c) How long is the stopover in Winnipeg?

(d) What is the total flying time from Winnipeg to Vancouver?

5. A direct flight between Edmonton and Toronto is approximately 4 h long. Find the local arrival time, given each of the following departure times.

(a) 08:00 departure from Toronto
(b) 17:20 departure from Edmonton

6. Shown below are the direct flights from Vancouver to Toronto, and Toronto to Vancouver.

Vancouver to		Toronto to	
Toronto EST/	F $622 Y $389	Vancouver PST/	F $622 Y $389
09.15 16.25 ✕ AC136		09.35 11.25 ✕ AC105	
13.00 20.12 ✕ AC148		14.50 16.40 ✕ AC147	
15.00 22.12 ✕ AC152		18.35 20.25 ✕ AC149	
23.59 +07.11 ✕ AC156		19.50 21.40 ✕ AC151	

(a) Which is the fastest flying time from Vancouver to Toronto?

(b) Which is the fastest flying time from Toronto to Vancouver?

(c) What are some possible reasons for the differences in flying times?

3

Evaluating Numerical Expressions

When you receive your bill at a restaurant, you want to be sure that the calculations were done correctly.

DAVE'S DELI	
CUSTOMER ORDERS	
2 corned beef @ 4.19	8.38
2 special @ $3.59	7.18
4 large milk (.95)	3.80
SUBTOTAL	19.36
10% TAX	1.94
TOTAL	21.30

The bill was calculated by multiplying first and then adding.

The **BEDMAS** rule can help you remember the correct order of operations.

B	rackets
E	xponents
D	ivision
M	ultiplication
A	ddition
S	ubtraction

$40 - 36 \div 3^2 \times (8 \div 2) + 1$ Brackets

$= 40 - 36 \div 3^2 \times 4 + 1$ Exponents

$= 40 - 36 \div 9 \times 4 + 1$ Division and Multiplication in order as they appear

$= 40 - 4 \times 4 + 1$

$= 40 - 16 + 1$

$= 24 + 1$ Addition and Subtraction
$= 25$ in order as they appear

Many numerical expressions that you encounter will contain integers.

Example 1

Evaluate using **BEDMAS**.
$-24 \div 4 \times (-2) - 5(-3 - 1)^2$

$$= -24 \div 4 \times (-2) - 5(-4)^2$$
$$= -6 \times (-2) - 5(16)$$
$$= 12 - 80$$
$$= -68$$

Many applications will require a good understanding of decimals.

Example 2

Evaluate.
$$\frac{0.052 \div 0.01 + 1200 \div 100}{0.002 \times 40}$$
$$= \frac{5.2 + 12}{0.08}$$
$$= \frac{17.2}{0.08}$$
$$= 215$$

Exercise

A **1.** State the value of each expression.

(a) $25 - 15 + 6$ (f) 4×3^2
(b) $24 - 4 \times 3$ (g) $(4 \times 3)^2$
(c) $100 \div 2(5)$ (h) $(6 + 2)(3 + 4)$
(d) $5 \times 12 - 4 \div 4$ (i) $6 + 2(3 + 4)$
(e) $5 \times (12 - 4) \div 4$ (j) $5[5 + 5(5)]$

2. State the value of each integer expression.

(a) $-8 + 3$ (f) $8 - 15 - (-1)$
(b) $-8 - 3$ (g) $-6 - 8 + 20$
(c) $-7 - 6 - 4$ (h) $-2 - 9 + 11$
(d) $21 - (-4)$ (i) $-(-3) - 3$
(e) $-6 - (-4) - 1$ (j) $12 - (5 - 9)$

3. State the value of each.

(a) $9 \times (-4)$ (h) $\frac{-12}{2} - \frac{-60}{-6}$
(b) $(-15) \times (-2)$ (i) 1.5×1000
(c) $-84 \div (-7)$ (j) $1.5 \div 10\ 000$
(d) $-40 \div 10$ (k) 1.5×0.0001
(e) $36 \div (-6) \div 2$ (l) $1.5 \div 0.01$
(f) $5 \times (-2) \times (-3)$ (m) $0.48 \div 0.001$
(g) $24 \div (-6)(-2)$ (n) $\frac{45}{-9} \times \frac{-36}{4}$

B 4. Evaluate.

(a) $3.5 + 0.35 + 35$ (f) 12×0.2
(b) $8.23 + 47 \times 0.3$ (g) 0.12×2
(c) 13.45×0.001 (h) $0.12 \div 2$
(d) $34.7 \div 0.01$ (i) $12 \div 0.2$
(e) $0.075 \div 0.000\,01$ (j) $0.12 \div 0.2$

5. Evaluate using **BEDMAS**.

(a) $(24 + 8) \div (4 \times 2)$
(b) $(24 + 8) \div 4 \times 2$
(c) $24 + 8 \div 4 \times 2$
(d) $60 \div (8 - 2) \div (4 - 3 + 1)$
(e) $5 + 3(16 - 4 + 2)$
(f) $(6^2 - 4^2) \div (6 - 4)^2$
(g) $5 \times 4^2 + (5 \times 4)^2$
(h) $3 + 3[3 + 3(3 + 3)]$
(i) $240 \div 20(8 - 7 + 1)$
(j) $\dfrac{6^2 - 6(2)}{2 + 8 \div 2} + \dfrac{24 + 8}{24 - 8}$
(k) $\dfrac{(8 \div 2 + 2 \times 3)[3 + 4(3)]}{(8 \div 4 + 1)(48 \div 12 \div 2)}$

6. Evaluate each of the following.

(a) $(-8 - 16) \div (-2 + 6)$
(b) $-8 - 16 \div (-2 + 6)$
(c) $-10[-4(-7) + 2(-6)]$
(d) $(-16) \div 2(-4) + (-5)(-3)$
(e) $-6 + 2(-10 - 6 + 4)$
(f) $3(-2) - 6(7) + (-9)(-1)$
(g) $3 \times (-4)^2 \div (-8)$
(h) $(-55) \div 5 - 8(-4)$
(i) $7[-12 \div 3 + 3(3 - 11) \div (2 - 6)]$
(j) $\dfrac{27 - 9}{27 \div (-9)} + \dfrac{-8 - 4(10)}{-8 \div 4 - 10}$
(k) $\dfrac{16 - 4(-3)}{-10 - 3 - 1} - \dfrac{(16 - 4)(-3)}{-10 - (3 - 1)}$
(l) $[12 - (-3) - 3(-8)][-4 + 2(-3)]$
(m) $(-3 - 2 + 1)[24 - (-12) - 2]$

7. In a figure-skating competition, a skater's final score is calculated by a *place standing* composed of:
- compulsory figures (C in the table);
- short program (S);
- long program (L).

The skater's score is calculated as shown, and the skater with the *lowest* score is the winner.

$$\begin{array}{l} C \times 0.6 \\ S \times 0.4 \\ + L \times 1.0 \\ \hline \text{Score} \end{array}$$

The following table shows the place standings of the best skaters at a competition. The first calculation is done for you. Copy and complete the table to find the winner.

Skater	C	S	L	Score
Lee	5th	16th	6th	$5(0.6) + 16(0.4) + 6$ $= 15.4$
Ann	10th	2nd	12th	
John	1st	9th	8th	
Sue	8th	11th	4th	
Dan	15th	4th	3rd	
Deb	8th	7th	6th	
Andy	2nd	18th	1st	

8. Use **BEDMAS** to evaluate.

(a) $9.2(16.1 - 13.46)$
(b) $(3.2 - 21 \times 0.1)(0.88 \div 0.4 \div 0.2)$
(c) $0.01(13.44 - 8.62 + 1.33)$
(d) $(12 \div 0.02 + 58 \div 0.02) \times 0.03$
(e) $\dfrac{0.055 - 0.007 + 1.02}{16.4 \div 4 - 0.1}$

Positive and Negative Fractions

Follow the rules below to evaluate fractional expressions correctly.

1. To add or subtract fractions, you must have a common denominator.
2. To multiply fractions, multiply the numerators and denominators separately. Change mixed numbers to improper fractions first.
3. To divide fractions, invert the divisor and multiply. Change mixed numbers to improper fractions first.

Stock brokers work with positive and negative fractions every day.

The table shows how stocks are listed in the daily papers.

Stock	High	Low	Close	Change	Volume
PQR Mines	$54\frac{1}{8}$	$52\frac{3}{4}$	$53\frac{1}{2}$	$-\frac{3}{4}$	3100
X-Oil	$12\frac{1}{2}$	$11\frac{1}{4}$	$11\frac{3}{4}$	$+\frac{5}{8}$	2200

To find yesterday's closing price, subtract the change in price from today's closing price.

$$\text{Yesterday's Price} = \text{Closing Price} - \text{Change}$$

Example 1

Find yesterday's closing price of PQR Mines.

$$\begin{aligned}\text{Yesterday's Price} &= 53\frac{1}{2} - \left(-\frac{3}{4}\right)\\ &= 53\frac{2}{4} + \frac{3}{4}\\ &= 54\frac{1}{4}\end{aligned}$$

$$\frac{2}{4} + \frac{3}{4} = \frac{5}{4} = 1\frac{1}{4}$$

The closing price yesterday was $54\frac{1}{4}$, or $54.25.

Example 2

Find the profit or loss if 320 shares of X-Oil, originally purchased for $12\frac{1}{8}$, were sold at today's closing price.

$$\begin{aligned}\text{Amount Received} &= 320 \times \$11\frac{3}{4}\\ &= 320 \times \$\frac{47}{4}\\ &= \$3760\end{aligned}$$

$$\begin{aligned}\text{Amount Paid} &= 320 \times \$12\frac{1}{8}\\ &= 320 \times \$\frac{97}{8}\\ &= \$3880\end{aligned}$$

Now subtract the amount paid from the amount received to find the profit or loss of the sale.

Profit or Loss	=	Amount Received	–	Amount Paid

$$= \$3760 - \$3880$$
$$= -\$120$$

The shares of X-Oil are sold at a loss of $120.

You can evaluate numerical expressions involving positive and negative fractions using **BEDMAS**.

Example 3

Use **BEDMAS** to evaluate.

$$\left(-\frac{3}{4} - \frac{7}{10}\right) \div \left(\frac{3}{10} \times 4\frac{1}{6}\right)$$

$$= \left(-\frac{15}{20} - \frac{14}{20}\right) \div \left(\frac{3}{10} \times \frac{25}{6}\right)$$

$$= \left(-\frac{29}{20}\right) \div \frac{5}{4}$$

$$= -\frac{29}{20} \times \frac{4}{5}$$

$$= \frac{-29}{25}$$

$$= -\frac{29}{25}$$

$$= -1\frac{4}{25}$$

Exercise

A 1. State in simplest terms.

(a) $\frac{-4}{8}$ (d) $-\left(\frac{2}{-3}\right)$

(b) $\frac{10}{-15}$ (e) $-\left(\frac{-4}{-2}\right)$

(c) $\frac{-7}{-2}$ (f) $-\left(\frac{-12}{15}\right)$

2. Evaluate.

(a) $\frac{3}{4} - \frac{1}{4}$ (f) $\frac{5}{6} \times 24$

(b) $\frac{5}{8} - \frac{7}{8}$ (g) $\left(-\frac{2}{3}\right) \times \frac{4}{7}$

(c) $-\frac{3}{5} - \frac{2}{5}$ (h) $8 \div \frac{1}{5}$

(d) $-\frac{7}{12} + \frac{1}{12}$ (i) $\frac{1}{5} \div 8$

(e) $\frac{5}{8} - \left(-\frac{7}{8}\right)$ (j) $\left(-\frac{1}{3}\right) \div \left(\frac{1}{2}\right)$

3. True or false?

(a) $\frac{5}{8} - \frac{2}{3} = \frac{3}{5}$

(b) $\frac{2}{3} \times \frac{4}{3} = \frac{8}{3}$

(c) $\frac{3}{4} \div \frac{5}{8} = \frac{3}{4} \times 1\frac{3}{5}$

(d) $2\frac{1}{2} \times 4\frac{1}{3} = 8\frac{1}{6}$

(e) $5\frac{5}{8} - 2\frac{3}{8} = 3\frac{1}{4}$

(f) $6 \times \frac{3}{5} = \frac{18}{30}$

B 4. Evaluate the following.

(a) $-\frac{2}{3} + \frac{1}{2} - \frac{5}{6}$

(b) $-5\frac{1}{2} + 1\frac{1}{3} - \frac{5}{6}$

(c) $-\frac{8}{9} - 1\frac{1}{4} - 2\frac{1}{3}$

(d) $1\frac{1}{3} - (\frac{5}{8} - \frac{1}{12})$

(e) $(-\frac{5}{6} + \frac{1}{8}) - (1\frac{1}{3} - 2\frac{3}{4})$

5. Multiply and divide as indicated.

(a) $2\frac{4}{5} \times (-1\frac{3}{7})$

(b) $-8(2\frac{3}{4})(-\frac{5}{22})$

(c) $\frac{7}{8} \div (-\frac{4}{5}) \div 1\frac{5}{16}$

(d) $-1\frac{5}{9} \div 2\frac{1}{3} \times (-\frac{4}{9})$

(e) $2\frac{6}{7} \div (-10) \div (-1\frac{5}{9})$

(f) $\frac{4}{27} \times (-3\frac{1}{2}) \times 1\frac{4}{5} \div 2\frac{4}{5}$

6.

Stock	High	Low	Close	Change
WXY Ltd.	$9\frac{3}{4}$	$8\frac{5}{8}$	$9\frac{1}{4}$	$-\frac{7}{8}$
SOS Inc.	14	$12\frac{7}{8}$	$13\frac{3}{8}$	$+\frac{3}{4}$

(a) What was yesterday's closing price of WXY Ltd? SOS Inc?

(b) If 500 shares of WXY were purchased at $10\frac{1}{4}$, and sold at today's low price, calculate the profit or loss.

(c) If 480 shares of SOS were purchased at $8\frac{3}{4}$ and sold at today's closing price, calculate the profit or loss.

(d) If 400 shares of WXY were purchased today, how much could be saved by purchasing the shares at the day's lowest price instead of the day's highest price?

7. Use **BEDMAS** to simplify.

(a) $(\frac{5}{6} + \frac{3}{4}) \div (1\frac{1}{3} - \frac{1}{8})$

(b) $\frac{5}{12} - \frac{5}{6} \times \frac{4}{15}$

(c) $-\frac{5}{9} \div (2\frac{1}{2}) + (-\frac{3}{14}) \times 3\frac{1}{2}$

(d) $-\frac{3}{4} + \frac{1}{14}(-\frac{2}{3} - \frac{1}{2})$

(e) $\dfrac{-\frac{2}{5} - \frac{1}{2} + \frac{1}{4}}{\frac{1}{3} + \frac{1}{8} + \frac{1}{12}}$

(f) $-1\frac{1}{3} \div (-\frac{3}{4} \div \frac{2}{3})$

(g) $(-\frac{3}{8} - 1\frac{1}{3} + \frac{3}{4}) \div \frac{5}{12}$

(h) $(-1\frac{3}{4}) \div 14 + (-\frac{1}{15}) \times 1\frac{1}{2}$

(i) $\dfrac{4\frac{1}{2} \times \frac{1}{2} + \frac{3}{5} \times (-\frac{1}{2})}{(-\frac{5}{12})(\frac{14}{15})(1\frac{2}{7})}$

(j) $(-\frac{5}{12} - \frac{4}{9} + \frac{1}{2}) \div (-\frac{4}{9} + \frac{1}{6})$

Percent

Percents are used in many applications.

A percent is a fraction with denominator 100.

$$23\% \text{ is } \tfrac{23}{100}.$$

Many calculations with percent are easier to perform if you express the percent in decimal form.

Example 1

Express in decimal form.

$$27\% = \tfrac{27}{100} \qquad\qquad 9\tfrac{1}{4}\% = \tfrac{9.25}{100}$$
$$\quad\; = 0.27 \qquad\qquad\qquad\quad = 0.0925$$

You can also express percents as fractions.

Example 2

Express each percent as a fraction.

$$35\% = \tfrac{\cancel{35}^{7}}{\cancel{100}_{20}}$$

$$= \tfrac{7}{20} \longleftarrow$$

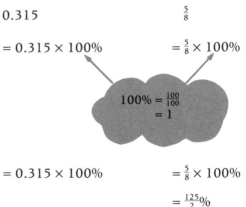
Reduce to lowest terms.

$$2\tfrac{1}{2} = \frac{2\tfrac{1}{2}}{100}$$

$$= \tfrac{\cancel{5}^{1}}{2} \times \tfrac{1}{\cancel{100}_{20}}$$

Invert and multiply.

$$= \tfrac{1}{40}$$

Decimals and fractions can also be converted to percents.

Example 3

Rewrite as percents.

$$0.315 \qquad\qquad\qquad\qquad \tfrac{5}{8}$$

$$= 0.315 \times 100\% \qquad = \tfrac{5}{8} \times 100\%$$

$$100\% = \tfrac{100}{100}$$
$$= 1$$

$$= 0.315 \times 100\% \qquad = \tfrac{5}{8} \times 100\%$$

$$\qquad\qquad\qquad\qquad = \tfrac{125}{2}\%$$

$$= 31.5\% \qquad\qquad\qquad = 62\tfrac{1}{2}\%$$

One of the most common applications of percent involves finding the percent of a number.

Example 4

If sales tax is 7% of the selling price, find the sales tax for an item selling for $12.10.

Sales tax is 7% of $12.10.

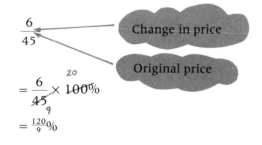

Change percent to decimal.

Sales tax = 0.07 × $12.10
= $0.847

The sales tax is $0.85, rounded to the nearest cent.

Other applications involve finding a percent.

Example 5

A $45 pair of shoes is reduced to a price of $39. What percent of the original price do you save if you buy the shoes on sale?

$$\frac{6}{45}$$

Change in price

Original price

$$= \frac{6}{\overset{9}{45}} \times \overset{20}{100}\%$$

$$= \frac{120}{9}\%$$

$$= 13.\dot{3}\%$$

You would save about 13% buying the shoes on sale.

Exercise

A **1.** State as decimals.

(a) 12%   (c) 250%   (e) $13\frac{1}{2}\%$

(b) 7%   (d) 127%   (f) $7\frac{1}{4}\%$

2. State as fractions.

(a) 37%   (c) 1%   (e) 75%

(b) 40%   (d) 5%   (f) 150%

3. State as percents.

(a) 0.72   (e) $\frac{1}{2}$ (i) $\frac{3}{4}$

(b) 0.05   (f) $\frac{1}{4}$ (j) $\frac{1}{3}$

(c) 1.23   (g) $\frac{4}{5}$ (k) $\frac{2}{3}$

(d) 0.325   (h) $\frac{9}{10}$ (l) $\frac{7}{20}$

B **4.** Rewrite as percents.

(a) 0.38   (h) $\frac{3}{8}$

(b) 0.125   (i) $\frac{15}{16}$

(c) 0.057   (j) $\frac{8}{9}$

(d) 0.005   (k) $\frac{5}{12}$

(e) 1.2   (l) $1\frac{1}{4}$

(f) 3.075   (m) $9\frac{5}{8}$

(g) 0.0125   (n) $11\frac{5}{9}$

5. Rewrite as decimals.

(a) 6%
(b) 9.8%
(c) 72.23%
(d) $35\frac{1}{2}$%
(e) $1\frac{1}{4}$%
(f) 10.05%
(g) 0.6%
(h) 148.2%
(i) $\frac{1}{2}$%
(j) $\frac{3}{4}$%
(k) $12\frac{1}{4}$%
(l) $6\frac{3}{4}$%
(m) 15.7%
(n) $1\frac{3}{4}$%
(o) $16\frac{4}{5}$%

6. Rewrite as fractions.

(a) 25%
(b) 55%
(c) 120%
(d) $33\frac{1}{3}$%
(e) $6\frac{1}{4}$%
(f) $8\frac{1}{3}$%

7. Evaluate each of the following.

(a) 20% of $50
(b) 40% of $75
(c) 3% of $800
(d) 15% of $12
(e) 2.5% of $120
(f) 160% of $80
(g) 12.5% of $30
(h) 0.5% of $60
(i) 8.12% of $3000
(j) $3\frac{1}{4}$% of $36

8. (a) 16 is what percent of 40?
(b) 3 is what percent of 40?
(c) 72 is what percent of 96?
(d) 25 is what percent of 10?
(e) 21 is what percent of 400?

9. Julie earns $24 000/a and receives an increase in pay of $7\frac{1}{2}$%. What will her new salary be?

10. Frank works as a waiter at a local restaurant, where he usually receives a 15% tip.

(a) What tip should Frank receive if the bill is $22.40?

(b) A customer left a $4 tip for a meal costing $24. What percentage did Frank earn as a tip?

11. A maker of granola bars increased the price of each bar from 45¢ to 55¢. What was the percentage increase in price?

12. A bicycle originally sells for $140 and is put on sale at 15% off.

(a) What is the selling price of the bike?
(b) What must you pay for the bike, including 8% sales tax?

13. An airline company has increased their fares. The airline claims the cause of the increase is a 9% increase in fuel prices. A $320 ticket now costs $360. Is the new price due solely to the increase in fuel prices?

14. A credit card company charges $1\frac{3}{4}$% of the balance of the account each month. How much would the company charge on a balance of $860?

Evaluating Algebraic Expressions ⚡

Many people working in business and technology rely on formulas to get their work done quickly and efficiently.

$$A = P(1 + rt)$$

The formula above can be used to calculate the amount, A, in an account that pays interest at the rate of $r\%$ per annum for t years if P is deposited initially.

Leslie needs to use this formula to calculate how much will be in an account in 3 a if $200 is deposited today. The account pays interest at the rate of 8%/a.

To use the formula, Leslie follows the steps below to evaluate by substitution.

1. Copy the expression and list the values to be substituted.
2. Rewrite the expression, replacing each variable with a pair of brackets.
3. Substitute the value for each variable.
4. Evaluate the resulting expression, using **BEDMAS**.

Here are the calculations Leslie makes to find how much will be in the account after 3 a.

$A = P(1 + rt)$ $\quad$ $\begin{array}{l} P = \$200 \\ r = 0.08 \\ t = 3 \end{array}$ $\quad$ Step 1

$A = (\blacksquare)[1 + (\blacksquare)(\blacksquare)]$ $\quad$ Step 2

$\quad = (200)[1 + (0.08)(3)]$ $\quad$ Step 3

$\quad = (200)[1 + 0.24]$

$\quad = 200[1.24]$ $\quad$ Step 4

$\quad = 248$

There will be $248 in the account after 3 a.

Example 1

Evaluate $\dfrac{4x - y}{x + y}$, given $x = -\frac{1}{6}$ and $y = \frac{2}{3}$.

$$\frac{4x - y}{x + y} = \frac{4(\ ) - (\ )}{(\ ) + (\ )}$$

You can combine Steps 2 and 3.

$$= \frac{4\left(-\frac{1}{6}\right) - \left(\frac{2}{3}\right)}{\left(-\frac{1}{6}\right) + \left(\frac{2}{3}\right)}$$

$$= \frac{-\frac{2}{3} - \frac{2}{3}}{-\frac{1}{6} + \frac{4}{6}}$$

$$= \frac{\frac{-4}{3}}{\frac{3}{6}}$$

$$= -\frac{4}{3} \times \frac{6}{3}$$

$$= -\frac{8}{3}$$

$$= -2\frac{2}{3}$$

Exercise

B 1. Evaluate by substitution.

(a) $5a - 6b + 2c$; $a = 4$, $b = 7$, $c = 3$

(b) $h(p + q)$; $p = 12$, $q = 14$, $h = 5$

(c) $a(2b + 5c)$; $a = 8$, $b = 9$, $c = -1$

(d) $\dfrac{2m - 4n}{m + 2n}$; $m = -6$, $n = 5$.

(e) $P(1 + i)$; $P = 300$, $i = 0.05$

(f) $\dfrac{A}{1 + rt}$; $A = 88$, $r = 0.2$, $t = 0.5$

(g) $(ab - 1)(a + b)$; $a = 1.6$, $b = -0.4$

(h) $\dfrac{I}{Pr}$; $I = 4$, $P = 500$, $r = 0.04$

(i) $\dfrac{a + b}{a - b}$; $a = 1\frac{1}{4}$, $b = \frac{3}{8}$

(j) $pq + 2p$; $p = -\frac{5}{8}$, $q = -\frac{3}{10}$

(k) $\dfrac{2x - y}{xy - 1}$; $x = -\frac{2}{5}$, $y = \frac{1}{4}$

2. There is a formula to calculate typing speed.

$$T = \frac{w - 10m}{t}$$

T is speed in words per minute; w is number of words typed in t minutes; m is the number of mistakes made. Find the typing speed of the 2 students below.
(a) Lee typed 110 words in 2 min and made 3 mistakes.
(b) Kim typed 205 words in 3 min and made 1 mistake.

3. The combined resistance R of 2 resistors, R_1 and R_2, that are connected in parallel is given by a formula.

$$R = \frac{R_1 R_2}{R_1 + R_2}$$

Find the value of R for each given pair of values of the 2 resistors.

(a) $R_1 = 60\ \Omega$, $R_2 = 30\ \Omega$
(b) $R_1 = 40\ \Omega$, $R_2 = 10\ \Omega$
(c) $R_1 = 12.2\ \Omega$, $R_2 = 12.2\ \Omega$

Electrical resistance is measured in ohms (Ω).

4. The area of a trapezoid is given by a formula.

$$A = \tfrac{1}{2}(a + b)h$$

Find the area of each of the following trapezoids.

(a)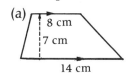
8 cm
7 cm
14 cm

(b)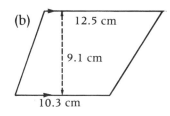
12.5 cm
9.1 cm
10.3 cm

5. $1 + 2 + 3 + 4 + \ldots + n$
The sum of the numbers (S) from 1 to n, where n is the highest number in the series, is given by a formula.

$$S = \frac{n(n + 1)}{2}$$

Find the following sums.
(a) the sum of the numbers from 1 to 20
(b) the sum of the numbers from 1 to 100

6. The formula $C = \frac{100l}{K}$ calculates the rate of fuel consumption (C) in litres per 100 km, if l litres are needed to drive a distance of K kilometres. Find C for each of the following cases, correct to 1 decimal place.

(a) 15 L of fuel are needed to drive 250 km.
(b) 7 L are needed to drive 210 km.
(c) 9.5 L are needed to travel 300 km.

7. The cross-sectional area $(C$ square centimetres) of the end of a drainage pipe can be found from a formula.

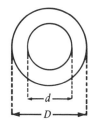

$$C = 0.79(D + d)(D - d)$$

D is the outer diameter of the pipe and d is the inner diameter. Find the cross-sectional area for each of the following cases.

(a) $D = 12$ cm, $d = 10$ cm
(b) $D = 5.6$ cm, $d = 5.4$ cm

13

8. The formula $t = g - h \times 0.0062$ gives the temperature ($t°C$) at an altitude of h metres if the ground temperature is $g°C$. Use the formula to find the temperature outside an aircraft given the altitude and ground temperature.

   (a) $h = 1000$ m, $g = 19°C$
   (b) $h = 2000$ m, $g = 15.7°C$
   (c) $h = 4200$ m, $g = -8.4°C$

9. There is a formula for finding a baseball player's fielding percentage, F.
$$F = \frac{100(p + a)}{p + a + e}\%$$
   p is the number of put-outs, a is the number of assists, and e is the number of fielding errors. Find the fielding percentages for each of the following player records.

   (a) 82 put-outs, 98 assists, 20 errors
   (b) 63 put-outs, 86 assists, 11 errors

10. The formula below calculates the amount ($\$P$) that you would need to deposit today to guarantee $\$S$ in t years if interest is paid at $r\%$ per annum.
$$P = \frac{S}{1 + rt}$$
   Find P for each of the following.

   (a) $S = \$200$, $r = 10\%$, $t = 10$ a
   (b) $S = \$6000$, $r = 8\%$, $t = 5$ a
   (c) $S = \$500$, $r = 20\%$, $t = 2.5$ a

11. Instead of calculating a baseball player's batting average, some teams calculate the player's "slugging percentage." The slugging percentage, SP, is calculated using a formula.
$$SP = \frac{s + 2d + 3t + 4H}{s + d + t + H + p}$$

There are s singles, d doubles, t triples, H homeruns, and p put-outs. The slugging percentage is expressed as a 3-digit decimal, like 0.450. Which player has the greatest slugging percentage?

Name	s	d	t	H	p
Frank	40	20	10	5	125
Terry	30	30	5	5	130
Sue	15	10	10	20	145

Which player gets on base the most often? Is this the same player that has the greatest slugging percentage?

12. For a lens the focal length, f centimetres, can be found using a formula.

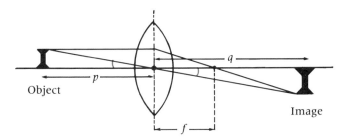

$$f = \frac{1}{\frac{1}{p} + \frac{1}{q}}$$

Find the focal length for each of the following cases.

   (a) $p = 12$ cm, $q = 12$ cm
   (b) $p = 6$ cm, $q = 12$ cm
   (c) $p = 8$ cm, $q = 6$ cm

Using a Calculator

Expressions can be evaluated quickly on a calculator. A calculator is a powerful tool, but the numbers must be entered accurately and in the correct sequence. To evaluate expressions using the **BEDMAS** rule, *you* must decide on the correct sequence.

$$154.76 + 2314 \div 17.4$$

Enter: 2314

$\boxed{\div}$

Enter: 17.4

$\boxed{=}$

$\boxed{+}$

Enter: 154.76

$\boxed{=}$

$$287.7485$$

The answer is 287.7485.

Many calculators have memory keys.

M+   or   STO

These keys *store* numbers *in* memory.

MR   or   RCL

These keys *recall* numbers *from* memory.

The memory of a calculator can temporarily store a result that is to be used again. You can use memory for storing intermediate results in calculations.

Example 1

Calculate $127.4 \div (12.1 \times 8.07)$

Enter:

12.1 $\boxed{\times}$ 8.07 $\boxed{=}$ STO $\boxed{C}$

Enter: 127.4 $\boxed{\div}$ RCL $\boxed{=}$

$$1.3046996$$

The bracket keys, $\boxed{(}$ and $\boxed{)}$, on a calculator can be a useful alternative to using memory.

Example 2

Calculate $5.8 \times 12.4 - 4.2 \div 0.95$

Using brackets:

5.8
$\boxed{\times}$
12.4
$\boxed{=}$
$\boxed{-}$
$\boxed{(}$
4.2
$\boxed{\div}$
0.95
$\boxed{)}$
$\boxed{=}$

Using memory:

4.2
$\boxed{\div}$
0.95
$\boxed{=}$
$\boxed{STO}$
$\boxed{C}$
5.8
$\boxed{\times}$
12.4
$\boxed{=}$
$\boxed{-}$
$\boxed{RCL}$
$\boxed{=}$

$$67.498947$$

It's a good idea to estimate the answer before doing a calculation with a calculator.

Example 3

Estimate, then check by evaluating on a calculator.

$$48.3 \times 97.6 \div 19.8$$
$$\doteq 50 \times 100 \div 20$$
$$= 5000 \div 20$$
$$= 250$$

Using a calculator, the value is 238.084 85.

Exercise

B **1.** Evaluate using a calculator.

(a) $274.5 + 827.4 \div 4.07$

(b) $96.2 \times 0.84 + 32.11 \div 1.74$

(c) $65.4 - 2.09(15.6 - 3.4 \times 2.82)$

(d) $\dfrac{4127.5}{16.72 \times 3.4 \div 6.7}$

2. Estimate, then check by evaluating on a calculator.

(a) $13.4 + 8.21 \div 1.67$

(b) $68.4 - (12.7 \times 3.77)$

(c) $11.4 \times 7.2 + 86.4 \div 0.82$

(d) $9.094 + 4.4(3.4 + 1.7 \times 2.3)$

(e) $158.7 \div 7.21 - 16.42 \div 1.82$

(f) $\dfrac{528.4 - (437.4 - 99.23)}{18.5 \div 3.1 \div 0.74}$

3. A Statistics Canada report stated that 10.48% of the available work force was unemployed. If the Canadian work force was estimated at 8 700 000, how many were unemployed?

4. Substitute the given values, estimate your answer, then check using a calculator.

(a) $\dfrac{S}{1 + rt}$; $r = 0.24$, $t = 5$, $S = 745$

(b) $h\left(1 + \dfrac{m}{v}\right)$; $m = 13.4$, $v = 20.5$, $h = 420$

(c) $\dfrac{1}{x} + \dfrac{1}{y}$; $x = 9.4$, $y = 5.4$

(d) $\dfrac{1 + rt}{1 - rt}$; $r = 0.08$, $t = 3.2$

5. You can use a calculator to find patterns in numbers. Copy and complete the tables below, using a calculator.

(a)

Expression	Value
66 × 65	
666 × 665	
6666 × 6665	

• Predict the value of 66 666 × 66 665.
• Can you check this value on a calculator? Explain.

(b)

Expression	Value
32 × 34	
332 × 334	
3332 × 3334	

• Predict the value of 333 332 × 333 334.

(c)

Expression	Value
93 × 93	
993 × 993	
9993 × 9993	

• Predict the value of 9 999 993 × 9 999 993.

Evaluating Formulas

The computer is a useful tool for evaluating formulas that are frequently used.

A secretary at a car rental company calculates customer's bills several times a day. The rental company charges $19.95/d plus $0.12/km driven.

The formula to calculate total cost (C) is $C = 19.95D + 0.12K$, where D is the number of days and K the number of kilometres driven.

Much of the secretary's day could be spent performing this calculation. But, with a computer and the following BASIC program, the work can be simplified.

```
10 PRINT "HOW MANY DAYS HAS THE CAR
     BEEN USED?"
20 INPUT D
30 PRINT "HOW MANY KILOMETRES DID THE
     CUSTOMER DRIVE?"
40 INPUT K
50 C = 19.95*D + 0.12*K
60 PRINT "THE CAR RENTAL COST IS $";C
70 GOTO 10
```

Notice line 50 in the program:

50 C = 19.95*D + 0.12*K

The symbol * is the computer symbol for multiplication. Computers will accept only * as a multiplication sign. The computer will multiply if you enter 5*8, but not if you enter 5X8, 5·8, or 5(8).

The symbol / is used for division.
17/5 means $17 \div 5$.

The symbol $\wedge$ or $\uparrow$ is used for exponents.
$5 \wedge 3$ or $5 \uparrow 3$ means 5^3.

In BASIC, the computer follows the rules of **BEDMAS**.

Example 1

Write the formula as it would be written in a computer program.
$$C = \frac{a(n^2 + 1)}{b + 2}$$

In BASIC:
C = A*(N$\wedge$2 + 1)/(B + 2)

Exercise

B 1. Evaluate each of the following BASIC expressions.

(a) $3 * 4 / 2$
(b) $3 \uparrow 2 + 3 * 2$
(c) $2 \uparrow 3 / 4$
(d) $(10 + 2 * 3)/(2 \uparrow 2 - 2)$
(e) $4 * 3 \uparrow 2 + (4 * 3) \uparrow 2$

2. Express each formula in a form acceptable by a computer.

(a) $I = PRT$
(b) $a = mv^2$
(c) $b = (3x - 2y) \div 5$
(d) $k = \dfrac{(a + b)(a - b)}{a^2 + 1}$

3. Write each of the following as an algebraic expression.

(a) $5 * x + x \uparrow 2$
(b) $4 * x * y + 3 / z$
(c) $(4 * x * y + 3)/z \uparrow 2$
(d) $3 * x \uparrow 2 + 5 * x + 7 = 0$
(e) $x = 3 / (y + 1) \uparrow 2$

4. Modify the given program to find the car rental cost if the company charged $23.50/d plus $0.09/km driven.

5. Suppose the car rental company had special rates for three-day weekends, when they charge $49 for the weekend plus $0.19/km driven.

(a) Modify the given program to find car rental cost using the special rates.
(b) Which is cheaper, renting under the regular rates or the special rates for a three-day weekend? It all depends on how far you expect to go. Copy and complete the table below, using the program and your modified program, to see which three-day weekend is cheaper for each given distance driven.

Distance Driven	Rental Charge	
	Regular Rates	Special Rates
100 km		
300 km		
500 km		
700 km		
1000 km		
1500 km		
2000 km		
3000 km		
4000 km		

6. Modify the given program so that it could be used by a video rental company that charges $15.90/d plus $7.98 per cassette used.

7. Modify the program to find interest earned on an investment over a number of years. Use the formula $I = PRT$. You will have to add 2 lines between lines 40 and 50 so that a third variable can be entered.

Structural Engineer

A structural engineer must know the strengths of the materials used in constructing buildings.

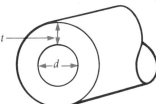

For instance, a pipe can be subjected to internal pressure that may cause it to burst. A structural engineer has to decide what type of pipe material is appropriate for a given construction project.

The different types of material available for making pipes are given a strength rating; s is tensile strength of the material. The engineer uses the rating of the material, together with the formula below, to find the required thickness, t centimetres, of a pipe.

$$t = \frac{pd}{1.3s}$$

d is the diameter of the pipe, p is the pressure exerted by the pipe's contents.

Example 1

Find the thickness of a metal pipe to withstand a pressure of 200 kPa if the diameter is 35 cm and the tensile strength is 3000 kPa.

$$t = \frac{pd}{1.3s}$$
$$= \frac{200 \times 35}{1.3 \times 3000}$$
$$= 1.8, \text{ to 1 decimal place}$$

$p = 200$ kPa
$d = 35$ cm
$s = 3000$ kPa

The pipe must be at least 1.8 cm thick.

Exercise

1. Use the given formula to determine the thickness of a pipe needed to withstand a pressure of 150 kPa if the pipe has a tensile strength of 2800 kPa and a diameter of 40 cm.

2. Determine maximum pressure in a pipe 1.5 cm thick and 30 cm in diameter if the tensile strength is 3200 kPa.

3. Another formula a structural engineer uses gives the safe load (S kilograms) on a wooden beam.

$$S = \frac{125wh^2}{l}$$

l is length in centimetres; h is height in centimetres; w is width in centimetres. The beam is supported at both ends.

(a) Find the safe load on a beam 10 cm wide, 15 cm high, and 320 cm long.
(b) Find the safe load on the same beam if it is turned so the width is 15 cm, height is 10 cm, and length is 320 cm.

4. Use the formula in Question 3 to find the width of a beam that will support 4000 kg if the beam is 700 cm long and 16 cm high.

Olympic Divers

Olympic athletes prepare for years before finally having the opportunity to compete with other athletes from around the world. When Olympic divers meet to perform, they are evaluated by seven judges who decide which athlete deserves the gold medal.

The athletes compete in men's and women's springboard and platform diving. Each diver selects a series of dives from an approved list. The dives usually rank in difficulty from 1.6 (a simple swan dive) to 3.6 (a complex dive that may include twists and somersaults).

As each athlete performs, each of the seven judges ranks the performance, using a number from 1 to 10.0. Once the judges have made their decisions, each dive is scored as follows.

• Of the seven scores posted by the judges, the highest and lowest marks are thrown out.

• The five other scores are added and multiplied by 0.6 (60%).

• The total score for each dive is obtained by multiplying the value in Step 2 by the difficulty factor (rank) of the dive.

Example 1

A gold-medal favorite performs a dive with a difficulty factor of 3.2. The diver receives marks of 9.5, 10, 10, 10, 10, 10, 10. What is the diver's total score?

The highest and lowest marks are thrown out. The marks left are 10, 10, 10, 10, 10.

Take 60% of the sum of these 5 marks.

$$60\% \text{ of } 50 = 0.6 \times 50$$
$$= 30$$

The degree of difficulty is 3.2. Multiply by this difficulty factor.

$$30 \times 3.2 = 96$$

The diver's score is 96.

Exercise

1. Calculate the total score for each diver.

   (a) Santos' dive, with a difficulty factor of 2.8, received scores of 9.0, 8.5, 8.0, 8.5, 8.5, 9.0, 7.5.

   (b) Lemieux' dive, with a difficulty factor of 2.5, received scores of 9.5, 8.0, 8.5, 9.5, 9.5, 8.5, 9.5.

   (c) Grando's dive, with a difficulty factor of 3.0, received scores of 7.0, 8.0, 7.0, 7.0, 6.0, 7.0, 7.0.

   (d) Stone's dive, with a difficulty factor of 2.3, received scores of 6.5, 5.5, 6.0, 6.5, 6.5, 7.0, 6.0.

   (e) O'Toole's dive, with a difficulty factor of 3.3, received scores of 8.0, 7.5, 7.5, 6.5, 6.5, 8.0, 7.0.

Unit 1 Review

1. Evaluate using **BEDMAS**.

   (a) $80 \div 4(5) - 200 \div 4 \div 2$
   (b) $(4 + 12) \div (6 - 2)$
   (c) $4 + 12 \div (6 - 2)$
   (d) $4 + 12 \div 6 - 2$
   (e) $7 + 4[8 - 2(6 - 3)]$
   (f) $\dfrac{6 + 6(12 \div 2 \div 2) \div 2}{2 + 4 \div 4}$
   (g) $-16 - 8(3 - 5)$
   (h) $(6^2 - 8^2) \div (6 - 8)^2$
   (i) $4 - 4[4 - 4(4 + 4)]$
   (j) $(5.7 - 3.4 + 0.2) \times 1.1$
   (k) $(2.4 \div 0.01) \div 0.4$

2. Evaluate the following fractional expressions.

   (a) $-\frac{5}{8} + \frac{1}{6} - \frac{3}{4}$
   (b) $24 \times 1\frac{1}{6} \times 3\frac{1}{2}$
   (c) $-\frac{7}{8} \div \frac{3}{4} + 1\frac{1}{10}$
   (d) $(\frac{5}{8} + \frac{1}{6}) \times 12$
   (e) $(-\frac{5}{9} - \frac{1}{6}) \div (\frac{1}{4} - \frac{2}{3})$
   (f) $\frac{5}{12} + (-4\frac{1}{5}) \div 1\frac{13}{15}$

3. Express as percents.

   (a) 0.27
   (b) 0.755
   (c) 2
   (d) 0.005
   (e) $1\frac{1}{2}$
   (f) $\frac{9}{20}$
   (g) $\frac{11}{25}$
   (h) $\frac{5}{8}$
   (i) $\frac{23}{19}$
   (j) $\frac{3}{74}$

4. Express as decimals.

   (a) 65%
   (b) 120%
   (c) 6.4%
   (d) $2\frac{1}{5}\%$
   (e) $93\frac{1}{2}\%$
   (f) $\frac{3}{4}\%$

5. Calculate the percentage for each student to find which student has the highest percentage.

   (a) Fred got 23 out of 30.
   (b) Anna got 33 out of 45.
   (c) Pat got 50 out of 72.

6. A metal alloy is 82% copper, 9% iron, 5.5% tin, 0.4% lead, 0.08% magnesium, and the remainder zinc.

   (a) Find the percentage of zinc in the alloy.
   (b) Calculate the number of kilograms of each element in 340 kg of the alloy.

7. Stu must pay $2\frac{1}{4}\%$ of his gross wages into a company pension plan. Find the amount that is owing if Stu earns $27 000/a.

8. The admission to an amusement park increased from $3.25 to $3.80. What is the percent increase in price?

9. Evaluate by substitution.

   (a) $9p + 4q - 5r$; $p = 6$, $q = 3$, $r = 5$
   (b) $(a - 2b)c$; $a = 30$, $b = 7$, $c = 3$
   (c) $\dfrac{2c - 3}{4e - c}$; $c = 9$, $e = 6$
   (d) $pq - \dfrac{p}{q}$; $p = -12$, $q = 4$
   (e) $P(1 + rt)$; $P = 50$, $r = 0.09$, $t = 4$
   (f) $\dfrac{x + y}{x - y}$; $x = \frac{9}{10}$, $y = \frac{5}{6}$
   (g) $2\pi(r + h)$; $r = 5.2$, $h = 4.8$, $\pi = 3.14$

10. There is a formula for calculating interest rate charged on a given loan.

$$r = \frac{2400C}{A(n-1)}$$

The rate of interest is $r\%$ per annum. A is the amount of the loan, to be repaid in n monthly payments, and $\$C$ is the interest charged.
Find the interest rate charged for the given values below.

(a) $A = \$500$, $n = 11$, $C = \$100$
(b) $A = \$200$, $n = 21$, $C = \$50$

11. There is a formula to find the approximate length (l centimetres) of a belt needed between the 2 pulleys shown.

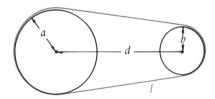

$$l = 3.3(a + b) + 2d$$

Find the length of the belt needed for each case given below.

(a) $a = 5$ cm, $b = 11$ cm, $d = 20$ cm
(b) $a = 12.5$ cm, $b = 7.5$ cm, $d = 25.1$ cm

12. Estimate, then check by evaluating on a calculator.

(a) $(29.4 + 42.7) \div 6.68$
(b) $178.9 \div (5.31 \times 1.88)$
(c) $45.7 \div 8.19 - 3.27 \times 0.814$
(d) $(14.274 - 3.82)(25.3 - 9.54)$
(e) $\dfrac{767.1 - 12.42 \times 31.49}{128.6 \div (87.43 \div 18.77)}$

Unit 2

Exponents

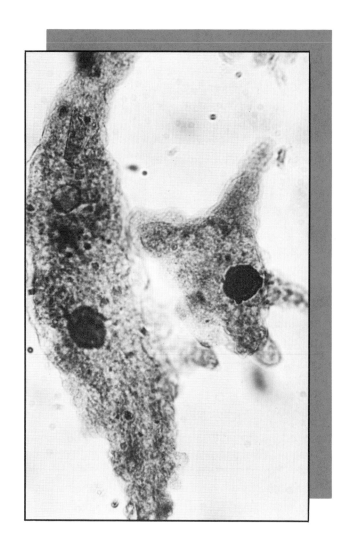

Evaluating Powers and Roots

To evaluate an expression with repeated multiplication, like the one below, would take a long time even with a calculator.

$1.3 \times 1.3 \times 1.3 \times 1.3 \times 1.3 \times 1.3 \times 1.3 \times 1.3 \times 1.3$

But if you can use a calculator with a power key, the calculation is easy.

First, express the list of *factors* as a *power*.

power $\longrightarrow a^n$
— exponent
— base

$1.3 \times 1.3 \times 1.3 \times 1.3 \times 1.3 \times 1.3 \times 1.3 \times 1.3 \times 1.3$
$= (1.3)^9$

Now evaluate on a calculator.

$\boxed{1}\ \boxed{\cdot}\ \boxed{3}\ \boxed{y^x}\ \boxed{9}\ \boxed{=}$

Some calculators have the key $\boxed{a^x}$

$(1.3)^9 = 10.604499\ldots$
$= 10.60$, to 2 decimal places

Example 1

Express as a power, then evaluate.

$500 \times 1.07 \times 1.07 \times 1.07 \times 1.07 \times 1.07 \times 1.07 \times 1.07 \times 1.07$
$= 500 \times (1.07)^8$
$= 500 \times 1.718\ 186$
$= 859.09$, to 2 decimal places

Follow BEDMAS —evaluate powers before multiplying.

Algebraic expressions may contain powers.

24

Example 2

If $x = -2$, evaluate the given expression.

$4x^2 + (4x)^2 + \sqrt{x^3 + 17}$
$= 4(-2)^2 + [4(-2)]^2 + \sqrt{(-2)^3 + 17}$
$= 4(4) + (-8)^2 + \sqrt{(-8)} + 17$
$= 16 + 64 + \sqrt{(-8)} + 17$
$= 80 + \sqrt{9}$
$= 80 + 3$
$= 83$

Example 3

Express as a power.

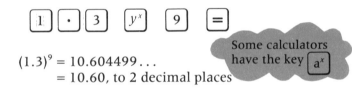

$6(y)(y)(x)(x)(y)(x)(y)(x)(x)$ x^5 y^4
$= 6x^5 y^4$

Exercise

A 1. Express each as a power.

    (a) $c \times c \times c \times c \times c \times c \times c \times c \times c \times c$
    (b) $p \times p \times q \times p \times q \times q \times q$
    (c) $1.6 \times 1.6 \times 1.6 \times 1.6 \times 1.6$
    (d) $9 \times 8 \times 8 \times 9 \times 8 \times 9 \times 9 \times 9$
    (e) $a \times a \times b \times 12 \times a \times a \times b \times a$
    (f) $5c \times 5c \times 5c \times 5c \times 5c \times 5c$
    (g) $5 \times c \times c \times c \times c \times c \times c$
    (h) $(1.02)(1.02)(700)(1.02)$
    (i) $(-y)(-y)(-y)(-y)(-y)$
    (j) $(-a)(-b)(-a)(-a)(-b)(-b)(-a)$

  2. True or false?

    (a) $(d)(d)(d)(d)(d) = 5d$
    (b) $(4x)^3 = 4x^3$
    (c) $(-a)^6 = -a^6$
    (d) $(-a)^7 = -a^7$
    (e) $-c^4 = -1 \times (c \times c \times c \times c)$
    (f) $(6x)(6x)(6x)(6x) = 6x^4$
    (g) $(-6)^2 = 36$
    (h) $-6^2 = 36$

B **3.** Evaluate without a calculator.

(a) 2^4

(b) $(-2)^4$

(c) -2^4

(d) $3^3 + (-3)^3$

(e) $2^5 - 5^2$

(f) $6^2 + 3^2$

(g) $(6 + 3)^2$

(h) $(2^3)^2$

(i) $(\frac{2}{5})^3$

(j) $(-1\frac{1}{2})^3$

(k) 5×2^4

(l) $(5 \times 2)^4$

(m) $-5(-2)^4$

(n) $(-1)^{100}$

(o) $(-1)^{237}$

(p) $-6(-1)^{19}$

(q) $(-1)^4 + (-1)^5$

(r) $(2 \times 4)^3$

(s) $2^3 \times 4^3$

(t) $\sqrt{9} + \sqrt{16}$

(u) $\sqrt{9 + 16}$

(v) $9\sqrt{16}$

(w) $\sqrt{9}\ \sqrt{16}$

(x) $\sqrt{9\sqrt{16}}$

(y) $\dfrac{(-2)^3}{2^2}$

(z) $(2 - 3^2)^2\ (3 - 2^2)^3$

4. Evaluate by substitution, using the given values.

(a) $5x^2 + (5x)^2$; $x = 2$

(b) $\sqrt{x^2 + y^2}$; $x = 6$, $y = -8$

(c) $\sqrt{a^3 - 4}$; $a = 5$

(d) $5\sqrt{a^2} + 5a^3$; $a = -3$

(e) $2x^3 - x^2y^3$; $x = \dot-2$, $y = 2$

(f) $(2x^3)^4$; $x = -1$

(g) $-3a^3 + (-3a)^3$; $a = -2$

(h) $a^b - b^a$; $a = 6$, $b = 2$

(i) $\sqrt{17 - x^3}$; $x = -2$

(j) $a\sqrt{a} + a^{\sqrt{a}}$; $a = 4$

(k) $\dfrac{2x^3 - 2y^2}{(y + 1)^2}$; $x = 3$, $y = -3$

(l) $-x^2 + (-x)^2 + (-x)^3$; $x = 4$

5. Express as a power, then evaluate.

(a) $(1.2)(1.2)(1.2)(1.2)(1.2)$

(b) $600(1.8)(1.8)(1.8)(1.8)(1.8)(1.8)$

(c) $(1.3)(1.5)(1.3)(1.3)(1.5)(1.3)(1.5)$

(d) $(2.31)(2.31)(90)(2.31)(2.31)$

6. Use a calculator to evaluate.

(a) $(1.03)^{21}$

(b) $600(1.05)^{12}$

(c) $45(1.14)^{10}$

(d) $\dfrac{(1.03)^7 - 1}{0.03}$

Side Trip

To convert a fraction to a decimal, you divide.

$\dfrac{5}{6} = 5 \div 6$

$= 0.8333\ldots$

$= 0.8\dot3$

1. Copy and complete the table, using a calculator.

Fraction	Decimal	Fraction	Decimal
$\dfrac{1}{7}$		$\dfrac{4}{7}$	
$\dfrac{2}{7}$		$\dfrac{5}{7}$	
$\dfrac{3}{7}$		$\dfrac{6}{7}$	

2. How are the numbered vertices of the hexagon related to your answer?

3. Complete a similar chart for the thirteenths: $\frac{1}{13}, \frac{2}{13}, \ldots \frac{12}{13}$. Find *two* hexagonal patterns for these fractions.

Exponent Rules

Exponent rules can simplify products and quotients of powers with the same base.

- $c^6 \times c^2 = \boxed{c \times c \times c \times c \times c \times c} \times \boxed{c \times c}$

  $= c^8 \longleftarrow$ 6 + 2

Product Rule
$a^m \times a^n = a^{m+n}$

- $c^6 \div c^2 = \dfrac{c^6}{c^2}$

  $= \dfrac{c \times c \times c \times c \times \boxed{c \times c}}{\boxed{c \times c}}$

  $= c^4 \longleftarrow$ 6 − 2

Division Rule
$a^m \div a^n = a^{m-n}$

The product rule and the division rule can be extended to give 2 more rules.

- $(c^6)^2 = (c^6)(c^6)$

  $= c^{6+6}$

  $= c^{12} \longleftarrow$ 6 × 2

Power of a Power Rule
$(a^m)^n = a^{m \times n}$

- $(a^2b^4)^3 = (a^2b^4)(a^2b^4)(a^2b^4)$

  $= (a^2 \times a^2 \times a^2)(b^4 \times b^4 \times b^4)$

  $= a^6b^{12} \longleftarrow$ 3 × 2   3 × 4

Power of a Product or Quotient
$(ab)^n = a^n b^n \qquad \left(\dfrac{a}{b}\right)^n = \dfrac{a^n}{b^n}$

You can use the rules to simplify expressions.

Example 1

Simplify each expression.

- $10m^{10} \times 2m^2 = (10 \times 2)(m^{10} \times m^2)$

  $= 20m^{10+2}$

  $= 20m^{12}$ Product rule

- $\left(\dfrac{2a^5}{b^2}\right)^4 = \dfrac{(2a^5)^4}{(b^2)^4}$

  $= \dfrac{2^4(a^5)^4}{b^{2 \times 4}}$

  $= \dfrac{16a^{20}}{b^8}$

- $(2a^4b^2)^3 \div (2a^6b) = \dfrac{(2a^4b^2)^3}{(2a^6b)}$

  $= \dfrac{(2)^3(a^4)^3(b^2)^3}{2a^6b}$

  $= \dfrac{8a^{12}b^6}{2a^6b}$

  $= 4a^{12-6}b^{6-1}$ Division rule

  $= 4a^6b^5$

Example 2

Simplify, then evaluate.

$3^{16} \times 3^8 \div (3^{10})^2 = 3^{16} \times 3^8 \div (3^{10 \times 2})$

$= 3^{16} \times 3^8 \div 3^{20}$

$= 3^{16+8-20}$

$= 3^4$ Evaluate.

$= 81$

Exercise

A 1. Simplify using the rules for multiplication and division.

(a) $y^5 \times y^8$

(b) $z^6 \times z$

(c) $3^8 \times 3^7$

(d) $4^{12} \times 4^5$

(e) $4x^{12} \times 4x^5$

(f) $2a^5 \times 2a^7$

(g) $2^5 \times 2^7$

(h) $a^3b^4 \times a^5b^7$

(i) $\dfrac{c^{10}}{c^2}$

(j) $d^{12} \div d^4$

(k) $b^5 \div b$

(l) $7^7 \div 7^2$

(m) $\dfrac{10^{30}}{10^{10}}$

(n) $(-15y^6) \div (3y)$

(o) $(x^6y^8) \div (x^2y^4)$

2. Simplify using the rule for powers of powers.

(a) $(y^4)^2$

(b) $(x^3)^3$

(c) $(a^7)^5$

(d) $(3^{10})^2$

(e) $(10^{12})^3$

(f) $(3a^{10})^2$

(g) $(4x^5)^2$

(h) $4(x^5)^2$

(i) $(a^6b^5)^4$

(j) $\left(\dfrac{a^7}{b^3}\right)^6$

B 3. Simplify using exponent rules.

(a) $a^{12} \times a^6 \times a^2$

(b) $(a^{12} \times a^6)^2$

(c) $[(a^{12})^6]^2$

(d) $a^{12} \div a^6 \div a^2$

(e) $(7x^5)^2$

(f) $7(x^5)^2$

(g) $(6y^6)(4y^4)$

(h) $(3^{70})(3^{50})$

(i) $(3x^{70})(3x^{50})$

(j) $(24x^{24}) \div (3x^3)$

(k) $(10^8)^3 \times (10^7)^2$

(l) $(7^5)^6 \div (7^4)^3$

(m) $(2x^{40})^3 \times 2(x^{40})^3$

(n) $(3^5 \times 3^7)^2$

(o) $(3a^5 \times 3a^7)^2$

4. Simplify.

(a) $\dfrac{(8x^5)^2}{(4x^2)^3}$

(b) $(a^7 \times a^{11} \div a^3)^4$

(c) $[(a^6)^5]^4$

(d) $(15a^{12} \div 3a^4)^3$

(e) $(-6x^{12})^2 \div (-x^6)$

(f) $\dfrac{(a^4)^6}{a^4 \times a^6}$

(g) $\dfrac{(a^3)^8}{a^{12} \div a^4}$

(h) $(2^{20} \div 2^5)^4$

(i) $\dfrac{(3^6 \times 3^4)^{10}}{(3^6)^4 \times 3^{10}}$

(j) $(10^{12} \div 10^4 \times 10^3)^5$

(k) $\dfrac{(4x^8)^2}{4(x^5)^2}$

(l) $\dfrac{(8a^5b^4)^2}{(2a^3b)^3}$

(m) $\dfrac{(9a^9)(4a^4)}{(-6a^6)^2}$

5. Simplify.

(a) $(a^{10} \times a^5)^4 \div (a^{12} \div a^6)^5$

(b) $\dfrac{(-2a^5b^4)(-12a^6b)}{(-a^2b^2)(9a^2b^2)}$

(c) $(8x^7y)(5x^5y^9) \div (10x^6y^2)$

(d) $(2x^4y^5)^5 \div (4x^6y)^2$

(e) $\dfrac{(c^5)^3 \times (c^3)^7}{c^{11} \times c}$

6. Simplify, then evaluate.

(a) $(2^{12} \times 2^{18}) \div (2^{15} \times 2^{11})$

(b) $(3^8 \times 3^{16}) \div (3^{25} \div 3^5)$

(c) $(4^3)^5 \div (4^2)^6$

(d) $\dfrac{(5^4)^6 \times 5^3}{(5^5)^5}$

(e) $\dfrac{(10^{11})^4 \times (10^5)^6}{[(10^7)^5]^2}$

Square Roots

$$m^2 = 36$$

There are 2 possible values that satisfy the equation above.

Since $(6)^2 = 36$ and $(-6)^2 = 36$, both 6 and -6 are square roots of 36.

The *positive* value, 6, is the **principal square root** of 36, and is written $\sqrt{36}$.

$$\sqrt{36} = 6$$

Numbers like $\sqrt{36}$, $\sqrt{13}$, $\sqrt{100}$, and $2\sqrt{5}$ are **radicals**. The symbol $\sqrt{\ }$ is a radical sign. The radical sign has the same priority as brackets in BEDMAS—that is, perform all operations under the radical sign in the same step as you perform operations within brackets.

Example 1

Evaluate using BEDMAS.

$$3 + 5\sqrt{16 - 9 + 2} = 3 + 5\sqrt{7 + 2}$$
$$= 3 + 5 \times \sqrt{9}$$
$$= 3 + 5 \times 3$$
$$= 3 + 15$$
$$= 18$$

Work within $\sqrt{\ }$ first.

Algebraic expressions may involve radical signs. The examples below show how to simplify some algebraic expressions containing radical signs.

Since $\sqrt{49} = \sqrt{7 \times 7}$
$\qquad = 7$

then $\sqrt{x^2} = \sqrt{x \times x}$ — *x* is positive.
$\qquad = x$

and $\sqrt{a^6} = \sqrt{a^3 \times a^3}$ — *a* is positive.
$\qquad = a^3$

To evaluate square roots like $\sqrt{87}$, you can use either a calculator or tables.

- On a calculator with a $\boxed{\sqrt{\ }}$ key, enter the following.

87 $\boxed{\sqrt{\ }}$ $\boxed{=}$

$\sqrt{87} \doteq 9.327\ 379\ 1$

$\doteq$ means approximately equal to.

- On a calculator with $\boxed{INV}$ and $\boxed{x^2}$, enter the following.

87 $\boxed{INV}$ $\boxed{x^2}$

$\sqrt{87} \doteq 9.327\ 379\ 1$

- Look on pages 442 and 443 or tables for the square roots of the numbers from 1 to 500.

$\sqrt{87} \doteq 9.33$

n	$\sqrt{n}$	n	$\sqrt{n}$
43	6.56	85	9.22
44	6.63	86	9.27
45	6.71	87	9.33
46	6.78	88	9.38
47	6.86	89	9.43
48	6.93	90	9.49
49	7.00	91	9.54
50	7.07	92	9.59
51	7.14	93	9.64
52	7.21	94	9.70
53	7.28	95	9.75
54	7.35	96	9.80
55	7.42	97	9.85
5	7.48	98	9.90
	7.55	99	9.95
	7.62	100	10.00
101			10.05

The tables give the values of the square roots correct to 2 decimal places.

The 2 examples below illustrate multiplication and division properties of square roots.

$$\sqrt{25} \times \sqrt{4} = \sqrt{25 \times 4}$$
$$= \sqrt{100}$$

$$\frac{\sqrt{100}}{\sqrt{4}} = \sqrt{\frac{100}{4}}$$
$$= \sqrt{25}$$

Check that these examples are correct by evaluating the left and right sides of each equation.

$$\sqrt{25} \times \sqrt{4} = 5 \times 2$$
$$= 10$$
$$\text{and } \sqrt{100} = 10$$

Use the properties of multiplication and division to simplify calculations involving products or quotients of square roots.

Example 2

Evaluate $\sqrt{8} \times \sqrt{5}$.

$$\sqrt{8} \times \sqrt{5} = \sqrt{40}$$
$$\doteq 6.324\,555\,32$$

This solution is quicker and more accurate than finding $\sqrt{8}$ and $\sqrt{5}$ separately and then multiplying.

$$\sqrt{8} \times \sqrt{5}$$
$$\doteq 2.828\,427\,1$$
$$\times 2.236\,068$$
$$\doteq 6.324\,5553$$

Example 3

Evaluate $\dfrac{\sqrt{28}}{\sqrt{7}}$.

$$\frac{\sqrt{28}}{\sqrt{7}} = \sqrt{\frac{28}{7}}$$
$$= \sqrt{4}$$
$$= 2$$

Exercise

A 1. Find all possible values of each variable.

  (a) $a = \sqrt{144}$ (f) $x = \sqrt{160\,000}$

  (b) $a^2 = 144$ (g) $r = \sqrt{9\,000\,000}$

  (c) $b = \sqrt{49}$ (h) $t^2 = 360\,000$

  (d) $b^2 = 49$ (i) $y = \sqrt{16} + \sqrt{9}$

  (e) $a^2 = 6400$ (j) $w = \sqrt{16 + 9}$

2. State the missing information.

  (a) $\sqrt{x^8} = \blacksquare^4$ (e) $\sqrt{a^{16}} = \blacksquare$

  (b) $\sqrt{b^{12}} = \blacksquare^6$ (f) $\sqrt{64y^{24}} = 8(\blacksquare)$

  (c) $\sqrt{d^{20}} = d^{\blacksquare}$ (g) $\sqrt{121a^{20}b^{64}} = \blacksquare$

3. What is the rule for finding the square root of a power?

B 4. Evaluate without a calculator.

  (a) $\sqrt{36} + \sqrt{64}$

  (b) $\sqrt{36 + 64}$

  (c) $\sqrt{36} \times \sqrt{64}$

  (d) $5\sqrt{64}$

  (e) $\dfrac{\sqrt{810\,000}}{\sqrt{900}}$

  (f) $\sqrt{49\,000\,000}$

  (g) $-5\sqrt{100 - 36}$

  (h) $2 - 6\sqrt{9 + 16}$

  (i) $\sqrt{10^2 - 8^2}$

  (j) $\sqrt{10^2} - \sqrt{8^2}$

  (k) $2 + 5\sqrt{26 + 5 \times (-2)}$

  (l) $4\sqrt{4} - 9\sqrt{9}$

  (m) $(9 - \sqrt{16})(9 + \sqrt{16})$

5. Evaluate, using a calculator or tables.

  (a) $\sqrt{5^2 + 6^2}$ (c) $10\sqrt{2^5 - 1}$

  (b) $\sqrt{9^2 - 2^2}$ (d) $\dfrac{\sqrt{4^2 + 9^2}}{\sqrt{3^3 - 2^3}}$

6. Evaluate.

(a) $\sqrt{3} \times \sqrt{12}$
(b) $\sqrt{20} \times \sqrt{5}$
(c) $\sqrt{11} \times \sqrt{3}$
(d) $\sqrt{15} \times \sqrt{5}$
(e) $\sqrt{3} \times \sqrt{7} \times \sqrt{2}$
(f) $(\sqrt{3})^3$
(g) $(\sqrt{2})^5$
(h) $\dfrac{\sqrt{50}}{\sqrt{5}}$

7. Simplify.

(a) $\sqrt{x^{14}y^2}$
(b) $\sqrt{9x^{20}y^6}$
(c) $\sqrt{5x^7 \times 20x^9}$
(d) $\sqrt{8a^5b^6 \times 18a^3b^4}$
(e) $\sqrt{(x^4)^3}$
(f) $\sqrt{(4x^{10})^3}$
(g) $\sqrt{72a^{13}b^9 \div (2ab^3)}$

8. Evaluate by substitution.

(a) $\sqrt{x^2 + 11}$; $x = 5$
(b) $a\sqrt{a - 1}$; $a = 10$
(c) $\sqrt{\dfrac{p}{q - 1}}$; $p = 50, q = 3$
(d) $\dfrac{x + 5}{2\sqrt{x + 1}}$; $x = 3$
(e) $\sqrt{x^2 + 2y^2}$; $x = -2, y = 4$
(f) $\sqrt{\dfrac{a^2 + b^3}{a + b}}$; $a = 8, b = -1$
(g) $\sqrt{9a^6b^2}$; $a = 2, b = 5$
(h) $\sqrt{a^2 - b^2}$; $a = 7, b = 3$
(i) $\sqrt{\dfrac{c}{\pi}}$; $c = 8$ $\qquad \pi \doteq 3.14$

9. The current (I amperes) in an electric circuit is given by a formula.

$$I = \sqrt{\dfrac{P}{R}}$$

R is resistance in ohms, P is power loss in watts. Find the current for each of the following.

(a) a 100 W bulb with a resistance of 20 Ω
(b) a 300 W bulb with a resistance of 150 Ω

10. If you know the area of a circle, you can find its radius from the formula below.

$$r = \sqrt{\dfrac{A}{\pi}}$$

Find the radius of a circle with area 82 cm^2.

11. The Law of Pythagoras can be extended to let you find the longest side of a right-angled triangle by using the formula given.

$$c = \sqrt{a^2 + b^2}$$

Find the length of c if $a = 4.7$ cm and $b = 7.2$ cm.

12. Fred wishes to rent a boat for a group of his friends to go fishing. The formula $l = 4\sqrt{2.5n}$ allows Fred to calculate the length l in metres of a small fishing boat that will safely carry n passengers. Find the length of boat that Fred should rent for each of the following number of passengers.

(a) 3 passengers
(b) 5 passengers

The Number System

Think of all the numbers that you use to tell others about yourself.

height, 165 cm   542 Main Street   S.I.N. 420 174 394   weight, 60 kg   bank account 725 422
locker combination 12-54-17   Amount in savings $160.23   579-1254
birthday April 18, 1969   age 16
driver's licence T374-00421-6237   shoe size, $8\frac{1}{2}$ locker number 527

The group of numbers that most of us encounter daily are **real numbers**. There are various sets of numbers that are contained in the real numbers.

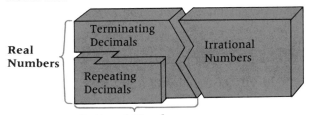

Rational Numbers

Rational numbers can be written as terminating or repeating decimals.

Terminating Decimals	Repeating Decimals
7.125	0.3̇
−0.0184	−9.45151515...
$\sqrt{9} = 3$	$2\frac{3}{7} = 2.428571428...$
$\frac{4}{5} = 0.8$	8.4̇329̇

Irrational numbers cannot be written as repeating or terminating decimals. Some examples of irrational numbers are given below.

0.123456789101112...
−3.454554555455554...

Since square roots like $\sqrt{87}$, $\sqrt{5}$, $\sqrt{7}$ are irrational numbers, no square root table or calculator can display an exact value.

Exercise

A 1. Classify each number as rational or irrational.

(a) 7.2
(b) −0.23
(c) π
(d) $2\frac{1}{4}$
(e) 0
(f) 3.400 000...
(g) 1.2020020002...
(h) 1.200200200...
(i) $\sqrt{49}$
(j) $\frac{32}{45}$
(k) −0.135719113...
(l) $\sqrt{12}$

B 2. Classify the following as repeating or terminating decimals.

(a) 3.45̇
(b) 8.2
(c) −7.0
(d) $\frac{5}{16}$
(e) $\frac{9}{11}$
(f) $-3\frac{23}{99}$

Side Trip

All repeating decimals can be written as fractions. A calculator can be used to first find a pattern.

1. Use your calculator to find the decimal expansion of each of the following.

(a) $\frac{7}{9}$
(b) $\frac{4}{9}$
(c) $\frac{23}{99}$
(d) $\frac{119}{999}$
(e) $\frac{53}{999}$
(f) $\frac{2}{999}$
(g) $\frac{4235}{9999}$

2. Use the results of Question 1 to determine the fractional equivalents of each of the following.

(a) 0.8̇
(b) 0.1̇
(c) 0.7̇1̇
(d) 0.2̇4̇
(e) 0.3̇52̇
(f) 0.005̇
(g) 0.1̇234̇
(h) −2.5̇2̇

31

Using the Computer to Find Patterns

All fractions are rational numbers: if the decimal equivalent of a fraction is not terminating, then there will be a repeating pattern of digits—although in some cases the pattern may be quite long.

$$\frac{31}{53} = 31 \div 53$$
$$= 0.584\ 905\ 660\ 377\ 3\ldots$$

Most calculators and computers have a display of only 8 digits, so you couldn't find the pattern of digits for a fraction like the one above unless you did it using pencil and paper.

However, you can program the computer to show the decimal expansion in small groups of digits. The following program will show the decimal expansion of a fraction in groups of 5 digits.

This program is only intended for fractions less than 1.

```
10   PRINT "ENTER THE NUMERATOR."
20   INPUT N
30   PRINT "ENTER THE DENOMINATOR."
40   INPUT D
50   IF N < = D THEN GOTO 90
60   PRINT "THE NUMERATOR MUST BE "
70   PRINT "SMALLER THAN THE
DENOMINATOR."
80   GOTO 10
90   A = N/D
100  X = INT(100000 * A)
110  PRINT "FIVE DECIMAL DIGITS ->";X
120  PRINT "DO YOU WANT TO CONTINUE
(Y/N)?"
130  INPUT R$
140  IF R$ = "N" THEN END
150  N = N * 100000 - D * X
160  GOTO 90
```

Here is a sample run for the fraction $\frac{31}{53}$.

```
ENTER THE NUMERATOR.
31
ENTER THE DENOMINATOR.
53
FIVE DECIMAL DIGITS -> 58490
DO YOU WANT TO CONTINUE(Y/N)?
Y
FIVE DECIMAL DIGITS -> 56603
DO YOU WANT TO CONTINUE (Y/N)?
Y
FIVE DECIMAL DIGITS -> 77358
DO YOU WANT TO CONTINUE (Y/N)?
Y
FIVE DECIMAL DIGITS -> 49056
DO YOU WANT TO CONTINUE (Y/N)?
N
```

List the digits that have been shown so far.

5 8 4 9 0 5 6 6 0 3 7 7 3 5 8 4 9 0 5 6

Look for a repeating pattern of digits.

$$\frac{31}{53} = 0.584\ 905\ 660\ 377\ 358\ 490\ 56\ldots$$
$$= 0.584\ 905\ 660\ 377\ \dot{3}$$

Exercise

1. Use the program to express the following as repeating decimals.

   (a) $\frac{14}{17}$

   (b) $\frac{12}{19}$

   (c) $\frac{17}{23}$

   (d) $\frac{44}{71}$

   (e) $\frac{26}{59}$

   Part (d) has a long pattern!

Fractional Exponents

What is the value of $64^{\frac{1}{2}}$?

Evaluate using a calculator.

64 $\boxed{y^x}$ $\boxed{\cdot}$ 5 $\boxed{=}$

Evaluate with your calculator:

- $25^{\frac{1}{2}} = 25^{0.5} = 5$

- $49^{\frac{1}{2}} = 49^{0.5} = 7$

- $16^{\frac{1}{2}} = 16^{0.5} = \blacksquare$

Now compare the following.

$$\begin{aligned}\sqrt{5} \times \sqrt{5} &= \sqrt{5 \times 5} \\ &= \sqrt{25} \\ &= 5\end{aligned} \qquad \begin{aligned}5^{\frac{1}{2}} \times 5^{\frac{1}{2}} &= 5^{\frac{1}{2}+\frac{1}{2}} \\ &= 5^1 \\ &= 5\end{aligned}$$

This result suggests that $5^{\frac{1}{2}} = \sqrt{5}$.
Similarly, $5^{\frac{1}{3}} = \sqrt[3]{5}$

$$5^{\frac{1}{4}} = \sqrt[4]{5}$$

> In general, $a^{\frac{1}{n}} = \sqrt[n]{a}$

Example 1

Evaluate.
$$\begin{aligned}64^{\frac{1}{3}} &= \sqrt[3]{64} \\ &= \sqrt[3]{4 \times 4 \times 4} \\ &= 4\end{aligned}$$

This means that the cube root of 64 is *one* of the *3* equal factors of 64.

Example 2

Evaluate.

$$\begin{aligned}((16^{\frac{1}{4}}))^3 &= (\sqrt[4]{16})^3 \\ &= (2)^3 \\ &= 8\end{aligned}$$

Frequently a calculator is needed to complete a calculation.

Example 3

Evaluate by using a calculator.

$18^{\frac{1}{7}}$

$18^{\frac{1}{7}} = \sqrt[7]{18}$

or

Fractional exponents are also used with algebraic powers.

Example 4

Simplify $(-8a^9)^{\frac{1}{3}}$.

$$\begin{aligned}(-8a^9)^{\frac{1}{3}} &= (-8)^{\frac{1}{3}}(a^9)^{\frac{1}{3}} \\ &= \sqrt[3]{-8}\,a^{9 \times \frac{1}{3}} \\ &= -2a^3\end{aligned}$$

33

Exercise

A 1. State the value of each expression.

(a) $25^{\frac{1}{2}}$

(b) $100^{\frac{1}{2}}$

(c) $\sqrt[3]{27}$

(d) $125^{\frac{1}{3}}$

(e) $\sqrt{64}$

(f) $\sqrt[3]{64}$

(g) $3\sqrt{64}$

(h) $\sqrt[3]{-64}$

(i) $32^{\frac{1}{5}}$

(j) $81^{0.25}$

2. State as a power.

(a) $\sqrt{7}$

(b) $\sqrt[3]{11}$

(c) $\sqrt[4]{19}$

(d) $\sqrt[5]{x}$

(e) $\sqrt[3]{a}$

(f) $\sqrt[3]{y^2}$

B 3. Evaluate each expression.

(a) $9^{\frac{1}{2}} + 16^{\frac{1}{2}}$

(b) $(9 + 16)^{\frac{1}{2}}$

(c) $64^{\frac{1}{2}} + 64^{\frac{1}{3}}$

(d) $(64^{\frac{1}{2}})^3$

(e) $(64^{\frac{1}{3}})^{\frac{1}{3}}$

(f) $(27^{\frac{1}{3}})^2$

(g) $(16^{\frac{1}{4}})^3$

(h) $1000^{\frac{1}{3}}$

(i) $(-1000)^{\frac{1}{3}}$

(j) $81^{\frac{1}{4}}$

(k) $32^{\frac{1}{5}} \times 125^{\frac{1}{3}}$

(l) $(-32)^{\frac{1}{5}}$

(m) $\dfrac{36^{\frac{1}{2}}}{(8^{\frac{1}{3}})^2}$

4. Evaluate.

(a) $(8^{\frac{1}{3}} + 25^{\frac{1}{2}})^2$

(b) $\dfrac{144^{\frac{1}{2}}}{\sqrt[3]{27}}$

(c) $\left(\dfrac{4}{9}\right)^{\frac{1}{2}}$

(d) $\left(\dfrac{4}{25}\right)^{\frac{1}{2}}$

(e) $\left(\dfrac{64}{27}\right)^{\frac{1}{3}}$

(f) $\left(\dfrac{1}{16}\right)^{\frac{1}{4}}$

(g) $36^{0.5}$

(h) $16^{0.25}$

(i) $(3^2 - 1)^{\frac{1}{3}}$

(j) $\left(1\dfrac{9}{16}\right)^{0.5}$

(k) $(-32)^{0.2}$

5. Simplify using exponent rules.

(a) $(c^{20})^{\frac{1}{2}}$

(b) $(x^{40}y^{12})^{\frac{1}{4}}$

(c) $(a^{15}b^3)^{\frac{1}{3}}$

(d) $(8a^{12})^{\frac{1}{3}}$

(e) $(36x^6)^{\frac{1}{2}}$

(f) $(c^{20})^{\frac{1}{4}}$

(g) $(a^{15}b^{50})^{\frac{1}{5}}$

(h) $(9x^8)^{\frac{1}{2}}$

(i) $(1000a^{24})^{\frac{1}{3}}$

(j) $(125x^{18}y^3)^{\frac{1}{3}}$

6. Simplify using exponent rules, and then evaluate.

(a) $2^{\frac{2}{5}} \times 2^{\frac{3}{5}}$

(b) $9^{\frac{3}{4}} \times 9^{\frac{1}{4}}$

(c) $100^{\frac{5}{16}} \times 100^{\frac{3}{16}}$

(d) $(8^{\frac{1}{6}})^2$

(e) $(64^{\frac{1}{30}})^5$

(f) $(25^{\frac{3}{8}} \div 25^{\frac{1}{8}})^2$

7. Evaluate using a calculator.

(a) $5^{\frac{1}{2}}$

(b) $7^{\frac{1}{3}}$

(c) $11^{\frac{1}{4}}$

(d) $100^{\frac{1}{5}}$

(e) $1000^{\frac{1}{8}}$

(f) $(75^{\frac{1}{3}})^2$

(g) $(400^{\frac{1}{10}})^3$

(h) $2400^{\frac{1}{12}}$

Side Trip

You can solve powers with more complex fractional exponents.

$$27^{\frac{2}{3}} = (27^{\frac{1}{3}})^2$$
$$= 3^2$$
$$= 9$$

$$\frac{2}{3} = \frac{1}{3} \times 2$$

Evaluate the following.

1. $8^{\frac{2}{3}}$

2. $16^{\frac{3}{4}}$

3. $25^{\frac{3}{2}}$

4. $27^{\frac{4}{3}}$

5. $64^{\frac{5}{6}}$

6. $32^{\frac{3}{5}}$

7. $(-32)^{\frac{2}{5}}$

8. $1000^{\frac{5}{3}}$

9. $81^{0.75}$

10. $(-64)^{1\frac{2}{3}}$

Integral Exponents

Here are 2 extensions of the division rule. Each example illustrates the rule given below it.

- $a^3 \div a^3 = a^{3-3}$ or $a^3 \div a^3 = \dfrac{a \times a \times a}{a \times a \times a}$
    $= a^0$ $= 1$

$$a^0 = 1$$

- $a^2 \div a^5 = a^{2-5}$ or $a^2 \div a^5 = \dfrac{a \times a}{a \times a \times a \times a \times a}$
    $= a^{-3}$ $= \dfrac{1}{a^3}$

$$a^{-n} = \frac{1}{a^n}, \ a \neq 0$$

Use the rules of exponents to simplify expressions containing powers.

Example 2

Simplify. $2^0 + 2^{-3} + (1\frac{1}{3})^{-2} = 1 + \dfrac{1}{2^3} + (\frac{4}{3})^{-2}$

$$= 1 + \tfrac{1}{8} + (\tfrac{3}{4})^2$$
$$= 1 + \tfrac{1}{8} + \tfrac{9}{16}$$
$$= \frac{16 + 2 + 9}{16}$$
$$= \frac{27}{16}$$

If you have a calculator with a reciprocal key, $\boxed{\frac{1}{x}}$, evaluate expressions like $7^{-\frac{1}{3}}$ by keying in the following.

Evaluate as $(7^{\frac{1}{3}})^{-1}$.

$\boxed{7}\ \boxed{y^x}\ \boxed{(}\ \boxed{1}\ \boxed{\div}\ \boxed{3}\ \boxed{)}\ \boxed{=}\ \boxed{\frac{1}{x}}$

$$7^{-\frac{1}{3}} \doteq 0.522\ 757\ 96$$

Exercise

A   **1.** State the value of each.

(a) 4^{-1} (h) $(-1)^{-1}$
(b) 3^{-1} (i) $(-7)^0$
(c) 4^{-2} (j) $(\frac{2}{3})^{-1}$
(d) 4^0 (k) $(\frac{1}{4})^{-1}$
(e) $(-4)^2$ (l) $(\frac{3}{5})^{-2}$
(f) $(-4)^{-2}$ (m) $(\frac{1}{2})^{-3}$
(g) $(-4)^{-1}$

2. State the result using exponent laws.

(a) $a^2 \times a^{-5}$ (f) $(c^{-5})^{-2}$
(b) $a^{-3} \times a^{-4}$ (g) $m^{10} \div m^2$
(c) $y^{-2} \times y^6$ (h) $m^{10} \div m^{-2}$
(d) $(c^{10})^{-2}$ (i) $m^{-10} \div m^{-2}$
(e) $(c^{-4})^3$ (j) $m^{-10} \div m^2$

3. True or false?

(a) $(6)^{-2} = -36$ (d) $(a^{-3})^{-5} = a^{15}$
(b) $x^{-4} \div x^{-7} = x^{-3}$ (e) $a^{-3} \times a^{-5} = a^{-2}$
(c) $(-5)^{-1} = \frac{1}{5}$ (f) $(\frac{2}{5})^{-2} = (\frac{5}{2})^2$

B   **4.** Evaluate.

(a) 2^{-4} (g) $(\frac{2}{3})^{-2}$
(b) $(-2)^4$ (h) $(\frac{4}{5})^{-3}$
(c) 5^{-3} (i) 10^{-4}
(d) $(-3)^{-2}$ (j) $(-10)^0 + (-10)^{-2}$
(e) $(-3)^{-3}$ (k) $(1\frac{2}{3})^{-2}$
(f) $(\frac{3}{4})^{-1}$

5. Evaluate.

(a) $8^{-\frac{1}{3}}$ (e) $(64^{-\frac{1}{3}})^2$ (i) $(\frac{1}{8})^{-\frac{1}{3}}$
(b) $9^{-\frac{1}{2}}$ (f) $(\frac{4}{9})^{-\frac{1}{2}}$ (j) $(-\frac{1}{8})^{\frac{1}{3}}$
(c) $16^{-\frac{1}{4}}$ (g) $32^{-\frac{1}{5}}$ (k) $(-\frac{1}{8})^{-\frac{1}{3}}$
(d) $25^{-\frac{1}{2}}$ (h) $(\frac{25}{36})^{-\frac{1}{2}}$ (l) $(\frac{1}{16})^{-\frac{1}{4}}$

6. Simplify.

(a) $2^0 + 2^{-1}$ (g) $4^{-1} + \left(\frac{4}{5}\right)^{-1}$

(b) $3^{-1} + 2^{-1}$ (h) $2^{-3} + \left(\frac{2}{3}\right)^{-2}$

(c) $4^{-1} + 2^{-1}$ (i) $(2^{-1} + 3^{-1}) \times 4^{-1}$

(d) $\left(\frac{1}{2}\right)^{-1} + \left(\frac{1}{3}\right)^{-1}$ (j) $(-4)^3 \times 4^{-3}$

(e) $(4^{-1})^{-2}$ (k) $\left(\frac{1}{8}\right)^{-2} \div \left(\frac{1}{2}\right)^{-4}$

(f) $(-2)^2 + 2^{-2}$

7. Simplify using exponent laws.

(a) $15a^4 \times 3a^{-7}$ (f) $36ab^{-12}a^{-3}b^4$

(b) $(7x^{-4})(9x^{-6})$ (g) $(x^{-6}y^5)^{-2}$

(c) $(a^{-6}b^5)(a^{-9}b^{-2})$ (h) $(3x^{-3})^{-2}$

(d) $(27a^2) \div (9a^6)$ (i) $(2x^5)^{-3}$

(e) $\dfrac{18x^7y^4}{2x^{-2}y}$ (j) $\dfrac{(a^5)^{-2} \times (a^{-2})^{-6}}{(a^{-6})^4}$

8. Simplify using power rules, then evaluate.

(a) $7^{-8} \times 7^{-4} \times 7^{10}$

(b) $15^{-10} \div 15^{-8}$

(c) $2^{12} \div 2^{18}$

(d) $12^{-4} \times 12^{10} \div 12^6$

(e) $(3^4)^{-5} \times (3^{-6})^{-3}$

(f) $8^{15} \div 8^{21} \times 8^4$

(g) $6^{-22} \div (6^{-3})^7$

(h) $\left(\frac{1}{4}\right)^{30} \times \left(\frac{1}{4}\right)^{-32}$

(i) $\left(\frac{2}{3}\right)^{-11} \div \left(\frac{2}{3}\right)^{-10}$

(j) $3^5 \times 2^7 \times 3^{-4} \times 2^{-5}$

9. Evaluate using a calculator.

(a) 17^{-1} (d) $64^{-\frac{1}{7}}$

(b) 3.5^{-2} (e) $(1.07)^{-\frac{1}{3}}$

(c) $(1.03)^{-5}$ (f) $(1.2)^{-\frac{1}{6}}$

10. Substitute, then evaluate.

(a) $(a^2 - 1)^{-n}$; $a = 3$, $n = 4$

(b) $(1 + i)^{-n}$; $i = 0.09$, $n = 7$

(c) $S(1 + i)^{-n}$; $i = 0.12$, $S = 400$, $n = 10$

(d) $(a - 1)^{-\frac{1}{m}}$; $a = 5$, $m = 3$

The Exponent Rules

Here is a complete list of all the exponent rules you have learned in this unit.

- Product Rule $\qquad a^m \times a^n = a^{m+n}$

- Division Rule $\qquad a^m \div a^n = a^{m-n}$

- Power of a Power Rule $\qquad (a^m)^n = a^{m \times n}$

- Power of a Product Rule $\qquad (ab)^m = a^m b^m$

- Power of a Quotient Rule $\qquad \left(\dfrac{a}{b}\right)^m = \dfrac{a^m}{b^m}$

- Fractional Exponents $\qquad a^{\frac{1}{m}} = \sqrt[m]{a}$

- Zero Exponent $\qquad a^0 = 1$

- Negative Exponents $\qquad a^{-n} = \dfrac{1}{a^n}$

Applications of Powers

There are many applications that involve evaluating expressions or formulas containing powers. Banking is an example of one situation where many formulas involve powers.

Given a specific interest rate, you can set yourself a target amount on an investment or an account, depending on how long you are willing to wait for the final amount.
Use the formula below.

$$P = A(1 + i)^{-n}$$

P is the deposit you would need to make today; A is the target amount; i is the interest rate, per year; n is the number of years.

How much money would you have to deposit to have a balance of $400 after 4 a, at 12%/a?

$A = 400$
$n = 4$
$i = 12\%$ or 0.12

$P = A(1 + i)^{-n}$
$\quad = 400(1 + 0.12)^{-4}$
$\quad = 400(1.12)^{-4}$
$\quad \doteq 400 \times 0.635\ 518\ 08$
$\quad \doteq 254.21$

You would need to deposit $254.21 today in order to receive $400 in 4 a.

Exercise

B **1.** Use the formula from the example to calculate the deposit needed for each of the following situations.

    (a) You want an amount of $1200 in 3 a and the account pays 6%/a.
    (b) You want an amount of $6000 in 10 a and the account pays 11%/a.

2. You can calculate the amount that will be in an account after a given number of years.

$$A = P(1 + i)^n$$

A is the amount that will be in the account; P is the deposit you make today; i is the interest rate, per year; n is the number of years. Find the amount in your account in each of the following cases.

    (a) $200 is invested at 7%/a for 4 a.
    (b) $3000 is invested at 15%/a for 10 a.
    (c) $500 is invested at 8%/a for 30 a.

3. To build the ramp shown in the diagram, you would need a board of length l.

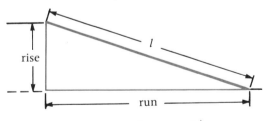

$$l = [(\text{rise})^2 + (\text{run})^2]^{\frac{1}{2}}$$

Find the length of board needed in each of the following cases.

    (a) rise = 6 m, run = 8 m
    (b) rise = 2 m, run = 10 m
    (c) rise = 4.2 m, run = 9.3 m

4. The surface area, SA, of a cube (or the total area of all 6 faces) can be found from the volume, V.

$$SA = 6(V^{\frac{1}{3}})^2$$

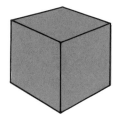

Find the surface area of a cube with each given volume.

(a) 27 cm³
(b) 125 cm³
(c) 50 cm³

5. There is a formula to calculate the interest rate, $i\%$ per annum, that will make an initial deposit, $\$P$, grow to a future value of $\$A$ in n years.

$$i = \left(\frac{A}{P}\right)^{\frac{1}{n}} - 1$$

Find i in each of the following cases.

(a) $100 grows to $200 in 8 a.
(b) $300 grows to $750 in 5 a.

6. The given formula is used to find the diameter of a circle if the area, A, is known. Find the diameter of each circle with the given area.

$$d = 1.13 \times A^{\frac{1}{2}}$$

(a) $A = 64$ cm²
(b) $A = 2500$ cm²
(c) $A = 40$ m²

7. When investigating car accidents, police use the skid marks of a car to calculate how fast a car was travelling when it collided.

Here is a formula that could be used in test situations—the car is assumed to come to a complete stop without colliding with any other objects.

$$S = 1.6(F \times L)^{\frac{1}{2}}$$

S is the car's estimated speed just before the brakes were applied, in kilometres per hour. L is the length of the skid, in metres. F is a "friction factor" that varies with the road conditions. The table below gives values of F under 3 different conditions.

F Value		
Dry Pavement	Wet Pavement	Gravel
80	62	49

Use the formula to calculate the speed of each car for the length of skid mark shown, under the road conditions given.

(a) 20 m on dry pavement
(b) 10 m on wet pavement
(c) 40 m on wet pavement
(d) 8 m on gravel
(e) 32 m on gravel

Compare your answers to items (b) and (c) and to items (d) and (e). What generalization could you make about the speeds of 2 cars if one car had a skid mark 4 times the length of the other, under the same road conditions?

8. The shipping clerks at a warehouse use string to tie up boxes. If the box is a cube, the formula below will give the amount of string, l centimetres, needed to tie up a box with a volume of V cubic centimetres.

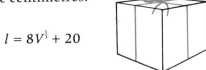

$$l = 8V^{\frac{1}{3}} + 20$$

Find the length of string for each box with the given volume.

(a) $V = 125$ cm³
(b) $V = 8000$ cm³
(c) $V = 200$ cm³

9. There is also a formula for finding the cost of wrapping up the box with paper.

$$C = 6p\left(V^{\frac{1}{3}}\right)^2$$

C is the cost in dollars; p is the price of the paper, in dollars per square centimetre; V is the volume of the box. Find the cost for each of the following.

(a) $V = 1000$ cm³, $p = \$0.002/\text{cm}^2$
(b) $V = 45\ 000$ cm³, p = $\$0.003\ 25/\text{cm}^2$

10. The formula below gives the time, T seconds, for one swing of a simple pendulum.

$$T = 2\pi g^{-\frac{1}{2}}l^{\frac{1}{2}}$$

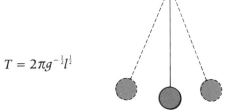

g is the gravitational constant and l is the length of the pendulum, in centimetres. Find T if $g = 980$ cm/s² and $l = 80$ cm. Use $\pi = 3.14$.

11. The radius r of a sphere with volume V can be found from a formula.

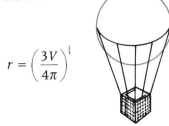

$$r = \left(\frac{3V}{4\pi}\right)^{\frac{1}{3}}$$

Find the radius of each sphere with the volume given.

(a) $V = 100$ cm³
(b) $V = 25$ m³
(c) $V = 5000$ m³

12. Leslie bought a used car and agreed to make equal monthly payments to pay for the car. If you knew how many monthly payments Leslie wanted to make, and the monthly rate of interest, you could calculate the monthly payments. Use the formula below.

$$R = \frac{P \times i}{1 - (1 + i)^{-N}}$$

N is the number of payments; i is the interest rate, per month; P is the price of the car.
Find the monthly payment in each case below.

(a) The car Leslie bought cost $1400. The interest rate was 2%, and Leslie is going to make 15 monthly payments.
(b) The car cost $1400. The interest rate was 4% and there are 15 monthly payments.

Compare your answers to parts (a) and (b). What is the increase in the monthly payment if the interest rate is doubled?

Estimating and Rounding

You're using estimation every time you make statements like the ones below.
"There were about 800 people at the game."
"It'll take approximately 2 h to drive home."

After taking inventory at a store, 493 albums were put on sale for $6.95 each. You could estimate the total value by rounding each figure.

$$500 \times \$7.00 = \$3500$$

When rounding, only important, or **significant**, digits are kept. The value of each album was rounded from $6.95 to $7.00—that is, to 1 significant digit.

Example 1

Round each number to 3 significant digits.

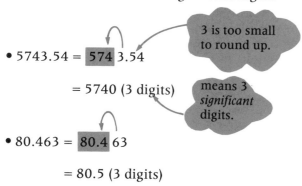

- 5743.54 = 574 3.54

  3 is too small to round up.

  = 5740 (3 digits)

  means 3 *significant* digits.

- 80.463 = 80.4 63

  = 80.5 (3 digits)

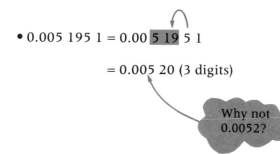

- 0.005 195 1 = 0.00 5 19 5 1

  = 0.005 20 (3 digits)

  Why not 0.0052?

Exercise

A 1. State a method that could be used to estimate each of the following.

(a) the number of words in a novel
(b) the height of a highrise
(c) the number of grade 11 students at your school
(d) the time it will take to save enough money to buy a motorbike
(e) the price to charge for admission to a dance

2. Choose the best estimate of the 3 given answers.

(a) 892×0.54 (45; 450; 4500)
(b) $0.514 \div 1.92$ (10; 2.5; 0.25)
(c) $71.4 \div 0.105$ (7; 70; 700)

3. Round to 2 significant digits.

(a) 7432.1   (e) 105 000
(b) 86 941   (f) 6.435
(c) 0.005 447   (g) 0.7953
(d) 0.000 603   (h) 0.042 49

4. Round to 4 significant digits.

(a) 987 654   (d) 0.495 897 5
(b) 1 590 000   (e) 10.498 567
(c) 2904.598   (f) 5687

5. Estimate each of the following.

(a) 1 L of stain will cover 5.2 m². How many litres would be needed to cover 66.6 m²?
(b) The total cost of a meal is shared by six people. If the total cost is $22.95, how much would each pay?
(c) There were 1383 people at the concert and the average price of a ticket was $8.10. What was the total value of ticket sales?

Scientific Notation

Very large and very small numbers can be found in science and technology.

Frequency of Light   390 000 000 000 000 Hz

Diameter of an   0.000 000 000 000 56 cm
Electron

Scientific notation expresses these numbers in an abbreviated form. Scientific notation expresses a number in the form

$$S \times 10^n,$$

where S is a number between 1 and 10, and n is an integer.

Here are examples of numbers expressed in scientific notation.

Frequency of Light 3.9×10^{14} Hz

Diameter of an 5.6×10^{-13} cm
Electron

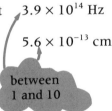

between 1 and 10

Example 1

Calculate $(5 \times 10^{-12}) \times (4 \times 10^7)$.

$(5 \times 10^{-12}) \times (4 \times 10^7)$
$= (5 \times 4) \times (10^{-12} \times 10^7)$
$= 20 \times 10^{-5}$
$= 0.0002$

Example 2

Express in scientific notation and evaluate to 2 significant digits.

$1\ 700\ 000\ 000\ 000 \div 590\ 000\ 000$
$= \dfrac{1.7 \times 10^{12}}{5.9 \times 10^8}$
$= (1.7 \div 5.9) \times (10^{12} \div 10^8)$
$\doteq (0.288\ 136) \times 10^{12 - 8}$
$\doteq 0.29 \times 10^4$

to 2 digits

$= 2900$

Example 3

Estimate the following.

$0.000\ 000\ 723 \div 0.000\ 018\ 54$
$= (7.23 \times 10^{-7}) \div (1.854 \times 10^{-5})$
$\doteq (7 \times 10^{-7}) \div (2 \times 10^{-5})$
$\doteq (7 \div 2) \times (10^{-7} \div 10^{-5})$
$= 3.5 \times 10^{-2}$
$= 0.035$
$\doteq 0.04$

Accurate value is 0.038 996 76.

Example 4

The circumference of the earth at the equator is 4.0024×10^7 m, and the speed of light is 2.998×10^8 m/s. Estimate the number of revolutions around the earth that a particle travelling at the speed of light could make in 1 s.

Number of revolutions

$$= (2.998 \times 10^8) \div (4.0024 \times 10^7)$$
$$= (3 \times 10^8) \div (4 \times 10^7)$$
$$= (3 \div 4) \times (10^8 \div 10^7)$$
$$= 0.75 \times 10^1$$
$$= 7.5$$

A particle can circle the earth approximately 7.5 times in 1 s.

Exercise

A **1.** Express each in decimal form.

    (a) 8.6×10^5 (e) 9.74×10^{-9}
    (b) 7.3×10^{-5} (f) 4×10^0
    (c) 6×10^8 (g) 3.07×10^1
    (d) 1.3×10^{-1} (h) 2.21×10^{-4}

2. Express each in scientific notation.

    (a) 950 000 000
    (b) 0.000 000 014
    (c) The diameter of the earth is 1 274 000 000 cm.
    (d) The mass of the earth is 5 983 000 000 000 000 000 000 000 kg.
    (e) The longest wavelength of visible red light is 0.000 076 cm.
    (f) The total volume of the oceans is 1 400 000 000 000 km³.
    (g) The speed of light is 300 000 000 m/s.
    (h) The Cray-1 computer can perform 4 800 000 000 operations every minute.

B **3.** Round each of the following to 3 significant digits and then express in scientific notation.

    (a) 57 378 000 000
    (b) 0.000 042 973
    (c) 0.010 006
    (d) 6 434 900
    (e) The world's population is 4 475 000 000.

4. Express the following in decimal form accurate to 2 digits.

   (a) 7.42×10^7
   (b) 3.055×10^{-6}
   (c) 7.962×10^3
   (d) 1.83×10^{-1}
   (e) 2.962×10^{-5}

5. Calculate the following to 2 digits.

   (a) $(7 \times 10^3) \times (4 \times 10^5)$
   (b) $(3 \times 10^{10}) \times (2 \times 10^{-14})$
   (c) $(5.1 \times 10^{-3}) \times (4.0 \times 10^{-5})$
   (d) $(8 \times 10^{12}) \div (4 \times 10^9)$
   (e) $(6.4 \times 10^7) \div (2 \times 10^{11})$
   (f) $(3 \times 10^5) \div (6 \times 10^{14})$
   (g) $(2.5 \times 10^{-18}) \div (6.3 \times 10^{-23})$
   (h) $(4.2 \times 10^7) \times (8.1 \times 10^3) \times (1.2 \times 10^{-4})$
   (i) $\dfrac{1.5 \times 10^{20}}{6.2 \times 10^{14}}$

6. Estimate the following.

   (a) $5\ 980\ 000\ 000 \times 0.000\ 002\ 91$
   (b) $87\ 800\ 000\ 000 \div 3\ 260\ 000\ 000$
   (c) $0.000\ 042\ 9 \div 0.000\ 223$
   (d) $48\ 300\ 000\ 000 \times 0.007\ 08$
   (e) $\dfrac{580 \times 0.3}{19\ 400}$
   (f) $\dfrac{0.000\ 136 \times 0.02}{0.000\ 83}$
   (g) $\dfrac{15\ 200 \times 0.034}{(43\ 200)^2}$

7. The speed of light is 3.0×10^8 m/s and the approximate distance from the earth to the sun is 1.5×10^{11} m. Calculate the time (in seconds) that it takes light to travel from the earth to the sun. *Hint*: to calculate time use the relationship

   $$\text{time} = \frac{\text{distance}}{\text{speed}}.$$

8. There are approximately 4.5×10^9 people on our planet, and it is estimated that there are 1.6×10^{21} L of water in the oceans. How many litres could be allotted to each person, correct to 1 digit?

9. The mass of the earth is approximately 6×10^{24} kg and the mass of the sun is approximately 2×10^{30} kg. How many times greater than the earth's mass is the sun's mass?

10. In a study made by Environment Canada, it was found that 8 million tonnes of hazardous waste are in dumps beside the Niagara River (U.S.). If 1% of this amount leaked into the river, the water would no longer be drinkable. How many tonnes is represented by 1%?

11. In Canada the surface area of water is 755 000 km². In total, the land area is 9 922 000 km². Express the surface area of water as a percent of the total land area.

12. A computer can perform up to 1.3 billion calculations per second. To process one income tax return, the computer could perform an average of about 200 calculations. How many average tax returns could the computer process in 8 h?

Pipe Fitter

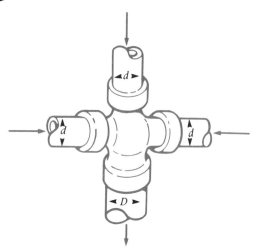

A pipe fitter works with various sizes of pipes. Often, water will flow from several small pipes into a larger, main pipe. A pipe fitter uses the formula below to find the diameter, D, of the larger pipe.

$$D = (n \times d^2)^{\frac{1}{2}}$$

d is the diameter of the smaller pipes, and n is the number of smaller pipes.

Example 1

Determine the diameter of a pipe that receives the flow from 3 pipes, each of which have diameter 1.5 cm.

$$D = (n \times d^2)^{\frac{1}{2}}$$
$$= (3 \times 1.5^2)^{\frac{1}{2}}$$
$$= (6.75)^{\frac{1}{2}}$$
$$= 2.6, \text{ to 1 decimal place}$$

$n = 3$
$d = 1.5$ cm

The large pipe must be 2.6 cm in diameter.

Exercise

1. Determine the diameter of a pipe that receives the flow from each of the following.

   (a) 2 pipes of diameter 2.5 cm
   (b) 5 pipes of diameter 6 cm

2. The formula below will determine the number, n, of smaller pipes, each of diameter d centimetres, that can flow into one large pipe of diameter D centimetres.

$$n = \frac{D^2}{d^2}$$

   (a) Determine the number of pipes of diameter 2 cm that can flow into 1 pipe of diameter 6 cm.
   (b) Determine the number of pipes of diameter 3.4 cm that can flow into 1 pipe of diameter 6.8 cm.
   (c) Determine the diameter of pipe so that 5 pipes of the same diameter can flow into 1 pipe of diameter 9 cm.

Unit 2 Review

1. True or false?

(a) $16^{\frac{1}{2}} = 8$

(b) $(x^5)^6 = x^{30}$

(c) $4^{-1} = -4$

(d) $(3x^4)^2 = 9x^8$

(e) $(3^4)^2 = 9^8$

(f) $(-6)^2 = -6^2$

(g) $5 \times 2^3 = 10^3$

(h) $(-2)^3 = -2^3$

(i) $(x^{16})^{\frac{1}{2}} = x^8$

(j) $(\frac{4}{5})^{-2} = (\frac{5}{4})^2$

2. Evaluate, if possible.

(a) 9^2

(b) $(-9)^2$

(c) -9^2

(d) 9^{-2}

(e) $9^{\frac{1}{2}}$

(f) $9^{-\frac{1}{2}}$

(g) $(9^{\frac{1}{2}})^3$

(h) $(\frac{1}{9})^{\frac{1}{2}}$

(i) $(-9)^{\frac{1}{2}}$

(j) $-9^{\frac{1}{2}}$

(k) $(\frac{4}{5})^{-1}$

(l) $(\frac{4}{5})^{-2}$

(m) $(-\frac{2}{3})^2$

(n) $(-\frac{1}{4})^3$

(o) $\sqrt{25 - 16}$

(p) $\sqrt{25} - \sqrt{16}$

(q) $(49)^{\frac{1}{2}} (\frac{4}{9})^{\frac{1}{2}}$

(r) $(\frac{25}{9})^{-\frac{1}{2}}$

(s) $27^{\frac{1}{3}}$

(t) $27^{-\frac{1}{3}}$

(u) $(-27)^{\frac{1}{3}}$

(v) $(-27)^{-\frac{1}{3}}$

3. Simplify, using exponent laws.

(a) $c^9 \times c^4 \times c^2$

(b) $(c^9 \times c^4)^2$

(c) $[(c^9)^4]^2$

(d) $m^{20} \div m^4 \times m^2$

(e) $(m^{20} \div m^4)^2$

(f) $(4x^6)^2$

(g) $4(x^6)^2$

(h) $(4^6)^2$

(i) $(6x^{12}y^5)(2xy^{10})$

(j) $(24a^{30}b^{10}) \div (2a^5b^5)$

(k) $(-5a^4b^5)^2$

(l) $(-2m^4 \times 2m^5)^3$

(m) $\sqrt{x^{36}}$

(n) $\sqrt{16x^{16}}$

(o) $\sqrt{4x^4y^2}$

(p) $\dfrac{c^{10} \times c^6}{(c^3)^2}$

(q) $\dfrac{(4a^4)(12a^{12})}{(-2a^2)^3}$

4. Simplify, then evaluate.

(a) $2^7 \times 2^8 \div 2^{12}$

(b) $(3^4)^2 \div (3^3)^2$

(c) $\dfrac{6^8 \times 6^{10}}{(6^9)^2}$

(d) $5^4 \times 5^{-6}$

(e) $10^{10} \div 10^{13}$

5. Simplify, using exponent laws.

(a) $(x^{-3})(x^7)$

(b) $c^{-6} \times c^{-10}$

(c) $(c^{-6})^{-10}$

(d) $c^{-6} \div c^{-10}$

(e) $(14a^{10}) \div (2a^{30})$

(f) $(-6x^{-6})(8x^8)$

(g) $(40x^{-2}y) \div (2x^4y^9)$

(h) $(a^{-4}b^3)^{-5}$

(i) $(22a^{10}b^{-8}) \div (-11a^3b^{-3})$

(j) $\sqrt{64a^{64}} \times 3a^{-30}$

6. Evaluate.

(a) $100^{\frac{3}{2}}$

(b) $1000^{\frac{2}{3}}$

(c) $81^{-\frac{1}{2}}$

(d) $81^{\frac{1}{4}}$

(e) $(\frac{8}{125})^{\frac{1}{3}}$

(f) $(\frac{4}{9})^{-2}$

(g) $(\frac{4}{9})^{-\frac{1}{2}}$

(h) $5^0 + 5^{-2}$

(i) $(\frac{1}{2})^3 + 2^{-2}$

(j) $(\frac{-1}{27})^{\frac{1}{3}}$

(k) $(\frac{2}{3})^{-1} + 4^{-\frac{1}{2}}$

(l) $(\frac{1}{10})^{-2} + (\frac{1}{10})^{-1}$

(m) $32^{\frac{1}{5}} + (\frac{1}{4})^{-2}$

(n) $16^{-\frac{1}{2}} - 16^0$

7. Substitute, then evaluate.

(a) $\sqrt{2as}$; $a = 6$, $s = 3$

(b) $\dfrac{x + 10}{\sqrt{x}}$; $x = 25$

(c) $(1 + x)^N$; $x = -2$, $N = 100$

(d) $-3x^2 + (-3x)^2$; $x = 2$

(e) $(a^2 - b^2)^{-N}$; $a = 3$, $b = 2$, $N = 1$

(f) $x\sqrt{y} - \sqrt{xy}$; $x = 4$, $y = 25$

(g) $\dfrac{4x^2}{3\sqrt{x + 6}}$; $x = 3$

(h) $\sqrt[a]{b} + a\sqrt{b}$; $a = 3$, $b = 64$

8. Evaluate using a calculator.

    (a) $(1.2)^{12}$
    (b) $(2.03)^8$
    (c) $(7.42)^3 - (2.31)^6$
    (d) $12^{\frac{1}{2}}$
    (e) $23^{\frac{1}{2}}$
    (f) $521^{\frac{1}{3}}$
    (g) $(12.5)^{-1}$
    (h) $(21.2)^{-2}$
    (i) $(1.07)^{-9}$
    (j) $59^{-\frac{1}{2}}$

9. Substitute and evaluate. Use a calculator.

    (a) $\sqrt{\dfrac{S}{T}}$; $S = 12.2$, $T = 3.5$
    (b) $(1 + i)^{-N}$; $i = 0.04$, $N = 6$
    (c) πx^3; $\pi = 3.14$, $x = 10$

10. Lee wants to connect 2 speakers to a stereo, running the speaker wire under the carpet as shown in the diagram.

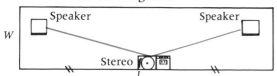

The formula to find the total length of wire needed is $T = (L^2 + 4W^2)^{\frac{1}{2}}$. Find the length of wire Lee needs if the room is 5.2 m by 3.1 m. Answer to 2 significant digits.

11. The formula below gives the amount, A, that will be in an account after n months, if R is deposited monthly and interest is $i\%$ per month.

$$A = R \times \left(\frac{(1 + i)^n - 1}{i} \right)$$

Find the amount in each case below.

    (a) $R = \$100$, $i = 2\%$, $n = 6$ months
    (b) $R = \$350$, $i = 3\%$, $n = 24$ months

12. A manufacturing company wants all of its soup cans to be exactly 9 cm high, for easy stacking on grocery shelves. The formula gives the diameter, d, of the can, using the volume, V.

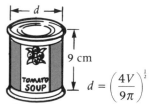

$$d = \left(\frac{4V}{9\pi} \right)^{\frac{1}{2}}$$

    (a) Find the diameter of a soup can with volume 500 cm³; with volume 1000 cm³.
    (b) Does the diameter double if volume is doubled? Explain.

13. Round each number to 3 significant digits; to 2 significant digits.

    (a) 75 327.4
    (b) 9.303×10^{40}
    (c) 0.000 059 951
    (d) 4.7451×10^{-7}

14. Express in scientific notation, to 2 significant digits.

    (a) 87 340 000 000
    (b) 0.000 002 549
    (c) 925 770 000 000 000
    (d) 0.000 000 000 054 3

15. Evaluate to 3 digits.

    (a) $(4.79 \times 10^7) \times (1.23 \times 10^{-4})$
    (b) $(3.54 \times 10^{-13}) \times (2.06 \times 10^8)$
    (c) $(7.32 \times 10^{-2}) \times (5.8 \times 10^{-7})$
    (d) $(3.5 \times 10^{15}) \div (3.77 \times 10^{12})$
    (e) $(9.21 \times 10^{30}) \div (7.38 \times 10^{36})$
    (f) $(2.47 \times 10^{-9}) \div (5.9 \times 10^{-12})$

16. Simplify *first*, using exponent laws. Then evaluate.

    (a) $(x^8)(x^{-6})$; $x = 3$
    (b) $a^{12} \times a^8 \div a^{20}$; $a = 8$
    (c) $(y^4)^7 \div (y^9)^3$; $y = 12$
    (d) $(a^5)^6 \div (a^4)^8$; $a = 9$
    (e) $\sqrt{x^8 y^2}$; $x = 2$, $y = 5$
    (f) $(a^{15} b^{-10})^{\frac{1}{5}}$; $a = -1$, $b = 3$

Unit 3

Polynomials

Terms and Polynomials

You may use algebraic ideas when some of the information needed to solve a problem is missing.

Suppose you applied for the job advertised. You'd probably want to know how much you could expect to earn each week. But you might not know how many hours you'd work.

Suppose you worked t hours per week.

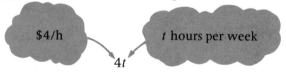

Your wages for one week would be $4t.

The expression $4t$ is an algebraic **term**. Here are some other examples of terms.

$5a$ $2xy$ $-6k$ $-8xy$ $33abc$ yx x^2y^3

$2xy$, $-8xy$, and yx are **like terms**.

$2xy$ and x^2y^3 are not like terms.

There are a few simple rules to follow when working with terms.

The rule to follow when adding or subtracting terms is given below.

> Only *like* terms can be added or subtracted.

Use the rule to simplify expressions containing like terms.

Example 1

$$2a + 5b - 4a + b = \underline{2a - 4a} + \underline{5b + b}$$
$$= \underline{-2a} \quad + \quad \underline{6b}$$

To subtract a term, *add* its *opposite*.

Example 2

$$-5x + 6x^2 - 7x - (-9x^2)$$
$$= -5x - 7x + 6x^2 + 9x^2$$
$$= -12x + 15x^2$$

A term or a sum of terms is a **polynomial**. Polynomials can also be added and subtracted.

Example 3

Simplify.

$$(7a + 3a^2) + (4a^2 - 2b) - (4a - a^2 + b)$$
$$= 7a + 3a^2 + 4a^2 - 2b - 4a + a^2 - b$$
$$= 3a + 8a^2 - 3b$$

Example 4

$$(5k + 7m - 4n) - (2k - 4m + 5n)$$
$$= 5k + 7m - 4n - 2k + 4m - 5n$$
$$= 3k + 11m - 9n$$

Like *or* unlike terms can be multiplied
or divided.

Example 5

$(8a)(5b) = (8 \times 5)ab$
$\qquad\quad = 40ab$

Example 6

$(-6x^6)(3x^3)$
$= (-6 \times 3)(x^6 \times x^3)$
$= -18x^9$

Simplify expressions by following the correct
order of operations.

BEDMAS!

Example 7

Simplify.

$$\frac{12a^3b - 20a^3b}{4ab} + 4a(-7a - 5a)$$

Brackets
first

$$= \frac{(12a^3b - 20a^3b)}{4ab} + 4a(-7a - 5a)$$

$$= \frac{-8a^3b}{4ab} + 4a(-12a)$$

Division and
multiplication next

$$= -2a^2 - 48a^2$$
$$= -50a^2$$

Addition and
subtraction last

Exercise

A **1.** Select pairs of like terms.

$5ab^2$	$5qp$
pq	$7b^2a$
$7q^2r$	$4r^2q$

2. State the perimeter as a polynomial.

(a)
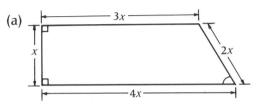

(b)
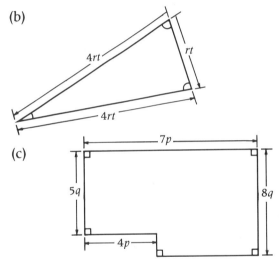

(c)

(d)
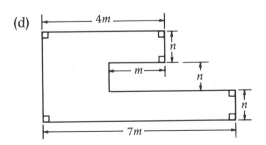

49

3. Simplify if possible.

(a) $15x - 8x$
(b) $-6m - 12m$
(c) $15c + 11a$
(d) $3a - 5x - 9a$
(e) $x^2 + x^2 + x^2$
(f) $x - 4y - 2x$
(g) $-a^3 - (-7a^3)$
(h) $8c^6 - 12c^2$
(i) $-a + b + a + b$
(j) $2x^2 - x - 3x^2$

4. Perform the indicated operation.

(a) $(2x)(-6y)$
(b) $(-5a^3)(-a^3)$
(c) $9xy \times 12xy$
(d) $(a^2b)(a^4b^2)$
(e) $(-10m^3k^2)(m^3k^2)$
(f) $(24b^8) \div (4b^2)$
(g) $(6abc) \div (2ac)$
(h) $(-45x^5) \div (5x)$
(i) $(a^{10}b^6) \div (a^2b)$
(j) $(-66x) \div (-2x)$

5. Add.

(a) $3x + 6y + 5z$
$\quad 8x + 9y - 3z$

(b) $6p - 7q - 2r$
$\quad p + 9q - 5r$

(c) $4ab - 6ac - b$
$\quad -5ab + ac - 9b$

(d) $7x^2 - 8x - 2$
$\quad 2x^2 - 8x + 9$

6. Subtract.

(a) $12s + 9t + 18w$
$\quad 8s + 6t + 9w$

(b) $17m + 12n + 6p$
$\quad 15m - 9n - 2p$

(c) $-12y + 4w - z$
$\quad 7y - 7w + z$

(d) $4q^2 - q - 15$
$\quad -q^2 + 3q - 28$

B **7.** Collect like terms.

(a) $24k + 15k - 3p + p$
(b) $12a + 13b - 7a - b + a$
(c) $-3x + 2y - 16x - 21y + 18x$
(d) $11a^2 - 15a - 10a - (-3a^2)$
(e) $4x - 7 - x + 24 - 3x - 8$
(f) $2x^2 + 4x - 6 + 17x^2 - 30x - 8$
(g) $-4a^2b^3 + a^3b^2 - 8a^2b^3 - 11a^3b^2$
(h) $6c^2 + 15cy - y^2 + 8cy - 14c^2 - 4y^2$
(i) $-5t^3 - (-8t^2) + 2t^3 - 14t^3 + 5t^2$
(j) $-6n^2 + 5n - 9n^2 - 5n - (3n^2 - 18n^2)$

8. Add or subtract polynomials as indicated.

(a) $(3a + 5b - c) + (a - 2b + 4c)$
(b) $(5x - 11y + 2z) - (x + 3y + 6z)$
(c) $(x + 4y) + (y - 5x) - (3x + 5y)$
(d) $(3p - q - 5r) - (p + 4r) + (3q - r)$
(e) $(3w^2 - 4w + 7) - (5w^2 - 8w - 2)$
(f) $(5ab - ac) + (-3a + ab) - (ac + 2a)$

9. Simplify using **BEDMAS**.

(a) $(3a + 2a)(7b - 10b)(-2c - 4c)$
(b) $(-4a)(2a) + (5a)^2$
(c) $(4x^2 - 11x^2)(3x + 2x)$
(d) $3a \times 7c + 15c \times (-2a)$
(e) $18y - 15y \times 2 + 7 \times (-2y)$
(f) $(12x^8)(3x^6) \div (-4x^2)$
(g) $21pqr \div 3p + 5r \times 8q$
(h) $\dfrac{9y^2 + 12y^2}{-y - 2y} + 4(6y - 8y)$
(i) $\dfrac{9x^2 - 24x^2}{-x + 6x} + \dfrac{2xy - (-8xy)}{-35x^2y^2 \div 7x^2y}$
(j) $18x^2 + 2x[5x + 4(x + 3x)]$

10. Find a polynomial expression for the perimeter of each figure.

(a)

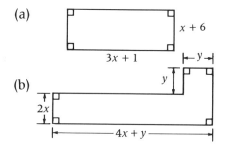

(b)

(c)

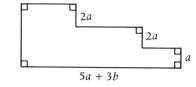

Expanding Expressions

The skills that you learn in these sections will show you how to present your work in a simpler form. You will also be able to use the skills to simplify many numerical calculations.

Lee applied for work on the kitchen staff at $4/h. When he started, he found out that his time would be split between the dining room and the banquet room.

One week, he worked x hours in the dining room and $5x$ hours in the banquet room. You can write an expression for his earnings for the week.

$$4(x + 5x)$$

This expression can be simplified by adding like terms.

$$4(x + 5x) = 4(6x)$$
$$= 24x$$

Here's another way to simplify the expression.

$$4(x + 5x) = 4x + 20x$$
$$= 24x$$

This is expanding.

Here, each term in the expression was multiplied by 4.

Often the terms inside the brackets are not like terms that can be added.

$$8(5x + 2y) = ?$$

To expand, multiply *each* term in the bracket by the term outside the bracket.

Example 1

Expand.

$$8(5x + 2y) = 8(\boxed{5x} + \boxed{2y})$$
$$= 8 \times 5x + 8 \times 2y$$
$$= 40x + 16y$$

Example 2

Expand and simplify.

$$4(9x + 5y) - 7(x - 15y)$$

$$= 4(\boxed{9x} + \boxed{5y}) - 7(\boxed{x} - \boxed{15y})$$
$$= 4(9x) + 4(5y) - 7(x) - 7(-15y)$$
$$= 36x + 20y - 7x + 105y$$
$$= 29x + 125y$$

$$3x(2x - 4) - (x^2 + 4x)$$

$$= 3x(\boxed{2x} - \boxed{4}) - 1(\boxed{x^2} + \boxed{4x})$$
$$= 3x(2x) + 3x(-4) - 1(x^2) - 1(4x)$$
$$= 6x^2 - 12x - x^2 - 4x$$
$$= 5x^2 - 16x$$

Use the **BEDMAS** rule to follow the correct order of operations when simplifying expressions.

Example 3

Simplify.

$13t - 5t[17t - 2(4t - 7)]$

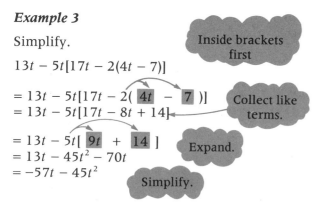

$= 13t - 5t[17t - 2(\boxed{4t} - \boxed{7})]$
$= 13t - 5t[17t - 8t + 14]$

$= 13t - 5t[\boxed{9t} + \boxed{14}]$
$= 13t - 45t^2 - 70t$
$= -57t - 45t^2$

The example below can be used to illustrate the expanding of an expression.

Example 4

Find an expression for the area of the given figure.

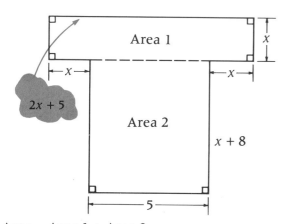

Area = Area 1 + Area 2
$= x(2x + 5) + 5(x + 8)$
$= 2x^2 + 5x + 5x + 40$
$= 2x^2 + 10x + 40$

Exercise

A 1. Expand each of the following.

(a) $5(7x + 3)$
(b) $8(4a - 3b)$
(c) $-2(4x + 9)$
(d) $-5(5z - 2w)$
(e) $-(8x - 3y)$
(f) $9(4a + 3b - 1)$
(g) $-12(3c - 11d)$
(h) $-2(6q - p - 4s)$
(i) $11(y + 3z - 8)$
(j) $-8(-t - 2s + 9)$

2. Expand.

(a) $a(a + 4)$
(b) $3x(2x - 3)$
(c) $x(2x - 4y)$
(d) $(b + c)a$
(e) $(3x - 4y)y$
(f) $-c(2c - 4)$
(g) $-12z(z + 3y)$
(h) $(2t - s)v$
(i) $(x - w)(-5w)$
(j) $a^2(a - 6)$

B 3. Expand.

(a) $a(3c - 5b)$
(b) $10z(x + 12y)$
(c) $-3r(2g - 9)$
(d) $-w(5w + 3a)$
(e) $2t^2(14t^4 - 18)$
(f) $6m(8 - 20m + a)$
(g) $-r(r^2 + 2r)$
(h) $9y(2y - 6)$
(i) $3x(x^2 - 6x + 16)$
(j) $-2ab(3a - 24ab)$

4. Expand and simplify.

(a) $7(x + 8) + 4(3x - 5)$
(b) $3(5x - 3y) + 6(x - 2y)$
(c) $12(4c - 5) + (10c + 7)$
(d) $4(8a - 3) - 3(2a + 6)$
(e) $7(2x + 4y) - (x - 9y)$
(f) $-4(2k - 5m) - 3(m - 4k)$
(g) $4(2t - 1) + (3t - 7) - (6t + 3)$
(h) $8(3a - 7b - 11c) - 2(9a + b - 5c)$
(i) $15r - 4(6r - 3) + 3(-5 + 3r)$
(j) $-8(3z - 2y + a) - (4a + y - 24z)$

5. Simplify.

(a) $4(2x - 8y) - 3(5y + x) - 2(-5x + 2y)$
(b) $-3(2a + 4b - 5c) - (8a - 6c + 2b)$
(c) $6(m^2 - 2m + 1) + 8(2m^2 - 3m - 2)$
(d) $7x(3a - 5y) + 5x(a + 6y)$
(e) $8x(2x - 3) - 4x(3x + 2)$
(f) $3a(2a - 4) - a(7a + 6) - 2a(a - 10)$
(g) $5w(2w + 3t) - 2t(11t - w)$
(h) $-7c(3c^2 - 2c + 1) + c(8 - 3c + c^2)$
(i) $-w(4w + 3) + 3w(w - 9) - (2w^2 - 30w)$
(j) $6xy(5x - 8xy) - 4xy(2y + xy)$

6. Expand and simplify. Use the **BEDMAS** rule.

(a) $8[5a + 3(4 - 3a)]$
(b) $-3[6x - 2(5x - 4)]$
(c) $-4a[5(2a - 1) + (3a + 2)]$
(d) $3y[4(2y - 3) - (y + 7)]$
(e) $6t + 5[-3(t + 4) + 11]$
(f) $7c - 4[3c - 2(c - 4)]$
(g) $3x + 3[3x + 3(3x + 3)]$
(h) $4a[6a(2a - 1) - a(4a - 5)]$
(i) $6z + 3[4(2z - 3) - 3(3z + 1)]$
(j) $12w^2 - w[2w(5w - 4) - w(w - 3)]$

7. Find an expression for the area of each shaded figure. Express the area in its simplest form.

(a)

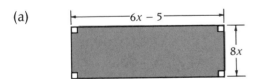

(b)

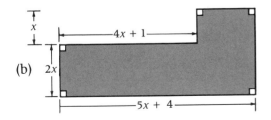

(c)

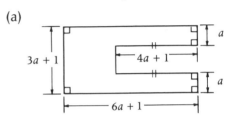

8. Determine an expression for the perimeter and area of each figure.

(a)

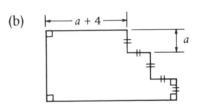

(b)

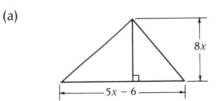

9. Find an expression for the area of each figure.

(a)

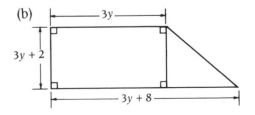

(b)

Multiplying Binomials

A binomial is a polynomial that contains 2 terms.

$$2y + 3z, \quad x + 7, \quad a^4b + 2ab$$

What would be the product of 2 binomials?

$$(\boxed{x} + \boxed{7})(\boxed{x + 2})$$
$$= x(x + 2) + 7(x + 2)$$
$$= x^2 + 2x + 7x + 14$$
$$= x^2 + 9x + 14$$

Notice that you multiply each term in the first pair of brackets by each term in the second pair of brackets. An easy way to remember these steps is **FOIL**: **F**irst terms; **O**uter terms; **I**nner terms; **L**ast terms.

Example 1

Expand and simplify.

$$(x + 5)(x + 8)$$

First, Outer, Inner, Last

$$\begin{aligned}
&\text{F} \quad \text{O} \quad \text{I} \quad \text{L} \\
&= x^2 + 8x + 5x + 40 \\
&= x^2 + 13x + 40
\end{aligned}$$

Pay attention to negative signs in solutions.

Example 2

Expand and simplify.

$$(2y - 4)(5y + 2) = 10y^2 + 4y - 20y - 8$$
$$= 10y^2 - 16y - 8$$

If a binomial is squared, it means "multiply it by itself."

Example 3

Expand.

$$(5t - 6s)^2 = (5t - 6s)(5t - 6s)$$
$$= 25t^2 - 30st - 30st + 36s^2$$
$$= 25t^2 - 60st + 36s^2$$

Now you can simplify expressions involving products of binomials.

Example 4

Expand.

$$-7(4w + 2)(3w - 1)$$

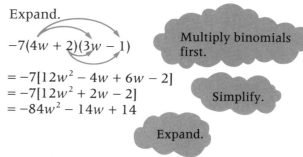

Multiply binomials first.

Simplify.

Expand.

$$= -7[12w^2 - 4w + 6w - 2]$$
$$= -7[12w^2 + 2w - 2]$$
$$= -84w^2 - 14w + 14$$

Example 5

Expand.

$$3(2x - 1)(x - 5) - 2(x + 3)^2$$
$$= 3(2x - 1)(x - 5) - 2(x + 3)(x + 3)$$
$$= 3[2x^2 - 10x - x + 5]$$
$$\quad - 2[x^2 + 3x + 3x + 9]$$
$$= 3[2x^2 - 11x + 5] - 2[x^2 + 6x + 9]$$
$$= 6x^2 - 33x + 15 - 2x^2 - 12x - 18$$
$$= 4x^2 - 45x - 3$$

Exercise

A 1. Find the missing term or terms.

(a) $(x + 8)(x + 3) = x^2 + 11x + \square$

(b) $(y - 9)(y + 5) = y^2 - 4y + \square$

(c) $(a - 4)(a - 6) = a^2 + \square + 24$

(d) $(4a + 3)(3a - 1) = \square + 5a + \square$

(e) $(z + 7)(z + 3) = z^2 + \square + 21$

(f) $(w - 9)(w + 5) = w^2 + \square + \square$

(g) $(a - 3b)(a - 4b) = a^2 + \square + \square$

B 2. Expand and simplify.

(a) $(t + 6)(t + 8)$

(b) $(2a + 5)(3a + 4)$

(c) $(x - 7)(x + 10)$

(d) $(d + 11)(d - 9)$

(e) $(y - 6)(y - 3)$

(f) $(2p - 5)(p + 4)$

(g) $(3r + 9)(2r - 1)$

(h) $(6c - 5)(2c - 4)$

(i) $6c - 5(2c - 4)$

(j) $(4s - 3)(4s + 3)$

(k) $(5x + 3)^2$

(l) $(4r - 7)^2$

(m) $(3a - 8)^2$

(n) $(3a)^2 - (8)^2$

3. Expand and simplify.

(a) $(a + 3c)(a + 2c)$

(b) $(2x + y)(3x + 2y)$

(c) $(3w - t)(2w + 3t)$

(d) $(5x + 4y)(6x - y)$

(e) $(3m - 4n)(7m - 8n)$

(f) $(5b - 2q)(4b - 3q)$

(g) $(a + 5x)^2$

(h) $(3c - 4b)^2$

(i) $(10y - 7t)(10y + 7t)$

(j) $(8q + 3a)(a - 2q)$

(k) $(3x^2 + 2x)(4x^2 + x)$

(l) $(7ab - 4)(2ab - 3)$

4. Expand and simplify.

(a) $(a - 4)(a - 6) + 5(3a - 2)$

(b) $(2w - 5)(w + 7) - 3(4w - 8)$

(c) $(x + 5)(x - 3) + (x - 4)(x + 2)$

(d) $(y - 10)(y + 3) + (2y + 5)(y - 7)$

(e) $(a - 5)(a + 6) + (2a - 5)(2a - 1)$

5. Simplify by first expanding binomials.

(a) $4(x + 6)(x - 4)$

(b) $3(2a - 9)(a + 2)$

(c) $-2(2w - 3)(w - 4)$

(d) $-5(a + 2)(3a - 2)$

(e) $6(2x - y)(x + 4y)$

6. Simplify.

(a) $(a - 6)(a + 8) + 3(a + 1)(a + 4)$

(b) $2(x - 9)(x - 2) + 4(x + 6)(x - 2)$

(c) $(a + 5)^2 + (a - 4)^2$

(d) $(y - 8)^2 + (y + 3)^2$

(e) $(2s - 3)^2 + 3(s - 4)(s + 2)$

(f) $2(x + 1)^2 + 3(x - 2)^2$

(g) $2(a - 5)(a - 4) + 3(a + 2)^2$

7. Simplify.

(a) $(a + 4)(a - 12) - 2(a + 3)(a + 2)$

(b) $(x + 5)(x - 5) - (x + 6)(x + 3)$

(c) $(4x - 3)(x - 7) - 3(x - 8)(x + 2)$

(d) $(c + 4)^2 - (c + 3)^2$

(e) $2(y - 6)(y - 4) - 3(y + 4)(y - 1)$

(f) $-3(2a + 1)(a - 4) + 2(2a + 3)(a + 2)$

(g) $4(w + 3)^2 - 3(w + 2)^2$

(h) $(x + 2)(x^2 + 5x + 7)$

(i) $(x - 3)(x^2 - 4x + 9)$

8. Find a simplified polynomial expression for the shaded area.

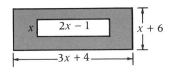

Common Factoring

You have already learned how to expand an expression like $5(30a + 15b)$.

$5(30a + 15b)$
$= 5(30a) + 5(15b)$
$= 150a + 75b$

> Multiply *each* term by 5.

You can divide polynomials in a similar way.

$$(150a + 75b) \div 5 = \frac{150a + 75b}{5}$$
$$= \frac{150a}{5} + \frac{75b}{5}$$
$$= 30a + 15b$$

> Divide *each* term by 5.

This division could be done in another way.

$$(150a + 75b) \div 5 = \frac{(150a + 75b)}{5}$$
$$= \frac{5(30a + 15b)}{5}$$
$$= 30a + 15b$$

This method involves finding the common factor of $150a + 75b$. To factor means to express as a product.

Example 1

Factor $12a + 16b$.

$$12a + 16b = \boxed{?} \times \boxed{?}$$

Look for terms that divide into both $12a$ and $16b$ exactly. The **common factors** are 2 and 4. The **greatest common factor** is 4.

$$12a + 16b = 4 (\boxed{?})$$
$$= 4(3a + 4b)$$

> 4 is the GCF.

Each term in the polynomial has been divided by the GCF.

You can check the factoring by expanding the answer.

$$4(3a + 4b) = 4 \times 3a + 4 \times 4b$$
$$= 12a + 16b$$

The answer is correct.

In some factoring problems, the GCF may contain variables as well as numbers.

Example 2

Factor $14a^2 + 21a$.

$$14a^2 + 21a = 7a(\boxed{?})$$
$$= 7a(2a + 3)$$

> The GCF of $14a^2$ and $21a$ is $7a$.

> Check: $7a(2a + 3)$
> $= 14a^2 + 21a$

The GCF may not be a single term. In the example below, the GCF is a binomial.

Example 3

Factor $2s(s + 6) - 7(s + 6)$.

> The GCF is $(s + 6)$.

$$2s\ (s + 6)\ - 7\ (s + 6)$$
$$= (s + 6)(\boxed{?})$$
$$= (s + 6)(2s - 7)$$

Exercise

A 1. Divide.

(a) $(8x + 6) \div 2$

(b) $(16a - 12b) \div 4$

(c) $(ab + ac) \div a$

(d) $(6xy - 9x) \div 3x$

(e) $\dfrac{4x - 12y}{-4}$

(f) $\dfrac{3x^2 + 2x}{-x}$

(g) $\dfrac{15b - 5}{-5}$

2. State the GCF, then factor.

(a) $4x + 8$
(b) $9a + 21$
(c) $12z - 36$
(d) $20p - 28$
(e) $8a - 4x + 12$
(f) $xy + xz$
(g) $ab - bc$
(h) $p^2 - 5p$
(i) $2st + 8at$
(j) $14s^2 - 21s$

B 3. Divide.

(a) $\dfrac{3x + 6n}{3}$

(b) $(8a - 4) \div 4$

(c) $\dfrac{18x + 24p}{-6}$

(d) $\dfrac{12ab - 15pb}{-3b}$

(e) $\dfrac{20x^2 + 35x}{5x}$

(f) $\dfrac{14a - 7b + 56c}{7}$

(g) $(2s^2 + 4s) \div 2s$

(h) $\dfrac{xy - 2x + x^2}{x}$

(i) $\dfrac{15w - 12q + 27r}{-3}$

(j) $\dfrac{4x^3 + 12x^2 - 16x}{-4x}$

4. Divide and simplify.

(a) $\dfrac{6t - 15}{3} + \dfrac{14t + 35}{7}$

(b) $\dfrac{28s + 36}{-4} + \dfrac{12s - 18}{-6}$

(c) $\dfrac{35r - 21s}{-7} + \dfrac{18r + 9s}{9}$

(d) $\dfrac{4x^2 + 10x}{2x} - \dfrac{15xy - 25x}{5x}$

(e) $\dfrac{16y^3 - 8y^2}{8y^2} - \dfrac{42y - 63}{-7}$

5. Factor each polynomial.

(a) $12w - 18$
(b) $50x + 20$
(c) $64a - 24$
(d) $5 - 30p$
(e) $6s - 9t + 12$
(f) $20x + 32y$
(g) $40w - 24 + 8t$
(h) $30s + 12q - 6$
(i) $16p - 56q$
(j) $90 + 15p$
(k) $ax + 6x$
(l) $21xy - 5y$
(m) $t^2 - 8t$
(n) $4x - x^2$
(o) $ap + pt - p$
(p) $9r - rs + r^3$
(q) $y^4 + 3y^3 - 2y^2$
(r) $a - a^3 + 3a^5$
(s) $6r^6 + 3r^3$
(t) $4s + 10st$

6. Factor each polynomial. Check your answer by expanding.

(a) $15x + 12xy$
(b) $32x^2 - 28x$
(c) $40t^4 + 8t^2$
(d) $12a^2 - 9ab$
(e) $60y - 45y^2$
(f) $75w^6 + 50w^2$
(g) $9n^5 - 3n^2$
(h) $2x^2 + 10x^4 - 8x^6$
(i) $35rs - 55st + 5s$
(j) $abc + abd - abe$
(k) $2bc - 7abc$
(l) $3m^3 + 9m^9 - 6m^6$
(m) $12w^2q - 15w^3$
(n) $120x^4 + 36x^6y$

7. Factor.

(a) $10pqr - 18qrt + 22qrs$
(b) $12mn + 42m^2n$
(c) $5rt^2 - 8r^2t - r^2t^2$
(d) $80z^4 - 32z^2 + 64z$
(e) $x(x + 9) + 6(x + 9)$
(f) $3a(a - 4) + 7(a - 4)$
(g) $5r(r + s) - 3s(r + s)$
(h) $m(3a - 6x) + 6(3a - 6x)$
(i) $p(p + 8) + (p + 8)$
(j) $4x(x - 6) - (x - 6)$

Side Trip

If you were given only 30 mL and 50 mL containers and a pail of water, how would you measure out exactly 40 mL of water?

Factoring Trinomials

Part I

Multiplying 2 binomials usually results in a 3-term expression called a **trinomial**.

binomials

$$(x + 10)(x + 2) = x^2 + 2x + 10x + 20$$
$$= x^2 + 12x + 20$$

trinomial

There is an important relationship here.

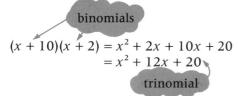

10×2

$$(x + 10)(x + 2) = x^2 + \boxed{12}\, x + \boxed{20}$$

$10 + 2$

You can often factor a trinomial by expressing it as the product of 2 binomials.

$$x^2 + 11x + 18 = (\ \boxed{?}\ +\ \boxed{?}\ )(\ \boxed{?}\ +\ \boxed{?}\ )$$
$$= (x +\ \boxed{?}\ )(x +\ \boxed{?}\ )$$

To factor the trinomial, find a pair of numbers that satisfy 2 conditions.

Multiply to 18	1×18
and	$\boxed{2 \times 9}$
add to 11.	3×6

The numbers that satisfy both conditions are 2 and 9.

$$x^2 + 11x + 18 = (x + 2)(x + 9)$$

You can check this factoring by expanding $(x + 2)(x + 9)$.

Example 1

Factor $a^2 + 8a + 12$.

$$a^2 + 8a + 12$$
$$= (a +\ ?\ )(a +\ ?\ )$$
$$= (a + 2)(a + 6)$$

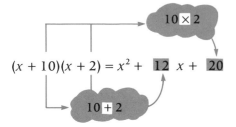

$12 = 1 \times 12$
$= \boxed{2 \times 6}$ → $2 + 6 = 8$
$= 3 \times 4$

After a little practice, you'll recognize the factors more quickly. Pay attention to negative signs in the trinomial.

Example 2

Factor $y^2 - 3y - 28$.
$$y^2 - 3y - 28$$
$$= (y - 7)(y + 4)$$

$(-7) \times (4) = -28$
$(-7) + (4) = -3$

Check the factoring by expanding.
$$(y - 7)(y + 4) = y^2 + 4y - 7y - 28$$
$$= y^2 - 3y - 28$$

Sometimes you can do common factoring first, then factor the resulting trinomial.

Example 3

Factor fully.
$$3t^2 - 30t + 48$$
$$= 3(t^2 - 10t + 16)$$
$$= 3(t - 8)(t - 2)$$

3 is a common factor.

$(-8) \times (-2) = 16$
$(-8) + (-2) = -10$

The trinomial you have to factor may contain more than one variable. Follow the same method to factor.

Example 4

Factor $x^2 + 6xy + 5y^2$.

$$x^2 + 6xy + 5y^2 = (x + \blacksquare y)(x + \blacksquare y)$$

Find 2 numbers that multiply to give 5 and add to give 6.

$$1 \times 5 = 5$$
$$1 + 5 = 6$$

$$x^2 + 6xy + 5y^2 = (x + y)(x + 5y)$$

On your own, expand to check the factoring.

Side Trip

Here are some puzzles and problems to test your thinking skills.

1. Jan's wrist watch loses 8 min/h. If it gives the correct time at 01:00, what is the correct time when the watch reads 18:00 the same day?

2. If a hen and a half lay an egg and a half in a day and a half, how many eggs do 6 hens lay in 6 days?

3. If 3 cats eat 3 mice in 3 min, how long will it take 50 cats to eat 50 mice?

Exercise

A 1. Find the missing information.

(a) $x^2 + 7x + 12 = (x + 4)(\square\square\square)$
(b) $y^2 + 11y + 38 = (\square\square\square)(y + 5)$
(c) $a^2 - 3a - 10 = (a + 2)(\square\square\square)$
(d) $w^2 + 4w - 12 = (\square\square\square)(w - 2)$
(e) $t^2 - 8t + 15 = (t - 3)(\square\square\square)$
(f) $a^2 + 12a + 20 = (a + \square)(a + \square)$
(g) $b^2 - 2b - 15 = (b + \square)(b - \square)$
(h) $c^2 + c - 6 = (c - \square)(c + \square)$
(i) $s^2 - 6s + 8 = (s - \square)(s - \square)$
(j) $p^2 - 9p + 8 = (p - \square)(p - \square)$

2. State the missing signs.

(a) $x^2 + 5x + 6 = (x \:\square\: 3)(x \:\square\: 2)$
(b) $z^2 + 3z - 28 = (z \:\square\: 7)(z \:\square\: 4)$
(c) $s^2 - 5s - 24 = (s \:\square\: 8)(s \:\square\: 3)$
(d) $a^2 - a - 12 = (a \:\square\: 3)(a \:\square\: 4)$
(e) $w^2 + 5w - 6 = (w \:\square\: 1)(w \:\square\: 6)$
(f) $p^2 - 7p + 10 = (p \:\square\: 5)(p \:\square\: 2)$
(g) $r^2 - 12r + 20 = (r \:\square\: 10)(r \:\square\: 2)$
(h) $t^2 - 8t - 20 = (t \:\square\: 10)(t \:\square\: 2)$
(i) $a^2 + 2a - 24 = (a \:\square\: 4)(a \:\square\: 6)$
(j) $t^2 - 9t + 18 = (t \:\square\: 6)(t \:\square\: 3)$
(k) $t^2 + 0t - 16 = (t \:\square\: 4)(t \:\square\: 4)$

B 3. Factor each trinomial.

(a) $x^2 + 7x + 12$ (k) $y^2 - 9y + 14$
(b) $x^2 + 8x + 12$ (l) $v^2 - 5v + 4$
(c) $x^2 + 13x + 12$ (m) $a^2 - 15a + 50$
(d) $x^2 + 13x + 22$ (n) $b^2 - 27b + 50$
(e) $a^2 + 13a + 30$ (o) $c^2 - 16c + 60$
(f) $y^2 + 9y + 20$ (p) $d^2 - 19d + 60$
(g) $s^2 + 14s + 40$ (q) $q^2 - 3q + 2$
(h) $f^2 + 2f + 1$ (r) $x^2 - 14x + 24$
(i) $w^2 + 6w + 5$ (s) $p^2 - 20p + 100$
(j) $m^2 + 5m + 6$ (t) $24 - 10s + s^2$

59

4. Factor.

(a) $x^2 - 3x - 10$ (k) $s^2 - 14s + 24$
(b) $y^2 - 2y - 15$ (l) $t^2 - 2t - 24$
(c) $a^2 + 2a - 15$ (m) $v^2 + 23v - 24$
(d) $b^2 + 7b - 30$ (n) $q^2 + 11q + 24$
(e) $c^2 - c - 20$ (o) $w^2 - 12w + 36$
(f) $z^2 - 6z - 27$ (p) $y^2 - 5y - 36$
(g) $q^2 + 11q - 12$ (q) $h^2 + h - 56$
(h) $k^2 - 3k - 40$ (r) $p^2 + 12p + 32$
(i) $t^2 + t - 42$ (s) $z^2 - 17z - 60$
(j) $n^2 + 8n - 48$ (t) $m^2 - 19m + 60$

5. Factor each trinomial.

(a) $x^2 + 6xy + 8y^2$
(b) $a^2 - 10ab + 16b^2$
(c) $c^2 - cd - 20d^2$
(d) $x^2 + 4xy - 45y^2$
(e) $p^2 - 2pq + q^2$
(f) $r^2 + 2rs - 48s^2$
(g) $q^2 + 16qr + 48r^2$
(h) $t^2 - 10tv + 9v^2$
(i) $q^2 - 7qw - 30w^2$
(j) $x^2y^2 + 5xy - 36$

6. Factor completely by first finding a common factor.

(a) $2a^2 + 12a + 18$
(b) $3x^2 - 21x + 30$
(c) $5z^2 - 5z - 30$
(d) $2b^2 + 10b - 48$
(e) $6c^2 - 12c - 18$
(f) $3q^2 + 15q - 42$
(g) $12m^2 - 84m + 72$
(h) $x^3 + 4x^2 - 21x$
(i) $2a^3 + 8a^2 + 6a$
(j) $xy^2 + xy - 72x$
(k) $4t^3 - 8t^2 - 60t$
(l) $2x^2 + 10xy + 12y^2$
(m) $4a^2 + 4ab - 48b^2$
(n) $s^3 - 14s^2t + 33st^2$
(o) $3a^2b + 9ab - 30b$

7. (a) Evaluate the expression $x^2 - 15x + 50$, given $x = 105$.
   (b) Factor the expression $x^2 - 15x + 50$. Now substitute $x = 105$ into the factored form to evaluate.
   (c) Which method of substitution is easier? Why?

8. Evaluate each expression for the value of the variable given. Use the method of your choice.

(a) $y^2 + 14y + 24$, when $y = 98$
(b) $z^2 - 16z + 60$, when $z = 1006$
(c) $x^2 + 19x - 20$, when $x = 1.08$
(d) $q^2 - 12q + 36$, when $q = 26$
(e) $w^2 - 4w - 45$, when $w = -5.1$

Side Trip

Many of the algebra skills that you are learning in this unit can be used to make some of your numerical calculations easier. For instance, your skills in expanding expressions could be used to help you do calculations like the one below mentally.

$$7 \times 112$$
$$\text{Think: } 7 \times 112 = 7(100 + 12)$$
$$= 700 + 84$$
$$= 784$$

Try each of the following calculations in your head. Check using a calculator.

1. 5×104 6. 7×905
2. 8×407 7. 7×95
3. 12×112 8. 4×1045
4. 11×709 9. 9×1208
5. 9×805 10. 8×8060

Part 2

You have factored trinomials in the following way.

$$2a^2 + 16a + 30 = 2(a^2 + 8a + 15)$$
$$= 2(a + 3)(a + 5)$$

The trinomial below requires a different method of factoring since there is no common factor.

$$2a^2 + 5a + 3$$

Start by factoring the first and last terms.

$$\overset{\frown}{2a^2 + 5a + 3}$$
$$2a \times a \qquad 1 \times 3$$

Now form pairs of binomial factors so that the first terms are $2a$ and a and the second terms are 1 and 3.

$$(\ 2a\ +\ \boxed{1}\ )(\ a\ +\ \boxed{3}\ )$$
$$(\ a\ +\ \boxed{1}\ )(\ 2a\ +\ \boxed{3}\ )$$

What combination of pairs will give you the correct middle term?

Once you expand these pairs, you will discover that only one combination gives the correct middle term.

$$(2a + 1)(a + 3) = 2a^2 + 6a + 1a + 3$$
$$= 2a^2 + 7a + 3$$

$$(a + 1)(2a + 3) = 2a^2 + 3a + 2a + 3$$
$$= 2a^2 + 5a + 3$$

The factors of $2a^2 + 5a + 3$ are $(a + 1)$ and $(2a + 3)$.

So $2a^2 + 5a + 3 = (a + 1)(2a + 3)$

Example 1

Factor $4r^2 + 11r + 6$.

Start by factoring the first and last terms.

$$\overset{\frown}{4r^2 + 11r + 6}$$
$$4r \times r \qquad 6 \times 1$$
$$2r \times 2r \qquad 2 \times 3$$

To combine these factors to make pairs of binomials, first choose one set of factors of the first term, like $4r \times r$, and combine it with a set of factors of the second term, like 6×1.

$$(4r + 6)(r + 1)$$
$$= 4r^2 + 4r + 6r + 6$$
$$= 4r^2 + \boxed{10r} + 6$$

> Expand.
> The middle term is not right.
> Try again!

$$(4r + 1)(r + 6)$$
$$= 4r^2 + 24r + r + 6$$
$$= 4r^2 + \boxed{25r} + 6$$

> Try another set of factors.

$$(4r + 3)(r + 2)$$
$$= 4r^2 + 8r + 3r + 6$$
$$= 4r^2 + \boxed{11r} + 6$$

> That's it!

The factors of $4r^2 + 11r + 6$ are $(4r + 3)$ and $(r + 2)$.

So $4r^2 + 11r + 6 = (4r + 3)(r + 2)$

The trial method is useful if the number of combinations is few. There is another method that does not require a long list of trials to find the answer, but does require a different first step.

Factor $10y^2 + 13y + 4$.

Multiplying by $\frac{10}{10}$ will not change the expression.

$$\frac{\boxed{10}\ (10y^2 + 13y + 4)}{\boxed{10}}$$
$$\frac{100y^2 + 130y + 40}{10}$$

The new coefficient of y^2 is a perfect square. The first term in each binomial factor will be $10y$.

$$= \frac{(\ \boxed{10y}\ + \triangle)(\ \boxed{10y}\ + \blacksquare)}{10}$$

Look for factor pairs, $\triangle$ and $\blacksquare$, that multiply to 40.

$$80y$$
$$(10y + 8)(10y + 5)$$
$$50y$$
$$80y + 50y = 130y, \text{ the middle term}$$

$$= \frac{(10y + 8)(10y + 5)}{10}$$
$$= \frac{2(5y + 4) \times 5(2y + 1)}{10} \quad \text{Now common factor.}$$
$$= (5y + 4)(2y + 1)$$

The first 2 steps in this method can be skipped because of the following fact.

$$\frac{(\ 10\ y + \boxed{8})(10y + \boxed{5}\ )}{10} \quad 10 \times 4 = 40$$

But $8 \times 5 = 40$
and $8 + 5 = 13$

The numbers 8 and 5 add to 13 (the middle coefficient) and multiply to 40 (the product of the first and last coefficients).

Let's use this shortcut to factor the following.

Example 2

Factor $6x^2 - 11x + 4$.
$$6x^2 - 11x + 4$$
$$= \frac{(6x + \triangle)(6x + \blacksquare)}{6}$$

$$6 \times 4 = 24$$
$$\triangle \times \blacksquare = 24$$
$$\triangle + \blacksquare = -11$$
$$\triangle = -8, \blacksquare = -3$$

$$= \frac{(6x + \boxed{-8})(6x + \boxed{-3})}{6}$$
$$= \frac{2(3x - 4) \times 3(2x - 1)}{6} \quad \text{Factor.}$$
$$= (3x - 4)(2x - 1) \quad \text{Divide.}$$

Example 3

Factor $4t^2 - 9t - 9$.
$$4t^2 - 9t - 9 \qquad 4 \times (-9) = -36$$
$$= \frac{(4t + \triangle)(4t + \blacksquare)}{4}$$
$$= \frac{(4t + 3)(4t - 12)}{4} \qquad 3 \times (-12) = -36$$
$$\qquad\qquad\qquad\qquad\qquad 3 + (-12) = -9$$
$$= \frac{(4t + 3) \times 4(t - 3)}{4}$$
$$= (4t + 3)(t - 3)$$

Example 4

Factor $6w^2 + 25wx - 9x^2$.
$$6w^2 + 25wx - 9x^2 = \frac{(6w + \triangle)(6w + \blacksquare)}{6}$$
$$= \frac{(6w + 27x)(6w - 2x)}{6}$$
$$= \frac{3(2w + 9x)2(3w - x)}{6}$$
$$= (2w + 9x)(3w - x)$$

Exercise

A 1. State the missing information.

(a) $3y^2 + 10y + 8$

$$= \frac{(\square y + 6)(\square y + 4)}{\square}$$

(b) $5y^2 + 12y + 4$

$$= \frac{(5y + \square)(5y + \square)}{5}$$

(c) $6y^2 + 7y + 2$

$$= \frac{(6y + \square)(\square y + 3)}{\square}$$

(d) $9y^2 - 19y + 2$

$$= \frac{(9y + \square)(9y + \square)}{\square}$$

2. State the numbers missing from the table.

	Products	Sum	Numbers
(a)	20	9	$\square,\square$
(b)	16	-10	$\square,\square$
(c)	-12	4	$\square,\square$
(d)	-18	-7	$\square,\square$
(e)	-42	1	$\square,\square$
(f)	48	-19	$\square,\square$

B 3. Use the result from Question 2 to factor each of the following.

(a) $2x^2 + 9x + 10$ (d) $6x^2 - 7x - 3$
(b) $16x^2 - 10x + 1$ (e) $21a^2 + a - 2$
(c) $4x^2 + 4x - 3$ (f) $12z^2 - 19z + 4$

4. Factor.

(a) $2a^2 + 7a + 3$ (g) $4t^2 - 8t + 3$
(b) $3x^2 + 16x + 5$ (h) $3a^2 + 4a - 7$
(c) $3x^2 + 8x + 5$ (i) $3x^2 - 4x - 4$
(d) $5x^2 + 8x + 3$ (j) $4y^2 + 8y - 5$
(e) $3x^2 - 10x + 7$ (k) $6t^2 - 13t - 5$
(f) $5y^2 - 36y + 7$ (l) $10x^2 - 11x + 3$

5. Factor the following using the method most suitable for each trinomial.

(a) $3a^2 + 8a + 4$ (g) $8x^2 + 22x + 5$
(b) $4x^2 - 13x + 3$ (h) $10a^2 - 19a - 2$
(c) $6x^2 - 13x + 5$ (i) $12w^2 + 11w + 2$
(d) $6y^2 + 17y + 5$ (j) $25a^2 - 5a - 2$
(e) $5x^2 - 17x + 6$ (k) $12c^2 + 16c + 5$
(f) $5t^2 + 29t - 6$ (l) $12c^2 + 17c + 5$

6. Factor the following.

(a) $3t^2 - t - 4$ (k) $2w^2 - 13w + 15$
(b) $4t^2 + t - 3$ (l) $2w^2 - 13w - 15$
(c) $6x^2 + 11x + 4$ (m) $2v^2 - 11v + 15$
(d) $16y^2 - 33y + 2$ (n) $10a^2 + 61a + 6$
(e) $5t^2 + 19t - 4$ (o) $6s^2 + 59s - 10$
(f) $5t^2 - t - 4$ (p) $2k^2 - 9k - 11$
(g) $15a^2 + 13a + 2$ (q) $8x^2 + x - 9$
(h) $9s^2 - 9s - 4$ (r) $8x^2 - 17x + 9$
(i) $9s^2 - 15s + 4$ (s) $8x^2 - 6x - 9$
(j) $9s^2 - 12s + 4$ (t) $10y^2 + 21y - 10$

7. Factor.

(a) $6x^2 + 13x + 6$ (f) $20t^2 - 20t + 5$
(b) $18x^2 + 13x + 2$ (g) $20t^2 + 21t - 5$
(c) $36x^2 + 13x + 1$ (h) $21s^2 - 13s + 2$
(d) $18x^2 - 5x - 2$ (i) $24r^2 + 2r - 5$
(e) $6x^2 + 5x - 6$ (j) $8w^2 - 63w - 8$

8. Factor by first finding a common factor.

(a) $4x^3 + 11x^2 + 6x$
(b) $9y^3 - 11y^2 + 2y$
(c) $5c^5 - 2c^4 - 3c^3$
(d) $8ab^2 + 6ab - 5a$
(e) $600x^2 - 1100x + 300$

Difference of Squares

You can factor many types of expressions quickly if you can recognize a pattern.

Consider the expansion of each of the following.

$$(x + 7)(x - 7) = x^2 - 7x + 7x - 49$$
$$= x^2 - 49$$
$$(3x - 4)(3x + 4) = 9x^2 + 12x - 12x - 16$$
$$= 9x^2 - 16$$

Note the difference in signs in the following.

$$(3x - 4)(3x + 4) = 9x^2 - 16$$
$$(3x)^2 \qquad (4)^2$$

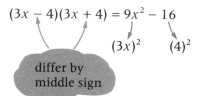

differ by middle sign

Expanding resulted in a binomial, and each term was a perfect square. These binomials are known as differences of squares.

$$9x^2 - 16, \quad 4y^2 - 25$$

Factoring can be done in one step.

$$4y^2 - 25 = (2y + 5)(2y - 5)$$

Example 1

Factor.

- $x^2 - 81y^2 = (x + 9y)(x - 9y)$

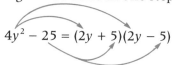

- $5a^3 - 45a = 5a \ (a^2 - 9)$
$$= 5a(a + 3)(a - 3)$$

common factor

Example 2

Factor completely.

$$x^4 - 5x^2 - 13$$
$$= (x^2 - 9)(x^2 + 4)$$

Factor trinomial.

$$= (x + 3)(x - 3)(x^2 + 4)$$

Factor difference of squares.

Exercise

A 1. State the two factors if possible.

(a) $x^2 - 81$
(b) $y^2 - 49$
(c) $a^2 - 100$
(d) $9 - x$
(e) $x^2 - y$
(f) $a^2 - 36b^2$
(g) $100z^2 - 9y^2$
(h) $400x^2y^2 - 1$
(i) $a^2b^2 - 64s^2t^2$
(j) $t^2 + 16$

B 2. Factor. Check for common factors first.

(a) $b^2 - 36$
(b) $25x^2 - 49$
(c) $9x^2z^2 - 4$
(d) $5a^2 - 5$
(e) $27 - 75c^2$
(f) $z^3 - 100z$
(g) $a^2b - 64b$
(h) $pq^2 - p$
(i) $20z^2 - 500y^2$
(j) $32x^2 + 8$
(k) $3x^2y^2 - 48$
(l) $8w - 18w^3$
(m) $t^3s^2 - t$
(n) $x^4 - 9$
(o) $y^6 - 100$
(p) $9z^6 - 121c^2$
(q) $x^7 - 144x$
(r) $10s^2 - 250t^2$
(s) $3z^3 - 75z$
(t) $28s^{10}t - 4t$

3. Factor completely.

(a) $y^4 - 81$
(b) $x^4 - 16$
(c) $16s^4 - 1$
(d) $81q^4 - 625$
(e) $a^4 - b^4$
(f) $x^4 - 256y^4$
(g) $a^4 + 7a^2 - 18$
(h) $x^4 - 18x^2 + 32$
(i) $y^4 - 3y^2 - 4$
(j) $s^4 - 11s^2 + 10$
(k) $x^4 - 10x^2 + 9$
(l) $p^4 - 13p^2 + 36$

A Factoring Summary

You have learned several types of factoring in this unit. The table summarizes the types of factoring possible for a given polynomial.

Number of Terms	Types of Factoring
2	• Common factoring • Difference of squares
3	• Common factoring • Trinomial
4 or more	• Common factoring

Follow the 2 steps below when given a factoring problem.

1. Always check for a common factor to all of the terms *first*.

2. Count the number of terms in the expression to be factored.

   • If it's a binomial, is it a difference of squares? If so, factor.

   • If it's a trinomial, is it of the form $ax^2 + bx + c$? If so, try to factor.

Example 1

Factor $6x^2 - 14x - 12$.

$6x^2 - 14x - 12$
$= 2[3x^2 - 7x - 6]$
$= 2(x - 3)(3x + 2)$

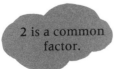
2 is a common factor.

Exercise

B 1. Factor and check by expanding.

(a) $pq - qr + 5q$
(b) $16a^2 - 14ab$
(c) $2x(x + 7) - 6(x + 7)$
(d) $q^2 - 14q + 48$
(e) $x^2 + 14x + 40$
(f) $y^2 - 3y + 2$
(g) $h^2 - 144$
(h) $3x^2 - 10x + 7$
(i) $6y^2 + 7y - 3$
(j) $9w^2 - 36b^2$
(k) $x^3 - 4x$
(l) $p^2 - 5pq - 66q^2$
(m) $x^3 + x^2 - 56x$
(n) $6x^3 - 6x$
(o) $4x^2 + 20x$
(p) $4x^2 + 20x - 11$
(q) $4x^2 + 20x - 24$
(r) $3x^2 - 15x + 12$
(s) $3x^3 - 12x$
(t) $3x^2 - 12x$
(u) $5w^2 + 30wr + 40r^2$
(v) $3z^2 + 13z - 10$
(w) $3z^2 - 13z + 10$
(x) $3z^2 - 15z - 150$

2. Factor.

(a) $w^2 - 16w$
(b) $w^3 - 16w$
(c) $w^5 - 16w$
(d) $w^2 - 16w + 28$
(e) $w^2 - 16w - 36$
(f) $w^3 - 16w^2 - 80w$
(g) $2w^2 - 16w - 40$
(h) $3w^2 - 16w - 12$
(i) $3w^3 - 16w^2 + 16w$
(j) $3w^2 - 3w - 36$

Using the Computer to Find GCF

$$945x - 560y = \blacksquare\ (\blacksquare)$$

To factor binomials with large coefficients, the first problem would be to find the largest number that divides *both* coefficients, or the greatest common factor.

Here is one way to find the GCF of 945 and 560.

1. Divide 945 by 560.

$$560\overline{)945} \\ \underline{560} \\ 385$$

with quotient 1.

larger number   smaller number

Use the divisor and the remainder in the next step.

2. Now divide 560 by 385.

$$385\overline{)560} \\ \underline{385} \\ 175$$

with quotient 1.

Again, use the divisor and the remainder in the next step.

3. Now divide 385 by 175.

$$175\overline{)385} \\ \underline{350} \\ 35$$

with quotient 2.

4. Now divide 175 by 35.

$$35\overline{)175} \\ \underline{175} \\ 0$$

with quotient 5.

When you get a remainder of 0, you're finished! The divisor is the GCF.

The GCF is 35, and
$$945x - 560y = 35(27x - 16y).$$

The calculations needed to find the GCF can be tedious. Fortunately, you can program a computer to perform the task for you.

```
10   PRINT "WHAT IS THE LARGER
     NUMBER?"
20   INPUT L
30   PRINT "WHAT IS THE SMALLER
     NUMBER?"
40   INPUT S
50   X = INT(L/S)
60   Y = L − X*S
70   IF Y <= 0 THEN GOTO 150
80   L = S
90   S = Y
100 GOTO 50
150 PRINT "THE GCF IS "; S"."
```

Exercise

1. Use the program to find the GCF for each of the following.

  (a) 182 and 312   (c) 585 and 990
  (b) 480 and 672   (d) 2077 and 4489

2. Use the program to help you factor the following binomials.

  (a) $184x + 115y$
  (b) $442a - 238b$
  (c) $1173x^2 - 3162x$

Unit 3 Review

1. Simplify.

   (a) $4a - 7b - 9a + b$
   (b) $5x^2 - 4x - (-3x^2) + 8x$
   (c) $5xy - 7xz + 4yz - xz + 2yz + 7xy$
   (d) $(7s)(-2t)$
   (e) $(3q)(-r)(-6p)$
   (f) $(5ab)(-6ac)$
   (g) $-12x^{12} \times (4x^4)$
   (h) $-12x^{12} \div (4x^4)$
   (i) $-12x^{12} + 4x^4$
   (j) $(-20x^6y^4)(-5x^6y^4)$
   (k) $(-20x^6y^4) \div (-5x^6y^4)$
   (l) $-20x^6y^4 - 5x^6y^4$
   (m) $(3x)^2 + 3x^2$
   (n) $(6t)(-4t) - (-3t)^2$
   (o) $\dfrac{24pqr}{-2pq} + \dfrac{14r^2}{7r}$
   (p) $(2w)(5w)^2$
   (q) $[(2w)(5w)]^2$
   (r) $(2w + 5w)^2$
   (s) $(3x - 6y + z) + (5x - y - 6z)$
   (t) $(5s + t - 7) - (8s - 4t + 5)$
   (u) $(2x^2 - 6x) - (x + 4x^2) + (5x^2 - 9x)$
   (v) $5a - (7ab - 3b + a) - (-3ab + 2b)$
   (w) $\dfrac{6x - 15y + 3z}{3}$
   (x) $\dfrac{8a - 28b + 4}{-4}$
   (y) $\dfrac{14x^3 - 56x^2 + 35x}{-7x}$
   (z) $\dfrac{18s^2t^6 - 9s^6t^3}{-9s^2t^3}$

2. Expand and simplify.

   (a) $5(4a - 6b + 9)$
   (b) $-8(3x - 4y + z)$
   (c) $8x(x - 5y)$
   (d) $-5t^2(-4t + 3)$
   (e) $-6(x^2 - 4x + 11)$
   (f) $5ab(2a + 3b - c)$
   (g) $-9x(5x - 6y)$
   (h) $9x - (5x - 6y)$
   (i) $6(b - 8) + 5(b + 7)$
   (j) $-3(6a - 9w) - (7w + a)$
   (k) $7z(2z - 8) - z(3z - 2) + 4z(z - 8)$
   (l) $7ab(3ab + 4a) - 3ab(a + 4ab)$

3. Expand and simplify.

   (a) $(y + 9)(y + 7)$
   (b) $(x - 12)(x - 4)$
   (c) $(a + 14)(a - 5)$
   (d) $(x - y)(x - 3y)$
   (e) $(8 + x)(5 - x)$
   (f) $7a + 4(6a - 2)$
   (g) $(7a + 4)(6a - 2)$
   (h) $(2b - 8p)(7b - 2p)$
   (i) $(6x - 2y)(x + 5y)$
   (j) $(5t - 4)^2$
   (k) $(4xy + 1)(3xy + 5)$
   (l) $(6q^2 - 8t)(6q^2 + 8t)$

4. Expand and simplify.

   (a) $(k - 8)(k + 6) + (k + 1)(k - 4)$
   (b) $6s(3s - 7) + (2s - 3)(5s - 2)$
   (c) $(t - 6)(2t + 1) - 5t(t + 3)$
   (d) $(y + 3)(y - 3) - (y + 4)(y - 8)$
   (e) $(4r + 3)^2 - (3r - 4)^2$
   (f) $[(4r + 3) - (3r - 4)]^2$
   (g) $-3(a - 2b)(a + 3b)$
   (h) $4(w + 3)(w - 1) + 2(w + 4)^2$
   (i) $2(a - 3)(2a - 5) - 3(a + 8)(a - 1)$
   (j) $(4x - 7)(3x^2 - x - 4)$

5. Simplify using BEDMAS.

   (a) $12x(-3y) + (-32x^2y^3) \div (4xy^2)$
   (b) $5[4x - 2(6x - 3)]$
   (c) $\dfrac{-14a^2 - 4a^2}{(3a)^2}$
   (d) $\dfrac{15x - 10}{5} + \dfrac{32xy + 16y}{-8y}$
   (e) $-6x[4(2x - 1) - 3(x + 4)]$
   (f) $(3x - 5)^2 + (3x)^2 + (-5)^2$
   (g) $\dfrac{14x^2 - 7x}{-7x} - \dfrac{24xy + 15y}{-y + 4y}$
   (h) $\dfrac{9t - 3(7t - 8)}{6}$

6. Common factor.

(a) $a^2 + 5a$
(b) $12ab - 15a^2 + 3a$
(c) $2xyz - 6wxz + 4xz$
(d) $3w(w - 5) + 7(w - 5)$
(e) $15x^2y + 27xy$
(f) $3a(4a - 3b) - (4a - 3b)$

7. Factor each trinomial.

(a) $c^2 - 9c + 8$
(b) $y^2 - 8y - 48$
(c) $z^2 + z - 90$
(d) $s^2 + 47s + 90$
(e) $q^2 - 6q - 55$
(f) $x^2 + 33x - 70$
(g) $a^2 - 17a + 70$
(h) $2a^2 + 5a + 3$
(i) $3a^2 + 7a + 2$
(j) $5a^2 - 23a - 10$
(k) $3y^2 + 11y + 10$
(l) $8s^2 - s - 9$
(m) $8s^2 - 22s + 9$
(n) $12w^2 + 4w - 5$
(o) $20a^2 - 21a - 5$
(p) $6r^2 - 67r + 11$
(q) $4y^2 + 9y - 9$
(r) $30t^2 - t - 3$

8. Factor.

(a) $q^2 - 25$
(b) $t^2 - 25t$
(c) $t^2 - 25t + 100$
(d) $t^2 - 25t - 26$
(e) $2a^2 + 14a + 20$
(f) $2a^3 - 14a^2 - 60a$
(g) $3w^2 + 14w + 11$
(h) $8q^2 + 31q - 4$
(i) $2a^2 + 3a - 20$
(j) $30t^2 - 120$
(k) $30t^3 - 120t$
(l) $30t^2 - 120t - 150$
(m) $30t^2 + 11t + 1$
(n) $r^2 - 2tr - 63t^2$
(o) $3y(4y + 5x) - x(4y + 5x)$
(p) $x^2y^2 + 12xy + 27$
(q) $2m^2 - 6mn - 56n^2$
(r) $2r^2 - 3rs - 9s^2$
(s) $50t^2 - 98s^2$
(t) $w^4 + w^2 - 20$

Side Trip

Factoring expressions like the one below can be done in 2 ways.

$$(x + 7)^2 - 9$$

- Expand the expression and simplify. Factor the result.

$$\begin{aligned} (x + 7)^2 - 9 &= (x + 7)(x + 7) - 9 \\ &= x^2 + 7x + 7x + 49 - 9 \\ &= x^2 + 14x + 40 \\ &= (x + 4)(x + 10) \end{aligned}$$

- Treat the expression as a difference of squares and factor.

$$\begin{aligned} (x + 7)^2 - 9 &= [(x + 7) - 3][(x + 7) + 3] \\ &= (x + 4)(x + 10) \end{aligned}$$

Compare the 2 methods given. Now factor the following expressions, using the method of your choice.

1. $(y + 2)^2 - 25$
2. $(x - 3)^2 - 9$
3. $(a + b)^2 - b^2$
4. $(x + 5)^2 - 36$
5. $(t + 6)^2 - (t + 2)^2$
6. $(s - 4)^2 - (s + 7)^2$
7. $(w - 8)^2 - (w - 3)^2$
8. $(2w + 5)^2 - (w + 4)^2$

Unit 4

Equations and Formulas

A Strategy for Solving Equations

Now that you have received some of the basic ideas of algebra, you can apply these skills to solve equations. To solve an equation is to find the value of the variable that makes the equation true.

An equation can be compared to an equal-arm balance.

$$LS \quad = \quad RS$$

To maintain a "balance" you must always perform the *same* operation on *both* sides of the equation.

Follow these 3 steps to solve equations.
1. **Multiply to eliminate fractions or brackets, and simplify.**
2. **Add or subtract to isolate the variable term, and simplify.**
3. **Divide to find the variable.**

Example 1

Solve and check.

$$3x - 2 + 4x = 5 - 2x + 11$$

Step 1

$$7x - 2 = 16 - 2x$$

$$7x - 2 + 2x = 16 - 2x + 2x$$

Step 2

$$9x - 2 + 2 = 16 + 2$$

$$\frac{9x}{9} = \frac{18}{9}$$

Step 3

$$x = 2$$

Check by substituting $x = 2$ into the original equation.

LS	RS
$3x - 2 + 4x$	$5 - 2x + 11$
$= 3(2) - 2 + 4(2)$	$= 5 - 2(2) + 11$
$= 6 - 2 + 8$	$= 5 - 4 + 11$
$= 12$	$= 12$

Since LS = RS, $x = 2$ is correct.

Equations may also involve decimal numbers. If brackets are present, simplify by expanding.

Example 2

Solve.

$$4.2(1.5x - 3.6) = 3(x - 9.5)$$
$$6.3x - 15.12 = -3x + 28.5$$
$$6.3x - 15.12 + 15.12 = 28.5 + 15.12$$
$$6.3x - 15.12 + 3x = -3x + 28.5 + 3x$$
$$\frac{9.3x}{9.3} = \frac{43.62}{9.3}$$
$$x = 4.69$$
$$\text{(to 2 decimals)}$$

After eliminating the brackets, simplify before attempting to isolate the variable term.

Example 3

Solve.

$$5(k - 3)(k + 1) + 41 = 2(k - 3)^2 + 3k(k - 2)$$
$$5(k^2 - 2k - 3) + 41 = 2(k^2 - 6k + 9) + 3k^2 - 6k$$
$$5k^2 - 10k - 15 + 41 = 2k^2 - 12k + 18 + 3k^2 - 6k$$
$$5k^2 - 10k + 26 - 5k^2 = 5k^2 - 18k + 18 - 5k^2$$
$$-10k + 26 + 18k = 18k + 18 + 18k$$
$$8k + 26 - 26 = 18 - 26$$
$$\frac{8k}{8} = \frac{-8}{8}$$
$$k = -1$$

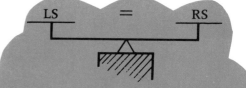

Whatever operation is performed on one side of an equation, the same operation must be performed on the other side.

Exercise

A **1.** State the first step you would use in solving each equation.

(a) $2a + 3 = 7$
(b) $4 - 5a = 19$
(c) $7.3 = 9 + m$
(d) $14t + 3 - t = 8 + 9t - 3$
(e) $3(y - 1.5) = 1.7$
(f) $(n + 1)(n - 2) = 4n - 7$
(g) $(p + 5) - 2(p - 1) = 4(p + 6) - 6$

2. State the solution in each case.

(a) $x - 3 = 19$ (e) $16 = 0.8 + n$
(b) $2t + 3 = 11$ (f) $27 + r = 20$
(c) $5k = -30$ (g) $4 - w = 7$
(d) $27 - s = 19$ (h) $60 = 2y + 30$

3. State whether the given value is a correct solution for the equation.

(a) $19 - k = 11;$ $k = 8$
(b) $0.3m + 1.2 = 4.2;$ $m = 10$
(c) $40 - 2k = 24;$ $k = 5$
(d) $2x + 9 = 14;$ $x = 2.5$
(e) $18 = 4y + 3;$ $y = 3$
(f) $-9 = -7 + 2w;$ $w = -1$

B **4.** Solve for each variable.

(a) $6n + 3 + 4n - 8n = -7$
(b) $6k - 12 = 9 - 4k + 3 + 7k$
(c) $-0.8y + 0.3 = 1.7 - 0.7y$
(d) $9 + 6g = -3 + 4g$
(e) $4m - 3 + 2m = 19 + 5m - 2$
(f) $5a - 9a + 4 - a + 16 = 0$
(g) $5x - 3 - 2x - 1 = 17 + 7x - 6$
(h) $43 - 25b + 11 = 7b + 31 + 8b$

5. Solve and check.

(a) $5u - (4u + 3) = 7$
(b) $4(y + 2) = 3(2y - 5)$
(c) $5(f - 2) = 3(f + 4)$
(d) $0.5(x - 7) + 6.3 = 0.9x$
(e) $20(k - 4) - 12(k - 5) = k - 6$
(f) $4(2a - 7) - (2a - 7) = 3(4a - 8)$

6. Solve for each variable.

(a) $5(d - 7) + 2 = 4(d - 6) + 3d$
(b) $3(y - 7) - 5(3y + 1) = -6 - 7y$
(c) $16.7 - 1.8(x - 10) =$
        $11.6 - 0.3(x - 17)$
(d) $3(5 - 6a) - 2(1 + 4a) = 2 - (3 - 2a)$
(e) $2m + 9(m + 1) = 3(5m - 2) - 5(m - 4)$
(f) $(2v + 3)(v + 3) = (2v + 1)(v + 1) + 14$
(g) $(3r + 8)(r - 5) - (r - 4)(3r - 2) = 8$

7. Solve each equation.

(a) $2(d + 1)(d + 3) = 2d(d - 5) + 6$
(b) $6(y^2 + 5) = (y - 4) + 6(y - 1)(y + 2)$
(c) $7 + 6(m - 3)^2 = (2m - 7)(3m + 1)$

8. Leslie needs to rent a chain saw. Company A charges $10 plus $7.50/h and Company B charges $20 plus $5/h.

(a) Which rental company should Leslie use for a rental of 3 h? 7 h?
(b) If x is the number of hours for which rental costs are equal, there is an equation to show equal charges for the 2 companies.

$$10 + 7.5x = 20 + 5x$$

Solve for x.

9. If $y = 3$ is a solution of $(y - 1)(y + 3) = (y - 5)(y - 7) + k$, find the value of k.

10. When $(2x - 3)(6x + 2)$ is subtracted from $(3x + 5)(4x - 3)$, the answer is 41. Find x.

71

Solving Equations Involving Fractions

It's often easier to perform operations with integers than with fractions.

Eliminating fractions from an equation gives a simpler equation. To eliminate fractions, multiply the terms on each side by the *common denominator* of all the fractions.

Example 1

Solve and check.

Multiply each side by 6, the common denominator.

$$\frac{x}{2} - \frac{x}{3} = 9$$

$$^3\!\!\not{6} \times \left(\frac{x}{\not{2}}\right) - ^2\!\!\not{6} \times \left(\frac{x}{\not{3}}\right) = 6 \times (9)$$

$$3x - 2x = 54$$

Simplify.

$$x = 54$$

Example 2

Solve.

Clear fractions.

$$\frac{m+1}{3} + \frac{2m-3}{4} = \frac{1}{2}$$

$$^4\!\not{12} \times \frac{(m+1)}{\not{3}_1} + \not{12} \times \frac{(2m-3)}{\not{4}_1} = \not{12} \times \frac{(1)}{\not{2}_1}$$

$$4(m+1) + 3(2m-3) = 6$$

$$4m + 4 + 6m - 9 = 6$$

$$10m - 5 + 5 = 6 + 5$$

$$10m = 11$$

$$m = \frac{11}{10}$$

If the equation contains both fractions and brackets, eliminate fractions first.

Example 3

Solve.

$$\frac{2(k-3)}{3} - \frac{5+k}{6} = \frac{k}{2} - 5(k-2)$$

$$^2\!\frac{\not{6} \times 2(k-3)}{\not{3}_1} - \frac{\not{6}(5+k)}{\not{6}_1} = \not{6}\!\left(\frac{k}{\not{2}_1}\right)^3 - 6 \times 5(k-2)$$

$$4(k-3) - (5+k) = 3k - 30(k-2)$$

$$4k - 12 - 5 - k = 3k - 30k + 60$$

$$3k - 17 + 27k = -27k + 60 + 27k$$

$$30k - 17 + 17 = 60 + 17$$

$$30k = 77$$

$$k = 2\frac{17}{30}$$

Fractional equations may also involve expanding binomials.

Example 4

Solve.

$$\frac{2(y-1)(5y+1)}{5} = \frac{y(3y-2)}{3} + y^2$$

$$^3\!\not{15}\!\left(\frac{2(y-1)(5y+1)}{\not{5}}\right) = \not{15}\!\left(\frac{y(3y-2)}{\not{3}}\right)^5 + 15(y^2)$$

$$6(y-1)(5y+1) = 5y(3y-2) + 15y^2$$

$$6(5y^2 - 4y - 1) = 15y^2 - 10y + 15y^2$$

$$30y^2 - 24y - 6 - 30y^2 = 30y^2 - 10y - 30y^2$$

$$-24y - 6 + 24y = -10y + 24y$$

$$-6 = 14y$$

$$\frac{-3}{7} = y$$

Check this answer by substituting $-\frac{3}{7}$ for y in the original equation, or by checking each step of your solution.

Exercise

A 1. State a common denominator for the fractions in each equation. How many terms must be multiplied by the common denominator in each case?

(a) $\dfrac{4s}{3} - \dfrac{s}{2} = \dfrac{1}{4}$

(b) $\dfrac{2(x+1)}{5} = \dfrac{3x}{6} - \dfrac{2}{3}$

(c) $\dfrac{1}{2}(m+1) = \dfrac{4m-1}{8} + \dfrac{m}{4}$

(d) $2 - \dfrac{y-2}{4} = \dfrac{5y}{3} + \dfrac{y-6}{5}$

(e) $\dfrac{2n+1}{4} - \dfrac{n}{6} = \dfrac{n}{3} + \dfrac{5n}{8} - 2$

2. Solve.

(a) $\dfrac{1}{2}x = 10$

(b) $\dfrac{m}{3} = -2$

(c) $5 = \dfrac{1}{4}k$

(d) $-\dfrac{t}{5} = 1$

(e) $-\dfrac{a}{10} = -6$

(f) $\dfrac{2}{3}r = 4$

(g) $\dfrac{5}{8}p = 10$

(h) $\dfrac{3}{4}$

B 3. Solve.

(a) $\dfrac{z}{3} - \dfrac{z}{8} = 5$

(b) $\dfrac{p}{7} = \dfrac{p}{2} - 5$

(c) $\dfrac{m-1}{2} = \dfrac{m+4}{3}$

(d) $\dfrac{2k}{3} - \dfrac{k}{4} = \dfrac{k-1}{2}$

(e) $\dfrac{x}{4} + \dfrac{x+2}{8} = \dfrac{2x+5}{8}$

(f) $\dfrac{3y+1}{3} + \dfrac{5y}{6} = -\dfrac{3}{2}$

4. Substitute to check whether the given value is a correct solution to the equation.

(a) $\dfrac{2k}{3} + 1 = \dfrac{k}{2}$; $k = 12$

(b) $\dfrac{4t-3}{3} = \dfrac{3+t}{2}$; $t = 3$

5. Solve and check.

(a) $\dfrac{x}{5} + \dfrac{x}{3} = 8$

(b) $\dfrac{m}{2} = \dfrac{m}{5} + \dfrac{m}{4} + 1$

(c) $\dfrac{r+5}{6} = \dfrac{r+3}{4} + \dfrac{r-1}{9}$

(d) $\dfrac{a+3}{4} + \dfrac{2a-1}{3} = 5$

(e) $\dfrac{1}{2}(k+4) + \dfrac{1}{3}(5k+4) = k + 1$

(f) $\dfrac{2w}{3} + w = \dfrac{1}{2}(w+7) - 14$

6. Solve each equation.

(a) $\dfrac{2n}{3} + 1 = \dfrac{n}{6} - \dfrac{7}{3}$

(b) $\dfrac{b-3}{4} - \dfrac{3b-5}{8} = \dfrac{2b-4}{5}$

(c) $\dfrac{1}{6}(w+3) + 1 = \dfrac{w+6}{4} - \dfrac{3w-16}{12}$

(d) $\dfrac{k-7}{3} - \dfrac{21-k}{2} + 5 = 4 - \dfrac{33-2k}{7}$

7. Solve for each variable.

(a) $\dfrac{c-1}{3} = \dfrac{3(c+2)}{5} - \dfrac{c}{2} + 5$

(b) $\dfrac{2(n-1)}{3} - \dfrac{5(n-2)}{2} = \dfrac{3(4-n)}{4} + 1$

(c) $\dfrac{1}{2}(a-3)^2 + 1 = \dfrac{(2a-1)(a+2)}{4}$

Solving Equations by Factoring

Joel must cut a solar panel according to specific directions. The length of solar panel is to be 3 m longer than its width, and the area of the panel is to be 28 m^2. Joel uses this equation to determine the dimensions of the panel.

$$x(x + 3) = 28$$

x is the panel width in metres.

To solve for x, Joel uses this rule.

> If $a \times b = 0$, then $a = 0$,
> or $b = 0$,
> or $a = b = 0$

Start by arranging one side of the equation to be zero.

$$x(x + 3) = 28$$
$$x(x + 3) - 28 = 0$$
$$x^2 + 3x - 28 = 0$$
$$(x - 4)(x + 7) = 0$$

Expand.

Trinomial factoring.

$$x - 4 = 0 \quad \boxed{\text{or}} \quad x + 7 = 0$$
$$x = 4 \qquad\qquad x = -7$$

The width of the solar panel is 4 m and its length is (4 + 3) m or 7 m. The value −7 is not a solution for this problem because negative measurements have no meaning in this situation.

Equations like $x^2 + 3x - 28 = 0$ are **quadratic** equations.

Example 1

Solve for m in the quadratic equation and check your answer by substitution.

$$m^2 = 8m - 15$$

Start by arranging one side of the equation to be zero.

$$m^2 - 8m + 15 = 8m - 15 - 8m + 15$$
$$m^2 - 8m + 15 = 0$$

Now factor the trinomial on the left side.

$$(m - 5)(m - 3) = 0$$
$$m - 5 = 0 \quad \text{or} \quad m - 3 = 0$$
$$m = 5 \qquad\qquad m = 3$$

Check.

$$m = 5 \qquad\qquad m = 3$$

LS	RS		LS	RS
m^2	$8m - 15$		m^2	$8m - 15$
$= (5)$	$= 8(5) - 15$		$= (3)$	$= 8(3) - 15$
$= 25$	$= 40 - 15$		$= 9$	$= 24 - 15$
	$= 25$			$= 9$

There are two values for m, 5 and 3.

Example 2

Solve $9k^2 - 25 = 0$.

The left side is a difference of squares, which can be factored.

$$(3k - 5)(3k + 5) = 0$$
$$3k - 5 = 0 \quad \text{or} \quad 3k + 5 = 0$$
$$3k = 5 \qquad\qquad 3k = -5$$
$$k = \frac{5}{3} \qquad\qquad k = -\frac{5}{3}$$

The two values for k are $\frac{5}{3}$ and $-\frac{5}{3}$.

Exercise

A **1.** State which of the following are quadratic equations.

(a) $m^2 - 9 = 0$ (d) $3a^4 - 2 = 8a$
(b) $2y - 5 = 16$ (e) $4w + 7 = 2w^2$
(c) $4k - 3k^2 = 11$ (f) $x - 5 = -12$

2. State 2 simple equations that result from each of the following.

(a) $x(x + 3) = 0$
(b) $(m - 1)(m - 2) = 0$
(c) $3y(y + 5) = 0$
(d) $(a - 7)(a + 2) = 0$
(e) $(t - 7)(t + 7) = 0$
(f) $4w(3w - 1) = 0$
(g) $(2k + 3)(k - 8) = 0$
(h) $(5a - 3)(4a + 1) = 0$

B **3.** Solve each part of Question 2.

4. Factor each expression.

(a) $m^2 + 8m + 15$ (e) $9k^2 - 16$
(b) $y^2 + 9y + 14$ (f) $3x + 9x^2$
(c) $x^2 - 5x + 6$ (g) $36n^2 - 1$
(d) $4a^2 - 8a$ (h) $2s^2 - 5s - 3$

5. Solve.

(a) $x^2 + 5x + 6 = 0$
(b) $y^2 + 4y + 3 = 0$
(c) $m^2 + 9m + 20 = 0$
(d) $p^2 + 9p + 18 = 0$
(e) $a^2 + 12a + 35 = 0$
(f) $n^2 - 8n + 12 = 0$
(g) $w^2 - 8w + 15 = 0$
(h) $k^2 + 7k - 18 = 0$
(i) $t^2 - 2t - 15 = 0$

6. Solve and check.

(a) $m^2 - 8m + 7 = 0$ (d) $3r^2 + 8r - 3 = 0$
(b) $k^2 - 2k - 15 = 0$ (e) $5s^2 - 7s = 0$
(c) $a^2 + 3a - 28 = 0$

7. Solve.

(a) $v^2 + 20 = -12v$
(b) $c^2 = 5c + 24$
(c) $7w = w^2 + 12$
(d) $a^2 + a = 56$
(e) $2k^2 = 7k + 15$

8. Solve for each variable.

(a) $2c(c - 2) = c(c + 3) - 6$
(b) $(m - 5)(m + 3) = 20$
(c) $x(x - 2) = 9 - 2x$
(d) $(g - 3)(g - 2) = 6(g - 3)$
(e) $2h(h + 3) = 5(h + 6) - 2$

9. A rectangular specifications plate on a machine is increased by x centimetres in each dimension. Find the new dimensions of the plate if the new plate has an area of 99 cm².

$$(x + 6)(x + 4) = 99$$

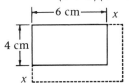

10. The lengths of the sides of a right-angled triangle are related by this equation.

$$(2x + 1)^2 = x^2 + (x + 7)^2$$

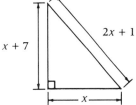

Solve for x to determine the length of the shortest side of the triangle.

11. If the quantity $5(m - 3)^2$ is reduced by $9m$, the result is equal to the product of m and $4m - 25$. Determine the values of m.

Substituting into Formulas

Greta works as an estimator for a landscaping firm. One job involves determining the cost of sod for a sports field when the cost per square metre is $1.25.

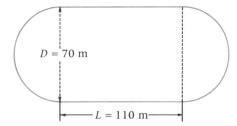

Greta uses a formula for cost.

$$C = \frac{UD}{4}(\pi D + 4L)$$

C is the total cost and U is the cost per square metre of the sod. To use this formula, she follows the steps in *evaluation by substitution*.

1. Copy the expression or formula, with the values to be substituted.
2. Rewrite the expressions, replacing each variable or letter with brackets.
3. Substitute the value for each variable.
4. Evaluate the resulting expression, using BEDMAS.

$U = 1.25$
$D = 70$
$L = 110$
$\pi = 3.14$

$$C = \frac{UD}{4}(\pi D + 4L)$$
$$= \frac{(1.25)(70)}{4}[(3.14)(70) + 4(110)]$$
$$= (2.1875)[219.8 + 440]$$
$$= (21.875)659.8$$
$$= 14433.125$$

Greta's calculation shows that the cost of sod for the field is approximately $14 400.

Example 1

Andy has had $455.07 in his savings account for the past 6 months. When he has his passbook updated, the information below is entered.

Date	Particulars	Withdrawal	Deposit	Balance
APR 30 84	INT		14.79	469.86

To find the rate of interest paid by the bank, he uses the formula for interest.

$$I = Prt$$
$$14.79 = (455.07)(r)(0.5)$$
$$14.79 = 227.535r$$
$$r = 0.065$$
$$r = 6.5\%$$

$I = 14.79$
$P = 455.07$
$t = 0.5$

The rate of interest paid is 6.5%.

Example 2

Pat is an apprentice in a custom machine shop. Pat has to design 2 meshing gears to rotate at speeds of 60 r/min and 108 r/min. One gear has 36 teeth; how many teeth should the other gear have? Pat can use a formula.

$$\frac{S_1}{S_2} = \frac{N_2}{N_1}$$

Read as "N-two"

S is the speed of each gear and N is the number of teeth.

If $S_1 = 60$ r/min
$S_2 = 108$ r/min
$N_1 = 36$

$$\frac{60}{108} = \frac{N_2}{36}$$
$$\frac{108N_2}{108} = \frac{60 \times 36}{108}$$
$$N_2 = 20$$

60 r/min
36 teeth

Gear 1

Gear 2

There must be 20 teeth on the smaller gear.

Exercise

B **1.** For each formula, values are given for all but one of the variables. Substitute these given values and determine the value of the remaining variable.

(a)

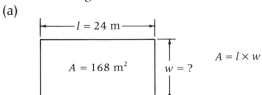

$l = 24$ m
$A = 168$ m²
$w = ?$
$A = l \times w$

(b)

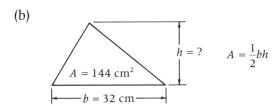

$h = ?$
$A = 144$ cm²
$b = 32$ cm
$A = \frac{1}{2}bh$

(c)

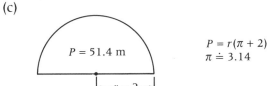

$P = 51.4$ m
$r = ?$
$P = r(\pi + 2)$
$\pi \doteq 3.14$

(d)

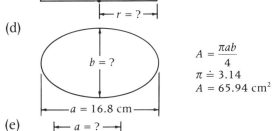

$b = ?$
$a = 16.8$ cm
$A = \frac{\pi ab}{4}$
$\pi \doteq 3.14$
$A = 65.94$ cm²

(e)

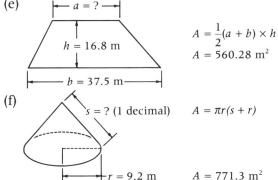

$a = ?$
$h = 16.8$ m
$b = 37.5$ m
$A = \frac{1}{2}(a + b) \times h$
$A = 560.28$ m²

(f)

$s = ?$ (1 decimal)
$r = 9.2$ m
$A = \pi r(s + r)$
$A = 771.3$ m²

2. The mass (M kilograms) of a certain metal rod (length L metres) is determined by the formula $M = DL$, where D is the mass per unit length (kilograms per metre) of the metal.

(a) If $M = 8.2$ kg and $D = 2.5$ kg/m, solve for L.
(b) If $M = 16.5$ kg and $L = 11.63$ m solve for D, correct to 2 decimals.

3. The current (I amperes) in an electric heater is determined by the power (P watts) and the voltage (V volts). The formula is
$$I = \frac{P}{V}.$$

(a) If $I = 12.5$ A and $V = 120$ V, find the value of P.
(b) If $I = 8.3$ A and $P = 1000$ W, find the value of V.

4. The simple interest formula, $I = Prt$, is used to determine the interest ($\$I$) on the principal ($\$P$) invested at r percent for t years.

(a) What sum invested at 7% will earn $21.86 interest in 57 d? (Use $t = \frac{57}{365}$.)
(b) What sum at 6.75% will earn $68.43 in 5 months?

5. In order to qualify as an electrical apprentice, Les has to be able to determine resistances in electric circuits. For 3 resistors connected in parallel, the formula is
$$\frac{1}{R_t} = \frac{1}{R_1} + \frac{1}{R_2} + \frac{1}{R_3}.$$

All resistances are measured in ohms (Ω).

Find R_2 if $R_1 = 6\ \Omega$, $R_3 = 24\ \Omega$, and $R_t = 3\ \Omega$.

Rewriting Formulas

Sometimes you can make your work easier by rewriting a formula before substituting values.

Jason must make several calculations of resistances, R, in an electrical circuit using the formula $V = IR$.

> In the formula $V = IR$, V is the **subject** of the formula.

Since $V = IR$,

$$\frac{V}{I} = \frac{IR}{I}$$

$$R = \frac{V}{I}$$

Here, R is the subject of the formula.

To rewrite a formula, follow the 3 steps for solving equations.

1. Eliminate fractions or brackets.
2. Isolate the term containing the new subject.
3. Find the new subject.

Some formulas will contain square roots.

Example 1

The impedance of an electric circuit is given by a formula.

$$Z^2 = X^2 + R^2$$

Z is impedance, X is reactance, and R is resistance, all measured in ohms.

Rewrite the formula with X as the subject.

Isolate the term containing X.

$$Z^2 = X^2 + R^2$$
$$Z^2 - R^2 = X^2 + R^2 - R^2$$
$$Z^2 - R^2 = X^2$$

Take the square root of each side to find X.

$$\sqrt{X^2} = \sqrt{Z^2 - R^2}$$
$$X = \sqrt{Z^2 - R^2}$$

Example 2

Stephanie knows that the formula for the total surface area of a cone is $A = \pi r(s + r)$.

She needs to evaluate s when $A = 2092$ cm^2, $r = 19.7$ cm, and $\pi \doteq 3.14$.

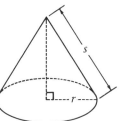

First, rewrite the formula with s as the subject.

$$A = \pi r(s + r)$$
$$\frac{A}{\pi r} = s + r$$
$$s = \frac{A}{\pi r} - r$$

Now substitute and evaluate.

$$s = \frac{2092}{(3.14)(19.7)} - 19.7$$
$$= 33.8 - 19.7$$
$$= 14.1, \text{ to 1 decimal place}$$

The slant height, s, is about 14.1 cm.

Exercise

A 1. State each formula with the letter in brackets as the subject.

(a) $A = 2\pi rh$; [r]   (f) $y = mx + b$; [b]
(b) $P = 2W + T$; [W]   (g) $y = mx + b$; [m]
(c) $P = a + b + c$; [c]   (h) $ax + 10 = k$; [x]
                           (i) $C = 2s + 50$; [s]
(d) $A = \dfrac{1}{2}bh$; [b]

(e) $v^2 = u^2 + 2as$; [a]   (j) $P = 21 + 2w$; [w]

B 2. Rewrite each formula so that the variable in the brackets is the subject.

(a)

$C = \pi d$; [d]

(b)

$V = \pi r^2 h$; [h], [r]
$A = 2\pi r^2 + 2\pi rh$; [h]

(c)

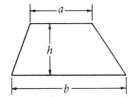

$A = \dfrac{1}{2}h(a + b)$; [a]

(d)

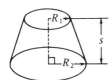

$L = \pi s(R_1 + R_2)$; [R_2]

(e)

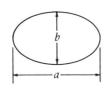

$\dfrac{p^2}{\pi^2} = \dfrac{a^2 + b^2}{2}$; [b]

3. An experimental solar energy panel is to be circular in shape. The formula that relates the area of the panel to its diameter is $A = 0.7854D^2$.

(a) Rewrite this formula with D as the subject.
(b) Calculate the diameter of the solar panel if its area is 5600 cm².

4. The power in an electric circuit is determined using a formula.

$$P = I^2R$$

P is power (watts); I is current (amperes); R is resistance (ohms).

(a) Rewrite the formula with R as the subject, then find R when $P = 1100$ W and $I = 12$ A.
(b) Rewrite the formula with I as the subject, and find I when P when $P = 4355$ W and $R = 9.6$ Ω.

5. The volume of a cylindrical shipping container is given by a formula.

$$V = \pi r^2h$$

V is volume, r is radius, h is height, and $\pi \doteq 3.14$.

(a) Rewrite the formula with h as the subject, then calculate the value of h when $V = 18\ 460$ cm³ and $r = 14$ cm.
(b) Rewrite the formula so that r is the subject, then find r if $V = 12\ 900$ cm³ and $h = 34$.

Machinist

For as long as she can remember, Lori has been interested in working with machines. In high school, she took several shop courses, and graduated near the top of her class in technical subjects. She then apprenticed for 3 a with a company that manufactures industrial diesel-electric motors, and now works full time with the company as a machinist.

One of Lori's jobs is to make tapered steel rods on a lathe.

Lori uses a formula to calculate the taper of the steel rod.

$$T = \frac{D - d}{L}$$

T is the taper;
D is the diameter of the larger end;
d is the diameter of the smaller end;
L is the length of the taper.

Find T, given that $L = 20$ cm, $D = 3.2$ cm, and $d = 1.8$ cm.

$$T = \frac{D - d}{L}$$
$$= \frac{3.2 \text{ cm} - 1.8 \text{ cm}}{20 \text{ cm}}$$
$$= \frac{1.2 \text{ cm}}{20 \text{ cm}}$$
$$= 0.06$$

The taper is 0.06.

Lori can rewrite the formula for taper to get a formula for the length of the rod, L.

$$T = \frac{D - d}{L}$$
$$L \times T = \frac{D - d}{L} \times L$$
$$\frac{L \times T}{T} = \frac{D - d}{T}$$
$$\boxed{L = \frac{D - d}{T}}$$

If Lori wanted a formula for diameter of the larger end, she could rewrite the formula for taper as below.

$$T = \frac{D - d}{L}$$
$$L \times T = \frac{D - d}{L} \times L$$
$$L \times T = D - d$$
$$L \times T + d = D - d + d$$
$$LT + d = D$$
$$\boxed{D = LT + d}$$

Exercise

1. Calculate the taper in each case.

   (a) D = 6.8 cm
       d = 5.4 cm
       L = 36.8 cm

   (b) D = 4.9 cm
       d = 3.1 cm
       L = 18.4 cm

   (c) D = 7.05 cm
       d = 6.13 cm
       L = 72.38 cm

   (d) D = 5.26 cm
       d = 3.79 cm
       L = 1.1371 m

2. Determine the length of the steel rod for each set of measurements.

   (a) D = 5.7 cm
       d = 2.6 cm
       T = 0.111

   (b) D = 11.1 cm
       d = 9.2 cm
       T = 0.0208

   (c) D = 4.6 cm
       d = 1.9 cm
       T = 0.108

   (d) D = 7.6 cm
       d = 5.8 cm
       T = 0.0469

3. Calculate the diameter of the larger end for each.

   (a) L = 19.65 cm
       T = 0.0952
       d = 3.85 cm

   (b) L = 12.6 cm
       T = 0.0952
       d = 2.5 cm

   (c) L = 76.95 cm
       T = 0.0220
       d = 4.13 cm

   (d) L = 48.2 cm
       T = 0.0394
       d = 7.6 cm

4. Rewrite the taper formula so that the subject is the diameter of the smaller end, d. Then calculate the diameter of the smaller end in each case.

   (a) D = 6.54 cm
       L = 21.7 cm
       T = 0.113

   (b) D = 5.6 cm
       L = 29.4 cm
       T = 0.0816

   (c) D = 5.82 cm
       L = 50.8 cm
       T = 0.0325

   (d) D = 6.2 cm
       L = 63.1 cm
       T = 0.0206

Applications with Formulas

The skills you've learned in this unit can help you solve applied problems in trade and technology.

Example 1

A cylindrical oil storage tank is to hold 130 m³. Calculate its radius (to 1 decimal place) if its height is 4.3 m. Use the formula

$$V = \pi r^2 h$$
$$(\pi \doteq 3.14)$$

There are 2 ways to solve this problem.

• Substitute directly into the formula.

$$V = \pi r^2 h$$
$$130 = (3.14)r^2(4.3)$$
$$\frac{130}{13.502} = \frac{13.502 r^2}{13.502}$$
$$r^2 = 9.628$$
$$r = \sqrt{9.628}$$
$$r = 3.1 \text{ (to 1 decimal place)}$$

• Solve for r, then substitute.

$$\frac{V}{\pi h} = \frac{\pi r^2 h}{\pi h}$$
$$r^2 = \frac{V}{\pi h}$$
$$\sqrt{r^2} = \sqrt{\frac{V}{\pi h}}$$
$$r = \sqrt{\frac{V}{\pi h}}$$
$$= \sqrt{\frac{130}{(3.14)(4.3)}}$$
$$= \sqrt{9.628}$$
$$= 3.1 \text{ (to 1 decimal place)}$$

By either method, the radius of the tank is about 3.1 m.

Example 2

In $\triangle ABC$ below, the perimeter is 72 units. Determine the length of BC.

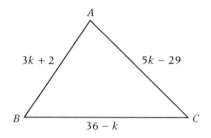

$$AB + BC + CA = 72$$
$$3k + 2 + 36 - k + 5k - 29 = 72$$
$$7k + 9 = 72$$
$$7k = 63$$
$$k = 9$$

Since $36 - k = 27$, the length of BC is 27 units.

Example 3

Determine the dimensions of rectangle $PQRS$.

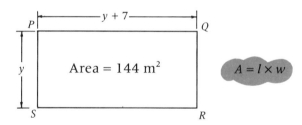

Since the area is 144 m² then $y(y + 7) = 144$.

$$y^2 + 7y = 144$$
$$y^2 + 7y - 144 = 0$$
$$(y - 9)(y + 16) = 0$$
$$y - 9 = 0 \text{ or } y + 16 = 0$$
$$y = 9 \qquad y = -16$$

Since length cannot be negative, this answer is inadmissable (not allowed)!

The width is 9 m, and the length is 9 + 7, or 16 m.

Exercise

B **1.** Determine the value of the variable in each case.

(a)

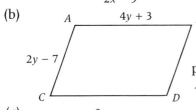

Perimeter of $\triangle KMN$ is 55.

(b)

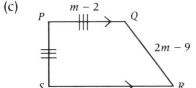

Perimeter of parallelogram $ABCD$ is 106.

(c)

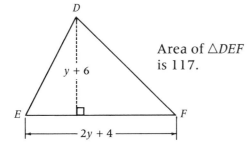

Perimeter of trapezoid $PQRS$ is 47.

2. Determine the value of the variable in each case.

(a)

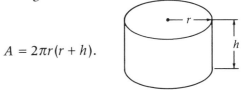

Area of $\triangle DEF$ is 117.

(b)

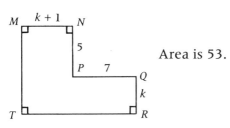

Area is 53.

3. The height of a ball thrown into the air is determined by the equation $S = ut - 5t^2$.

(a) Rewrite the formula with u as the subject.
(b) Calculate the value of u if $t = 3$ and $S = 100$.

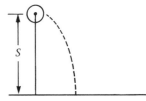

4. On a construction site the length of a brace to support a framed wall is found from the formula below.

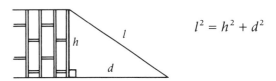

$$l^2 = h^2 + d^2$$

(a) Solve the formula for d.
(b) Calculate the value of d (to 1 decimal place), if $h = 2.5$ m and $l = 4.9$ m.

5. The total surface area of a cylindrical storage tank is

$$A = 2\pi r(r + h).$$

(a) Substitute $A = 102.9$ m^2, $\pi = 3.14$, $r = 2.6$ m, then evaluate h (to 1 decimal place).
(b) Solve for h, then substitute the same values as in part (a).
(c) How do your answers to (a) and (b) compare?

83

Unit 4 Review

1. What first step would you perform in solving each equation?

   (a) $5(a - 3) = 4(a + 1)$
   (b) $2x + 3 + 5x = 19$
   (c) $\dfrac{4k - 3}{2} - \dfrac{1}{3} = \dfrac{2 + k}{5}$

2. Solve.

   (a) $m - 5 = 27$ (d) $\dfrac{n}{13} = 8$

   (b) $4r = 20$ (e) $13 + s = 8$
   (c) $3.6 - t = 2.4$ (f) $15 = 3y + 6$

3. State which of the following are quadratic equations.

   (a) $4 - k^2 = 9$ (d) $m(m - 2) = 0$
   (b) $3 + 2r = r^2$ (e) $2y + 3 = 4y$
   (c) $5x - 3 = 11$ (f) $(a - 2)(a - 5) = 0$

4. State 2 simple equations that result from each statement.

   (a) $m(2m + 1) = 0$ (c) $(a + 3)(a - 3) = 0$
   (b) $0 = 2k(k - 5)$ (d) $(2y - 5)(3y + 7) = 0$

5. Rewrite each formula with the letter in brackets as the subject.

   (a) $I = Prt$; $[t]$ (c) $E = mc^2$; $[m]$
   (b) $v = u + at$; $[u]$ (d) $A = \pi r^2$; $[r]$

6. Substitute to check whether the given value is a correct solution to the equation.

   (a) $4k - 2 = 3k + 6$; $k = 8$
   (b) $2(m - 3) = 8 - 3(m - 2)$; $m = 4$
   (c) $x(x + 1) = x^2 - 5$; $x = 5$
   (d) $\dfrac{y}{5} + \dfrac{3y}{2} = 2y - 3$; $y = 10$
   (e) $\dfrac{4 - n}{3} + \dfrac{n}{4} = \dfrac{n + 1}{3}$; $n = 8$
   (f) $w(w + 3) + 5 = w^2 - 1$; $w = -2$

7. Solve and check.

   (a) $3t + 4 = 21 - 20t + 6$
   (b) $5(x - 2) = 6(x - 3) + 2$
   (c) $7 = 5(2a - 1) - 3(4a - 6)$
   (d) $\dfrac{m - 4}{5} + \dfrac{m}{3} = 4$
   (e) $\dfrac{2k + 7}{3} + \dfrac{k}{4} = \dfrac{1}{2}$
   (f) $(s - 2)^2 = 10 - 3s$

8. Solve each quadratic equation.

   (a) $2k^2 - 6k = 0$ (d) $a^2 + 8a = -16$
   (b) $c^2 - 7c = 0$ (e) $m^2 = m + 12$
   (c) $4x^2 - 25 = 0$ (f) $2y^2 + 3y + 1 = 0$

9. Solve for each variable.

   (a) $3 - 2(1 - 3r) = 5(2 - r) - 31$
   (b) $5x(x - 2) - x(x + 3) = (2x - 1)^2 - 28$
   (c) $\dfrac{7m}{2} + \dfrac{m - 3}{5} = 29$
   (d) $\dfrac{5y}{4} - 3 = \dfrac{2y}{3} + 7$
   (e) $m(m - 3) = m(4 - m) + 3 - 2m$
   (f) $\dfrac{4 - x}{3} + \dfrac{x^2}{4} = x + 5$

10. A plant is 41 cm tall and grows at the rate of 3 cm/week. Another plant is 18 cm tall and grows at the rate of 4 cm/week. After k weeks, the 2 plants are equal in height. Solve the equation $41 + 3k = 18 + 4k$ to determine the number of weeks before both plants are the same height.

11. A rectangular garden with the dimensions shown has a cement walk of uniform width built around it. The area of both garden and walk is 70 m². Solve the equation $(2x + 7)(2x + 4) = 70$ to determine the width of the walk.

12. Substitute the appropriate values in each formula, then solve for the remaining variable.

(a)

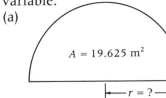

$A = 19.625 \text{ m}^2$

$A = \pi r^2$
$\pi \doteq 3.14$

$A = \dfrac{\pi r^2}{2}$

(b)

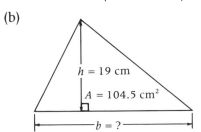

$h = 19 \text{ cm}$
$A = 104.5 \text{ cm}^2$
$b = ?$

$A = \dfrac{1}{2}bh$

(c)

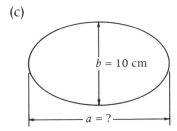

$b = 10 \text{ cm}$
$a = ?$

$A = \dfrac{\pi ab}{4}$
$\pi \doteq 3.14$
$A = 128.74 \text{ cm}^2$

(d)

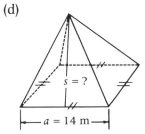

$s = ?$
$a = 14 \text{ m}$

$A = 2as + a^2$
$A = 672 \text{ m}^2$

(e)

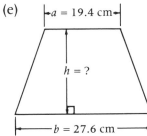

$a = 19.4 \text{ cm}$
$h = ?$
$b = 27.6 \text{ cm}$

$A = \dfrac{1}{2}(a + b)h$
$A = 481.75 \text{ cm}^2$

13. If $k = -2$ is a solution of $(k - 1)(2k - 3)$ $= (3k + 2)^2 + m$, find the value of m.

14. When 50 is subtracted from the product of $(c + 4)$ and $(2c + 9)$, the result is $5c(c + 6)$. Find c.

15. The bearing area of a washer is found by using a formula.

$A = \pi(R^2 - r^2)$

(a) Calculate the bearing area of a washer if $r = 3.8$ cm and $R = 1.2$ cm.
(b) Determine the value of r for a washer if $R = 3.8$ cm and bearing area is equal to 38.3 cm².
(c) If the bearing area is 74.7 cm² and $r = 2.1$ cm, find R.

16. The speed of rotation of a certain grinding wheel is determined by a formula.

$V = \dfrac{v}{\pi d}$

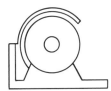

V is the speed of rotation (rotations per minute); v is the maximum surface speed of the wheel (centimetres per minute), and d is the wheel diameter (centimetres).

(a) Calculate the value of V if $v = 150\ 000$ cm/min and $d = 13.8$ cm.
(b) If the wheel rotates at 1800 r/min and has a diameter of 17.7 cm, what is the surface speed of the wheel?
(c) What is the wheel's diameter if it is on a shaft turning at 1675 r/min, and its surface speed is 120 000 cm/min?

17. To calculate true interest rate of a loan, Sharon uses a formula.

$$r = \frac{24C}{P(n + 1)}$$

r is the true interest rate; C is finance charges; P is the amount owing; n is number of monthly payments. Determine the number of monthly payments by solving for n if $C = \$1400$, $P = \$7000$, and $r = 19.2\%$.

18. The volume of an electrolytic capacitor is given by a formula.

$$V = \frac{\pi d^2 h}{4}$$

V is the volume (cubic centimetres); d is the diameter (centimetres); h is the height (centimetres). Rewrite this formula so that d is the subject, then solve for d (to 1 decimal place) if $V = 6.36$ cm³, $\pi \doteq 3.14$, and $h = 2.5$ cm.

19. Current in an electric circuit is found from a formula.

$$I^2 = \frac{P}{R}$$

I is current (amperes); P is power (watts); R is resistance (ohms). Solve for R if $P = 1000$ W and $I = 6.3$ A.

20. An elliptical dining room table has the dimensions shown.

$$\frac{p^2}{\pi^2} = \frac{a^2 + b^2}{2}$$

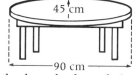

45 cm

90 cm

Use the formula to calculate the length (to 1 decimal place) of a strip of veneer to cover the outer edge of the table. (Use $\pi \doteq 3.14$.)

21. Leo works for a firm that designs industrial equipment. In designing a grinding wheel, he uses a formula to determine the speed of the wheel.

$$V = \frac{S}{\pi d}$$

V is the speed of the wheel (rotations per minute), S is the speed of the grinding surface (centimetres per minute), and d is the diameter of the wheel (centimetres).

(a) For a certain wheel, $d = 15$ cm and $S = 120\ 000$ cm/min. Using $\pi \doteq 3.14$, calculate the speed of the wheel (to the nearest 10 r/min).
(b) Solve the formula for d, and find d (to the nearest centimetre) if $S = 115\ 000$ cm/min, $\pi \doteq 3.14$, and $V = 1665$ r/min.

22. The power loss for an electric circuit is given by a formula.

$$P = \frac{V^2}{R}$$

P is power loss (watts); V is voltage (volts); and R is resistance (ohms).

(a) Calculate the power loss in a circuit if $V = 120$ V and $R = 980$ Ω.
(b) Find the resistance in a circuit if $V = 75$ V and $P = 20$ W.
(c) What voltage causes a circuit with a resistance of 280 Ω to lose 13.2 W of power?

Unit 5

Rational Algebraic Expressions

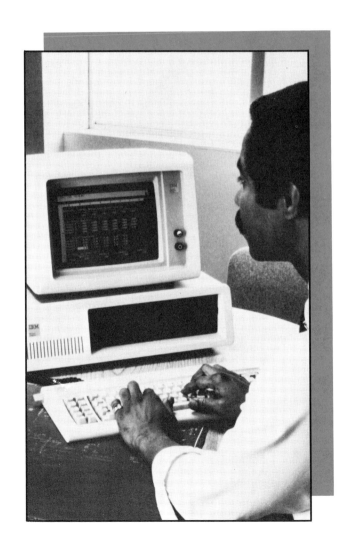

Reducing to Lowest Terms

Algebraic expressions like the ones below are examples of algebraic rational expressions.

$$\frac{x + 2}{x - 7}; \quad \frac{a^2}{2a + 1}; \quad \frac{1}{y}; \quad \frac{x^2 - 9}{3}$$

Expressions like these often appear in real life. An automative design engineer, for instance, uses the formula below to calculate the change (δ) in the length (L) of a piston rod with cross-sectional area A, under a combustion force of P.

$$\delta = 3.3 \times 10^{-8}\left(\frac{PL}{A}\right)$$

Rational numbers can be simplified by dividing numerator and denominator by a common factor.

- $\dfrac{27}{30} = \dfrac{3 \times 9}{3 \times 10}$
  $= \dfrac{9}{10}$

- $\dfrac{-72}{108} = -\dfrac{36 \times 2}{36 \times 3}$
  $= -\dfrac{2}{3}$

You can simplify rational variable expressions in a similar way.

> Divide numerator and denominator by a common factor.

The examples below show how this is done.

- $\dfrac{25ab}{5a} = \dfrac{5a \times 5b}{5a}$
  $= 5b$

- $\dfrac{3m^3n^4}{15m^2n^7} = \dfrac{\overset{1}{\cancel{3}}}{\underset{5}{\cancel{15}}} \times \dfrac{\overset{m}{\cancel{m^3}}}{\underset{1}{\cancel{m^2}}} \times \dfrac{\overset{1}{\cancel{n^4}}}{\underset{n^3}{\cancel{n^7}}}$
  $= \dfrac{m}{5n^3}$

Since division by 0 is not permitted, it is assumed that whenever we divide by an expression, the value of the expression is not 0.

Expressions in brackets may also be treated as factors.

- $\dfrac{(k + 1)(k + 3) \times 2(k - 2)}{(k - 2)(k + 1) \times k(k + 3)}$
  $= \dfrac{(\cancel{k + 1})(\cancel{k + 3}) \times 2(\cancel{k - 2})}{(\cancel{k - 2})(\cancel{k + 1}) \times k(\cancel{k + 3})}$
  $= \dfrac{2}{k}$

- $\dfrac{2xy(x - y)}{5xy^2(x - y)}$
  $= \dfrac{2xy(\cancel{x - y})}{5xy^2(\cancel{x - y})}$
  $= \dfrac{2}{5y}$

Exercise

A 1. State which of the following are rational algebraic expressions.

   (a) $\dfrac{2}{3}$

   (b) $\dfrac{x}{4}$

   (c) $-\dfrac{5}{7}$

   (d) $\dfrac{16n}{2}$

   (e) $\dfrac{5}{k}$

   (f) $\dfrac{r}{y}$

2. State the answer in each case.

   (a) $\dfrac{12}{16}$

   (b) $\dfrac{5m}{2m}$

   (c) $\dfrac{4x^2}{2x}$

   (d) $\dfrac{3(4y)}{4(9)}$

   (e) $\dfrac{xy^2}{x^2y}$

   (f) $\dfrac{2(k + 3)}{(k + 3)7}$

   (g) $\dfrac{4a(2a + b)}{(2a + b)3b}$

   (h) $\dfrac{(m + 4)(m - 7)}{(m - 7)(m + 4)}$

B 3. Reduce to lowest terms.

   (a) $\dfrac{4ab}{2b}$

   (b) $\dfrac{x^3y^7}{xy^5}$

   (c) $\dfrac{m^5}{n^2} \times \dfrac{n^9}{m}$

   (d) $\dfrac{6(x - 1)}{12}$

   (e) $\dfrac{5(k - 3)}{7(k - 3)}$

   (f) $\dfrac{(a + b)^4}{(a + b)^2}$

   (g) $\dfrac{3(y + 7)}{(y + 7)(y + 2)}$

   (h) $\dfrac{4(r + 1)(r - 3)}{(r - 3)2(r + 1)}$

Multiplying and Dividing Rational Expressions

You can multiply and divide rational expressions by following the same rules as you do for rational numbers.

> To multiply 2 rational expressions, multiply both numerators and both denominators together.

- $\dfrac{\overset{1}{\cancel{3}}}{\underset{1}{\cancel{4}}} \times \dfrac{\overset{2}{\cancel{8}}}{\underset{3}{\cancel{9}}} = \dfrac{2}{3}$

- $\dfrac{\overset{1}{\cancel{4a^2b}}}{\underset{1\ 1\ 1}{\cancel{3ab}}} \times \dfrac{\overset{3}{\cancel{9b}}}{\underset{2\ 1}{\cancel{8a}}} = \dfrac{3b}{2}$

> To divide, invert the divisor and multiply.

- $\dfrac{15}{16} \div \dfrac{25}{4} = \dfrac{15}{16} \times \dfrac{4}{25} = \dfrac{3}{20}$

- $\dfrac{3(m + 1)}{2(m - 3)} \div \dfrac{9(m + 1)}{4(m + 3)} = \dfrac{\cancel{3}(\cancel{m+1})}{2(m - 3)} \times \dfrac{\overset{2}{\cancel{4}}(m + 3)}{\cancel{9}(\cancel{m+1})}$
  $$= \dfrac{2(m + 3)}{3(m - 3)}$$

The above expressions have been simplified by dividing common factors from numerator and denominator.

Sometimes you'll be surprised at how far a rational expression can be simplified!

- $\dfrac{(x - 1)(x + 2)}{(x + 2)(x - 3)} \times \dfrac{(x - 3)(x + 5)}{(x - 5)(x - 7)} \div \dfrac{(x + 5)(x - 1)}{(x - 7)(x - 5)}$

  $= \dfrac{(\cancel{x-1})(\cancel{x+2})}{(\cancel{x+2})(\cancel{x-3})} \times \dfrac{(\cancel{x-3})(\cancel{x+5})}{(\cancel{x-5})(\cancel{x-7})} \times \dfrac{(\cancel{x-7})(\cancel{x-5})}{(\cancel{x+5})(\cancel{x-1})}$

  $= \dfrac{1}{1}$

  $= 1$

Exercise

B 1. Determine each product. Give your answer in lowest terms.

(a) $\dfrac{2a(a - 1)}{a^2} \times \dfrac{a^3}{(a - 1)}$

(b) $\dfrac{k}{(k - 1)(k - 2)} \times \dfrac{(k - 1)}{3}$

(c) $\dfrac{3r^2}{5(r - 6)} \times \dfrac{10(r - 6)}{9r}$

(d) $\dfrac{4y(y + 5)}{16y^2} \times \dfrac{8}{(y + 5)}$

2. Express each as a product, then simplify.

(a) $\dfrac{11k}{4m} \div \dfrac{3k}{8}$

(b) $\dfrac{6xy}{5y} \div \dfrac{3x^2}{10y}$

(c) $\dfrac{15f^2g^3}{2fg^2} \div \dfrac{5f^3g}{8fg}$

(d) $\dfrac{4a^2b}{12ab^4} \div \dfrac{16ab^3}{27a^5b^2}$

(e) $-\dfrac{x^2}{y^2} \div \dfrac{4x^3}{-y^7}$

(f) $\dfrac{a + b}{3} \div \dfrac{(a + b)^2}{6}$

(g) $\dfrac{4w}{w - 1} \div \dfrac{8w^3}{w - 1}$

(h) $\dfrac{5m^2}{(m + 3)^2} \div \dfrac{25m^3}{(m + 3)^5}$

3. Perform the operations indicated.

(a) $\dfrac{4a(a + b)}{5a^2b} \div \dfrac{15a^2(a + b)}{2a}$

(b) $\dfrac{16r(r + 3)}{4r(r + 2)} \div \dfrac{12r^2(r + 3)}{5r(r + 2)}$

(c) $\dfrac{2a}{(a + 1)} \div \dfrac{5a}{(a + 1)^2} \times \dfrac{4a^3}{(a + 1)}$

(d) $\dfrac{2a}{(a + 1)} \div \left[\dfrac{5a}{(a + 1)^2} \times \dfrac{4a^3}{(a + 1)} \right]$

Factoring to Simplify Rational Expressions

Sometimes it seems that a rational expression cannot be simplified, since there are no obvious factors common to both numerator and denominator.

$$\frac{15x^2 + 30x}{3x + 6} = ?$$

But the expression can be simplified if you start by factoring both numerator and denominator.

$$15x^2 + 30x = 15x(x + 2)$$
$$3x + 6 = 3(x + 2)$$

Now $\dfrac{15x^2 + 30x}{3x + 6} = \dfrac{\overset{5}{\cancel{15}}x\cancel{(x + 2)}}{\cancel{3}\cancel{(x + 2)}}$
$$= 5x$$

Similarly,
$\dfrac{6m^2 + 12m}{2mn + 4n} = \dfrac{\overset{3}{\cancel{6}}m\cancel{(m + 2)}}{\cancel{2}n\cancel{(m + 2)}}$
$$= \frac{3m}{n}$$

For an answer to be in lowest terms, *all* possible factors common to numerator and denominator must be divided. This means you should factor *completely* first, before simplifying.

Use the 3 main methods of factoring, as necessary.

- common factor
- trinomial
- difference of squares

Factoring may be involved in finding a missing dimension for a geometric figure.

Determine the length of the rectangle given below.

Since $A = l \times w$, then $l = \dfrac{A}{w}$

$l = \dfrac{A}{w}$
$ = \dfrac{18x^3 + 27x^2 - 36x}{9x}$
$ = \dfrac{9x(2x^2 + 3x - 4)}{9x}$
$ = 2x^2 + 3x - 4$

More than one method of factoring may be involved in a single problem.

Factor, then simplify.

- $\dfrac{2a^2 - a - 1}{a^2 - 1} \div \dfrac{2a^2 + 7a + 3}{4a^2 + 4a}$
$= \dfrac{2a^2 - a - 1}{a^2 - 1} \times \dfrac{4a^2 + 4a}{2a^2 + 7a + 3}$
$= \dfrac{(2a + 1)(a - 1)}{(a - 1)(a + 1)} \times \dfrac{4a(a + 1)}{(2a + 1)(a + 3)}$
$= \dfrac{4a}{a + 3}$

All 3 methods are used!!

After factoring, there may not be any common factor to divide.

$\dfrac{4w + 8}{3w + 9}$
$= \dfrac{4(w + 2)}{3(w + 3)}$

This cannot be simplified!

Exercise

A **1.** State the factors of each expression.

(a) $2r + 8$

(b) $y^2 + 5y + 6$

(c) $a^2 + 3a$

(d) $a^2b + ab$

(e) $m^2 - 7m + 10$

(f) $3a^2 + 6a$

(g) $x^2 + 11x + 28$

(h) $25s^2 - 16t^2$

2. True or false?

(a) $n^2 - 4 = (n - 2)(n - 2)$

(b) $3k^2 + 12k = 3k(k + 4)$

(c) $t^2 - 4t + 3 = (t + 1)(t + 3)$

(d) $4a^3b - 8a^2 = 4a^2(ab - 2)$

(e) $c^2 + 8c + 12 = (c + 3)(c + 4)$

(f) $x^2 + 3x - 10 = (x + 2)(x - 5)$

B **3.** Factor completely.

(a) $4k^2 - 81$

(b) $m^2 - 13m - 48$

(c) $u^2 - 14u - 72$

(d) $x^2 - 10x + 21$

(e) $c^2 - 3c + 2$

(f) $6x^2 - 26x - 20$

(g) $5a^3 - 45a$

4. Determine common factors for each numerator and denominator; then simplify, if possible.

(a) $\dfrac{2x + 2}{3x + 3}$

(b) $\dfrac{5y - 10}{10y - 20}$

(c) $\dfrac{6k^2 + 3k}{8k + 4}$

(d) $\dfrac{3m^2 - 5m}{3m^3 - 5m^2}$

(e) $\dfrac{8w^3 + 24w^2}{2w^2 + 6w}$

(f) $\dfrac{15x - 30x^2}{3x^2 - 6x^3}$

(g) $\dfrac{2r^2 + 2rs - 6r}{4r + 4s - 12}$

(h) $\dfrac{3a + 3b + 3}{2a - 2b - 2}$

5. Use trinomial factoring, then simplify.

(a) $\dfrac{k^2 + 3k + 2}{k^2 + k - 2}$

(b) $\dfrac{m^2 + 8m + 15}{m^2 + 6m + 5}$

(c) $\dfrac{y^2 + 7y + 12}{y^2 + 5y + 6}$

(d) $\dfrac{x^2 - 5x - 14}{x^2 - 4x - 21}$

(e) $\dfrac{a^2 - 7a + 10}{a^2 - a - 20}$

(f) $\dfrac{n^2 - 5n - 24}{n^2 - 9n + 8}$

(g) $\dfrac{2y^2 + 3y + 1}{2y^2 + 7y + 3}$

(h) $\dfrac{a^2 - 2a - 3}{a^2 + 6a + 8}$

6. Factor, then simplify.

(a) $\dfrac{a^2 + 4a}{2a + 2} \times \dfrac{a + 1}{2a + 8}$

(b) $\dfrac{m^2 - 9}{4m + 12} \times \dfrac{2m + 2}{3m - 9}$

(c) $\dfrac{k^3 + k^2}{k^2 - 2k} \times \dfrac{k^2 - 4}{k^2 + 3k + 2}$

(d) $\dfrac{x^2 - 9}{x^2 + 11x + 24} \times \dfrac{x^2 - 64}{x^2 + 7x - 30}$

7. Express each as a product, then factor and simplify.

(a) $\dfrac{m^2 + 3m + 2}{m^2 - 4} \div \dfrac{4m + 4}{3m - 6}$

(b) $\dfrac{2n^2 - 18}{n^2 + 2n - 15} \div \dfrac{4n + 24}{n^2 + 11n + 30}$

(c) $\dfrac{2c^2 - 6c}{c^2 - 9} \div \dfrac{4c^3 + 28c^2}{c^2 + 10c + 21}$

(d) $\dfrac{2y^2 - 9y + 10}{4y^3 - 24y^2} \div \dfrac{2y^2 + 7y - 30}{y^3 - 36y}$

8. Perform the operations indicated.

(a) $\dfrac{y^2 + 4y - 21}{y^2 + 16y + 63} \times \dfrac{y^2 + 7y - 18}{y^2 + 3y - 18}$

(b) $\dfrac{d^2 + 5d - 14}{d^2 - d - 12} \div \dfrac{d^2 + 9d + 14}{d^2 - 2d - 8}$

(c) $\dfrac{k^2 - 11k + 30}{k^2 - 8k - 9} \times \dfrac{k^2 - 3k - 54}{k^2 - 13k + 40} \div$
$\dfrac{k^2 - 5k - 6}{k^2 - 7k - 8}$

(d) $\dfrac{a^2 + 6a + 8}{8a^2 - 24a} \times \dfrac{a^2 - 2a - 3}{a^2 - 4} \times$
$\dfrac{4a^2 - 8a}{a^2 + 5a + 4}$

(e) $\dfrac{m^2 - m - 12}{2m^2 + 5m - 3} \div \dfrac{m^2 + m - 20}{m^2 - 25} \div$
$\dfrac{m^3 - 5m^2}{10m^2 - 5m}$

9. Determine the average rate of speed if it takes $(3x^2 - 4x + 1)$ hours to travel $(6x^2 + 10x - 4)$ kilometres.

10. Determine each missing dimension.

(a)

(b)

(c)

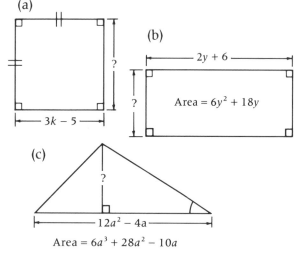

Adding and Subtracting Rational Expressions

Adding and subtracting rational expressions is very similar to the same operations with rational numbers. Compare the 2 columns below.

Rational Number Expressions

Rational Algebraic Expressions

Both numerical fractions have a common denominator.

$$\bullet \frac{4}{5} + \frac{3}{5} = \frac{4+3}{5}$$
$$= \frac{7}{5}$$

$$\bullet \frac{4}{x} + \frac{3}{x} = \frac{4+3}{x}$$
$$= \frac{7}{x}$$

Both algebraic fractions have a common denominator.

Always reduce answers to lowest terms!

$$\bullet \frac{3}{8} + \frac{1}{8} = \frac{3+1}{8}$$
$$= \frac{4}{8}$$
$$= \frac{1}{2}$$

$$\bullet \frac{a}{2y} + \frac{3a}{2y} = \frac{a+3a}{2y}$$
$$= \frac{4a}{2y}$$
$$= \frac{2a}{y}$$

8 is the lowest common denominator (LCD) for 8 and 4.

$$\bullet \frac{1}{8} - \frac{5}{4} = \frac{1}{8} - \frac{10}{8}$$
$$= \frac{1-10}{8}$$
$$= -\frac{9}{8}$$

$$\bullet \frac{5}{4x} - \frac{3}{2x} = \frac{5}{4x} - \frac{6}{4x}$$
$$= -\frac{1}{4x}$$

$4x$ is the LCD for $2x$ and $4x$.
$$\frac{3}{2x} = \frac{3 \times 2}{2x \times 2} = \frac{6}{4x}$$

12 is the LCD for 4 and 3.
$$\frac{3}{4} = \frac{3 \times 3}{4 \times 3} = \frac{9}{12}$$
$$\frac{2}{3} = \frac{2 \times 4}{3 \times 4} = \frac{8}{12}$$

$$\bullet \frac{3}{4} - \frac{2}{3} = \frac{9}{12} - \frac{8}{12}$$
$$= \frac{1}{12}$$

$$\bullet \frac{3}{a} - \frac{2}{b} = \frac{3b}{ab} - \frac{2a}{ab}$$
$$= \frac{3b - 2a}{ab}$$

ab is the LCD for a and b.
$$\frac{3}{a} = \frac{3 \times b}{a \times b} = \frac{3b}{ab}$$
$$\frac{2}{b} = \frac{2 \times a}{b \times a} = \frac{2a}{ab}$$

These examples illustrate the steps in adding or subtracting rational algebraic expressions.

- Determine the LCD for the fractions.
- Express each fraction with the LCD as the denominator.
- Combine the fractions by adding or subtracting numerators and placing the result over the LCD.
- Simplify (if possible).

For more complex expressions, it's important to use the *lowest* common denominator to make your work easier.

Example 1

$$\frac{3x}{4} + \frac{5x}{3} = \frac{9x}{12} + \frac{20x}{12}$$

$$= \frac{9x + 20x}{12}$$

$$= \frac{29x}{12}$$

Collect like terms.

12 is the LCD for 4 and 3.

$$\frac{3x}{4} = \frac{3x \times 3}{4 \times 3} = \frac{9x}{12}$$

$$\frac{5x}{3} = \frac{5x \times 4}{3 \times 4} = \frac{20x}{12}$$

A numerator or denominator may involve more than one term.

• $$\frac{x - y}{2x} + \frac{x + y}{5x}$$

$$= \frac{5(x - y)}{10x} + \frac{2(x + y)}{10x}$$

$$= \frac{5(x - y) + 2(x + y)}{10x}$$

$$= \frac{5x - 5y + 2x + 2y}{10x}$$

$$= \frac{7x - 3y}{10x}$$

Expand numerators.

Collect like terms.

10x is the LCD for 2x and 5x.

$$\frac{x - y}{2x} = \frac{(x - y) \times 5}{2x \times 5} = \frac{5(x - y)}{10x}$$

$$\frac{x + y}{5x} = \frac{(x + y) \times 2}{5x \times 2} = \frac{2(x + y)}{10x}$$

• $$\frac{5}{a + b} - \frac{3}{a - b}$$

$$= \frac{5(a - b)}{(a + b)(a - b)} - \frac{3(a + b)}{(a + b)(a - b)}$$

$$= \frac{5(a - b) - 3(a + b)}{(a + b)(a - b)}$$

$$= \frac{5a - 5b - 3a - 3b}{(a + b)(a - b)}$$

$$= \frac{2a - 8b}{(a + b)(a - b)}$$

If 2×3 is the LCD for 2 and 3 and 4×7 is the LCD for 4 and 7, then $(a + b)(a - b)$ is the LCD for $(a + b)$ and $(a - b)$.

$$\frac{5}{a + b} = \frac{5(a - b)}{(a + b) \times (a - b)} = \frac{5(a - b)}{(a + b)(a - b)}$$

$$\frac{3}{a - b} = \frac{3 \times (a + b)}{(a - b) \times (a + b)} = \frac{3(a + b)}{(a + b)(a - b)}$$

Exercise

A 1. State the answer in each case.

(a) $\dfrac{9}{5} - \dfrac{6}{5}$ (e) $\dfrac{6}{ab} - \dfrac{3}{ab}$

(b) $\dfrac{5}{8} - \dfrac{3}{8}$ (f) $\dfrac{19}{x-y} - \dfrac{13}{x-y}$

(c) $\dfrac{6a}{2} - \dfrac{5a}{2}$ (g) $\dfrac{4a}{5b} + \dfrac{6a}{5b}$

(d) $\dfrac{5m}{4} + \dfrac{7m}{4}$ (h) $\dfrac{3t}{2u+v} + \dfrac{6t}{2u+v}$

2. State the LCD for each question.

(a) $\dfrac{1}{5} + \dfrac{3}{4}$ (d) $\dfrac{5k}{2m} - \dfrac{3}{4m}$

(b) $\dfrac{5a}{9} - \dfrac{a}{6}$ (e) $\dfrac{19}{y-x} - \dfrac{11}{y+x}$

(c) $\dfrac{8}{x} - \dfrac{5}{y}$ (f) $\dfrac{4}{n(n+3)} + \dfrac{7}{(n+5)}$

B 3. Add.

(a) $\dfrac{2x}{3} + \dfrac{x}{3}$ (c) $\dfrac{2t+1}{4} + \dfrac{3t-4}{3}$

(b) $\dfrac{2m}{7} + \dfrac{12m}{7}$ (d) $\dfrac{y-2}{6} + \dfrac{3y-2}{8}$

4. Subtract.

(a) $\dfrac{c}{4} - \dfrac{c}{2}$ (d) $\dfrac{a+2}{5} - \dfrac{a+1}{6}$

(b) $\dfrac{5k}{4} - \dfrac{2k}{3}$ (e) $\dfrac{y-2}{7} - \dfrac{3+y}{4}$

(c) $\dfrac{7n}{8} - \dfrac{5n}{4}$ (f) $\dfrac{6-2x}{5} - \dfrac{3x-4}{15}$

5. Add.

(a) $\dfrac{7}{m} + \dfrac{8}{m}$ (c) $\dfrac{4}{5r^2} + \dfrac{6}{5r^2}$

(b) $\dfrac{9}{2y} + \dfrac{7}{2y}$ (d) $\dfrac{24}{7xy} + \dfrac{4}{7xy}$

6. Subtract.

(a) $\dfrac{5}{3a} - \dfrac{9}{3a}$ (c) $\dfrac{17}{2k} - \dfrac{5}{2k}$

(b) $\dfrac{6}{5m} - \dfrac{1}{5m}$ (d) $\dfrac{17b}{6ab^2} - \dfrac{29b}{6ab^2}$

7. Add or subtract as indicated.

(a) $\dfrac{7}{3y} - \dfrac{5}{12y}$ (d) $\dfrac{4}{2s^2} + \dfrac{3}{5s}$

(b) $\dfrac{16}{15xy} - \dfrac{11}{10xy}$ (e) $\dfrac{a+b}{7} + \dfrac{a-3b}{14}$

(c) $\dfrac{2}{4ab} - \dfrac{5}{12a}$ (f) $\dfrac{3x-y}{2x} - \dfrac{x+y}{3y}$

8. Perform the operations indicated.

(a) $\dfrac{x-1}{x} + \dfrac{x-3}{x+4}$ (c) $\dfrac{k+2}{k-1} - \dfrac{k-1}{k+2}$

(b) $\dfrac{r+5}{r-3} + \dfrac{r}{r+2}$ (d) $\dfrac{3}{y-2} + \dfrac{4}{y} + \dfrac{6}{y^2}$

9. Determine an expression for the perimeter of each figure and simplify.

(a)   (b)

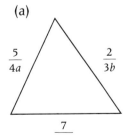

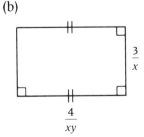

95

Evaluating Rational Expressions

Use your knowledge of reducing to lowest terms, the 3 main methods of factoring, and operations for rational expressions to simplify your work in evaluating expressions.

If $m = 6$, evaluate the expression in 2 different ways.

$$\bullet \; \frac{m^2 + 5m + 6}{m^2 + 2m - 3} \div \frac{m^2 - 4}{m^3 - m^2}$$

> Substitute $m = 6$.

$$= \frac{(6)^2 + 5(6) + 6}{(6)^2 + 2(6) - 3} \div \frac{(6)^2 - 4}{(6)^3 - (6)^2}$$

$$= \frac{72}{45} \div \frac{32}{180}$$

$$= \frac{\cancel{72}^{9}}{\cancel{45}_{1}} \times \frac{\cancel{180}^{4}}{\cancel{32}_{4}}$$

$$= 9$$

Instead of substituting first, the expression could be simplified and *then* evaluated.

$$\frac{m^2 + 5m + 6}{m^2 + 2m - 3} \div \frac{m^2 - 4}{m^3 - m^2}$$

> Simplify.

$$= \frac{\cancel{(m + 2)}\cancel{(m + 3)}}{\cancel{(m + 3)}\cancel{(m - 1)}} \times \frac{m^2\cancel{(m - 1)}}{\cancel{(m - 2)}\cancel{(m + 2)}}$$

$$= \frac{m^2}{m - 2}$$

$$= \frac{6^2}{6 - 2}$$

> Evaluate.

$$= \frac{\cancel{36}^{9}}{\cancel{4}_{1}}$$

$$= 9$$

Exercise

B

1. If $a = 1.8$, evaluate the expression $\dfrac{a^2 - 3a}{a^2 - 9}$ in 2 different ways, and compare your answers.

2. Evaluate each expression if $m = -5$.

(a) $\dfrac{2m^2 - 8m}{5m - 20}$

(b) $\dfrac{m^2 - 3m}{2m + 8} \times \dfrac{m^2 + 5m + 4}{m^2 - 2m - 3}$

(c) $\dfrac{m + 1}{2m} - \dfrac{m - 1}{3m}$

3. Simplify each expression, then evaluate using the given value.

(a) $\dfrac{y^2 - 4}{2y + 4}$; $y = 9.26$

(b) $\dfrac{w^2 + 5w + 6}{2w + 6} \times \dfrac{w^2 + 3w - 10}{w^2 - 4}$; $w = 19.8$

(c) $\dfrac{2k^2 + 5k - 3}{8k - 4} \div \dfrac{3k + 9}{2k + 10}$; $k = 16.6$

4. Calculate the perimeter of $\triangle ABC$ if $m = 2.5$.

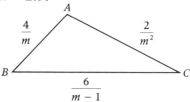

5. Determine the area of rectangle $PQRS$ if $a = 4.8$ and $b = 16$.

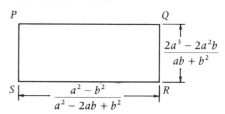

Unit 5 Review

1. Reduce to lowest terms.

   (a) $\dfrac{2(m + 3)}{(m + 3)}$

   (b) $\dfrac{9t(t - 1)}{5t(t - 1)}$

   (c) $\dfrac{4a^2b}{8ab^2}$

   (d) $\dfrac{3mn}{4m^2}$

2. Simplify.

   (a) $\dfrac{2xy}{4x}$

   (b) $\dfrac{5(a + b)}{2(a + b)}$

   (c) $\dfrac{k^4}{n^2} \times \dfrac{n^3}{k}$

   (d) $\dfrac{(y - 1)^5}{(y - 1)^2}$

   (e) $\dfrac{5(w - 1)(w + 2)}{4(w + 2)}$

   (f) $\dfrac{3(a + 1)}{6(a - 2)} \times \dfrac{4(a - 2)}{(a + 1)}$

3. Express as a product, then reduce to lowest terms.

   (a) $\dfrac{4a}{3b} \div \dfrac{5a^2}{6b^2}$

   (b) $\dfrac{3mn}{4n} \div \dfrac{9m^2}{16n^3}$

   (c) $\dfrac{-9a^3}{5b^2} \div \dfrac{-3a^2}{-4b^2}$

   (d) $\dfrac{14}{x + y} \div \dfrac{21}{x + y}$

4. Perform the operations indicated.

   (a) $\dfrac{6y(y - 3)}{2(y + 1)} \times \dfrac{(y + 1)(y - 2)}{(y - 3)(y + 5)}$

   (b) $\dfrac{9a(a - 1)(a + 2)}{3a^2(a + 4)} \times \dfrac{2(a + 4)^2}{(a - 1)(a + 4)}$

   (c) $\dfrac{(5m - 3)(m + 2)}{(m + 2)(m - 1)} \div \dfrac{4m(5m - 3)}{3m^2(m + 1)}$

   (d) $\dfrac{12x^2 + 12x}{x^2 - 25} \div \dfrac{x^2 - 1}{x^2 + 4x - 5}$

5. Factor completely, then simplify.

   (a) $\dfrac{2k^2 - 8k}{3k^2 - 12k}$

   (b) $\dfrac{m^2 - 3m}{m^2 - 9}$

   (c) $\dfrac{a^3b - a^2b}{a^2 - 1}$

   (d) $\dfrac{c^2 - c - 2}{c^2 + 4c + 3}$

   (e) $\dfrac{2y^2 + 5y + 3}{10y + 15}$

   (f) $\dfrac{x^2 - 2x - 15}{x^2 - 4x - 21}$

6. State the LCD in each case.

   (a) $\dfrac{4}{3} + \dfrac{3}{5}$

   (b) $\dfrac{2k}{3} - \dfrac{k}{2}$

   (c) $\dfrac{4}{3m} + \dfrac{6}{4m}$

   (d) $\dfrac{a + b}{2a} - \dfrac{a - b}{4a^2}$

7. Add or subtract as indicated.

   (a) $\dfrac{4k}{3} + \dfrac{5k}{3}$

   (b) $\dfrac{5m}{7} - \dfrac{2m}{7}$

   (c) $\dfrac{3}{2y} + \dfrac{5}{2y}$

   (d) $\dfrac{6k}{m} + \dfrac{3k}{4m}$

   (e) $\dfrac{3y}{2x} - \dfrac{y}{3x}$

   (f) $\dfrac{3}{5a} + \dfrac{7}{10a}$

   (g) $\dfrac{4}{xy} - \dfrac{3}{x^2y}$

   (h) $\dfrac{5}{r^2s} + \dfrac{3}{rs}$

   (i) $\dfrac{x}{y^2} - \dfrac{2x}{y}$

   (j) $\dfrac{m - n}{2m} + \dfrac{3m + n}{3n}$

8. If $k = 2$, evaluate the expression $\dfrac{4}{k + 3} - \dfrac{2}{k}$ in 2 different ways, and compare your answers.

9. Simplify each expression, then evaluate using the given value.

   (a) $\dfrac{a^2 + a - 30}{a^2 - 6a + 5}$; $a = 3$

   (b) $\dfrac{m^2 - 16}{m^2 + 4m}$; $m = 4$

   (c) $\dfrac{k^2 + 3k}{k^2 - 9} \times \dfrac{k^2 + k - 12}{k^2 - 2k - 24}$; $k = 5$

   (d) $\dfrac{2r^2 - 3r - 5}{r^2 - 1} \div \dfrac{2r^3 - 5r^2}{r^2 + 6r - 7}$; $r = -1$

10. Determine an expression for the perimeter of each figure.

(a)
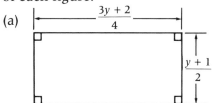

(b)
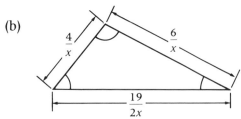

(c)
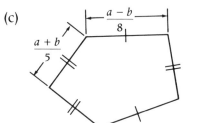

(d)
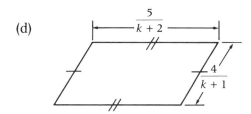

(e)
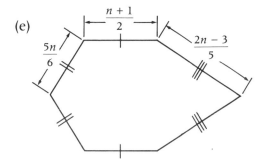

11. Evaluate the expression below if $x = 79$.

$$\frac{x^2 + 38x + 37}{x^2 - 26x - 27} \times \frac{2x^2 - 56x + 54}{x^2 + 36x - 37}$$

12. Find each missing dimension.

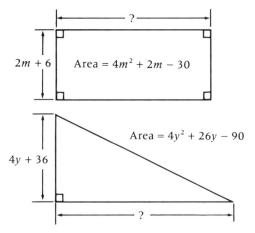

13. Determine the area of trapezoid $ABCD$ if $x = 2.3$.

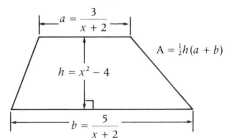

14. Find an expression (in simplified form) for the perimeter of the figure shown.

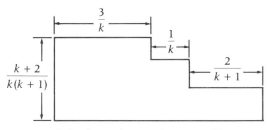

Calculate the perimeter if $k = 4$.

Unit 6

Coordinate Geometry

Graphing Ordered Pairs
Graphing Relations
Interpreting Graphs
Length of a Line Segment
Midpoint of a Line Segment
Exponential Curves
Unit 6 Review

Graphing Ordered Pairs

Working on coordinate grids is a skill used by navigators, air traffic controllers, and air search and rescue crews.

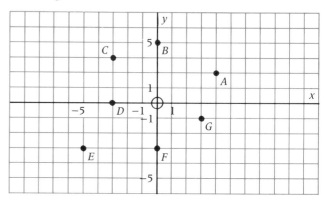

You should already know how to graph ordered pairs like (6,3) and (−5,−4).

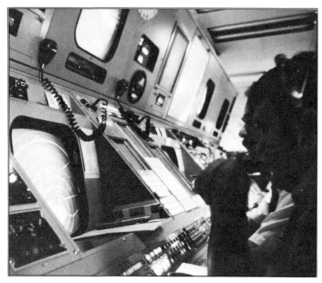

The exercise questions will help you review your graphing skills.

100

Exercise

A 1. State the coordinates of each point on the grid below.

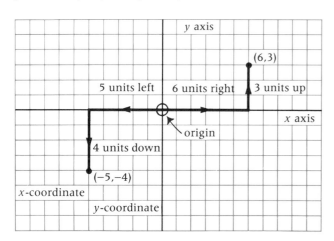

B 2. (a) Plot each of the following on a grid.
$M(3,3)$, $N(2,2)$, $O(0,0)$, $P(-1,-1)$, $Q(-2,-2)$

(b) Join the points. How are they related?

(c) Name coordinates of 2 other points that fit the pattern in part (a).

3. (a) Graph the following set of points and join the points in order.
$A(1,3)$, $B(0,2)$, $C(-1,1)$, $D(-2,0)$, $E(-3,-1)$

(b) Name the coordinates of 2 other points that fit the pattern in part (a).

4. (a) Graph the following set of points and join the points in order.
$G(2,4)$, $H(1,4)$, $J(0,4)$, $K(-1,4)$, $L(-2,4)$

(b) Name the coordinates of 2 other points that fit the pattern in part (a).

(c) Give the coordinates of 5 points that lie on another line parallel to the x axis.

5. Name the coordinates of 5 points that lie on a line parallel to the y axis.

6. (a) Plot the points $A(-3,2)$, $B(-3,-1)$, and $C(5,-1)$.
   (b) What are the coordinates of point D so that figure $ABCD$ is a rectangle?

7. (a) Plot the points $P(0,3)$ and $Q(0,-2)$.
   (b) Name the coordinates of 2 points R and S so that the figure $PQRS$ is a square.

8. (a) Describe the position of all the points located so that the x-coordinate is equal to 2.
   (b) Describe the position of all the points located so that the y-coordinate is equal to 3.

9. Graph each set of points on a separate set of axes. In each case use line segments to connect the points. Each set should form the geometric figure named.
   (a) $(2,3)$, $(-4,-1)$, $(2,-1)$;
       Right-angled triangle
   (b) $(-1,5)$, $(-6,-3)$, $(4,-3)$;
       Isosceles triangle
   (c) $(-2,3)$, $(5,3)$, $(2,-1)$, $(-5,-1)$;
       Parallelogram
   (d) $(2,2)$, $(-4,5)$, $(-4,-6)$, $(2,-3)$;
       Trapezoid

10. Draw each of the following figures on a grid and name the coordinates of the vertices you have used.
    (a) Isosceles right-angled triangle
    (b) Square

11. (a) Plot the points $A(-4,0)$, $B(0,-3)$, and $C(5,-3)$.
    (b) Name the coordinates of a point D so that figure $ABCD$ is a trapezoid. More than one solution is possible.

12. (a) Plot the points $M(0,4)$, $N(3,-1)$, and $P(5,-1)$.
    (b) Name the coordinates of point Q so that figure $MNPQ$ is a parallelogram. Can you find more than one solution?

13. Place a piece of graph paper horizontally. Mark x and y axes so that the origin is in the lower left-hand corner, as shown.

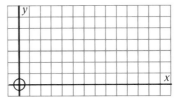

   (a) Plot the points $A(16,16)$, $B(16,24)$, $C(24,24)$, $D(24,16)$, $E(20,28)$, $F(28,28)$, $G(28,20)$, $H(20,20)$.
   (b) Join AB, AD, AH, BE, EF, EH, DG, FG, and GH with solid lines.
   (c) Join BC, CF, and CD with broken lines. What type of solid is represented by the graph?
   (d) Plot new points, on the same sheet of graph paper, with coordinates that are one-half of the corresponding coordinates of the points in part (a). You should obtain the points $A_1(8,8)$, $B_1(8,12)$, and so on to $H_1(10,10)$.
   (e) Draw in solid and broken lines as for parts (b) and (c) to form another cube.
   (f) Plot new points, on the same sheet of graph paper, with coordinates that are one-half of the corresponding coordinates of the points in part (d). You should obtain the points $A_2(4,4)$, $B_2(4,6)$, and so on to $H_2(5,5)$.
   (g) Draw in solid and broken lines as for parts (b) and (c) to form yet another cube.
   (h) Draw straight lines connecting B, B_1, B_2. Draw 2 other straight lines connecting D, D_1, D_2 and C, C_1, C_2. Extend the 3 lines so that they meet. Where do they meet?
   (i) Can you draw a smaller cube that lines up with the 3 you have already drawn? If so, do it.

101

Graphing Relations

Fix-It & Co. is a partnership of students who repair small electrical appliances. They charge $5/h plus a fixed charge of $8. This situation could be represented by an equation.

$$y = 5x + 8$$

x is the number of hours worked; y is the total charge.

You could use the equation to make a table of values and then draw a graph to illustrate the situation.

x	y	(x,y)
0	8	(0,8)
1	13	(1,13)
2	18	(2,18)
3	23	(3,23)

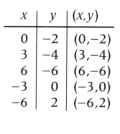

This situation can be stated in words: for each (x,y) the second number, y, is 5 times the first number, x, plus 8.

The points in the graph could be joined by a straight line. The graph represents a **linear relation**.

Any point on the graph will satisfy the equation $y = 5x + 8$. For example, (4,28) is on the graph. Check that it satisfies the equation.

LS	RS
y	$5x + 8$
$= (28)$	$= 5(4) + 8$
	$= 28$

You can graph any relation by first making a table of values, then plotting and joining the points.

Example 1

Graph the relation represented by $y = -\frac{2}{3}x - 2$.

x	y	(x,y)
0	−2	(0,−2)
3	−4	(3,−4)
6	−6	(6,−6)
−3	0	(−3,0)
−6	2	(−6,2)

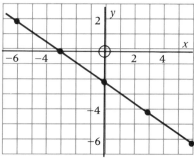

The line crosses the x axis at the point (−3,0). It crosses the y axis at the point (0,−2).

The graphs of some relations are not straight lines.

Example 2

Graph the relation represented by $y = x^2 + 1$.

x	y	(x,y)
2	5	(2,5)
1	2	(1,2)
0	1	(0,1)
−1	2	(−1,2)
−2	5	(−2,5)

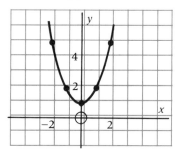

The points can be joined by a smooth curve. Since no straight line can be drawn through the points, this is called a **non-linear relation**.

Exercise

A 1. Use the graph to answer the questions below.

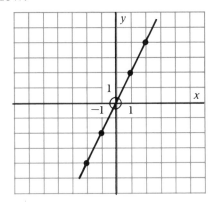

(a) State each missing coordinate.
$(1,\square)$, $(2,\square)$, $(-2,\square)$, $(\square,-1)$, $(\square,0)$, $(\square,6)$

(b) State the coordinates of 2 other points that follow the pattern.

(c) Formulate an equation that represents this relation.

2. State 5 ordered pairs (x,y) that belong to each relation.

(a) The second number, y, is the first number, x, plus two.

(b) The second number is twice the first, minus three.

(c) The second number is one-half the first.

3. State equations for each relation described in Question 2.

B 4. Write an equation that represents each of the following relations. Graph each relation.

(a) The second number, y, is three times the first, x, minus two.

(b) The second number is two-thirds the first, plus two.

(c) The second number is negative two times the first number, plus one.

(d) $(3,6)$, $(2,5)$, $(1,4)$, $(-1,2)$

(e) $(3,9)$, $(1,3)$, $(0,0)$, $(-3,-9)$

(f) $(0,4)$, $(2,4)$, $(7,4)$, $(-1,4)$, $(5,4)$, $(-3,4)$, $(1,4)$

(g) $(3,1)$, $(3,-2)$, $(3,5)$, $(3,0)$, $(3,-3)$, $(3,2)$, $(3,3)$

5. (a) Graph the relation $y = 2x - 3$ for $x = -1, 0, 1$.

(b) What are the coordinates of the point where the graph crosses the x axis? the y axis?

(c) From the graph, name each missing coordinate.
$(-2,\square)$, $(\square,1)$, $(3,\square)$, $(\square,-9)$

6. Graph each of the following linear relations on separate axes. For each graph name the coordinates of the points where the line crosses each of the axes.

(a) $y = x - 3$ (f) $y = \frac{1}{2}x + 2$

(b) $y = 2x - 4$ (g) $y = -\frac{1}{3}x + 4$

(c) $y = -x + 2$ (h) $y = \frac{3}{4}x - 2$

(d) $y = 3x - 1$ (i) $y = -\frac{2}{3}x + 2$

(e) $y = -2x + 3$ (j) $y = \frac{2}{5}x + 2$

7. Graph each of the following non-linear relations on separate axes.

(a) $y = x^2$ (e) $y = 2x^2 + 1$

(b) $y = x^2 + 2$ (f) $y = 2x^2 - 3$

(c) $y = x^2 - 4$ (g) $y = -x^2$

(d) $y = 2x^2$ (h) $y = -x^2 + 3$

Interpreting Graphs

A salesperson works on salary plus commission. The monthly pay ($P) is represented by the equation $P = 0.05S + 800$, where S represents the monthly sales, in dollars.

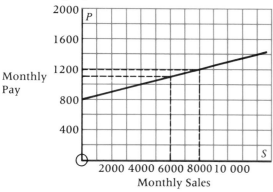

Here is a graph of the relation.

You could make the following observations from the graph.

- If sales are $6000, then pay for the month is $1100.
- If the salesperson earned $1200, then sales for the month totalled $8000.
- The line crosses the P axis at (0,800). This means that if there are no monthly sales then the salesperson earns $800 for the month.

The graph is drawn in the first quadrant only. Why is this appropriate in this situation?

Exercise

A 1. The graph below represents the situation in which a train 200 m from the station brakes to a stop.

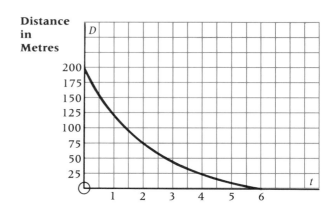

Time in Seconds

(a) In this situation, what information can be determined from the points (0,200) and (6,0)?

(b) How far from the station is the train 3 s after the brakes have been applied? 5 s after the brakes have been applied?

B 2. The cost of producing a yearbook is given by an equation.
$$C = 8n + 4000$$
C is the cost in dollars and n is the number of yearbooks.

(a) Draw a graph of the relation for $n = 0$ to 3000.

(b) From your graph, find the cost of producing 700 yearbooks; 1500 yearbooks; 2000 yearbooks.

(c) In this situation, what information can be determined from the point of intersection with the vertical axis?

3. Oil is being drained from a tank so that the amount of oil (R litres) remaining after a given time (t seconds) is given by an equation.

$$R = -10t + 500$$

(a) Draw a graph of this relation.
(b) How many litres are in the tank at the start?
(c) How long does it take to drain the tank?
(d) How many litres of oil remain in the tank after 20 s?

4. A Rent-All outlet uses a formula to calculate the charge for renting a snowblower.

$$C = 3.5t + 4$$

C is the cost in dollars and t is the rental time in hours.

(a) Draw a graph of this relation.
(b) What is the fixed charge?
(c) How much does it cost to rent a snowblower for 5 h?
(d) What is the rental charge per hour?

5. The fuel consumption of Ange's mid-size car is given by an equation.

$$N = -0.105D + 63$$

N is amount of fuel in litres; D is distance in kilometres.

(a) Draw a graph of this relation.
(b) How many litres are there in a full tank of gasoline?
(c) How far can Ange drive before the tank is empty?
(d) How many litres are left after driving 200 km?
(e) How many litres are used per 100 km?

6. When the mayor opened the new stadium with a kick off, the football followed a path given by the equation below.

$$d = -5t^2 + 20t + 1$$

t is the time in seconds and d is the distance above the ground, in metres.

(a) Draw the graph of the relation represented by the equation.
(b) What was the highest point reached by the football?
(c) If the ball was caught 1 m above the ground, how long was it in the air?
(d) How high above the ground was the ball when it left the mayor's foot?

7. A plane leaves Vancouver and flies 4000 km to Montreal. The average speed is 800 km/h. After t hours the distance, D kilometres, from Montreal is given by the equation $D = -800t + 4000$.

(a) Draw the graph of the relation represented by the equation.
(b) Lunch is served 2 h after takeoff. How far from Montreal is the plane when lunch is served?

(c) How long will it take to reach Montreal?
(d) After how many hours is the plane over Winnipeg, approximately 2000 km from Vancouver?

Length of a Line Segment

On a grid, you can find horizontal and vertical distances easily.

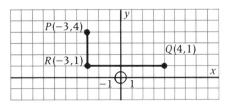

The length of RQ is the difference in x coordinates.

$$RQ = 4 - (-3)$$
$$= 4 + 3$$
$$= 7$$

The length of PR is the difference in y coordinates.

$$PR = 4 - 1$$
$$= 3$$

You can apply the Law of Pythagoras, now that you know the lengths of RQ and PR, to find the length of PQ.

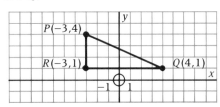

$$PQ^2 = PR^2 + RQ^2$$
$$= 3^2 + 7^2$$
$$= 9 + 49$$
$$= 58$$
$$PQ = \sqrt{58}$$
$$= 7.6, \text{ to 1 decimal place}$$

> $\triangle PQR$ is a right-angled triangle.

The length of PQ is about 7.6 units.

> In general, the length of a line segment AB on a grid is given by a formula.
>
> $$AB^2 = \left(\begin{array}{c}\text{Difference of}\\ x \text{ coordinates}\end{array}\right)^2 + \left(\begin{array}{c}\text{Difference of}\\ y \text{ coordinates}\end{array}\right)^2$$

You can use the formula to discover or prove properties of given figures.

Example 1

Show that the triangle with vertices $A(3,5)$, $B(-6,0)$, and $C(-2,-4)$ is isosceles.

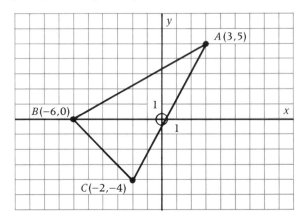

Calculate the length of each side of the triangle until you find 2 equal sides.

$$AB^2 = [3 - (-6)]^2 + (5 - 0)^2$$
$$= (9)^2 + (5)^2$$
$$= 81 + 25$$
$$= 106$$
$$AB = \sqrt{106}$$

$$BC^2 = [-2 - (-6)]^2 + (-4 - 0)^2$$
$$= (4)^2 + (-4)^2$$
$$= 16 + 16$$
$$= 32$$
$$BC = \sqrt{32}$$

$$AC^2 = [3 - (-2)]^2 + (5 - (-4))^2$$
$$= (5)^2 + (9)^2$$
$$= 25 + 81$$
$$= 106$$
$$AC = \sqrt{106}$$

Since $AB = AC$, then $\triangle ABC$ is isosceles.

Exercise

A 1. State the length of each line segment.

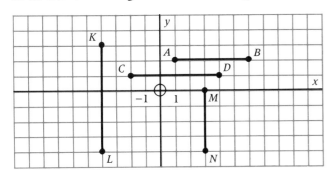

2. Find the area of rectangle $ABCD$.

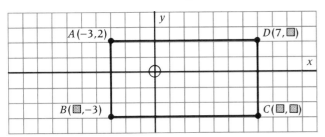

3. Find the area of $\triangle ABC$. Use the formula $A = \frac{1}{2}bh$.

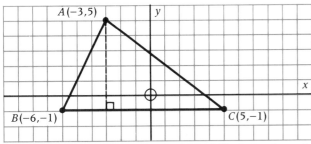

B 4. Plot each pair of points and find the length of the segment joining them.

(a) $(2,3)$, $(5,7)$ (f) $(-3,-2)$, $(1,5)$
(b) $(4,3)$, $(1,2)$ (g) $(-1,-3)$, $(-4,2)$
(c) $(-3,4)$, $(0,2)$ (h) $(4,-1)$, $(-5,-6)$
(d) $(0,0)$, $(7,8)$ (i) $(-2,-2)$, $(3,3)$
(e) $(-2,4)$, $(6,3)$ (j) $(-1,-6)$, $(4,7)$

5. Show that the triangle with vertices $D(-3,6)$, $E(0,2)$, and $F(4,5)$ is isosceles.

6. Three vertices of a rectangle $ABCD$ are $A(-2,3)$, $B(4,3)$, and $C(4,-2)$.

(a) What are the coordinates of point D?
(b) Determine the lengths of AC and BD.
(c) How are the lengths of the diagonals of the rectangle related?
(d) Calculate the perimeter of the rectangle.

7. The end points of the diameter of a circle are $A(-3,5)$ and $B(5,-1)$.

(a) Calculate the length of the diameter.
(b) What is the radius of the circle?
(c) Calculate the area and circumference of the circle, to one decimal place. $(A = \pi r^2, C = \pi d, \pi \doteq 3.14)$

8. The location of 3 islands is given by the points $A(50,40)$, $B(-60,70)$, and $C(0,-50)$, where the numbers represent distance in kilometres.

(a) Calculate the distance between each island.
(b) If a ship can sail 30 km/h, how long will it take to sail from island A to island C?

9. Given the 3 points $A(3,2)$, $B(6,6)$, and $C(9,10)$, answer the following.

(a) Find the lengths of AB, AC, and BC.
(b) Show that A, B, and C lie on the same straight line.

Midpoint of a Line Segment

You can find the midpoint of a line segment on a grid by using its end points.
Midpoints of horizontal and vertical lines are easy to find.

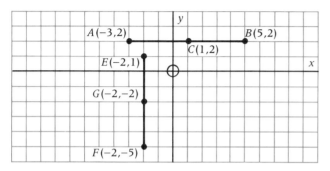

The midpoint of AB is $C(1,2)$, because
$AC = CB = 4$.
Similarly, the midpoint of EF is $G(-2,-2)$.

Find the midpoints of diagonal lines by drawing in right-angled triangles.

Example 1

Find M, the midpoint of the segment joining $P(1,1)$ and $Q(7,5)$.

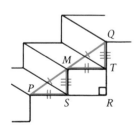 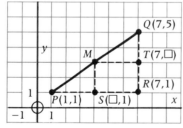

Start by drawing the right triangle PRQ.
Consider the x and y coordinates separately. The midpoint of RQ is $T(7,\boxed{3})$ and the midpoint of PR is $(\boxed{4},1)$.
Look at the graph. The midpoint of PQ is $M(\boxed{4},\boxed{3})$.

Another way of finding the coordinates of M is to find the *average* of the coordinates of P and Q.

x coordinate of M	y coordinate of M
$= \dfrac{7 + 1}{2}$	$= \dfrac{1 + 5}{2}$
$= 4$	$= 3$

Example 2

Find M, the midpoint of DE.

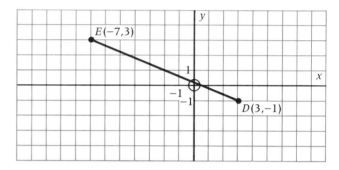

x coordinate of M	y coordinate of M
$= \dfrac{3 + (-7)}{2}$	$= \dfrac{-1 + 3}{2}$
$= \dfrac{-4}{2}$	$= \dfrac{2}{2}$
$= -2$	$= 1$

The midpoint is $M(-2,1)$.

In general, the coordinates of the midpoint of a line segment are the averages of the coordinates of its end points.

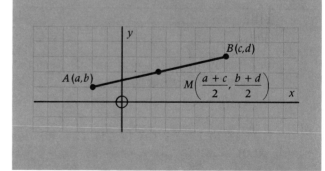

Exercise

A 1. State the midpoint of each segment.

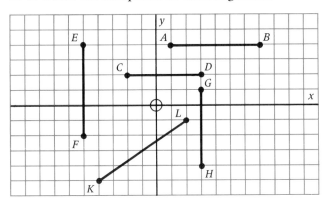

B 2. Determine the coordinates of the midpoints of the line segment joining each pair of points.

(a) (2,5), (8,9)   (f) (−4,−9), (−2,−3)
(b) (1,2), (8,10)   (g) (−3,−2), (4,8)
(c) (−3,4), (5,8)   (h) (−5,−2), (9,−6)
(d) (−2,7), (4,−3)   (i) (7,−5), (−12,8)
(e) (4,6), (10,6)   (j) (−3,5), (−3,−5)

3. (a) Plot the triangle with vertices $A(4,6)$, $B(−4,−2)$, and $C(12,−2)$.
   (b) Find the midpoints M and N of segments AB and AC. Join points M and N.
   (c) Find the length of MN.
   (d) Find the length of BC.
   (e) How are the lengths of MN and BC related?

4. The vertices of a parallelogram are $A(−2,3)$, $B(8,3)$, $C(4,−3)$, and $D(−6,−3)$.

   (a) Plot the parallelogram.
   (b) Find the midpoint of each diagonal (AC and BD).
   (c) What conclusion can you make about the diagonals of a parallelogram?

5. The vertices of a triangle are $A(4,10)$, $B(−4,2)$, and $C(6,−4)$.

   (a) Plot the triangle on a grid.
   (b) Find the midpoints of sides AB, BC, and AC.
   (c) Join each vertex to the midpoint of the opposite side.
   (d) How are the segments drawn in part (c) related?
   (e) What name is given to each segment in part (c)?

6. The end points of the diameter of a circle are $(0,5)$ and $(10,3)$.

   (a) Determine the coordinates of the centre of the circle.
   (b) Find the radius of the circle.
   (c) Find the area of the circle.

7. The midpoint of a line segment is $(4,5)$. One end point of the segment is $A(2,2)$. What are the coordinates of the other end point?

8. A rhombus $ABCD$ is determined by points $A(−3,6)$, $B(4,9)$, $C(1,2)$, and $D(−6,−1)$.

   (a) Plot the points A, B, C, and D, then join opposite vertices AC and BD.
   (b) By calculating the midpoints of AC and BD, show that the diagonals of the rhombus bisect one another.
   (c) If the diagonals meet at E, use lengths to show that each angle is $90°$.

Exponential Curves

A round-robin basketball tournament was held for the 16 senior school teams in a county. The diagram shows the results of the tournament.

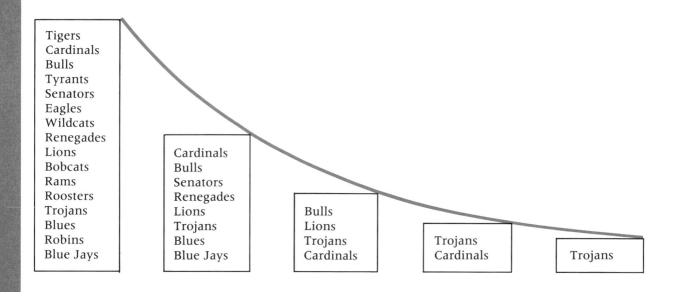

Tigers				
Cardinals				
Bulls				
Tyrants				
Senators	Cardinals			
Eagles	Bulls			
Wildcats	Senators			
Renegades	Renegades	Bulls		
Lions	Lions	Lions		
Bobcats	Trojans	Trojans	Trojans	
Rams	Blues	Cardinals	Cardinals	Trojans
Roosters	Blue Jays			
Trojans				
Blues				
Robins				
Blue Jays				

The lists of teams form a pattern. The curve drawn through the top right corner of each column is an **exponential curve**.

Exponential curves represent quantities that grow or decrease by successive multiplication. In the basketball example, each list of team names has one-half the number of the names in the list before it.

Another example of exponential curves can be found in music. The wave-length of a musical note is exactly twice the wave-length of the note that is exactly one octave higher.

Why is the shape of a grand piano in the form of an exponential curve?

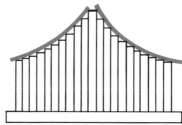

Money that is invested in a savings account to earn compound interest is another example of exponential growth. The graph below shows how your money would grow if you invested $1000 at 8%/a compounded annually. The situation has been represented by an exponential curve.

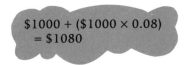

$1000 + ($1000 × 0.08)
= $1080

Time (years)	Amount
0	$1000.00
1	$1080.00
2	$1166.40
3	$1259.71
4	$1360.49
5	$1469.33
6	$1586.87
7	$1713.82
8	$1850.93
9	$1999.00
10	$2158.92

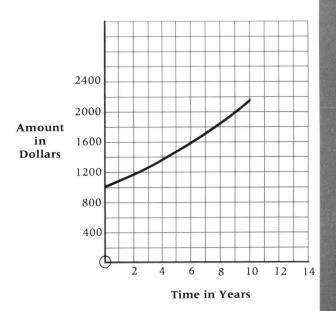

Exercise

1. Make a table of values to show how $1000 will grow at 10%/a compounded annually. Draw a graph from the table of values.

2. The population of Canada from 1871 to 1981 is given below, in millions.

1871; 3.7	1911; 7.2	1951; 14.0
1881; 4.0	1921; 8.8	1961; 18.2
1891; 4.8	1931; 10.4	1971; 21.6
1901; 5.4	1941; 11.5	1981; 24.0

   (a) Construct a graph to show the growth of Canada's population.
   (b) What type of curve represents the growth of Canada's population?
   (c) Has the population growth been regular?
   (d) Explain the growth pattern from the years 1901 to 1941 and from 1941 to 1981.
   (e) Canada's population is increasing at the rate of approximately 12% every 10 a. Estimate Canada's population in 1991 and 2001.

Unit 6 Review

1. Graph each of the following linear relations. For each graph, name the points where the line crosses each of the x and y axes.

   (a) $y = x + 3$

   (b) $y = 2x - 2$

   (c) $y = -3x + 4$

   (d) $y = \frac{1}{3}x - 2$

   (e) $y = -2x - 3$

   (f) $y = -\frac{1}{2}x + 2$

   (g) $y = \frac{2}{3}x - 5$

   (h) $y = -\frac{3}{4}x + 3$

2. Graph each of the following non-linear relations.

   (a) $y = x^2 - 1$

   (b) $y = x^2 + 3$

   (c) $y = x^2 - 2$

   (d) $y = 2x^2 + 2$

   (e) $y = -x^2 + 1$

   (f) $y = -2x^2 + 3$

3. The length (L centimetres) of a spring is measured for different masses (M kilograms) attached to it. The formula that relates M and L is $L = 14M + 60$.

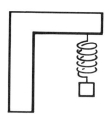

   (a) Draw a graph of this relation for $M = 0$ to 5.

   (b) What is the length of the spring if a 4 kg mass is attached?

   (c) What mass is attached to the spring if the length is 130 cm?

   (d) In this situation, what information can be interpreted from the intercept of the vertical axis?

4. A can of apple juice is placed in a refrigerator to cool. The relation between the temperature (T degrees Celsius) and the time (t minutes) after the pitcher is placed to cool is given by an equation.

$$T = -\tfrac{1}{10}t + 20$$

   (a) Graph this relation.

   (b) What is the initial temperature of the apple juice when it is placed in the refrigerator?

   (c) When will the juice reach a temperature of 5°C?

   (d) When will the temperature of the juice be 0°C? Explain why the cooling will eventually stop in this situation.

   (e) Under what condition would liquid placed in a refrigerator freeze? What would the graph look like in this situation?

5. Plot each pair of points and find the length of each segment.

   (a) (4,6), (6,10)

   (b) (−3,4), (2,0)

   (c) (0,0), (−2,4)

   (d) (−2,−3), (1,5)

   (e) (−3,−1), (2,−4)

   (f) (−6,−1), (7,4)

6. Determine the coordinates of the midpoint of each segment.

   (a) (4,7), (10,5)

   (b) (4,−3), (8,5)

   (c) (−9,−4), (−3,−2)

   (d) (8,9), (−2,−3)

   (e) (−2,−5), (−6,9)

   (f) (−5,7), (8,−12)

Unit 7

Geometry of a Straight Line

Slope

"Let's head for the slopes."

Slope refers to the steepness of a hill or road and is related to the pitch of a roof. On a coordinate grid, the slope of a line is defined as a ratio.

$$\text{Slope} = \frac{\text{Rise}}{\text{Run}}$$

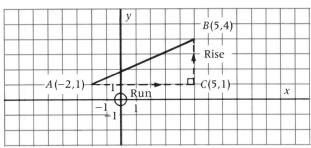

Rise = BC Run = AC
 = $4 - 1$ = $5 - (-2)$
 = 3 = 7

Rise is the difference between the y coordinates of A and B.
Run is the difference between the x coordinates of A and B.

$$\text{Slope of } AB = \frac{\text{Rise}}{\text{Run}}$$
$$= \tfrac{3}{7}$$

Use the same definition to find a general expression for the slope of a line segment joining two points $P_1(x_1, y_1)$ and $P_2(x_2, y_2)$.

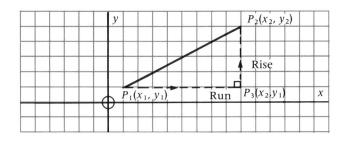

Rise = $y_2 - y_1$
Run = $x_2 - x_1$

$$\text{Slope of } P_1P_2 = \frac{y_2 - y_1}{x_2 - x_1}$$

Example 1

Calculate the slope of each line segment.

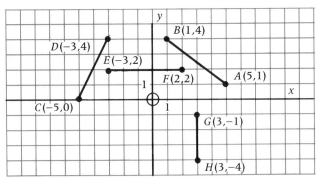

$$\text{Slope} = \frac{\text{Rise}}{\text{Run}}$$

Slope of AB
$$= \frac{4 - 1}{1 - 5}$$
$$= -\tfrac{3}{4}$$

Slope of CD
$$= \frac{4 - 0}{-3 - (-5)}$$
$$= \tfrac{4}{2}$$
$$= 2$$

Slope of EF
$$= \frac{2 - 2}{2 - (-3)}$$
$$= \tfrac{0}{5}$$
$$= 0$$

Slope of GH
$$= \frac{-4 - (-1)}{3 - 3}$$
$$= \tfrac{-3}{0}$$

The slope of GH is undefined.

On a grid system:
- the slope of a line slanting upward to the right is positive;
- the slope of a line slanting upward to the left is negative;
- the slope of a horizontal line is zero;
- the slope of a vertical line is undefined.

You can use your knowledge of slope to answer questions like the one below.

Example 2

Draw a line through the point $A(2,2)$ with slope $-\frac{2}{3}$.

Name 2 other points on the line.

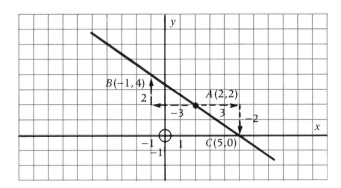

Since slope is negative, the line slants upward to the left.

Begin at $(2,2)$ and move 3 to the left and 2 up, or 3 to the right and 2 down. Two other points on the line are $B(-1,4)$ and $C(5,0)$.

Draw the line through A, B, and C.

Exercise

A **1.** State the slope of each of the following lines. In each case, state the coordinates of two other points on the line.

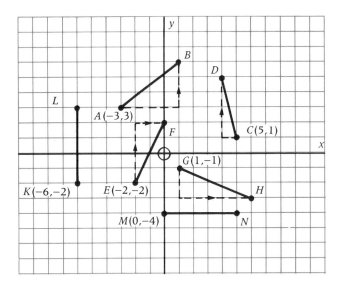

B **2.** For each pair of points:
- calculate the slope of the line segment through the points;
- tell whether the line is horizontal, vertical, or slants upward to the right or left.

(a) $A(3,5)$, $B(7,8)$
(b) $C(6,2)$, $D(-3,7)$
(c) $E(3,-7)$, $F(-7,0)$
(d) $G(6,5)$, $H(6,-1)$
(e) $J(3,-2)$, $K(-5,-4)$
(f) $L(3,7)$, $M(-2,7)$
(g) $N(-8,-3)$, $P(-4,-6)$
(h) $Q(-4,-2)$, $R(9,3)$
(i) $O(0,0)$, $S(8,5)$
(j) $T(\frac{3}{2},-3)$, $V(\frac{7}{2},-9)$

115

3. On a separate grid, draw the graph of each line passing through the given point and with the given slope. In each case, name two other points on the line.

(a) $A(3,5)$, slope $\frac{2}{3}$
(b) $B(-2,4)$, slope $-\frac{4}{5}$
(c) $C(4,-3)$, slope 0
(d) $D(-3,2)$, slope $-\frac{5}{2}$
(e) $E(-4,-5)$, slope $\frac{2}{7}$
(f) $F(2,7)$, slope undefined
(g) $(6,0)$, slope $-\frac{4}{3}$
(h) $G(5,-2)$, slope 3

4. (a) Plot the points $A(-6,0)$, $B(-3,1)$, $C(0,2)$, and $D(3,3)$ on a grid.
(b) Join the points in order. How are the points related?
(c) Calculate the slopes of AB, BC and CD.
(d) What conclusion can you make about the slopes of all segments of the same straight line?

5. The pitch of a roof is defined by a formula.
$$\text{Pitch} = \tfrac{1}{2}(\text{Slope})$$
Calculate the pitch of each roof.
(a)

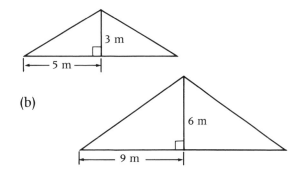

(b)

6. A road rises vertically 2 m for every horizontal run of 40 m to the right. What is the grade (slope) of the road?

7. A ski slope drops to the right 7.5 m for every horizontal run of 30 m. What is the slope of the ski hill?

8. A ramp for wheelchairs drops 7.5 cm for every 90 cm it runs horizontally. What is the slope of the ramp?

9. A stairway rises 12 cm for every 24 cm it runs horizontally. What is the slope of the stairs?

10. Plot the points $A(1,3)$ and $B(3,7)$.

(a) Determine the slope of AB.
(b) Using the slope from part (a), determine the missing coordinate for each of the following points that lie on the same line as A and B.

- $C(5,\blacksquare)$
- $D(-1,\blacksquare)$
- $E(\blacksquare,-5)$
- $F(9,\blacksquare)$

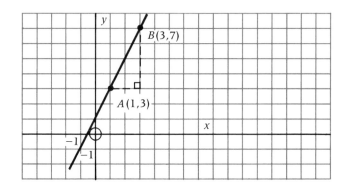

Graphing $y = mx + b$

The graph of the relation $y = \frac{2}{3}x + 1$ is a straight line. To graph the line, you may use a table of values from which you find points on the line.

$y = \frac{2}{3}x + 1$

x	y
0	1
3	3

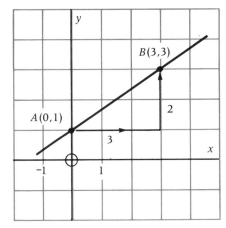

Another way to graph the line is to find its slope and a point on it as follows.

Slope of $AB = \dfrac{\text{Rise}}{\text{Run}}$

$\phantom{\text{Slope of } AB} = \dfrac{3 - 1}{3 - 0}$

The line crosses the y axis at the point $(0,1)$. The y coordinate of this point is the **y-intercept**. The y-intercept of this line is 1.

Notice that the slope, $\frac{2}{3}$, and the y-intercept, 1, appear in the equation $y = \frac{2}{3}x + 1$.

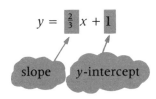

$$y = \boxed{\tfrac{2}{3}}\, x + \boxed{1}$$

slope y-intercept

In general, the line represented by $y = \boxed{m}\,x\, \boxed{+b}$ has slope m and y-intercept b.

Example 1

Name the slope and y-intercept for the line represented by the equation $y = -\frac{3}{4}x - 3$. Use this information to graph the line.

Compare to $y = mx + b$.

$$y = \boxed{mx} \quad \boxed{+b}$$
$$y = \boxed{-\tfrac{3}{4}x} \quad \boxed{-3}$$

The slope of the line is $-\frac{3}{4}$ and the y-intercept is -3.

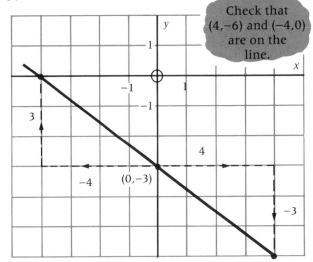

Check that $(4,-6)$ and $(-4,0)$ are on the line.

Example 2

Write an equation of the line with slope $\frac{4}{5}$ and y-intercept 3.

Since the slope, m, is $\frac{4}{5}$ and the y-intercept, b, is 3, an equation of the line is $y = \frac{4}{5}x + 3$.

117

Exercise

A **1.** Each equation defines a line. State the slope and y-intercept in each case.

   (a) $y = \frac{3}{4}x - 3$ (d) $y = 3x$
   (b) $y = 4x + 5$ (e) $y = -\frac{2}{3}x$
   (c) $y = -\frac{4}{3}x - 2$ (f) $y = 5 - 2x$

2. State an equation for each of the following lines.

   (a) $m = 4$; $b = 3$
   (b) $m = -\frac{2}{3}$; $b = -1$
   (c) slope 2, y-intercept 2
   (d)   (e)

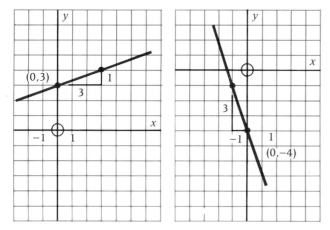

B **3.** Each of the following equations defines a line. For each line:
   • give the slope and y-intercept;
   • graph the line using its slope and y-intercept

   (a) $y = 2x + 1$ (f) $y = -2x - 3$
   (b) $y = \frac{3}{4}x - 2$ (g) $y = -\frac{3}{7}x + 1$
   (c) $y = \frac{5}{3}x + 3$ (h) $y = -3x$
   (d) $y = x + 4$ (i) $x = 3$
   (e) $y = -x + 2$ (j) $y = 4$

4. Write an equation for each of the following lines.

   (a) slope 3, y-intercept 1
   (b) slope $\frac{4}{3}$, y-intercept -2
   (c) slope $-\frac{4}{5}$, y-intercept $+3$
   (d) slope -2, y-intercept 0
   (e) slope $-\frac{2}{3}$, y-intercept -4

5. (a) Graph all of the given lines on one set of axes.
     • $y = 2x$ • $y = -3x$
     • $y = \frac{1}{2}x$ • $y = -\frac{2}{3}x$
     • $y = x$ • $y = \frac{5}{3}x$
   (b) Give the slope and y-intercept of each line in part (a).
   (c) How are the lines in part (a) related?

6. (a) Graph all of the given lines on one set of axes.
     • $y = 2x + 6$ • $y = 2x$
     • $y = 2x + 4$ • $y = 2x - 2$
     • $y = 2x + 2$ • $y = 2x - 4$
   (b) Give the slope and y-intercept of each line in part (a).
   (c) How are the lines in part (a) related?

7. Repeat Question 6 for the lines defined by each of the following equations:
     • $y = -3x + 6$ • $y = -3x$
     • $y = -3x + 4$ • $y = -3x - 2$
     • $y = -3x + 2$ • $y = -3x - 4$

8. From your results of Questions 6 and 7, what is the relationship between slopes of parallel lines?

Rewriting Equations

Now that you have graphed equations of the form $y = mx + b$ without using a table of values, you can extend that skill to graph the lines represented by other forms of equations.

$$3x + y = 2$$

Use your algebra skills to rewrite the equation in the form $y = mx + b$.

$$3x + y = 2$$

Subtract $3x$ from each side.
$$3x + y - 3x = 2 - 3x$$
$$y = 2 - 3x$$

Rewrite in the form $y = mx + b$.
$$y = -3x + 2$$

The slope of the line is -3 and the y-intercept is 2.

To graph a line without using a table of values, you can rewrite its equation in the form $y = mx + b$.

Example 1

Graph the line represented by
$2x - 3y - 12 = 0$.
$$2x - 3y - 12 = 0$$
$$-3y = -2x + 12$$
$$y = \tfrac{2}{3}x - 4$$

Divide by -3.

The line has slope $\tfrac{2}{3}$ and y-intercept -4.

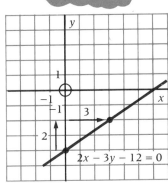

Exercise

B 1. Rewrite each of the following equations in the form $y = mx + b$. Then write the slope and y-intercept.

(a) $2x + y = 3$
(b) $3x + y - 4 = 0$
(c) $4x - y = 2$
(d) $x + y - 3 = 0$
(e) $2x + 3y = 6$
(f) $3x - 5y = 15$
(g) $4x + 3y - 12 = 0$
(h) $x + 2y = 4$
(i) $x - 3y = 9$
(j) $3x + 2y = 5$

2. Rewrite each of the following equations in the form $y = mx + b$ and then graph the line.

(a) $3x + y = 2$
(b) $2x - y = 4$
(c) $3x + 2y = 6$
(d) $4x - 3y - 12 = 0$

Side Trip

The equation of a line is $Ax + By + C = 0$.

(a) Rewrite the equation in the form $y = mx + b$.
(b) By comparing with $y = mx + b$, find the slope of the given line in terms of A and B.
(c) Use the results of part (b) to find the slope of each line below.

- $4x - 8y + 5 = 0$
- $3x + 5y + 15 = 0$
- $9x - 2y + 18 = 0$
- $10x + 5y + 7 = 0$

119

Graphing Using Intercepts

In the last section a line represented by the equation $2x - 3y = 12$ was graphed by rewriting it in the form $y = \frac{2}{3}x - 4$.

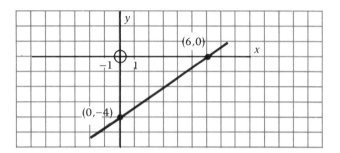

The point of intersection of the line with the y-axis is $(0,-4)$.
The y-intercept of this line is -4.

To find the y-intercept of a line substitute $x = 0$ in the equation and solve for y.

The line crosses the x-axis at the point $(6,0)$. The x coordinate of this point is the **x-intercept**. The x-intercept of this line is 6.

To find the x-intercept of a line substitute $y = 0$ in the equation and solve for x.

You can use the x- and y-intercepts of a line to graph the line.

Example 1

Graph the line represented by $3x + 4y = 12$ by finding the x- and y-intercepts of the line.

For the x-intercept, let $y = 0$.
$$3x + 4(0) = 12$$
$$3x = 12$$
$$x = 4$$

The x-intercept is 4.

For the y-intercept, let $x = 0$.
$$3(0) + 4y = 12$$
$$4y = 12$$
$$y = 3$$

The y-intercept is 3.

Two points on the line are $(4,0)$ and $(0,3)$. Plot the points and draw the line through them.

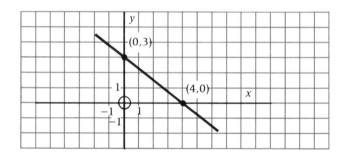

Exercise

B **1.** Determine the x- and y-intercepts for each of the following lines, then graph the line.

(a) $2x + 3y = 6$
(b) $x + 4y = 8$
(c) $3x + y = 6$
(d) $2x - y = 4$
(e) $x - 3y = 6$
(f) $4x - 3y = 12$
(g) $2x + 7y = 14$
(h) $5x - 3y = 15$
(i) $2x + 5y = 10$
(j) $5x - 2y = 10$
(k) $3x + 4y = 12$
(l) $2x + 5y = 12$
(m) $3x - 7y = 21$
(n) $6x + 5y = 18$

Finding the Equation of a Line

You can determine an equation of a line in the form $y = mx + b$ if you know the slope and one other point on the line.

Example 1

Determine an equation of the line with slope $\frac{3}{4}$ and passing through the point $(2,-3)$.

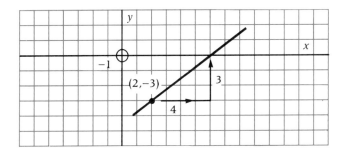

Substitute $m = \frac{3}{4}$ in $y = mx + b$.
The required equation is in the following form.

$$y = \frac{3}{4}x + b$$

Now find b by substituting $x = 2$ and $y = -3$.

$-3 = \frac{3}{4}(+2) + b$ Since $(2,-3)$ is on the line
$-3 = \frac{3}{2} + b$

$-6 = 3 + 2b$ ×2
$2b = -9$
$b = \frac{9}{2}$

An equation of the line is
$y = \frac{3}{4}x - \frac{9}{2}$.

You can also find an equation of a line if you know two points on the line.

Example 2

Determine an equation of the line passing through the points $A(4,-2)$ and $B(-3,4)$.

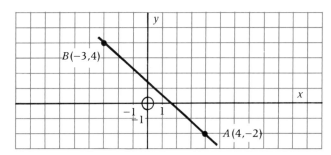

The slope m of the line is the same as the slope of segment AB.

$$\text{Slope of } AB = \frac{4 - (-2)}{-3 - 4}$$
$$= -\frac{6}{7}$$

Substitute $m = -\frac{6}{7}$ in $y = mx + b$. The required equation is in the following form.
$$y = -\frac{6}{7} + b$$

To determine b, select one of the points and substitute for x and y.
Since $A(4,-2)$ is on the line, substitute $x = 4$ and $y = -2$.

$-2 = -\frac{6}{7}(4) + b$ ×7
$-14 = -24 + 7b$
$7b = 10$
$b = \frac{10}{7}$

An equation of the line is:

$$y = -\frac{6}{7}x + \frac{10}{7}$$
$$\text{or } 7y = -6x + 10 \quad \text{×7}$$

In general, to determine an equation of a line in the form $y = mx + b$:
- determine the slope m;
- determine b by substituting values for x and y from a point on the line.

Exercise

A **1.** State the slope and y-intercept for each of the following lines.

(a) $y = \frac{7}{2}x + 3$ (c) $y = \frac{2}{3}x$
(b) $y = -2x - 4$ (d) $y = -\frac{4}{3}x - 8$

2. In each case, state an equation of the line in the form $y = mx + b$.

(a) $m = 4, b = 3$
(b) $m = -\frac{2}{3}, b = -2$
(c) $m = \frac{5}{3}, b = \frac{2}{3}$
(d) $m = -\frac{5}{2}, b = 3$

B **3.** Solve for b in each of the following:

(a) $4 = 3(2) + b$
(b) $9 = -2(3) + b$
(c) $7 = \frac{2}{3}(-6) + b$

4. Determine an equation of each of the following lines with the given slope and passing through the given point.

(a) $m = 3$; $A(2,5)$ (f) $m = \frac{1}{2}$; $F(4,2)$
(b) $m = 2$; $B(-3,-4)$ (g) $m = \frac{3}{4}$; $G(-4,1)$
(c) $m = -4$; $C(5,-3)$ (h) $m = -\frac{2}{5}$; $H(10,-1)$
(d) $m = -1$; $D(3,0)$ (i) $m = \frac{5}{3}$; $I(7,2)$
(e) $m = 5$; $E(0,-2)$ (j) $m = -\frac{4}{7}$; $J(-9,-3)$

5. (a) Plot the points $P(3,2)$ and $Q(9,6)$.
(b) Determine the slope of PQ.
(c) Determine an equation of the line passing through the points P and Q.

6. In each of the following, determine an equation of the line passing through each pair of points.

(a) $(2,3), (4,9)$ (e) $(4,5), (-4,-4)$
(b) $(3,-4), (6,2)$ (f) $(4,0), (0,3)$
(c) $(4,-2), (-2,10)$ (g) $(0,0), (4,-3)$
(d) $(-3,-5), (2,3)$ (h) $(-5,1), (-8,-1)$

7. (a) Determine the equation of the line passing through the points $A(2,3)$ and $B(6,6)$.
(b) Show that the coordinates of the point $C(10,9)$ satisfy the equation in part (a).
(c) Explain why the points A, B, and C lie on the same line.

8. (a) For the points $A(2,3)$, $B(6,6)$, and $C(10,9)$, find the slopes of AB and AC.
(b) What property of a line does the result in part (a) illustrate?

9. Use the results of Questions 7 and 8 to show that the three points, $P(3,-5)$, $Q(1,-2)$, and $R(-1,1)$ lie on a straight line (that is, are collinear).

10. Show that the points $M(-4,-2)$, $N(1,1)$, and $P(6,4)$ are collinear.

Applications of Linear Equations

A pine tree is 24 cm high when it is 1 a old. When it is 3 a old it is 56 cm high. Assuming a steady rate of growth, determine a linear equation to approximate the tree's growth (G centimetres) at age t years.

Draw a graph of the relation.

This is the given data.

t	G
1	24
3	56

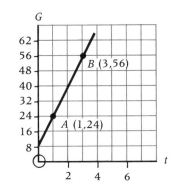

Since you know 2 points on the graph, you can find the equation of the form $G = mt + b$.

$$\text{Slope of } AB = \frac{56 - 24}{3 - 1}$$
$$= \tfrac{32}{2}$$
$$= 16$$

$y = mx + b$

Substitute $m = 16$ in $G = mt + b$.

$$G = 16t + b$$

Select the point $A(1,24)$ to determine b and substitute $t = 1$ and $G = 24$.
$$24 = 16(1) + b$$
$$b = 8$$

The equation representing the tree's growth is
$$G = 16t + 8.$$

The slope ($m = 16$) represents an annual rate of growth of 16 cm/a. The G-intercept ($b = 8$) represents the height (8 cm) of the tree when it was planted.

Exercise

B 1. (a) The growth of a tree is given by the equation $G = 16t + 18$ (G in centimetres and t in years). Calculate the height of the tree after 10 a; 25 a.

(b) After how many years is the height of the tree 162 cm? 4.0 m? 5.68 m?

2. The following chart shows the cost ($\$c$) of running a car for 1 a if the distance driven is d kilometres.

d (kilometres)	1000	5000	10 000
c (dollars)	2150	2750	3500

(a) Draw a graph to show how c is related to d.
(b) Determine a linear equation that relates c and d.
(c) In this situation, what does the slope and vertical c-intercept represent?
(d) What is the annual cost of driving the car 20 000 km?
(e) How far was the car driven in the year if the total cost of running the car is $5300?

3. The following chart shows the cost (C) of printing various lengths (L metres) of wallpaper.

L (metres)	3	5	8
C (dollars)	13	17	23

(a) Draw a graph to show how C is related to L.
(b) Determine a linear equation that relates C and L.
(c) What is the slope and the vertical C-intercept of the line representing the equation found in part (b)?
(d) In this situation, what do the slope and vertical C-intercept represent?
(e) What is the cost of printing 150 m of wallpaper?
(f) How much wallpaper can be printed for $321?

4. The property tax (T) on the assessed value (A) of various homes is shown in the table below.

A (dollars)	$4000	$6000	$10000
T (dollars)	$720	$1080	$1800

(a) Draw a graph to show how T and A are related.

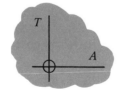

(b) Determine a linear equation that relates T and A.
(c) What is the slope and the vertical T-intercept of the line representing the equation found in part (b)?
(d) In this situation, what does the slope and the vertical T-intercept represent?
(e) What are the taxes on a home assessed at $12 000? $8500?
(f) What is the assessed value of a home that is taxed for $900? $1500?

5. The following chart shows the amount (N litres) of water remaining in a swimming pool t minutes after draining of the pool begins.

t (minutes)	10	15	30
N (litres)	18 800	18 200	16 400

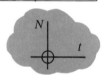

(a) Draw a graph to show how N is related to t.
(b) What is happening to the quantity of water in the pool as time passes?
(c) Determine a linear equation that relates N and t.
(d) What is the slope and the vertical N-intercept of the line representing the equation found in part (b)?
(e) In this situation, what do the slope and N-intercept represent?
(f) How long does it take to empty the pool?

Slopes of Parallel and Perpendicular Lines

There is a relationship between the slopes of parallel lines.

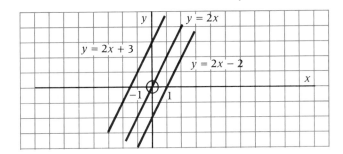

The slope of each line is 2. The lines all slant in the same direction and are parallel to each other.

> Slopes of parallel lines are equal. Also, if 2 lines have equal slopes, then the lines are parallel.

There is also a relationship between slopes of perpendicular lines.

If a line is drawn through points A, P, and B, and a set square is placed with one vertex at point P as shown, then one of its edges passes through point $Q(2,5)$.

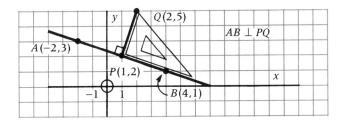

Calculate the slopes of the perpendicular segments to find the relationship between them.

Slope of AB

$= \dfrac{1 - 3}{4 - (-2)}$

$= \dfrac{-2}{6}$

$= \dfrac{-1}{3}$

Slope of PQ

$= \dfrac{5 - 2}{2 - 1}$

$= 3$

Since $3 \times \frac{-1}{3} = -1$, then 3 and $\frac{-1}{3}$ are negative reciprocals.

> Slopes of perpendicular lines are negative reciprocals. Also, if 2 lines have slopes that are negative reciprocals, then the lines are perpendicular.

Example 1

The points $A(3,2)$, $B(-24)$, and $C(-4,-1)$ are vertices of a triangle. Use slopes to determine whether or not $\triangle ABC$ is a right-angled triangle.

It appears that $AB \perp BC$.

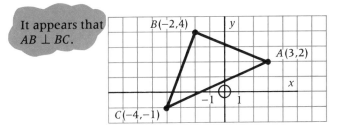

Slope of AB

$= \dfrac{4 - 2}{-2 - 3}$

$= -\dfrac{2}{5}$

Slope of BC

$= \dfrac{-1 - 4}{-4 - (-2)}$

$= \dfrac{-5}{-2}$

$= \dfrac{5}{2}$

Since the slopes of AB and BC are negative reciprocals, then AB is perpendicular to BC and $\triangle ABC$ is a right-angled triangle at B.

Exercise

A 1. State the negative reciprocal for each of the following.

(a) 2   (b) $\frac{3}{4}$ (c) $-\frac{1}{5}$ (d) -4

2. State the slope of another line that is:
- parallel to the given line;
- perpendicular to the given line.

(a) $y = 5x + 2$
(b) $y = \frac{2}{3}x + 1$
(c) $y = -\frac{4}{7}x - 2$
(d) $y = -2x + 4$

3. $ABCD$ is a parallelogram.

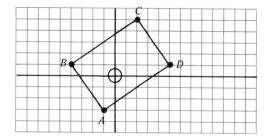

The slope of AB is $-\frac{4}{3}$ and the slope of BC is $\frac{2}{3}$. State the slopes of AD and CD.

4. For each item, two lines have the given slopes, m_1 and m_2. In each case, state whether the lines are parallel, perpendicular, or neither.

(a) $m_1 = \frac{2}{3}$, $m_2 = \frac{4}{6}$
(b) $m_1 = \frac{5}{3}$, $m_2 = -\frac{3}{5}$
(c) $m_1 = -5$, $m_2 = -\frac{1}{5}$
(d) $m_1 = 1$, $m_2 = -1$
(e) $m_1 = -\frac{3}{5}$, $m_2 = -\frac{9}{15}$

B 5. Calculate the slope of the line segment joining each pair of points. Name pairs of line segments, AB, CD, EF, . . . , that are parallel. Name pairs that are perpendicular.

(a) $A(4,3)$, $B(-2,7)$
(b) $C(-1,0)$, $D(-7,4)$
(c) $E(4,-2)$, $F(6,1)$
(d) $G(3,4)$, $H(7,8)$
(e) $I(-1,0)$, $J(11,12)$
(f) $K(9,7)$, $L(-4,-3)$
(g) $M(-7,2)$, $N(-4,5)$
(h) $P(-4,-3)$, $Q(-7,0)$

6. Each set of points gives the vertices of a triangle. Graph each triangle and use slopes to determine whether or not it is a right-angled triangle.

(a) $A(3,2)$, $B(-4,6)$, $C(8,1)$
(b) $K(-1,7)$, $L(-6,1)$, $M(0,-4)$
(c) $P(0,6)$, $Q(-5,0)$, $R(6,-2)$

7. Place a set square with its right-angle vertex at $A(0,12)$ on graph paper.

(a) Show that sides of the set square can pass through the following pairs of points on the x-axis.
- $B(-12,0)$, $C(12,0)$
- $B(-9,0)$, $C(16,0)$
- $B(-8,0)$, $C(18,0)$

(b) Find the slopes of AB and AC for each of the pairs of points in part (a).

(c) How are the slopes of AB and AC related?

FOCUS ON

Roofing Estimator

Dale is an estimator for a roofing contractor. To determine the area of a gable or hip roof, Dale uses the given formula.

Area of Roof = Area of Foundation $\times \sqrt{4P^2 + 1}$

P represents the pitch of the roof.

Gable Roof

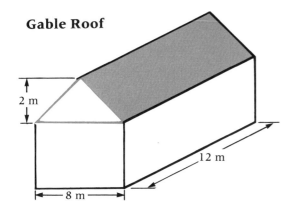

What is the area of the gable roof?

Area of Foundation = Length $\times$ Width
$$= 8 \times 12$$
$$= 96 \text{ m}^2$$

Pitch $= \frac{1}{2} \times$ Slope
$$= \frac{1}{2} \times \left(\frac{2}{4}\right)$$
$$= \frac{1}{4}$$

Rise = 2
Run = 4

Area of Roof $= 96 \times \sqrt{4\left(\frac{1}{4}\right)^2 + 1}$
$$= 96 \times \sqrt{4\left(\frac{1}{16}\right) + 1}$$
$$\doteq 96 \times 1.12$$
$$= 107.52$$

When ordering roofing material, Dale adds 10% for ridges, starters, and waste.
$$10\% \text{ of } 107.52 = 10.752$$
Dale would order materials based on an area of 107.52 + 10.75, or about 118 m² for the gable roof.

Exercise

Determine the roof area for each of the following.

1. Pitch $= \frac{1}{5}$

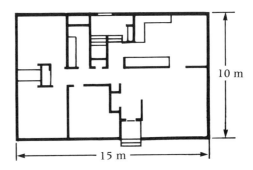

10 m

15 m

2. Pitch $= \frac{1}{2}$

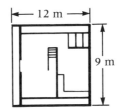

12 m

9 m

3. Pitch $= \frac{2}{5}$

21.5 m

9 m

4. Length of house = 25 m

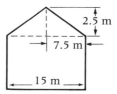

2.5 m

7.5 m

15 m

Side view of house

Unit 7 Review

1. For each pair of points, calculate the slope of the line segment joining them.

   (a) $A(4,6)$, $B(9,15)$
   (b) $C(-1,3)$, $D(-5,9)$
   (c) $E(4,3)$, $F(9,3)$
   (d) $G(-6,3)$, $H(\frac{1}{2}, \frac{3}{2})$

2. On a separate grid, draw the graph of each line passing through the given point and with the given slope.

   (a) $A(2,7)$, slope $\frac{1}{5}$
   (b) $B(-3,0)$, slope $\frac{5}{3}$
   (c) $C(0,4)$, slope 3
   (d) $D(-3,4)$, slope $-\frac{2}{3}$
   (e) $E(-2,-5)$, slope -2

3. Calculate the pitch of each roof.

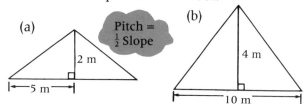

   Pitch = $\frac{1}{2}$ Slope

4. A ski hill drops 9.75 m for every horizontal run to the right of 35 m. What is the slope of the ski hill?

5. (a) A guy wire supporting a telephone pole is fastened to the ground 10 m from the base of the pole. If the guy wire has a slope of $\frac{9}{5}$, what is the height of the pole?
   (b) Find the length of the guy wire.

6. Each of the following equations defines a line. In each case:
   • give the slope and y-intercept;
   • name the coordinates of the point where the line crosses the y axis;
   • use the slope and the point to graph the line.

   (a) $y = 3x + 2$
   (b) $y = -2x - 1$
   (c) $y = \frac{1}{3}x + 2$
   (d) $y = \frac{5}{2}x + 1$
   (e) $y = -\frac{3}{5}x - 4$
   (f) $y = -\frac{2}{3}x$
   (g) $y = -2$
   (h) $x = -4$

7. Write an equation for each line.

   (a) slope 2, y-intercept -1
   (b) slope $\frac{5}{3}$, y-intercept 2
   (c) slope -1, y-intercept -3
   (d) slope 1, y-intercept 0
   (e) slope $-\frac{4}{3}$, y-intercept $+2$
   (f) slope $-\frac{3}{5}$, y-intercept -4

8. Rewrite each of the following equations in the form $y = mx + b$. Then write the slope and y-intercept of each line.

   (a) $3x + y = 2$
   (b) $4x - y = 4$
   (c) $3x + 2y = 8$
   (d) $4x - 3y = 12$
   (e) $3x + 5y - 15 = 0$
   (f) $x + 4y = 12$
   (g) $4x - 5y = 9$

9. Determine the x- and y-intercepts for each of the following lines, then graph the line.

   (a) $3x + 2y = 12$
   (b) $x - 4y = 8$
   (c) $4x - 5y = 20$
   (d) $3x + 5y = 15$
   (e) $7x - 3y = 21$

10. Determine an equation for each of the following lines with the given slope and passing through the given point.

(a) $m = 2$, $A(3,5)$
(b) $m = -3$, $B(-2,1)$
(c) $m = \frac{1}{4}$, $C(3,5)$
(d) $m = \frac{3}{5}$, $D(4,0)$
(e) $m = -\frac{1}{2}$, $E(-2,4)$
(f) $m = -\frac{4}{3}$, $F(-3,-5)$
(g) $m = \frac{7}{2}$, $G(3,-2)$
(h) $m = -\frac{4}{5}$, $H(-7,-5)$

11. In each case, determine an equation of the line passing through the given pair of points.

(a) $(3,2)$, $(9,4)$
(b) $(4,-3)$, $(2,6)$
(c) $(-2,4)$, $(10,2)$
(d) $(0,4)$, $(-3,0)$
(e) $(0,0)$, $(4,-2)$
(f) $(1,-5)$, $(-1,-8)$

12. The chart below compares the total cost (C dollars) of renting a car to the distance driven (D kilometres).

D (kilometres)	100	300	500
C (dollars)	50	90	130

(a) Draw a graph to show how C is related to D.
(b) Determine a linear equation that relates C and D.

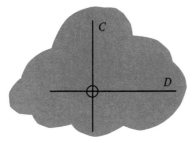

(c) In this situation, what does the slope represent?
(d) In this situation, what does the C-intercept represent?
(e) Determine the total charge if you drive the car 250 km; 1000 km.
(f) How far did you drive if the total charge was $170? $95?

13. On a holiday in July, the temperature at sea level is 30°C. The table below shows the decrease in temperature ($T°$ Celsius) with an increase in altitude (H metres).

H (metres)	0	2000	4000
T (°C)	30	17	4

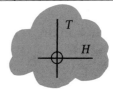

(a) Draw a graph to show how T is related to H.
(b) What happens to the temperature as the altitude increases?
(c) Determine a linear equation that relates T and H.
(d) What is the slope and the vertical T-intercept of the line representing the equation found in part (b)?
(e) In this situation, what do the slope and T-intercept represent?
(f) What is the temperature at an altitude of 3000 m? 6000 m?
(g) What is the altitude when the temperature is 23.5°C? −18°C? 0°C?

14. The table below shows the total cost (C) of printing a number (N) of advertising pamphlets for a school production.

N	100	200	300
C (dollars)	53	56	59

(a) Draw a graph to show how C is related to N.
(b) Determine a linear equation that relates C and N.
(c) What is the slope and the vertical intercept C of the line represented by the equation found in (b)?
(d) What is the fixed cost of printing?
(e) What is the cost of printing each pamphlet?
(f) What is the cost of printing 1000 pamphlets? 3500 pamphlets?
(g) How many pamphlets can be printed for $110?

15. On expressways, bridges have expansion joints that are small gaps between one bridge section and the next.

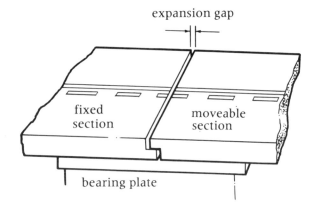

expansion gap

fixed section

moveable section

bearing plate

The gaps allow for expansion of the bridge deck in hot weather. The table below shows the width of the gap (G centimetres) as the temperature ($T°$ Celsius) changes.

T	28	8
G	1	2

(a) Draw a graph to show how G is related to T if the relation is linear.
(b) What happens to the gap as the temperature rises?
(c) Determine a linear equation that relates G and T.
(d) What is the slope and the vertical G-intercept of the line representing the equation in part (c)?
(e) In this situation, what does the slope and vertical G-intercept represent?
(f) What is the width of the gap when the temperature is 0°C? 10°C? 30°C? −10°C?
(g) What is the temperature when the gap is 1.5 cm wide?

16. Calculate the slope of the line segment joining each pair of points. Name pairs of line segments that are parallel or perpendicular.

(a) $A(1,2)$, $B(5,5)$
(b) $C(-4,3)$, $D(0,6)$
(c) $E(-1,-3)$, $F(-4,1)$
(d) $G(2,0)$, $H(-1,4)$

17. Use slopes to show that the triangle with vertices $A(3,0)$, $B(2,-4)$, and $C(-5,2)$ is a right-angled triangle.

Unit 8

Solving Pairs of Equations

Solving Pairs of Equations by Graphing
Solving Pairs of Equations
   by Elimination
Solving Pairs of Equations
   by Substitution
Solving Word Problems
Finding Patterns
Unit 8 Review

Solving Pairs of Equations by Graphing

Graphing equations is a skill that can be used in business situations. Graphing more than one equation on the same axes can help you to make comparisons and solve problems.

Example 1

A company that manufactures video cassette tapes calculates that it has a fixed cost of $10 500 for overhead plus a cost of $3.50 for each tape produced. The dealers pay $5.60 for each tape.

Determine how many tapes must be sold to the dealers so that income from the sales equals production costs.

The cost, $C, of manufacturing n tapes is given by $C = 3.50n + 10\ 500$.
The income, $I, from selling n tapes is given by $I = 5.60n$.

Graph each equation on the same axes to compare cost and income.

$C = 3.50n + 10\ 500$

n	C
0	10 500
1000	14 000

$I = 5.60n$

n	I
0	0
1000	5600

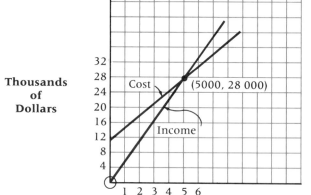

Thousands of Dollars

Thousands of Tapes

When the company sells 5000 tapes, income and costs are both equal to $28 000. This is the **break-even point**.

The ordered pair (5000, 28 000) satisfies (or makes true) both equations.

Check by substituting $n = 5000$ in each equation.

$C = 3.50(5000) + 10\ 500$
$\quad = 28\ 000$

$I = 5.60(5000)$
$\quad = 28\ 000$

Example 2

Solve the pair of equations by graphing.

$$2x + y = 6$$
$$x + y = 2$$

To graph the lines, find the x- and y-intercepts of each line.

$2x + y = 6$

x	y
3	0
0	6

$x + y = 2$

x	y
2	0
0	2

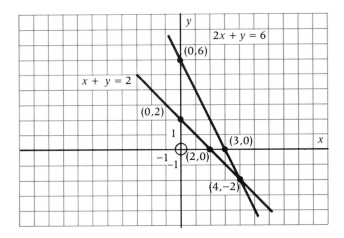

The lines intersect at $(4, -2)$. Check by substituting $x = 4$ and $y = -2$ in each equation.

$2x + y = 6$

LS	RS
$2x + y$ $= 2(4) + (-2)$ $= 6$	6

$x + y = 2$

LS	RS
$x + y$ $= 4 - 2$ $= 2$	2

Since LS = RS in both cases, $(4, -2)$ satisfies both equations.

Exercise

A **1.** State the intersection point for each of the following pairs of lines, if possible.

(a)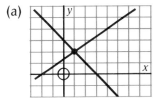

(c)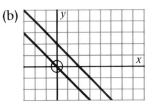

(b)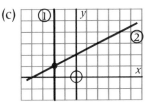

(d)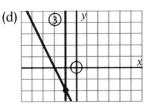

2. Use the graphs in Question 1 to answer the following.
   (a) State the equation of line ①.
   (b) State the x- and y-intercepts of line ②.
   (c) State the slope of line ②.
   (d) State the equation of line ③.

B **3.** Solve each of the following pairs of equations by graphing. Check your answers by substitution.

(a) $y = x + 1$
    $y = 2x + 4$

(b) $y = 2x + 3$
    $y = x$

(c) $y = \frac{2}{3}x + 2$
    $y = 2x - 2$

(d) $y = 3x - 5$
    $x + y = 7$

(e) $2x + y = 4$
    $x + y = 3$

(f) $2x + y = 5$
    $x - y = 7$

(g) $3x - 2y = 6$
    $2x + 3y = -9$

(h) $5x - 3y = 15$
    $2x - 3y = 8$

(i) $4x - 3y = 12$
    $x = 6$

(j) $3x + 2y = 18$
    $y = 3$

133

4. Graph each of the following to find the break-even point for producing and selling n items.

   (a) Cost: $C = 0.5n + 700$
       Income: $I = 3n$
   (b) Cost: $C = 2.5n + 900$
       Income: $I = 4.0n$

5. Two salespeople, John and Mary, work for salary plus commission. Their monthly pay is represented by the following equations.

   Mary: $P = 0.07S + 500$
   John: $P = 0.05S + 800$

   P represents the monthly pay in dollars and S represents the monthly sales in dollars.

   (a) Solve the two equations graphically.

   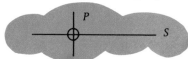

   (b) What does the intersection point represent in this situation?
   (c) For what monthly sales does Mary make more than John?
   (d) For what monthly sales does John make more than Mary?

6. A daughter challenges her father to a 500 m race. The daughter allowed her father to start 35 m ahead of her. The equations relating the distance run (d kilometres) after a certain time (t seconds) are given below.
   Father: $d = 2.5t + 35$
   Daughter: $d = 3.2t$

   (a) Solve the two equations graphically.
   (b) In this situation, what does the point of intersection represent?
   (c) Who finishes first? By how many seconds and by how many metres?

7. A manufacturer of hockey sticks uses a sanding machine to form the blade of each stick. The daily cost, C, of operating this machine per day is given by the equation below.

   $$C = 6.0n + 1000$$

   n is the number of hockey sticks sanded. A new sanding machine would allow the company to manufacture sticks according to the equation below.

   $$C = 4.5n + 1600$$

   (a) Solve the two equations graphically.
   (b) In this situation, what does the point of intersection represent?
   (c) For what number of sticks produced per day would it be economical to use the new machine?
   (d) What is the difference in cost if the company produces 300 sticks a day? 1000 sticks a day?

8. A homeowner must choose between two types of heating systems. The cost, C, of heating the home each year is given by the following equations.
   Type A: $C = 750t + 3600$
   Type B: $C = 400t + 5000$
   t is the time in years.

   (a) Solve the two equations graphically.
   (b) In this situation, what does the point of intersection represent?
   (c) Which system is more economical at the end of 6 a? By how much?
   (d) What does the slope and C-intercept of the line in each graph represent?

9. The following pair of equations represents the annual cost, C, of operating a gasoline-powered car and a diesel-powered car.

Gasoline: $\quad C = 0.25d$
Diesel: $\quad C = 0.21d + 2000$

d is the distance driven, in kilometres.

(a) Solve the two equations graphically.
(b) In this situation, what does the point of intersection represent?
(c) Which type of car is more economical for driving 20 000 km? 80 000 km? What's the difference in cost in each case?
(d) What does the slope and the C-intercept of the line in each graph represent?

10. The average annual cost of heating a home with solar energy is about $200 with an initial investment of $9000. The average annual cost of heating a home with oil is $900 with an initial investment of $2700.

$$C = 200t + 9000$$
$$C = 900t + 2700$$

(a) When is the breakeven point (that is, when the costs are equal)?
(b) How much more does it cost to heat with solar energy than with oil for the first 5 a?

11. Two cars leave Bridgetown along the same road. The equations relating the distance travelled (d kilometres) after a certain time (t hours) are given below.
Car A: $\quad d = 70t$
Car B: $\quad d = 80t - 160$

(a) Solve the two equations graphically.
(b) In this situation, what does the point of intersection represent?

Side Trip

The Portable Cassette Company found that the daily supply for their portable cassette players is represented by the equation below.

(Supply) $P = 0.5n - 10$

P is the unit price in dollars of each player and n is the number of players supplied.

The demand equation for the cassette players is given below.

(Demand) $P = -n + 170$

(a) Solve the 2 equations graphically in order to determine the price at which the quantity demanded is equal to the quantity supplied.
(b) The point found in part (a) is called the **equilibrium point**. What is the desirable price per player for market equilibrium?
(c) How many cassette recorders must be sold to result in market equilibrium?

Solving Pairs of Equations by Elimination

Solving a pair of equations by graphing may sometimes provide only an approximate solution. Tony's graph for $x - y = 2$ and $4x + y = 4$ is shown below.

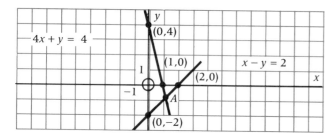

Tony can only guess at the coordinates for A, the point of intersection of the 2 lines.

Tony found an exact solution by applying his skills in algebra.

$$x - y = 2 \qquad ①$$
$$4x + y = 4 \qquad ②$$

Since the coefficients of the y terms are opposites, add the left sides and right sides to eliminate the y terms.

$$
\begin{array}{r}
x \boxed{-y} = 2 \qquad ① \\
4x \boxed{+y} = 4 \qquad ② \\
\hline
\text{(Add)} \quad 5x = 6 \\
x = \tfrac{6}{5}
\end{array}
$$

To find y substitute $x = \tfrac{6}{5}$ in equation ①.

$$\tfrac{6}{5} - y = 2$$
$$6 - 5y = 10$$
$$-5y = 4$$
$$y = -\tfrac{4}{5}$$

The solution is $x = \tfrac{6}{5}$ and $y = -\tfrac{4}{5}$.

The previous pair of equations was solved by adding. Look at Example 1 to see how subtraction can be used to solve equations.

Example 1

Solve. Check by substitution.

$$4x - 3y = 11 \qquad ①$$
$$4x - y = 9 \qquad ②$$

Since the coefficients of the x terms are equal, subtract left sides and right sides to eliminate x terms.

$$
\begin{array}{r}
\boxed{4x} - 3y = 11 \qquad ① \\
\boxed{4x} - y = 9 \qquad ② \\
\hline
\text{(Subtract)} \quad -2y = 2 \\
y = -1
\end{array}
$$

 Add the opposite.

Substitute $y = -1$ in equation ①.
$$4x - 3(-1) = 11$$
$$4x + 3 = 11$$
$$4x = 8$$
$$x = 2$$

Check that $x = 2$ and $y = -1$ is correct.

$4x - 3y = 11$

LS	RS
$4x - 3y$	11
$= 4(2) - 3(-1)$	
$= 8 + 3$	
$= 11$	

$4x - y = 9$

LS	RS
$4x - y$	9
$= 4(2) - (-1)$	
$= 8 + 1$	
$= 9$	

Since LS = RS in both cases, $(2, -1)$ satisfies both equations.

The solution $x = 2$ and $y = -1$ is correct.

Example 2

Solve.
$$4x + 9y = 2 \quad \text{①}$$
$$3x - 2y = 5 \quad \text{②}$$

Since the coefficients of neither the *x* terms nor the *y* terms are equal or opposite, multiply each equation by a different constant before adding or subtracting.

$$
\begin{array}{ll}
\text{①} \times 2 & 8x + 18y = 4 \\
\text{②} \times 9 & 27x - 18y = 45 \\
\text{(Add)} & 35x = 49 \\
& x = \frac{49}{35} \text{ or } \frac{7}{5}
\end{array}
$$

To find *y*, either substitute $x = \frac{7}{5}$ in equation ① or eliminate the *x* term.

$$
\begin{array}{ll}
\text{①} \times 3 & 12x + 27y = 6 \\
\text{②} \times 4 & 12x - 8y = 20 \\
\text{(Subtract)} & 35y = -14 \\
& y = -\frac{14}{35} \text{ or } -\frac{2}{5}
\end{array}
$$

The solution is $x = \frac{7}{5}$ and $y = -\frac{2}{5}$.

Example 3

Solve.
$$2y = 2 - 3x \quad \text{①}$$
$$2x - y = 6 \quad \text{②}$$

Rewrite equation ① and solve.

$$
\begin{array}{ll}
& 3x + 2y = 2 \\
\text{②} \times 2 & 4x - 2y = 12 \\
& 7x = 14 \\
& x = 2 \\
& \text{and } y = -2
\end{array}
$$

The solution is $x = 2$ and $y = -2$.

Exercise

A 1. Add.

(a) $4x - 3y$
    $5x + 3y$

(b) $9x - 5y$
    $-2x + 5y$

(c) $3x - 2y = 6$
    $5x + 2y = 10$

(d) $4x - 5y = -9$
    $-4x + 3y = -3$

2. Subtract.

(a) $4x + 5y$
    $3x + 5y$

(b) $9x - 3y$
    $9x - 5y$

(c) $2x - 4y = 12$
    $5x - 4y = 3$

(d) $3x - 7y = -14$
    $3x + 2y = 4$

3. Suppose you wanted to solve equations ① and ②.

$$3x + 4y = 7 \quad \text{①}$$
$$5x - y = 27 \quad \text{②}$$

(a) What would you do to eliminate the *y* terms? the *x* terms?

(b) Which method is easier? Why?

B 4. Solve by adding or subtracting and check.

(a) $x + y = 9$
    $x - y = 3$

(b) $x + y = 7$
    $2x - y = 2$

(c) $3x + 2y = 5$
    $x - 2y = -1$

(d) $5x + 2y = 19$
    $3x + 2y = 5$

(e) $4x + 3y = 9$
    $4x + y = 3$

(f) $4x - 3y = 11$
    $7x - 3y = 17$

(g) $6x + 5y = 22$
    $6x + 3y = 10$

(h) $-2x - 5y = 4$
    $2x + 3y = 2$

5. Solve by multiplying first. Check your answers by substitution.

(a) $5x - 3y = 4$
$3x + y = 8$

(b) $2x + 3y = 5$
$x + 7y = 8$

(c) $2x - y = 2$
$7x - 3y = 8$

(d) $4x + y = 5$
$x - 2y = 8$

6. Solve each of the following pairs of equations. Check your answers by substitution.

(a) $4x + 3y = -3$
$2x - 3y = 21$

(b) $x + 2y = 5$
$3x - y = 1$

(c) $2x + 3y = -5$
$5x + 2y = 4$

(d) $3x + y = 10$
$5x + 2y = 16$

(e) $2x - 3y = -4$
$4x + 7y = 5$

(f) $4x - 4y = 15$
$2x - 3y = 7$

(g) $2x + 3y = -22$
$3x - 2y = 6$

(h) $3x + 2y = 8$
$x - 3y = 10$

(i) $5x + 2y = 9$
$2x + 3y = -3$

(j) $2x + 3y = 2$
$6x - 5y = -8$

(k) $3x + 4y = 19$
$5x - 6y = 0$

(l) $5x + 2y = 1$
$2x - y = 3$

7. Rewrite each equation in the form $\blacksquare x + \blacksquare y = \blacksquare$. Then solve each pair of equations.

(a) $6x - 3y = 12$
$x = y - 3$

(b) $2x = 9 - 3y$
$2y = 5x - 13$

(c) $2x = 7 - 3y$
$x - 5y - 10 = 0$

(d) $2x + y + 5 = 0$
$3y = 10 - 2x$

8. (a) For a school play, x represents the number of adult tickets sold and y represents the number of student tickets sold.
Solve the equations to find the number of adults and students who bought tickets.

$x + y = 1000$
$5x + 3y = 3700$

(b) If each adult ticket cost \$5 and each student ticket cost \$3, what does equation ② represent?

9. A music store sells tapes and albums.

(a) If x represents the number of tapes the store sells in one day and y the number of albums, solve the equations to find the number of each sold.

$x + y = 80$
$8x + 12y = 720$

(b) What does equation ① represent?

(c) If each tape costs \$8 and each album costs \$12, what does equation ② represent?

10. Steve cashed his cheque and received the money in \$5 and \$10 bills.

(a) If x represents the number of \$5 bills, and if y represents the number of \$10 bills, solve the equations to find the number of each type of bill Steve received.

$x + y = 18$
$5x + 10y = 135$

(b) What does each equation represent?

Solving Pairs of Equations by Substitution

Here is another algebraic method of solving pairs of equations.

$y = 4x + 3$ ①
$y = 2x - 1$ ②

From equation ②, use $(2x - 1)$ as a *value* of y, and substitute into equation ①.

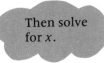

$y = 4x + 3$
$2x - 1 = 4x + 3$
$2x - 4x = 1 + 3$
$-2x = 4$
$x = -2$

Then solve for x.

Now substitute $x = -2$ in equation ①.
$y = 4(-2) + 3$
$y = -5$

On your own, check that the solution is $x = -2$ and $y = -5$.

Example 1

Solve.
$2x + 3y = 7$ ①
$y = 3x - 5$ ②

Substitute $y = 3x - 5$ in equation ①.
$2x + 3(y) = 7$
$2x + 3(3x - 5) = 7$
$2x + 9x - 15 = 7$
$11x = 22$
$x = 2$

Substitute $x = 2$ in equation ②.
$y = 3(2) - 5$
$y = 1$

The solution is $x = 2$ and $y = 1$.
Check this solution on your own.

Exercise

B **1.** Use the method of substitution to solve each of the following pairs of equations.

(a) $y = 2x + 5$
   $y = 4x - 3$

(b) $y = 4x - 5$
   $y = 2x + 9$

(c) $y = 2x - 3$
   $y = 1 - 6x$

(d) $2x + y = 8$
   $y = 3x - 7$

(e) $2x + 3y = 7$
   $y = -2x + 1$

(f) $5x - 2y = 16$
   $y = 2x - 3$

(g) $y = \frac{x - 5}{2}$
   $y = \frac{2x - 7}{7}$

(h) $y = \frac{x + 3}{2}$
   $y = \frac{2x + 4}{3}$

2. Use any algebraic method to solve each of the following pairs of equations.

(a) $y = 3x + 4$
   $y = 5x - 2$

(b) $4x + 3y = 11$
   $y = -2x + 5$

(c) $3x + y = -5$
   $4x + 5y = 18$

(d) $2x + 3y = 17$
   $3x + y = 8$

3. The costs of renting a car from two car rental companies are given by the equations below.

Company A: $C = 0.3d + 18$
Company B: $C = 0.27d + 27$

C is the cost in dollars and d is the distance the car is driven, in kilometres. Use an algebraic method to find the number of kilometres that the cars must be driven so that the costs are equal.

Solving Word Problems

The E-Z Ride Taxicab Company charges an initial fee of $1.50 and a rate of $1.20/km. The Cushionaire Taxicab Company charges an initial fee of $1.75 and a rate of $1.15/km. For what distance would the charges by the 2 cab companies be equal?

Many problems involve more than 1 unknown quantity. Follow the 4 problem-solving steps below to solve problems with two unknowns.

1. **Identify the problem.**
   Choose two variables to represent the unknowns.

2. **Determine the necessary data.**
   Since there are 2 unknowns, there are 2 sets of data. Use the data to form two equations in two unknowns.

3. **Do the required calculations.**
   Solve the equations. Check your answer.

4. **Make a final statement.**

To solve the taxicab problem, let $C represent the total cost of a trip. Let d kilometres represent the distance travelled.

Write an equation to represent the cost for each company.

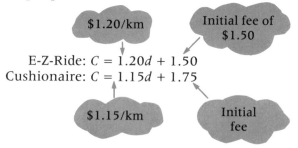

E-Z-Ride: $C = 1.20d + 1.50$
Cushionaire: $C = 1.15d + 1.75$

In this case, solve the pair of equations by substitution.

$$1.20d + 1.50 = 1.15d + 1.75$$
$$1.20d - 1.15d = 1.75 - 1.50$$
$$0.05d = 0.25$$
$$d = \frac{0.25}{0.05}$$
$$d = 5$$

The costs of the two companies are equal on a trip of 5 km.

Check in the problem that 5 km gives the same cost from each company.

E-Z-Ride charges $1.50 plus ($1.20 × 5), which is $1.50 + $6.00, or $7.50.

Cushionaire charges $1.75 plus ($1.15 × 5), which is $1.75 + $5.75, or $7.50.

Example 1

John invested $4000 for 1 a, part at 7%/a and part at 9%/a. The interest on the investment is $300. How much did John invest at each rate?

Let $x represent the principal invested at 7%.
Let $y represent the principal invested at 9%.
The table helps to clarify the problem.

Investment	Principal	Interest
7%	x	$0.07x$
9%	y	$0.09y$

$I = Prt$
$= x(0.07)(1)$

Total investment

$x + y = 4000$ ①
$0.07x + 0.09y = 300$ ②

Interest earned

Solve by elimination.

$$\begin{array}{ll} ② \times 100 & 7x + 9y = 30\ 000 \\ ① \times 7 & 7x + 7y = 28\ 000 \\ \text{(Subtract)} & 2y = 2000 \\ & y = 1000 \end{array}$$

Substitute in equation ①.

$$x + 1000 = 4000$$
$$x = 3000$$

Check that $x = 3000$ and $y = 1000$.
Interest on $3000 at 7%/a is $210.
Interest on $1000 at 9%/a is $90.
The total interest is $210 + $90, or $300.

John invested $3000 at 7%/a and $1000 at 9%/a.

Exercise

A 1. Translate each sentence into an equation with 2 variables.

(a) The sum of two numbers x and y is 25.
(b) The total annual interest received from x dollars invested at 8% per annum, and y dollars invested at 9% per annum, is $658.
(c) The amount collected from selling x adult tickets at $5 each and y students tickets at $3 each is $850.

B 2. The U-Drive Car Rental Company charges a fixed amount of $18.00 plus 20¢/km for renting a car. The U-Steer Car Rental Company charges a fixed amount of $24 plus 16¢/km.

(a) For what distance would the cost of renting a car from the 2 companies be the same?
(b) What is this cost?
(d) For what distance is it cheaper to rent from U-Drive?

3. A construction company is investigating the cost of renting a power cement mixer. They find that Company A charges a fixed amount of $50 plus $10/d. Company B charges a fixed amount of $40 plus $12/d.

(a) After how many days would the cost of renting the cement mixer be the same?
(b) What is this cost?
(c) What is the difference in cost if the mixer is rented for 10 d?

4. Jim has $50 in savings and plans to save $10/week. Marcia has $20 in savings and plans to save $15/week.
   (a) After how many weeks will they have the same amount of savings?
   (b) What is this amount?

5. Melanie, a recent high school graduate, is deciding between two jobs in selling computers. Company A is offering a fixed salary of $800/month plus 5% commission on the monthly sales. Company B is offering $500/month plus 8% commission on sales.
   (a) For what amount of sales would the monthly salary be the same?
   (b) What is this salary?
   (c) What would be the difference in the monthly salaries if monthly sales total $20 000?

6. The A-Z printing shop charges $25 for making an engraving plate for printing engraved stationery, plus 15¢/sheet printed. The B-Y printing shop charges $15 for the plate plus 25¢/sheet. For how many sheets of stationery will the cost from each shop be the same?

7. Anne-Marie invested $10 000 for 1 a. She invested part at 8% per annum and the remainder at 10% per annum. The total interest earned for 1 a on this investment was $940. How much did she invest at each rate?

8. Dan invested his $3000 lottery win, partly in bonds paying 9% interest per annum, and the remainder in stocks paying 6% interest per annum. The total interest earned for 1 a on this investment was $240. How much did he invest at each rate?

9. Tickets for a school dance cost $3/person with an activity card and $4 without an activity card. The total amount received from the sale of tickets was $2300. Seven hundred students attended the dance.
   (a) Let x represent the number of students attending with activity cards and y the number of students without activity cards. Write an equation relating x, y, and the 700 students attending the dance.
   (b) Write an expression for the amount of money collected from selling x tickets at $3 each.
   (c) Write an expression for the amount of money collected from selling y tickets at $4 each.
   (d) Write an equation relating the quantities in (b) and (c) to the total amount received ($2300).
   (e) Solve the two equations to determine the number of students with activity cards attending the dance.

10. A hockey team scored a total of 112 points in a season. Each win earned the team 2 points and each tie earned the team 1 point. The team won or tied a total of 60 games. How many games did they win?

11. In a soccer league each goal is worth 3 points and each assist is worth 2 points. A player scored a total of 95 points. His goals and assists totalled 35. How many goals did he score?

12. Two trucks move 136 m^3 of earth by taking 8 loads each. They can move 178 m^3 of earth if one truck takes 15 loads and the other takes 4 loads. What is the capacity of each truck?

13. Plain pizzas cost $7 each and deluxe pizzas cost $9 each. To feed the cast and crew of a high school production $560 was spent. A total of 70 pizzas were ordered. How many plain and how many deluxe pizzas were ordered?

14. Gregory bought some nuts for a class party at a special sale. He bought 2 kg of peanuts and 3 kg of almonds for $15.50. Because of the special sale he returned to the store and bought 3 kg of peanuts and 4 kg of almonds for $21.50.

    (a) If x dollars represents the price of 1 kg of peanuts, what is the cost of 2 kg? of 3 kg?
    (b) If y dollars represents the price of 1 kg of almonds what is the cost of 3 kg? of 4 kg?
    (c) Use the information obtained in parts (a) and (b) to write two equations that represent the amount Greg spent each time.
    (d) Solve the equation to determine the cost per kilogram for each kind of nut.

15. A gasoline station sells leaded and unleaded gasoline. On Friday 2000 L of leaded and 4000 L of unleaded were sold for $2690. On Saturday 2700 L of leaded and 4500 L of unleaded were sold for $3222. How much did each type of gasoline cost per litre?

16. On Saturday Mary Ann babysat for 2 h and worked 4 h at the variety store. She earned $21. On Sunday she babysat for 3 h and worked 5 h at the variety store. She earned $27.50. How much per hour does she earn on each job?

17. A carpenter ordered 8 kg of spikes and 3 kg of finishing nails for $15.75. Three days later she ordered 10 kg of spikes and 5 kg of finishing nails for $21.25. How much does each type of nail cost?

18. Three times a number plus seven times a second number equals 49. Five times the first number minus 4 times the second equals 19. Find the two numbers.

19. A rectangular garden is 5 m longer than it is wide.

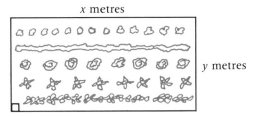

x metres

y metres

The perimeter of the garden is 110 m.

    (a) What are the dimensions of the garden?
    (b) What is the area of the garden?

20. A test contains 45 questions. Some of the questions are worth 3 marks and some are worth 2 marks. A perfect score is 100 marks. How many questions of each type are on the test?

Finding Patterns

1. Judy has both chickens and cows on her farms. Together the animals have 54 legs. How many cows and how many chickens might she have?

Complete a table to organize the given information.

Number of Chickens	Legs	Number of Cows	Legs	Total Number of Legs
1	2	13	52	54
3	☐	12	☐	54
⋮	⋮	⋮	⋮	⋮
5	10	☐	☐	54

Is it possible to have exactly 2 chickens, or 4 chickens, and so on? Why?

2. Twelve couples have been invited to a party. The couples will be seated at a row of small square card tables, placed end to end so as to form one long table. How many of these tables are needed to seat all 24 people?

Find the answer by looking for a pattern. The table below is one way of organizing information to help you find a pattern.

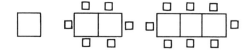

Number of Tables	1	2	3	4
Number of People	4	6	8	10

How many of these tables are needed to seat 20 couples?

3. A cube (of dimensions 12 cm by 12 cm by 12 cm) is painted completely green on all 6 faces. The cube is then cut into 27 smaller cubes, each having the dimensions 4 cm by 4 cm by 4 cm. Of these 27 smaller cubes:
   • how many have exactly 3 faces painted green?
   • how many have exactly 2 faces painted green?
   • how many have exactly 1 face painted green?
   • how many have no faces painted green?

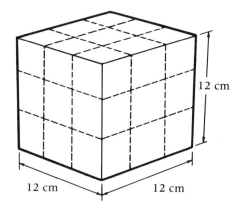

4. (a) There are 9 football teams in the Canadian Football League. To conduct their annual draft, teams from each city must have a direct telephone line to each of the other cities. How many direct telephone lines must be installed to accomplish this?

Number of Cities	1	2	3	4	5	6
Number of Lines	0	1	3	6	10	▨

   (b) How many direct telephone lines must be installed if there are 16 teams in the league?

Unit 8 Review

1. Solve each of the following pairs of equations graphically. Check your answers by substitution.

   (a) $y = x - 1$
   $y = 2x - 4$
   (b) $y = -3x + 1$
   $y = 2x + 6$
   (c) $y = \frac{1}{2}x - 3$
   $y = 2x - 6$
   (d) $4x - y = 8$
   $x + y = 7$
   (e) $4x - 3y = 0$
   $2x + y = 0$
   (f) $2x + 5y = 10$
   $x = 4$

2. A machine shop owner investigates the cost of renting a drilling press. The equations relating the cost (C) and the number of weeks, W, that the machine is rented is given below.

   Company A: $C = 60W + 120$
   Company B: $C = 65W + 100$

   (a) Solve the two equations graphically.
   (b) In this situation, what does the solution represent?
   (c) What is the difference in cost if the shop owner rents the machine for 10 weeks?

3. The cost, C, of making advertising buttons by 2 companies is given by the following equations.

   Company X: $C = 0.40n + 25$
   Company Y: $C = 0.45n + 18$

   n is the number of buttons ordered.

   (a) Solve the two equations graphically.
   (b) For what number of buttons is it cheaper to order from Company X?
   (c) What is the difference in cost if you order 2000 buttons?

4. Solve each of the following pairs of equations algebraically and check your answers.

   (a) $x - y = 9$
   $x + y = 5$
   (b) $x + y = 5$
   $2x - y = 10$
   (c) $4x - 3y = 12$
   $2x - 3y = 6$
   (d) $x + 2y = 5$
   $2x + y = 1$
   (e) $2x + 3y = 9$
   $5x - 2y = 13$
   (f) $2x - 5y = 9$
   $3x + 2y = 4$
   (g) $3x + 2y = 4$
   $4x + 4y = 3$
   (h) $4x + 2y = 13$
   $5x - 3y = 19$
   (i) $2x + 3y = 4$
   $3x + 4y = 5$
   (j) $3x - 2y = -7$
   $2x - 5y = 10$

5. Use the method of substitution to solve each of the following pairs of equations.

   (a) $y = 5x + 2$
   $y = 2x - 7$
   (b) $y = 2x$
   $x - 2y = 9$
   (c) $y = 3x - 1$
   $2x + 5y = 22$
   (d) $y = \frac{1 - 3x}{2}$
   $y = \frac{2x - 18}{3}$

6. The following pair of equations represents the cost, C, of renting a bicycle from 2 bicycle shops for a time t hours.

   $$C = 3 + 4t$$
   $$C = 10 + 0.5t$$

   Solve the 2 equations to determine the time for equal costs.

7. If d represents the number of dimes and q the number of quarters in a parking meter box, the two equations to determine the number of each coin are given below.
$$d + q = 35$$
$$10d + 25q = 725$$

   (a) What does the equation $10d + 25q = 725$ represent?
   (b) How many coins of each type are there in the box?

8. A tennis club charges a $90 membership fee plus $3.50/h for court fees. Another club charges a $120 membership fee plus $3/h court fees.
   For how many hours will the cost at each club be the same?

9. Kathy invested $6000 for 1 a. She invested part at 8% per annum and the remainder at 11% per annum. The interest earned for 1 a on these investments was $600. How much did she invest at each rate?

10. A fixed charge is made for each car carried across a river by ferry and an additional charge is made for each person in the car. If 10 cars containing 30 people are carried $95 is collected. If 12 cars containing 40 people are carried $120 is collected. What is the cost for each car and for each person?

11. For a school fund-raising campaign, Robert sold 20 boxes of apples, and 25 cartons of oranges, collecting $400. Sandra sold 22 boxes of apples and 23 cartons of oranges for $386. How much did each box of apples and each carton of oranges cost?

12. A leading scorer in a football league scored 111 points in a single season. The player accumulated these points by scoring touchdowns (worth 6 points each) and field goals (worth 3 points each). The number of points scored by touchdowns and field goals totalled 27. How many of each were scored?

Side Trip

Arrange 12 toothpicks in squares as shown below.

Now move only 3 toothpicks so that you will have only 3 squares, not 4.

Move 3 coins so that the figure on the left will look like the figure on the right.

146

Summary of Units 1 to 8

Unit 1   Math Skills You Need

What you have learned to do	For review, see page...
• Calculate time differences	2
• Read maps, tables, and schedules	2, 6
• Evaluate numerical expressions using BEDMAS	4
• Evaluate expressions involving fractions	6
• Write percents as fractions or decimals	9
• Solve problems involving percent	10
• Evaluate algebraic expressions and apply formulas	12, 15-16, 17, 19, 20

Unit 2   Exponents

What you have learned to do	For review, see page...
• Evaluate powers and square roots	24, 28
• Evaluate expressions with powers by applying the power rule, division rule, power of a power rule, or the rule for power of a product or quotient	26, 36
	33, 36
• Evaluate a power involving a fractional exponent	35, 36
• Evaluate a power involving integral exponents	37, 44
• Solve problems involving powers	40
• Estimate, round, and round to significant digits	41, 42
• Work with numbers in scientific notation	

Unit 3   Polynomials

What you have learned to do	For review, see page...
• Identify like terms	48
• Add and subtract like terms	48
• Multiply and divide like or unlike terms	49
• Simplify algebraic expressions	49
• Expand expressions that involve a monomial multiplied by a polynomial	51-52
• Multiply pairs of binomials	54
• Find the common factor of a polynomial and divide	56
• Factor trinomials	58-59, 61-62
• Factor a difference of squares	64
• Factor any given polynomial, if possible	65

147

Unit 4 Equations and Formulas

What you have learned to do | **For review, see page...**

- Solve equations by performing the same operation on left side and right side — 70, 72
- Solve equations by factoring or simplifying first — 74
- Substitute given variables into formulas — 76
- Rewrite a given formula to isolate a specified variable — 78, 80
- Apply formulas to solve problems — 82

Unit 5 Rational Algebraic Expressions

What you have learned to do | **For review, see page...**

- Simplify rational algebraic expressions by reducing to lowest terms — 88
- Multiply and divide rational expressions — 89
- Simplify a given rational algebraic expression by factoring first, then reducing to lowest terms — 90
- Find the lowest common denominator of a pair of rational algebraic expressions — 93
- Add and subtract rational algebraic expressions — 93, 94

Unit 6 Coordinate Geometry

What you have learned to do | **For review, see page...**

- Plot ordered pairs on a grid — 100
- Name points on a graph — 100
- Graph a relation from a given equation — 102
- Read information from a given graph — 104
- Calculate the length of a line segment — 106
- Find the midpoint of a line segment — 108

Unit 7   Geometry of a Straight Line

What you have learned to do   **For review, see page...**

Unit 8   Solving Pairs of Equations

What you have learned to do   **For review, see page...**

Units 1 to 8 Review

Unit 1   *Math Skills You Need*

1. Evaluate using Bedmas.

   (a) $9 + 24 \div 2^2 + 3(6 - 2)$
   (b) $(-5 + 2)^2 \div [-9 - (-7)]$
   (c) $(7.5 - 2.3 + 3.4) \times 0.001$
   (d) $\dfrac{4.3 \times 0.5 + 6.35}{14\ 000 \div 1000 - 1.23 \times 10}$

2. Evaluate the following fractional expressions.

   (a) $\frac{1}{3} - \frac{1}{2} + \frac{3}{4}$
   (b) $1\frac{4}{5} \div \frac{3}{5} - \frac{2}{3}$
   (c) $(\frac{3}{5} - 1\frac{1}{4}) \times 20$

3. Calculate each of the following.

   (a) 12% of $150
   (b) $3\frac{1}{2}$% of $45

4. A manufacturer of light bulbs states that 5.5% of all light bulbs sold by the company will be faulty. If a department store buys 3000 of these bulbs, how many of them might be expected to be usable?

5. A student obtains 68 marks out of 80 on an examination. What was the percentage mark?

6. Evaluate by substitution.

   (a) $7x - 3y$; $x = 4$, $y = 3$
   (b) $6x + wy$; $w = 2$, $x = 3$, $y = 4.5$
   (c) $\dfrac{3x + 4y}{2(x + w)}$; $x = 2$, $y = 3$, $w = 2.5$

7. The formula $P = VI$ calculates the electrical power, P watts, used by an electrical appliance with voltage V volts and current I amperes.
   Calculate P for each of the following appliances.

   (a) A toaster with voltage 110 V and current 12 A.
   (b) A clothes dryer with voltage 220 V and current 30 A.
   (c) A light bulb with voltage 110 V and current 1.25 A.

Unit 2   *Exponents*

8. Evaluate.

   (a) 3^2 (f) 4^0
   (b) $(-3)^2$ (g) $25^{\frac{1}{2}}$
   (c) -3^2 (h) $(-8)^{\frac{1}{3}}$
   (d) 3^{-2} (i) $(\frac{4}{9})^{0.5}$
   (e) $(\frac{3}{4})^2$ (j) $(-2)^3$

9. Simplify using exponent rules.

   (a) $a^3 \times a^5 \times a^2$
   (b) $3m^9 \times 4m^{-3}$
   (c) $(3x^3)^2$
   (d) $a^{15} \div a^5 \times a^2$
   (e) $\dfrac{(3a^5) \times 8a^{15}}{(2a^3)^2}$
   (f) $15a^7 \div (3a^9)$
   (g) $36x^7y^{-2} \div (3x^9y^7)$
   (h) $\dfrac{15t^{-2} \times 4t^8}{10t^4}$

10. Evaluate.

   (a) $\sqrt{25}$ (e) $\sqrt{225 + 64}$
   (b) $7\sqrt{81}$ (f) $\sqrt{25} \times \sqrt{36}$
   (c) $\sqrt{25} + \sqrt{36}$ (g) $\sqrt{13^2 - 5^2}$
   (d) $\dfrac{\sqrt{36}}{\sqrt{9}}$ (h) $\sqrt{13^2} - \sqrt{5^2}$

11. Simplify, then evaluate.

 (a) $10^5 \times 10^2 \div 10^4$
 (b) $10^7 \div 10^5 \times 10^{-2}$
 (c) $\dfrac{5^3 \times (5^5)^2}{5^7 \times 5^4}$
 (d) $4^0 + 2^3 - (-2)^2$
 (e) $9^{\frac{1}{2}} + 2^{-1}$

12. Substitute, then evaluate.

 (a) $x^2 + 3x + 10;\ x = 2$
 (b) $\sqrt{3xy};\ x = 4,\ y = 12$
 (c) $4a^2 - \sqrt{a + 3};\ a = 6$

13. Express each answer in scientific notation, correct to 2 digits.

 (a) $(1.7 \times 10^4) \times (5.0 \times 10^{-2})$
 (b) $(9.6 \times 10^5) \div (3.0 \times 10^{-5})$
 (b) $\dfrac{(8.47 \times 10^3) \times (4.7 \times 10^{-3})}{2.0 \times 10^{-2}}$

14. The perimeter, P, of a square with area A can be found by using the formula $P = 4A^{\frac{1}{2}}$. A square window is to provide for 900 cm^2 of illumination. Find the length of weather stripping needed to seal the window.

15. The formula $d = 3.6\sqrt{h}$ gives the distance (d kilometres) of the horizon from an observer at a height h metres. How far is the horizon from each of the following?

 (a) The 457 m observation level of the CN Tower
 (b) Eye level, 1.75 m, when you are standing at the water's edge (Use eye level as 1.75 m above the water surface.)

16. Simplify.

 (a) $3x + 4y + 9x - 10y$
 (b) $(4a + 7b) + (9a - 13a) - (-4b)$
 (c) $(4w^2 - 6w + 7) - (9w^2 - 5w - 13)$
 (d) $5a \times 7b + 15abc \div 3c$
 (e) $\dfrac{9x - 15y + 24w}{3}$
 (f) $\dfrac{6c^3 - 4c}{-2c}$
 (g) $(-5a^2b)(6ab^2)$

17. Expand and simplify.

 (a) $5y + 3(2 - 3y) - (4y + 3)$
 (b) $4p(3p - 5) - 2p(5p - 12)$
 (c) $(a + 3)(a + 5)$
 (d) $(2x - 5)(x - 3)$
 (e) $(4x + 7)(2x - 3)$
 (f) $(6x - 5y)(x + 5y)$
 (g) $(3t - 2)^2$
 (h) $(x - 6)(x - 5) + (x + 4)(x + 3)$
 (i) $(2a - 3b)(2a + 3b) - (a + b)(a - 3b)$
 (j) $3(w - 5)(2w + 7) + 2(3w - 5)^2$
 (k) $(3x + 4)^2 - (2x - 5)^2$
 (l) $(3x - 2)(x^2 - 3x + 7)$

18. Factor completely.

 (a) $8q^2 - 2q$
 (b) $25ab - 10b^2 + 5b$
 (c) $4x(x - 5) + 3(x - 5)$
 (d) $x^2 - 8x + 15$
 (e) $y^2 - 5y - 6$
 (f) $a^2 + 8a + 16$
 (g) $p^2 + 7p - 44$
 (h) $3x^2 + 17x + 10$
 (i) $3a^2 - 11a + 10$
 (j) $6q^2 - 17q - 10$
 (k) $10y^2 - 31y - 14$
 (l) $x^2 - 25$
 (m) $9x^2 - 25$

19. Solve.

(a) $3x - 7 = 8$
(b) $9x - 5 = 2x + 23$
(c) $6m + 3 - 2m - 14 = 7m + 21 + 1$
(d) $4(x + 1) = 2(x + 5)$
(e) $5(2a - 7) + 3(4a - 3) = 2a + 7(2a - 2)$
(f) $15 - [2x - 7(x + 3)] = 31$
(g) $\dfrac{3x - 7}{3} = \dfrac{2x - 5}{4}$
(h) $\dfrac{x}{2} - \dfrac{3x}{5} = \dfrac{7}{4}$
(i) $\dfrac{2a + 2}{5} + \dfrac{2a + 5}{3} = -1$
(j) $\dfrac{2}{3}(3y - 5) - \dfrac{y - 2}{2} = -2$

20. Solve for the variable in each quadratic equation.

(a) $x^2 - 25 = 0$
(b) $3k^2 - 6k = 0$
(c) $y^2 - 5y + 6 = 0$
(d) $x^2 - 9x - 22 = 0$
(e) $2x^2 + x - 15 = 0$

21. Substitute the appropriate values in each formula, then solve for the remaining variable.

(a) $K = Wa + b$; $a = 3$, $b = 5$, $K = 80$
(b) $P = \dfrac{RT}{V}$; $P = 144$, $R = 56$, $V = 7$
(c) $V = \pi r^2 h$; $V = 536.94$, $\pi \doteq 3.14$, $r = 3$

22. Rewrite each formula so that the variable in the brackets is the subject.

(a) $c = \pi d$; $[d]$
(b) $V = u + at$; $[a]$
(c) $V = \dfrac{2R}{R - r}$; $[r]$

23. Determine the value of x, given that the perimeter of the rectangle is 28 cm.

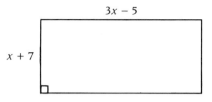

24. Simplify.

(a) $\dfrac{2}{3} \times \dfrac{3}{4}$
(b) $\dfrac{5x}{6} \times \dfrac{3}{x}$
(c) $\dfrac{4(x + 3)}{2(x + 3)}$
(d) $\dfrac{5xy}{4w} \div \dfrac{2w}{5y}$
(e) $\dfrac{8a^3b^2}{2a^5b^3} \times \dfrac{9a^2c^3}{6b^6}$
(f) $\dfrac{a^4b^3}{-ac} \div \dfrac{-a^2b}{c^3}$
(g) $\dfrac{9(w + 5)(w - 4)}{3(w + 5)(w + 4)}$
(h) $\dfrac{5(x + 3)}{3(x - 4)} \div \dfrac{7(x + 3)}{6(x - 4)}$
(i) $\dfrac{(x + 4)(x + 5)}{(x + 7)(x + 4)} \times \dfrac{x(x + 7)}{(x + 5)(x + 2)}$

25. Factor completely, then simplify.

(a) $\dfrac{4x + 4y}{2x + 2y}$
(b) $\dfrac{y^2 - 2y - 15}{y^2 - y - 20}$
(c) $\dfrac{a^2 - 25}{a^2 + 5a}$
(d) $\dfrac{3x^2 - 10x + 3}{9x - 3}$

(e) $\dfrac{x^2 - 4}{2x^2 + 9x + 9} \div \dfrac{4x - 8}{10x + 15}$

(f) $\dfrac{7c + 35}{c^2 - 25} \times \dfrac{3c - 15}{c^2 - 9}$

26. Simplify.

(a) $\dfrac{3a}{4} - \dfrac{a}{5}$

(b) $\dfrac{x - 3}{4} - \dfrac{x}{3}$

(c) $\dfrac{x}{2} - \dfrac{(x - 3)}{3}$

(d) $\dfrac{2a + 3b}{3} - \dfrac{a - 2b}{2}$

(e) $\dfrac{3}{2x} + \dfrac{2}{3x}$

(f) $\dfrac{m}{x} - \dfrac{3m}{2x} + \dfrac{5m}{3x}$

(g) $\dfrac{4}{x - 1} + \dfrac{3}{x + 1}$

(h) $\dfrac{y}{y - 2} - \dfrac{y + 3}{y - 1}$

Unit 6 *Coordinate Geometry*

27. Graph each of the following linear relations on separate axes.

(a) $y = 2x - 2$ (c) $y = \frac{1}{2}x - 4$
(b) $y = -3x + 5$ (d) $y = -\frac{2}{3}x + 2$

28. Graph each of the following non-linear relations on separate axes.

(a) $y = x^2 - 5$ (c) $y = -2x^2$
(b) $y = 3x^2$ (d) $y = 2x^2 + 3$

29. In an experiment, one end of a solid metal rod was heated over a burner. The temperature at the opposite end of the rod was recorded every 2 min.

time (minutes)	0	2	4	6	8	10	12	14	16	18
Temperature (°C)	15	35	55	75	78	80	82	120	150	180

(a) Plot the points corresponding to each pair of numbers (t, T) in the table. Join the points in order with line segments.
(b) What was the temperature for the opposite end of the rod after 1 min? 5 min? 11 min?
(c) After how many minutes was the temperature at the far end of the rod 50°C? 70°C? 100°C? 170°C?

30. The cost of organizing an athletic banquet is given by an equation.
$$C = 6n + 100$$

C is the cost in dollars and n is the number of people attending the banquet.

(a) Draw a graph of this relation.
(b) From your graph, find the cost for 200 people; 350 people.
(c) In this situation, what information can be determined from the point of intersection of the line with the vertical axis?

31. As dry air moves upward it expands and, in so doing, cools at a rate of about 1°C for each 100 m rise, up to about 12 km. This situation is represented by an equation.
$$T = -0.01h + 10$$

T is the temperature in degrees Celsius and h is the height above the ground in metres.

(a) Draw a graph of this relation.
(b) What is the ground temperature?
(c) What is the temperature 800 m above the ground? 2 km above the ground?
(d) What is the height above the ground if the temperature is $-50°C$?

32. Plot each pair of points and find the length of the segment joining them.

(a) $(2, 5)$, $(9, 10)$
(b) $(-2, 6)$, $(3, -5)$

33. Determine the coordinates of the midpoint of the segment joining each pair of points.

(a) $(3, 9)$, $(7, 12)$
(b) $(-5, -3)$, $(7, -5)$

Unit 7 *Geometry of a Straight Line*

34. Calculate the slope of the line segment joining each pair of points.

(a) $A(3, 4)$, $B(7, 9)$
(b) $C(-2, 5)$, $D(4, -3)$
(c) $E(-9, -2)$, $F(3, -2)$

35. A railway grade runs vertically 5 m for every horizontal distance of 100 m.

(a) Express the grade (slope) as a percentage.
(b) On the grade, what vertical height would correspond to a horizontal distance of 1500 m?

36. Calculate the pitch of each roof.

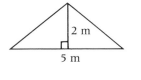

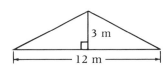

37. Each of the following equations defines a line. In each case:
• give the slope and y-intercept;
• use the slope and the y-intercept to graph the line.

(a) $y = 2x - 3$
(b) $y = \frac{2}{3}x + 4$
(c) $y = -\frac{5}{2}x - 2$
(d) $2x + y = 4$
(e) $5x - 2y = 10$

38. Determine the x- and y-intercepts for each of the following lines, then graph the line.

(a) $3x - 4y = 12$ (d) $2x - 5y = 12$
(b) $3x - y = 9$ (e) $3x + 5y = 15$
(c) $3x + 7y = 21$ (f) $2x + 3y = 9$

39. Determine an equation for each of the following lines.

(a) slope 3, y-intercept -2
(b) $m = -\frac{1}{3}$, y-intercept 4
(c) $m = \frac{2}{5}$, passing through the point $A(5, 7)$
(d) $m = -\frac{7}{2}$, passing through the point $C(-4, 3)$
(e) passing through the points $A(4, 1)$ and $B(7, 5)$
(f) passing through the points $C(5, -2)$ and $D(0, 5)$

40. The table below shows the total cost (C) charged by a plumbing contractor for a job requiring t hours to complete.

t	1	3	5
C	58	118	178

(a) Draw a graph to show how C is related to t.
(b) Determine a linear equation that relates C and t.
(c) What do the slope and vertical intercept represent in this situation?
(d) What is the cost of a 5.5 h job?
(e) How many hours did the plumber work if the total cost was $268?

41. The table below shows the length of stretch (L centimetres) of a spring as various objects of mass m grams are attached to it.

m	20	40	60
L	33	36	39

(a) Draw a graph to show how L is related to m.
(b) Determine a linear relation that relates L and m.
(c) What does the vertical intercept represent in this situation?
(d) What is the stretch of the spring if a mass of 50 g is attached to it?
(e) What mass is required to stretch the spring to a length of 40.5 cm?

42. Calculate the slope of the line segment joining each pair of points. Name pairs of line segments that are parallel or perpendicular.

(a) $A(3, 5)$, $B(7, 10)$
(b) $C(-2, 3)$, $D(4, -8)$
(c) $E(-3, -4)$, $F(5, 6)$
(d) $G(3, 4)$, $H(14, 10)$

Unit 8   Solving Pairs of Equations

43. Solve each of the following pairs of equations by graphing. Check your answers by substitution.

(a) $y = 2x + 1$ (b) $2x + y = -5$
$y = -x + 7$ $x + 3y = 10$

44. For each of the following, determine graphically the break-even point for producing and selling n items.

(a)   Cost: $C = 1.5n + 600$
Income: $I = 4n$
(b)   Cost: $C = 0.8n + 500$
Income: $I = 3.3n$

45. Two salespeople, Ivan and Michelle, work for salary plus commission. Their monthly pay is represented by the following equations.

Ivan: $P = 0.02S + 800$
Michelle: $P = 0.06S + 300$

P represents the monthly pay in dollars and S represents the monthly sales in dollars.

(a) Solve the two equations graphically.
(b) What does the intersection point represent in this situation?
(c) For what monthly sales does Michelle make more than Ivan?

155

46. Solve each of the following pairs of equations.

(a) $3x + y = 1$
    $2x - y = 9$

(b) $x - 3y = -4$
    $x + 7y = 11$

(c) $x - y = 5$
    $2x + 3y = -20$

(d) $3x + 2y = 6$
    $4x + 3y = 10$

(e) $3x - 2y = -7$
    $2x - 5y = 10$

(f) $4x - 2y = 3$
    $3x - 2y = 4$

(g) $12x - 4y = 5$
    $6x + 8y = 5$

(h) $y = 2x + 7$
    $y = 5x - 2$

(i) $y = 2x - 1$
    $5x + 3y = 8$

(j) $3x = 2y - 1$
    $4y = 3 - x$

47. The Too-Wheel Bicycle Rental Company charges a fixed amount of $5, plus $2/d for renting a bicycle. The U-Balance Bicycle Rental Company charges a fixed amount of $2, plus $3.50/d.

(a) Write an equation to represent the cost of renting from each company.
(b) For how many days would the cost of renting a bicycle from the 2 companies be the same?
(c) What is this cost?

48. Robert invested $5000 for 1 a. He invested part at 7% per annum and the remainder at 10% per annum. The total interest earned for 1 a on this investment was $440. How much did he invest at each rate?

49. On Saturday, Amy worked for 3 h at one job and 4 h at another job. She earned $34. If she had worked 2 more hours at each job, she would have earned $54. How much did she earn per hour at each job?

Side Trip

Could you draw the envelope without lifting your pencil off the paper?

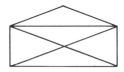

The diagram below shows you how.

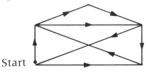

Start

If you can draw a figure with one continuous line where no line is passed over more than once, then the figure is drawn **unicursally**.

Make copies of each of the following figures unicursally.

1.

3.

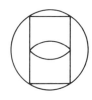

2.

4.

Unit 9

Earning Money

Earning Wages
Earning Commission
Calculating Net Earnings
Interpreting Wage Graphs
Comparing Earnings on Graphs
Unit 9 Review

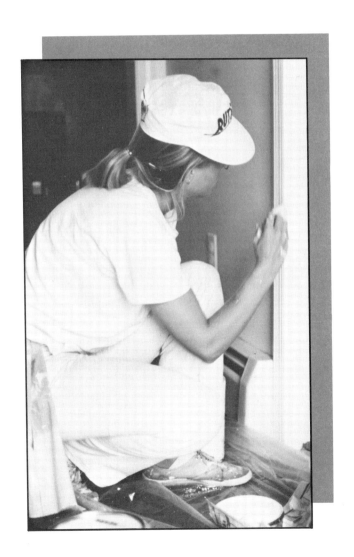

Earning Wages

Once you leave school, you will probably want a full-time job. The wages you earn may be paid in several different ways.

WANTED

Goundskeeper for golf course.
Duties: mowing lawns, some gardening, maintaining pathways
Send résumé to Pat Chan.

Karl answered the ad and got the job as a groundskeeper at a public golf course. He is paid an hourly wage of $8.20 for a 37.5 h week. Karl is paid overtime at a rate of time-and-one-half. One week in early spring, Karl works 50 h. Calculate his total wages, or his **gross pay**, for the week.

- Regular pay
  = $8.20/h × 37.5 h
  = $307.50

- Overtime rate of pay
  = $8.20/h × 1.5
  = $12.30/h

- Overtime pay
  = $12.30/h × 12.5 h
  = $153.75

  Overtime hours
  = 50 − 37.5
  = 12.5

- Gross pay
  = Regular pay + Overtime pay
  = $307.50 + $153.75
  = $461.25

Karl's gross pay for the week is $461.25.

Many people earn *tips* as well as hourly wages.

As a waiter, Henry earns $4.10/h for a 40 h week and keeps 80% of his tips. In one week, his tips amounted to $248. Calculate Henry's gross pay for the week.

- Regular pay
  = $4.10/h × 40 h
  = $164

- Earnings in tips
  = $248 × 0.80
  = $198.40

  80%

- Gross pay
  = Regular pay + Tips
  = $164 + $198.40
  = $362.40

Henry's gross pay was $362.40.

Some employers give bonuses to encourage greater productivity.

Leslie's summer job as a truck driver hauling topsoil pays $9.75/h for an 8 h day with a bonus of $2.50 for every tonne of soil hauled in excess of 50 t. Determine Leslie's gross pay for hauling 59 t in one day.

- Regular pay
  = $9.75/h × 8 h
  = $78

- Bonus pay
  = $2.50/t × 9 t
  = $22.50

- Gross pay
  = Regular pay + Bonus
  = $78 + $22.50
  = $100.50

Leslie's gross pay for the day was $100.50.

Exercise

A **1.** State several reasons why an employer would pay more than the regular rate (that is, time-and-one-half) for overtime work.

2. In a restaurant, waiters and waitresses often keep only *part* of their tips. Who else would share in the tips they earn?

3. State why a bonus or incentive plan is a good thing from an employee's viewpoint, and from an employer's viewpoint.

B **4.** In each case, determine the gross pay if overtime is at time-and-one-half.

Job	Regular Hours Worked	Regular Hourly Rate	Overtime Hours Worked
Clerk	40	$8.50	5
Shipper	37.5	$9.60	12
Typist	40	$7.95	7
Custodian	35	$8.45	13
Teller	40	$7.20	2

5. Han works as a word processing operator for a small computer firm. She is paid $11.50/h for a 37.5 h week, with overtime at the rate of time-and-one-half. Calculate her gross pay for a week in which she works 52.5 h.

6. Sergi is employed by a landscape firm at $7.50/h for a 40 h week. To meet a project deadline, the company asks its employees to work through a weekend. Pay is at time-and-one-half for Saturday and double time for Sunday. Calculate Sergi's gross pay for a week when he worked his regular hours, then 8 h on Saturday and 6 h on Sunday.

7. As a waitress, Sarah earns $4.90/h for a 40 h week and shares 25% of her tips with other employees. In one week, her tips were $318. What was Sarah's gross pay for the week?

8. Armondo is a busboy at Sam's Pizza and is paid $4.25/h. He also receives 1.8% of the tips collected by all table servers during the week. In one week, Armondo worked for 32 h and $2856.80 was collected in tips. How much did Armondo earn that week?

9. Heidi works in a plant that assembles television sets. Her job is to solder connections for the electrical components in each set. Her base pay is $9.50/h for a 40 h week, but she also receives a bonus of $0.90 for every set processed in excess of 75 in one day. Use the information in the table to calculate Heidi's gross pay for the week.

Day of Week	M	T	W	T	F
Number of Sets Processed	72	88	103	91	96

Earning Commission

With salespeople, an incentive to sell is provided by *commission* earnings.

Julie is a beauty consultant for Lotus Cosmetics and is paid $150/week plus a commission of 38% of sales. Her sales for one 4-week interval are shown in the table. How much did she earn in that period of time?

Week Number	1	2	3	4
Amount of Sales	$785	$472	$1052	$976

- Regular pay
  = $150/week × 4 weeks
  = $600

- Commission earned
  = Total Sales × 0.38
  = ($785 + $472 + $1052 + $976) × 0.38
  = $3285 × 0.38
  = $1248.30

Julie earned $600 + $1248.30 or $1848.30 in 4 weeks.

Your knowledge of algebra is helpful in solving certain types of commission problems. If Julie wants to earn $700 in 1 week, what would her sales have to be?

Let the amount of her sales be k.
Weekly Pay + Commission = Earnings
$$150 + 0.38k = 700$$
$$0.38k = 550$$
$$k = 1447.37$$

Julie's sales would have to be $1447.37.

Sometimes commission earnings are graded or go up by steps. This is called **step commission**.

Grant is a salesperson for Crabgrass and Mangletoe, a fertilizer company. He is paid $350/week, plus a step commission based on the value of the fertilizer he sells. He receives 5% on sales up to $1000, 10% on sales between $1000 and $2000, and 20% on sales over $2000. Calculate Grant's total earnings for 2 weeks with sales as shown in the table.

Week Number	1	2
Amount of Sales	$1680	$2250

Week 1

Salary	$350
Commission	
• 5% on first $1000	
= $1000 × 0.05	50
• 10% on next $680	
= $680 × 0.10	68
Total Pay	$468

Week 2

Salary	$350
Commission	
• 5% on first $1000	
= $1000 × 0.05	50
• 10% on next $1000	
= $1000 × 0.10	100
• 20% on next $250	
= $250 × 0.20	50
Total Pay	$550

Grant's total earnings were $468 + $550 or $1018.

Exercise

A **1.** State the commission earned in each case.

	Amount of Sales	Rate of Commission
(a)	$500	10%
(b)	$2000	40%
(c)	$1500	5%
(d)	$3000	8%

B **2.** Calculate the commission earnings in each case.

	Amount of Sales	Rate of Commission
(a)	$1453	15%
(b)	$7216.50	2.5%
(c)	$898.20	18%
(d)	$17641	1.9%
(e)	$2843.92	7.6%

3. A real estate agent earns 2.4% on the sale of a house priced at $89 950. Calculate the amount of the commission.

4. Rick is a salesclerk in a bicycle shop. He's paid $6.25/h for a 37.5 h week, plus a commission of 6% of his sales for the week. In one week, Rick's sales were $2319.75.

(a) Calculate Rick's total earnings for the week.
(b) What was Rick's average hourly wage for the week?
(c) What would Rick's sales for the week have to be for him to earn $400 in one week?

5. Calculate each value missing from the table.

	Rate of Commission	Amount of Sales	Commission Earned
(a)	4%	$1673.19	▨
(b)	10.5%	$3621.95	▨
(c)	27%	▨	$412.19
(d)	▨	$4275	$363.38
(e)	18%	▨	$208.12
(f)	▨	$3584.32	$1505.41

6. Ingrid is a salesperson for a firm specializing in microprocessors. She is paid $450/week, plus a step commission based on sales. She receives 3% on sales up to $5000 and 5% on sales over $5000. Use the information in the table to calculate her earnings each week and her total earnings for the 4 weeks.

Week	1	2	3	4
Sales	$4930	$5800	$6213	$5235

If Ingrid worked a total of 150 h, calculate her hourly wage.

7. Step commission on sales is calculated as follows.
- 8% on the first $1000
- 12% on the next $2000
- 20% on sales above $3000

Calculate the total commission if sales are as indicated.

(a) $970
(b) $632.85
(c) $1500
(d) $2760.42
(e) $1229
(f) $3716
(g) $2345
(h) $5728.63
(i) $412.78
(j) $4563.81

161

Calculating Net Earnings

When you get a regular job, your *net earnings* (or *take-home* pay) will be less than your gross pay. This difference is due to *deductions*. Federal law requires that your employer make certain deductions for the government. When you start work, your employer will have you fill out a Tax Exemption Return (TD1 form).

On her first job, Teresa LeBlanc fills out a TD1 Form, part of which is shown below.

Teresa's TD1 form gives her employer the information needed to determine how much money is to be deducted from her weekly wages. The 3 federal deductions are described below. Teresa's employer uses tables like the ones given to find the weekly deductions for a weekly gross pay of $230.

- **Canada Pension Plan (C.P.P.)** This money is collected by the government and is used to provide income for workers after they retire at age 65.

  Teresa's deduction for C.P.P. is $3.52.

C.P.P. R.P.C.	Remuneration Rémunération		C.P.P. R.P.C.
	From-de	To-à	
	229.34 –	229.88	3.51
	229.89 –	230.44	3.52
	230.45 –	230.99	3.53
	231.00 –	231.55	3.54
	231.56 –	232.10	3.55

- **Unemployment Insurance (U.I.)** This money is paid to workers who become unemployed.

  Teresa's deduction for U.I. is $5.29.

  > Deductions for C.P.P. and U.I. are made *before* income tax is calculated.

  Teresa's deductions for C.P.P. and U.I. total $3.52 + $5.29, or $8.81.
  The calculation of income tax will then be based on wages of $230 − $8.81, or $221.19, with net claim code 3.

U.I. Premium Prime d'a.-c.	Remuneration Rémunération		U.I. Premium Prime d'a.-c.
	From-de	To-à	
4.84	229.78 –	230.21	5.29
4.85	230.22 –	230.64	5.30
4.86	230.65 –	231.08	5.31
4.87	231.09 –	231.51	5.32
4.88	231.52 –	231.95	5.33
4.89	231.96 –	232.38	5.34
90	232.39 –	232.82	5.35
	232.83 –	233.25	5.36
	233.26 –	233.69	5.37

- **Income Tax** The government uses this money to provide the country with services like the following.
  - public transportation
  - public buildings
  - highways
  - development of natural resources

  Construction and maintenance

WEEKLY PAY Use appropriate bracket PAIE PAR SEMAINE Utilisez le palier approprié	IF THE EMPLOYEE'S "NET CLAIM CODE EMPLOYÉ S				
	1	2	3	4	5
	DEDUCT FROM EA				
208.00 – 209.99	23.00	21.15	17.90	14.75	11.55
210.00 – 211.99	23.55	21.70	18.45	15.30	12.10
212.00 – 213.99	24.10	22.30	19.00	15.85	12.60
214.00 – 215.99	24.65	22.85	19.60	16.40	13.15
216.00 – 217.99	25.20	23.40	20.15	16.95	13.65
218.00 – 219.99	25.75	23.95	20.70	17.50	14
220.00 – 221.99	26.35	24.50	21.25	18.10	
222.00 – 223.99	26.90	25.05	21.80	18.65	
224.00 – 225.99	27.45	25.60	22.35		
226.00 – 227.99	28.05	26.20			

Teresa's income tax deduction will be $21.25.

Teresa's pay stub might look like this.

```
            Statement of Earnings
  Name: TERESA LEBLANC  Date: SEPT 28 19 84

  Regular Earnings                    $230·00
  Other Earnings                      $  —
  Total Earnings                      $230·00

  Deductions:

  Canada Pension Plan             $   3·52
  Unemployment Insurance          $   5·29
  Income Tax                      $  21·25
  Health Insurance                $
                                  $
                                  $
                                  $
                                  $

          Total Deductions:         $30.06
          Net Payment:             $199·94
```

Example 1

Arthur earns $412/week and has net claim code 2. In addition to weekly deductions for C.P.P., U.I., and income tax, he has other deductions as shown.
- Charities $3.00
- Health insurance $1.90
- Union dues $2.85

Calculate Arthur's take-home pay.

From tables,
- C.P.P. deduction $ 6.74
- U.I. deduction $ 9.48
     Total $16.22
- Income tax deduction
  (based on $412 − $16.22 = $395.78) $75.65
- Charities $ 3.00
- Health Insurance $ 1.90
- Union dues $ 2.85
     Total Deductions $99.62

Arthur's take-home pay is $412 − $99.62, or $312.38.

Example 2

Pat is paid $5.50/h for a 37.5 h week and earns double-time for overtime. Pat has net claim code 1 and other deductions of $14.73. Determine Pat's net pay for a week in which overtime worked was 4.5 h.

"Other deductions" are in addition to C.P.P., U.I., and income tax.

Calculate Pat's gross wages.

- Regular pay
  = $5.50/h × 37.5 h $206.25
- Overtime pay
  = $5.50/h × 2 × 4.5 h   49.50

Double time

  Gross Wages $255.75

Calculate Pat's deductions.

- C.P.P. $ 3.91
- U.I.   5.88
- Income tax (based on
  $255.75 − $9.79 = $245.96) 33.40
- Other deductions   14.73
     Total Deductions $57.92

Pat's net pay is $255.75 − $57.92, or $197.83.

164

Exercise

Use the C.P.P., U.I., and income tax tables on pages 444 to 455.

A 1. State the weekly deductions for C.P.P. and U.I. according to the weekly income shown.

(a) $178
(b) $316.48
(c) $259
(d) $385.91
(e) $401.75
(f) $493

2. State the amount deducted for income tax in each case.

	Weekly Income (After C.P.P. and U.I. Deductions)	Net Claim Code
(a)	$298.50	2
(b)	$528.72	1
(c)	$316.08	3
(d)	$401.79	5

3. In each case, calculate:
• taxable earnings after C.P.P. and U.I.;
• income tax payable.

	Gross Weekly Income	Net Claim Code
(a)	$263.05	4
(b)	$327.80	1
(c)	$237.17	3
(d)	$483.75	6
(e)	$392.68	2

4. Helga's weekly gross pay is $380.45. Her net claim code is 3. If she has only the standard deductions for C.P.P., U.I., and income tax, calculate her net pay.

5. Jason earns $328 weekly as an assistant in a printing shop, and has net claim code 2. Determine Jason's take-home pay if he has other deductions of $8.19, in addition to C.P.P., U.I., and income tax.

In problems 6 to 9, all deductions noted are in addition to C.P.P., U.I., and income tax.

6. Selina is paid $6.90/h for a 40 h week. She has net claim code 4. Her other deductions amount to $6.15. Calculate her net pay for 1 week.

7. Arnold works as an apprentice electrician and is paid $10.50/h for a 37.5 h week, with overtime paid at time-and-one-half. His net claim code is 1 and his other deductions total $16.84. Calculate Arnold's take-home pay for a week in which he worked 43 h.

8. As a salesperson for a small business machines firm, Gail is paid $300/week, plus a commission of 5% of the value of her sales. In 1 week, Gail sold $2118 worth of machines. If her net claim code is 3, and she has other deductions of $19.50, calculate Gail's net pay for the week.

9. Sam earns $285/week, plus a step commission of 8% on the first $1000 of sales, 10% on the next $500, and 14% on sales over $1500. Sam has deductions for health insurance ($2.19), life insurance ($3.10), charities ($4.00) and Canada Savings Bond ($10.00). If Sam has net claim code 4, and his sales for the week total $1640, calculate his net pay for the week.

Interpreting Wage Graphs

An interesting way to look at wages is through a wage-time graph. The properties of the graph can be related to the wages earned.

Lucille has a part-time job as a clerk. Her wages and hours worked during 1 week are given in the table.

Hours Worked	2	4	7
Wages Earned	$9	$18	$31.50

Information from the table can be used to construct a graph.

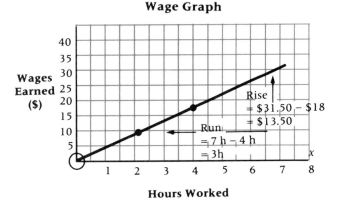

Wage Graph

Hours Worked

The slope of AB is $\dfrac{\$13.50}{3\text{ h}}$, or $4.50/h.

This *slope* is the *hourly rate* at which Lucille is paid. How much would Lucille earn in 5 h? How long would she have to work to earn $36?

A graph gives a lot of information at a glance, but may not be very *accurate*. If Lucille works 6.5 h, it would be better to calculate her wages ($4.50/h × 6.5 h = $29.25) rather than try to read them from the graph.

David is paid a weekly salary of $200/week. In addition, he earns a step commission based on his weekly sales. The graph below shows David's wages compared to his weekly sales.

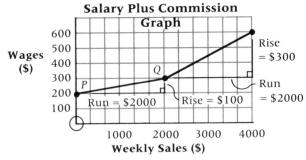

Salary Plus Commission Graph

Weekly Sales ($)

Notice that the *y*-intercept (on the wages axis) is $200. This tells you that David receives a guaranteed salary of $200/week. (As before, sales determine the amount of commission.)

Calculate the slopes of PQ and QR.

Slope of PQ

$= \dfrac{\$100}{\$2000}$

$= 0.05$ or 5%

Slope of QR

$= \dfrac{\$300}{\$2000}$

$= 0.15$ or 15%

These slopes are *rates of commission*. David earns 5% commission for sales of up to $2000. If sales amount to over $2000, he earns 15% commission.

- For sales of $100, David would earn $250 ($200 salary + $50 commission).
- If David earned $450 in 1 week, his sales must have been $3000.

Calculate David's wages for sales of $3216.
- Commission on first $2000 $100
  (5% of $2000)
- Commission on sales over $2000
  (15% of $1216) $182.40
- Salary $200
  Total wages $482.40

David's wages are $482.40.

Exercise

B 1. The graph shows Garth's earnings from his part-time job selling greeting cards.

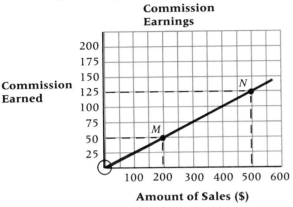

Commission Earnings

Commission Earned

Amount of Sales ($)

(a) Use points *M* and *N* to calculate the slope of the line. What rate of commission does Garth earn?

(b) Determine Garth's earnings if his sales are $300; $600; $1470.

(c) What would Garth's sales have to be for him to earn $100? $175? $316?

2. The graph shows Leslie's weekly wages for hours worked on a step commission basis.

Commission Wages

Wages ($)

Weekly Sales ($)

(a) How much does Leslie earn on sales of $500? $1500?

(b) Determine Leslie's sales for a week in which she earns $300; $700.

(c) Calculate the slope of segment *OP*. What is Leslie's rate of commission for weekly sales up to $1000?

(d) Calculate the slope of segment *QR*. What is Leslie's rate of commission for weekly sales over $1000?

(e) Calculate Leslie's wages for a week in which her sales are $2860.

3. The graph shows Soji's weekly wages based on his weekly sales.

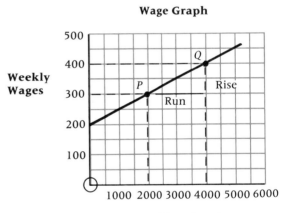

Wage Graph

Weekly Wages

Weekly Sales ($)

(a) What is Soji's guaranteed weekly salary?

(b) What are Soji's wages for sales of $1000? $3000? $5000?

(c) What sales will provide wages of $200? $400?

(d) What rate of commission does Soji earn on weekly sales?

(e) Calculate Soji's wages for weekly sales of $4823.

167

4. The graph below shows Karen's weekly wages based on a step commission.

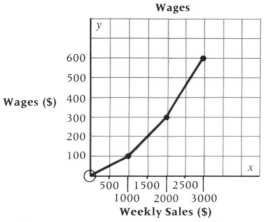

(a) What are Karen's wages for weekly sales of $500? $2000? $2500?
(b) What would Karen's weekly sales have to be to earn $100? $200? $600?
(c) Determine Karen's commission on sales up to $1000? between $1000 and $2000? above $2000?
(d) Calculate Karen's wages for sales of $1193; $865; $2819.

5. Dina's wages are based on salary plus commission, as shown in the graph.

(a) What is Dina's guaranteed monthly salary?
(b) What are Dina's wages for sales of $10 000? $20 000? $30 000?
(c) What sales would provide wages of $1000? $4000?
(d) Calculate Dina's rate of commission for sales up to $20 000, above $20 000.
(e) Determine Dina's wages for sales of $18 562, $31 263.48.

6. Derek is paid a weekly salary and a step commission based on sales.

Salary Plus Commission Wages

(a) What is Derek's guaranteed weekly salary?
(b) What are Derek's wages for sales of $1000? $1500? $2000? $2500?
(c) What sales will provide wages of $300? $450? $900?
(d) Calculate the slopes of segments AB, BC, and CD. What rate of commission does Derek earn on weekly sales up to $1000? from $1000 to $2000? over $2000?
(e) Calculate Derek's total wages for sales of $852, $1638, and $2145.

Comparing Earnings on Graphs $

Graphs can provide a convenient way of comparing 2 or more types of earnings.

The graph below shows wages and hours worked for Melinda and Tony.

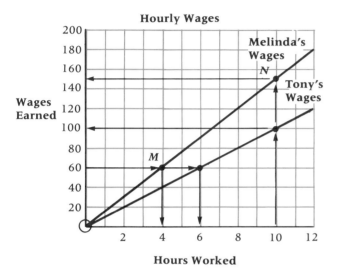

Hourly Wages

From the graph, you can see that Melinda's hourly wage is greater than Tony's.
- If they each work 10 h, Melinda would earn $150, while Tony would earn only $100.
- To earn $60, Melinda would only have to work 5 h, while Tony would have to work 6 h.
- If they both worked 12 h, Melinda would earn $180 − $120, or $60 more than Tony.
- Melinda's hourly wage is given by the slope of the segment MN.

$$\text{Hourly Wage} = \frac{\$150 - \$60}{6\ h}$$
$$= \frac{\$90}{6\ h}$$
$$= \$15/h$$

Ted and Claire work for 2 different sales companies.

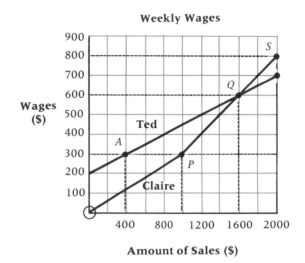

Weekly Wages

You can read information from the graph.
- Both people earn the same wages for sales of $1600. For sales less than $1600, Ted earns the greater amount; for sales greater than $1600, Claire earns the greater amount.
- For sales of $2000, Claire earns $100 more than Ted.
- If both people earn $300, Ted's sales were $400, and Claire's sales were $1000.
- The slope of segment AQ is $\dfrac{\$300}{\$1200}$ or 25%.

Ted is guaranteed a weekly salary of $200 plus a straight commission of 25% of sales.

Slope of OP	Slope of PS
$= \dfrac{\$300}{\$1200}$	$= \dfrac{\$500}{\$1000}$
$= 0.30$	$= 0.50$

Claire's wages are based on step commission of 30% for sales of $1000 or less, and 50% for sales greater than $1000.

Exercise

A 1. Graham earns a fixed weekly salary as shown.

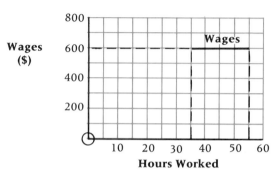

(a) What is Graham's weekly salary?
(b) What is the range of hours that Graham works from week to week?
(c) State several reasons (or job situations) that might account for this range of hours worked.

2. Jill is paid on a commission basis according to her weekly sales.

(a) What are Jill's wages for weekly sales of $1000? $2500? $4000?
(b) What would Jill's weekly sales have to be to earn $100? $400? $700?
(c) For segment *OP*, what is the rise? the run? the slope?
(d) What is Jill's rate of commission?

3. Fiona's wages are made up of a guaranteed monthly salary plus a commission based on sales, as shown in the graph.

(a) What is Fiona's guaranteed monthly salary?
(b) What are Fiona's wages for sales of $5000? $15 000? $20 000?
(c) What monthly sales would provide wages of $2000? $2500?
(d) For segment *MN*, what is the rise? the run? the slope?
(e) What rate of commission does Fiona earn?
(f) Why is it not possible to determine Fiona's wages for sales of $8416.30 from the graph?

B **4.** Pat's and Mike's weekly wages are shown in the graph. Pat is a stationary engineer on a fixed weekly salary (earnings don't change with hours worked). Mike is a bricklayer earning hourly wages.

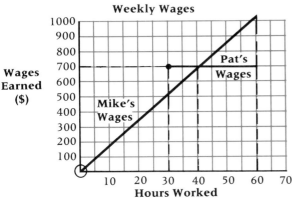

Weekly Wages

(a) What is Pat's weekly wage?
(b) What is the range of hours that Pat works from week to week?
(c) Under what condition do both people earn the same wages?
(d) Calculate Mike's hourly wage.
(e) If each person works 30 h, how much more does Pat earn than Mike?
(f) If each person works 60 h, how much more does Mike earn than Pat?

5. Alice is paid a straight commission and Joanne is paid a salary plus commission. The graph shows possible earnings.

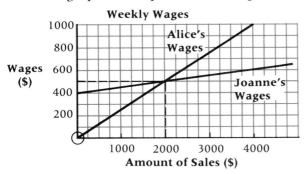

Weekly Wages

(a) What weekly salary is Joanne guaranteed?
(b) What rate of commission does Joanne earn?
(c) What rate of commission does Alice earn?
(d) For what amount of sales does each person earn the same wage?
(e) For sales of $1000, how much less than Joanne does Alice earn?
(f) For $3500 in sales, how much more than Joanne does Alice earn?

6. Al earns a straight commission and Joe earns a step commission. Use the graph to answer the questions below.

Monthly Wages

(a) For what amount of sales does each person earn the same amount?
(b) What is Al's rate of commission?
(c) What are Joe's rates of step commission?
(d) For sales of $4000, how much more than Joe does Al earn?
(e) For sales of $10 000, how much more than Al does Joe earn?

171

Unit 9 Review

1. In each case, calculate the total wages. Overtime is 1.5 times the regular rate.

	Regular Hours Worked	Regular Hourly Rate	Overtime Hours Worked
(a)	37.5	$11.00	3
(b)	40	$ 7.40	6
(c)	40	$ 9.55	2.5
(d)	37.5	$10.40	4.5
(e)	35	$ 8.65	8

2. Mel works as a carpenter and is paid $15.50/h for a 40 h work week. If he works more than 40 h in one week, Mel is paid for the extra hours at time-and-one-half. Calculate Mel's gross pay for a week in which he works 47.5 h.

3. As a welder, Tony earns $11.90/h for a 37.5 h week, with overtime at time-and-one-half. On a pipeline project, he works 50 h one week and 54.5 h another. Determine his total wages for the 2 week period.

4. Rick works as a waiter in his father's restaurant. In addition to regular pay of $5.20/h for a 40 h week, Rick keeps 65% of all the tips he receives. Calculate his gross pay for a week in which he received $92.30 in tips.

5. Gus is part of a four-member crew that produces metal castings for automobile transmission housing. Each member of the team is paid $10.75/h for a 40 h week, as well as a bonus of $1.80 per casting for the number of castings in excess of 40 produced in an 8 h shift. Calculate Gus' earnings for the week with production figures summarized in the table.

Day of Week	M	T	W	T	F
Number of Castings	43	51	56	48	50

6. Calculate the commission earnings in each case.

	Amount of Sales	Rate of Commission
(a)	$695	35%
(b)	$4263	2.5%
(c)	$598	15%
(d)	$1250	18.5%
(e)	$1300	45%

7. Bette sells furniture in a department store. She's paid $8.45/h for a 37.5 h week plus 5.5% commission. In 1 week Bette's sales were $2855.

   (a) Calculate Bette's total earnings for the week.
   (b) What was Bette's average hourly wage for the week?
   (c) What would her total weekly sales have to be for Bette to earn $500 in 1 week?

8. Calculate each value missing from the table.

	Rate of Commission	Amount of Sales	Commission Earned
(a)	6%	$1475	▨
(b)	12.3%	$978.52	▨
(c)	15%	▨	$ 62.95
(d)	▨	$1968.50	$167.32
(e)	23%	▨	$923.91

9. Step commission on sales is calculated as follows.
  • 5% on the first $2000
  • 8% on the next $3000
  • 12% on sales over $5000

Calculate the total commission for the given sales.

(a) $1875
(b) $2950
(c) $3614
(d) $4590.11
(e) $1268.42
(f) $2216
(g) $5500
(h) $3219.42
(i) $4873.02
(j) $6572.19

10. As salesperson for a farm implement company, Tammy is paid $435/week, plus a step commission based on sales.
  • 1.5% on sales up to $20 000
  • 3% on sales of $20 000 or over

Tammy's sales for the 4 weeks in May are given in the table.

Week	1	2	3	4
Sales	$12 000	$21 650	$3580	$49 500

Calculate Tammy's earnings for each week as well as her total earnings for the month.

11. In each case, calculate:
  • taxable earnings after deduction for C.P.P. and U.I.;
  • income tax payable.

	Gross Weekly Income	Net Claim Code
(a)	$265.03	2
(b)	$238.19	1
(c)	$328.60	3
(d)	$478.32	5
(e)	$389.91	2

12. Cathy's weekly gross pay is $392.07. Her net claim code is 4. If she has only the standard deductions for C.P.P., U.I., and income tax, calculate her net pay.

13. Carl earns $403.50 weekly as a plasterer's apprentice, and has net claim code 1. Determine Carl's takehome pay if he has other deductions of $7.94 in addition to C.P.P., U.I., and income tax.

14. As an auto mechanic, Henri is paid $12.65/h for a 40 h week, and has net claim code 3. His other deductions total $10.08. Calculate Henri's net weekly pay.

15. Fiona is a waitress who earns $215/week and keeps 70% of the tips she receives. She has net claim code 2 and other deductions totalling $4.85, as well as standard deductions for C.P.P., U.I., and income tax. Calculate Fiona's net pay for a week in which she receives $104 in tips.

16. Geraldine is paid a guaranteed salary of $328/week, plus a commission of 4.5%. In 1 week the value of her sales was $2165.17. If Geraldine has net claim code 3 and her other deductions total $14.67, calculate her net pay for the week.

17. Karin earns $250/week, plus a step commission of 3% on the first $5000 of sales, and 5% on sales over $5000. She has deductions for charities ($3.50), health insurance ($1.75), and credit union ($25). If Karin has net claim code 2 and her sales for the week total $7158.40, calculate her net pay for the week.

18. Lois earns a guaranteed weekly salary, plus a step commission based on sales. The graph shows possible earnings.

(a) What weekly salary is Lois guaranteed?
(b) What are Lois' wages for sales of $1000? $1600? $2000?
(c) What sales will give Lois wages of $400? $600? $900?
(d) Calculate the slopes of segments AB and BC. What rate of commission does Lois receive on sales of up to $1000? On sales over $1000?

19. Use the graph to answer the questions below.

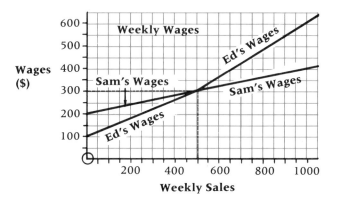

(a) What weekly salary is each person guaranteed?
(b) Which person earns step commission?
(c) For what amount of sales does each person earn the same wage?
(d) What is Sam's rate of commission?
(e) What are Ed's rates of step commission?
(f) For sales of $250, how much less than Sam does Ed earn?
(g) For sales of $1000, how much more than Sam does Ed earn?
(h) Calculate how much each person would earn on sales of $968.17.

174

Unit 10

Calculating Income Tax

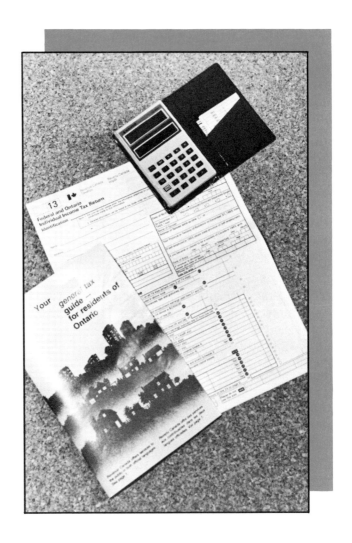

Income Tax and the T4 Slip

As you start to work regularly, you will be responsible for reporting your income each spring. This unit outlines the basics of that responsibility.

The information that is presented here is based on tax regulations in effect in 1984. The basic procedures outlined in this section have been in effect for many years and are unlikely to change in the near future. However, certain amounts do change yearly and certain regulations may have been changed. *To work through this unit and its exercises, get copies of recent tax forms and a General Tax Guide*.

Income tax is just that: a tax on your income. If you are not self-employed your employer deducts the income tax, Canada Pension Plan (C.P.P.) and Unemployment Insurance (U.I.) from your wages. The tax deduction is based on the amount of your wage and your tax category, which can be found from your TD1 form (see page 163).

The federal government first began to collect income tax as a source of funds to support the military during the First World War. Money presently raised from income tax accounts for a large portion of total revenue. People may complain about having to pay taxes, but most realize that it is necessary to collect revenue to fund the many government services, as shown on the allocation diagram.

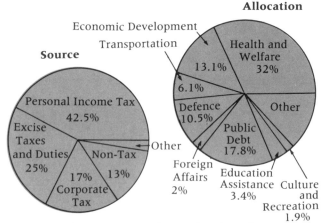

The Canadian system of taxation has the taxpayers volunteer information about their finances when they complete their tax returns. Canadian taxpayers have the right and the responsibility to check the amount of income tax collected from them the previous year.

Not all countries have the same regulations. In the Soviet Union, workers have income tax deducted from their paycheques, but do not file returns to verify that they were correctly assessed. In France, the taxes are not deducted from wages, but instead the government sends out an annual bill to taxpayers based on earnings. The U.S. system of taxation is similar to the Canadian system, but the tax return is far more complicated due to extra deductions and regulations.

A completed tax return provides a check on the amount of tax you should have paid during the year. There are many reasons for the amount of tax paid varying from the amount you should have paid. You may not have worked for the full year, or may have deductions that result in your over-paying your taxes. You may be working at two jobs, or have income from other sources, like bank interest, that results in your being in a higher tax bracket.

One of the items you'll need to file your income tax return is a T4 slip. A T4 slip is an official record of your total taxes and payments made to C.P.P. and U.I. Your employer sends you the T4 slip during January or February. It's a good idea to check your employer's figures against your own records.

Lee works at a hardware store part-time. Here is the T4 slip that Lee's employer sent.

- Box C gives the total income received from the employer for the previous calendar year.
- Box D gives the amount that the employer deducted for Canada Pension Plan. Most working Canadians between the ages of 18 and 70 contribute to this plan. The employer must pay 1.4 times the amount contributed by each employee.
- Box E gives the amount that the employer deducted for Unemployment Insurance. The employer must pay 1.4 times the amount contributed by each employee.
- Box F gives the amount contributed to a pension plan at the place of employment.
- Box G gives the amount that has already been paid in income tax during the taxation year.

As shown on the T4 slip, the employer will often record any fees paid to a union through payroll deduction.

The tax return form is basically very simple. The form is divided into 4 main sections.

• A section where you identify yourself

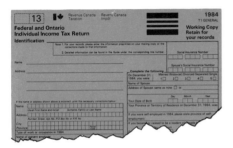

It's important that you are careful when completing the Identification section, so that any payments made to C.P.P. are attributed to you, and also so that any refund due from Revenue Canada can be sent to you.

• A section to report all income

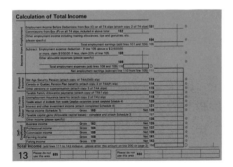

Many Canadian residents have sources of income other than wages, like interest from savings, pensions, commissions, and so on. The first page of the tax return lists the other sources of income that are taxable.

• A section to report all deductions

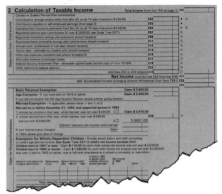

Taxpayers don't pay tax on *all* their income. If money is spent on items like tuition for school, union dues, or child care, some or all of the money spent *may* be eligible as a deduction. It's important to realize that a deduction isn't money that the government is giving you; it's just a reduction in your income that is subject to tax. Read page 2 of a tax return to see some of the deductions that the government allows.

• A section to calculate the refund or balance owing

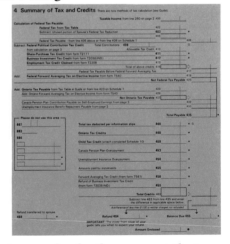

The last page checks the amount that you *should* have paid in taxes for the previous year against what you *did* pay in taxes.

178

Exercise

A 1. The Canadian income tax system is based on "self-assessment." Explain what is meant by self-assessment.

2. What government departments does an employer make contributions to?

3. List some reasons a taxpayer may receive a refund of some or all of last year's income tax.

4. Name the three most important sources of income for the government in addition to income tax.

B 5. Use the Allocation graph on page 176 to answer the following: If the federal government had an annual expenditure of $29 billion, how much was allocated for each of the following (rounded to the nearest thousand dollars)?

(a) Health and Welfare
(b) Defence
(c) Culture and Recreation

Refer to a current tax form to answer Questions 6 and 7.

6. (a) What is the maximum C.P.P. contribution?
(b) What is the maximum Unemployment Insurance premium?

7. Classify as income or deduction.

(a) $40 interest earned on a savings account
(b) $220 tuition paid for a night school course
(c) $5 tip received as a waiter
(d) $400 commission earned as a sales clerk
(e) $45 in compulsory union dues

Refer to a General Tax Guide to find the information for Questions 8, 9, and 10.

8. If you owe tax money, what are the penalties for filing a late return?

9. When is the last date for filing a tax return?

10. Is it possible for anyone to get information from your tax return from the government without your permission? What measures have been take to guarantee confidentiality?

Refer to Lee's T4 slip to answer Questions 11 and 12.

11. (a) How much income tax has Lee paid?
(b) How much did Lee contribute to a company pension plan?
(c) How much did Lee pay to the Canada Pension Plan? How much did Lee's employer pay to C.P.P.?
(d) How much did Lee pay to Unemployment Insurance? How much did Lee's employer pay to U.I.?

12. Look at the entries in boxes C, D, E, F, and G of the T4 slip.

(a) Which of these are deductions and which are income?
(b) Refer to a tax return to find the number of the line on which each would be entered on the tax form.

Calculating Net Income $

Jessie worked at a cinema last year. Here is Jessie's T4 slip.

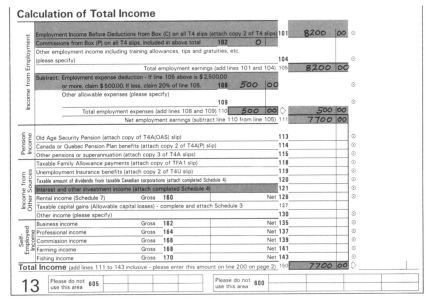

Revenue Canada Taxation	Revenu Canada Impôt	T4-1984 Supplementary - Supplémentaire	STATEMENT OF REMUNERATION PAID ÉTAT DE LA RÉMUNÉRATION PAYÉE

(C) EMPLOYMENT INCOME BEFORE DEDUCTIONS — 8200 00 — REVENUS D'EMPLOI AVANT RETENUES

(D) EMPLOYEE'S PENSION CONTRIBUTION CANADA PLAN — 111 00 / QUEBEC PLAN — DU CANADA / DU QUÉBEC COTISATION DE PENSION (EMPLOYÉ)

(E) U.I. PREMIUM — 141 00 — PRIME D'A.-C.

(F) REGISTERED PENSION PLAN CONTRIBUTION — 200 00 — COTISATIONS RÉGIME ENREGISTRÉ DE PENSIONS

(G) INCOME TAX DEDUCTED — 810 00 — IMPÔT SUR LE REVENU RETENU

(H) U.I. INSURABLE EARNINGS — GAINS ASSURABLES A.-C.

(I) C.P.P. PENSIONABLE EARNINGS — GAINS OUVRANT DROIT À PENSIONS - R.P.C.

(J) EXEMPT — EXONÉRATION

BOX (C) AMOUNT INCLUDES ANY AMOUNTS IN BOXES (K), (L), (M), (N), (O) AND (P) — LE MONTANT DE LA CASE (C) COMPREND TOUS LES MONTANTS FIGURANT AUX CASES (K), (L), (M), (N), (O), ET (P)

(K) BOARD AND LODGING / TAXABLE ALLOWANCES AND BENEFITS — AVANTAGES IMPOSABLES / NOURRITURE ET LOGEMENT

(L) RENT FREE AND LOW RENT HOUSING — LOGEMENT GRATUIT OU À COÛT MODIQUE

(M) PERSONAL USE OF EMPLOYER'S AUTO — USAGE PERSONNEL DE L'AUTO DE L'EMPLOYEUR

(N) INTEREST FREE AND LOW INTEREST LOANS — PRÊTS SANS INTÉRÊT OU À FAIBLE INTÉRÊT

(O) OTHER TAXABLE ALLOW. AND BENEFITS — AUTRES AVANTAGES IMPOSABLES

(P) EMPLOYMENT COMMISSIONS — COMMISSIONS D'EMPLOI

(Q) PENSION PLAN REGISTRATION NUMBER — N° D'ENREGISTREMENT RÉGIME DE PENSIONS

(R) PAYMENTS TO DPSP — PAIEMENTS À UN RPDB

(S) CHARITABLE DONATIONS — DONS DE CHARITÉ

(T) UNION DUES — 60 00 — COTISATIONS SYNDICALES

(A) PROVINCE OF EMPLOYMENT — ONT — PROVINCE D'EMPLOI

(B) SOCIAL INSURANCE NUMBER — 734 120 567 — N° D'ASSURANCE SOCIALE

(U) EMPLOYEE NO. — N° DE L'EMPLOYÉ

EMPLOYEE: SURNAME FIRST (in capital letters), USUAL FIRST NAME AND INITIALS AND FULL ADDRESS — EMPLOYÉ: NOM DE FAMILLE D'ABORD (en capitales), PRÉNOM USUEL ET ADRESSE COMPLÈTE

→ JESSIE JONES

NAME AND ADDRESS OF EMPLOYER OR PAYOR — NOM ET ADRESSE DE L'EMPLOYEUR OU DU PAYEUR

ABC CINEMAS INC.

• Attach to your 1984 Income Tax Return SEE INFORMATION ON REVERSE

• Annexer à votre déclaration d'impôt sur le revenu de 1984 VOIR LES RENSEIGNEMENTS AU VERSO

2

After completing the Identification section of the tax return, Jessie's next step is to calculate Total Income on page 1.

Total Earnings from T4 slips

- Record the total paid in wages and commissions, from all sources of employment.
- This amount is recorded in Box C of the T4 slip.

Other Employment Income

- If tips are earned, keep a record of the amount earned and report it as income.
- There are penalties for people who do not report all earned income.

Employment Expense Deduction

- The amount of this deduction may vary from what is shown.
- This deduction covers expenses like travelling to and from work, or dry cleaning work clothes.

Interest Income

- The interest earned from savings accounts, bonds, and so on, is income and must be reported.

Calculation of Total Income

Income from Employment

Employment Income Before Deductions from Box (C) on all T4 slips (attach copy 2 of T4 slips)	101	8200 00
Commissions from Box (P) on all T4 slips, included in above total	102	0
Other employment income including training allowances, tips and gratuities, etc. (please specify)	104	
Total employment earnings (add lines 101 and 104)	105	8200 00
Subtract: Employment expense deduction - If line 105 above is $2,500.00 or more, claim $500.00. If less, claim 20% of line 105.	108	500 00
Other allowable expenses (please specify)	109	
Total employment expenses (add lines 108 and 109)	110	500 00 / 500 00
Net employment earnings (subtract line 110 from line 105)	111	7700 00

Pension Income

Old Age Security Pension (attach copy of T4A(OAS) slip)	113	
Canada or Quebec Pension Plan benefits (attach copy 2 of T4A(P) slip)	114	
Other pensions or superannuation (attach copy 3 of T4A slips)	115	

Income from Other Sources

Taxable Family Allowance payments (attach copy of TFA1 slip)	118	
Unemployment Insurance benefits (attach copy 2 of T4U slip)	119	
Taxable amount of dividends from taxable Canadian corporations (attach completed Schedule 4)	120	
Interest and other investment income (attach completed Schedule 4)	121	
Rental income (Schedule 7) Gross 160	Net 126	
Taxable capital gains (Allowable capital losses) - complete and attach Schedule 3	127	
Other income (please specify)	130	

Self-Employed Income

Business income Gross 162	Net 135	
Professional income Gross 164	Net 137	
Commission income Gross 166	Net 139	
Farming income Gross 168	Net 141	
Fishing income Gross 170	Net 143	

Total Income (add lines 111 to 143 inclusive - please enter this amount on line 200 on page 2) 150 — 7700 00

13 Please do not use this area 605

Please do not use this area 600

180

There are a number of deductions that can be claimed on page 2 of the tax return before calculating Net Income.

Contributions to C.P.P.
- The total amount Jessie paid is in Box D of the T4 slip.

Unemployment Insurance
- The total amount paid is in Box E of the T4 slip.

Registered Pension Plan
- Jessie enters the amount paid into a company plan.

Union Dues
- This is the annual membership fee to a trade union or association of public servants.

2 Calculation of Taxable Income

Total Income (from line 150 on page 1) 200 — 7700 00

Deductions from Total Income			
Canada or Quebec Pension Plan contributions			
Contributions through employment from Box (D) on all T4 slips (maximum $338.40)	202	111 00	• ⊙
Contribution payable on self-employed earnings (from page 3)	203		•
Unemployment Insurance premiums from Box (E) on all T4 slips (maximum $508.56)	204	141 00	• ⊙
Registered pension plan contributions (if over $3,500.00, see Guide "Line 207")	207	200 00	⊙
Registered retirement savings plan premiums (attach receipts)	208		⊙
Registered home ownership savings plan contributions (attach receipts)	211		⊙
Annual union, professional or like dues (attach receipts)	212	60 00	⊙
Tuition fees - claimable by student only (attach receipts)	213		⊙
Child care expenses (complete and attach Schedule 5)	214		⊙
Allowable business investment losses	217		⊙
Indexed Security Investment Plan - allowable capital losses (attach copy of form T5 ISIP)	218		⊙
Other deductions (please specify)	222		⊙
Add lines 202 to 222 inclusive 223	512 00	▷	512 00

Net Income (subtract line 223 from line 200) 224 — 7188 00

Tuition Fees
- There are restrictions on the minimum tuition allowed.
- Only the student may claim the deduction even though someone else may have paid the fees.

Net Income determines whether the taxpayer can be claimed as a Dependant. If the taxpayer has a net income below $3870 (this amount is subject to change) then the taxpayer is designated as a dependant, which may qualify a parent, spouse, or guardian for a tax deduction on their return.

With a Net Income of $7188, Jessie is classified as a non-dependant.

Example 1

The following information is given on Joyce's T4 slip.

- Total Income $2300.00
- C.P.P. $ 11.50
- U.I. Payments $ 13.00
- Union Dues $ 35.00

Calculate Joyce's Net Income.

Total Earnings from T4 slip	$2300.00
Other Employment Income	—
Total Employment Earnings	$2300.00

Employment Expense Deduction	
20% × $2300 = $460	−460.00

Net Employment Earnings	$1840.00
Other Income	—
Total Income	$1840.00

C.P.P.	$11.50
U.I. Payment	$13.00
Union Dues	$35.00
Total	$59.50
	−59.50

Net Income	$1780.50

Joyce has a net income of $1780.50 and is, therefore, a dependant.

Exercise

B 1. Determine the Employment Expense Deduction and the Net Employment Earnings given each of the following Total Employment Earnings.

(a) $800
(b) $1400
(c) $2200
(d) $6500
(e) $56 000

2. Calculate the net income for each of the following.

(a) George received the following information on his T4 slip.

Total Income	$1500.00
C.P.P.	—
U.I. Payment	$8.00

(b) Betty received the following information on her T4 slip.

Total Income	$3200.00
C.P.P.	$25.20
U.I. Payment	$41.00
Union Dues	$66.00

(c) Fran received the following information on her T4 slip.

Total Income	$2050.00
C.P.P.	$5.00
U.I. Payment	$11.00

Fran also earned approximately $420 from tips at work.

(d) Jack received the following information from 2 part-time jobs.

	Job #1	Job #2
Total Income	$1500.00	$4000.00
C.P.P.	—	$39.60
U.I. Payment	$12.00	$70.00
Union Dues		$95.00

3. The answers to the following questions can be found in the Guide Book or the tax return.

(a) What is the only deduction before calculating Total Income on the tax return?
(b) Name 5 sources of income, other than wages and tips.
(c) Name 4 sources of income that are not taxable.
(d) Bill's father paid for Bill's tuition to college. Who claims the tuition deduction, Bill or his father?
(e) What is the minimum amount of tuition that may be claimed as a deduction?

Calculating Tax Payable

Once Jessie has calculated Net Income, there are a number of further deductions that can be subtracted before arriving at the Taxable Income.

Basic Personal Exemption
- Every taxpayer can claim this exemption (the amount may vary from year to year).
- There are further exemptions possible for taxpayers who have dependents, such as children, spouses, and so on.

Medical/Charity Deduction
- To claim this deduction the calculation must be completed and all receipts attached to the tax return.

Interest Deduction
- A deduction is available equal to the amount of interest, dividends, and capital gains claimed as income on page 1 of the return.
- The maximum deduction is $1000. For many taxpayers, interest from a bank account appears as income on page 1, and the same amount appears as a deduction on page 2.

Education Deduction
- Students may claim a $50/month deduction for each month in which they were in full-time attendance, at a university or college.

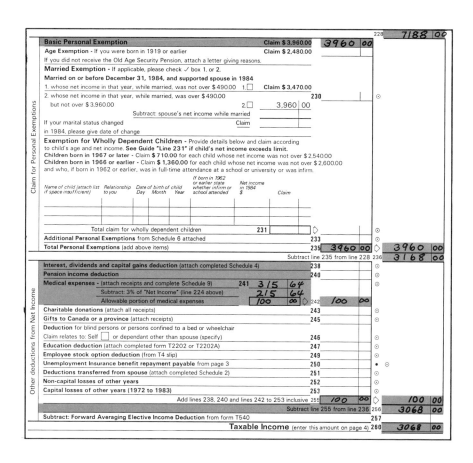

The amount called Taxable Income is the income received during the year on which income tax must be paid.

The last page is used to calculate a refund or balance due.

The tables at the back of the Guide Book are used to find the Federal and Provincial Tax Payable, based on the amount of Taxable Income. These figures vary from year to year.

4 Summary of Tax and Credits
There are two methods of tax calculation (see Guide).

Taxable Income from line 260 on page 2	400	**3068**	00

Calculation of Federal Tax Payable:

Federal Tax from Tax Table	402	**222**	00
Subtract: Unused portion of Spouse's Federal Tax Reduction	403	•	
	405		
Federal Tax Payable - from line 405 above or from line 406 on Schedule 1	406	**222**	00

from tables based on Taxable Income of $3068

Subtract: **Federal Political Contribution Tax Credit** Total Contributions	409		⊙	
from calculation on page 3	Allowable Tax Credit	410		
Share-Purchase Tax Credit from form T2111	411	•	
Business Investment Tax Credit from form T2038 (IND.)	412	•	
Employment Tax Credit Claimed from form T2208	413		
Total of above credits	416		◇
Federal Tax Payable Before Federal Forward Averaging Tax	417		
Add: **Federal Forward Averaging Tax on Elective Income** from form T540	418		
Net Federal Tax Payable	420	**222**	00

Add: **Ontario Tax Payable** from Tax Table in Guide or from line 423 on Schedule 1	423	**203**	90
Add: Ontario Forward Averaging Tax on Elective Income from form T540	426		
Net Ontario Tax Payable	427	**203**	90 ◇
Canada Pension Plan Contribution Payable on Self-Employed Earnings from page 3	432		
Unemployment Insurance Benefit Repayment Payable from page 3	433		
Total Payable	435	**425**	90 •

Box G of Jessie's T4

Many provinces offer tax credits.

Please do not use this area

667
683
684

Total tax deducted per information slips	440	**810**	00 • ⊙
Ontario Tax Credits	448	•	
Child Tax Credit (attach completed Schedule 10)	450	•	
Canada Pension Plan Overpayment	453	•	
Unemployment Insurance Overpayment	454	•	
Amounts paid by instalments	455	•	
Forward Averaging Tax Credit (from form T581)	458	•	
Refund of Business Investment Tax Credit (from form T2038-IND.)	459	•	
Total Credits	463	**810**	00 ◇ **810** 00

Subtract line 463 from line 435 and enter the difference in applicable space below.
384 10

810.00 – 425.90

A difference of less than $1.00 is neither charged nor refunded.

Refund 464	**384** 10 •	Balance Due 465		•

Refund transferred to spouse
468 •

Since Total Credits is greater than Total Payable, a refund is claimed.

IMPORTANT: The inside front cover of your guide tells you when to expect your refund.

Amount Enclosed •

Please attach cheque or money order **payable to the Receiver General. Do not mail cash.**
Payment is due not later than April 30, 1985.

Name and address of any individual or firm, other than the taxpayer, who has prepared this return for compensation.
Name
Address
Telephone

I hereby certify that the information given in this return and in any documents attached is true, correct and complete in every respect and fully discloses my income from all sources.

Please sign here *Jessie Jones*
Date **APRIL 17/85** Telephone **293-8141**

It is a serious offence to make a false return.

Remember to sign the tax return!

Form authorized and prescribed by order of the Minister of National Revenue for purposes of Part I of the Income Tax Act, Part I of the Canada Pension Plan and Part VIII of the Unemployment Insurance Act, 1971.

Privacy Act Personal Information Bank number RC-T-P20

Example 1

Calculate any refund or balance owing given the following information.
- Net Income is $6400.00.
- Total tax deducted, as given on T4 slip, is $350.00.

The taxpayer is single and has made a charitable donation of $200.

• Net Income		$6400.00
• Basic Personal Exemption	$3770.00	
• Medical/Charity Deduction	200.00	
Total	$3970.00	3970.00
Taxable Income		$2430.00

- Federal Tax Payable — from tax table → $ 70.00
- Provincial Tax Payable — from tax table → 130.30
- Total Payable — $200.30
- Total Credits — 350.00
- Difference — $149.70

Since Total Credits is more than Total Payable, a refund of $149.70 is claimed.

Example 2

Determine the Medical/Charity Deduction for Sam who has $120 in medical expenses and $140 donated to charity, with net income of $5000.

• Medical Expenses	$120
• Subtract 3% of Net Income 3% × $5000	− 150
• Allowable Portion	$ 0 _(cannot be negative)_
• Add Charitable Donation	140
Total	$140

The Medical/Charity deduction is $140.

Exercise

B 1. Use the tables in the Guide Book to find the Federal and Provincial Tax Payable given the following Taxable Incomes.

(a) $0 (d) $7532
(b) $1255 (e) $12 379
(c) $4302 (f) $28 450

2. Determine the amount of the Medical/Charity Deduction for each of the following cases.

(a) $55 in medical expenses (net income is $1000.)
(b) one charitable donation of $175
(c) $65 donated to one charity and $85 to another
(d) $300 in medical expenses (net income is $80 000)
(e) $400 in allowable medical expenses (net income $6500) and $80 donated to various charities
(f) $155 in allowable medical expenses (net income $3000) and $25 donated to a charity

3. Determine any refund or balance owing given the following information. Complete for a single person with no extra deductions.

	Net Income	Total Tax Deducted
(a)	$ 7 300.00	$ 450.00
(b)	$ 6 800.00	$ 32.00
(c)	$ 2 300.00	$ 89.00
(d)	$ 4 150.00	$ 0.00
(e)	$17 050.00	$1250.00
(f)	$31 400.00	$7320.00

Completing a Tax Return

The following cases are meant to be completed using up-to-date tax forms. It should be noted that many provinces offer provincial tax credits (at present, credits are given by Manitoba, Ontario, Alberta, Nova Scotia, British Columbia, the Yukon, and the North West Territories). Your teacher may include extra information pertaining to a particular provincial tax credit.

Case 1

This is the first tax return for Harvey Wallace, who was born August 11, 1970 and works part-time at a local gas station. Harvey is a student at J.W. Dyck Secondary School. He received the T4 slip shown below from his employer. Complete Harvey's tax return.

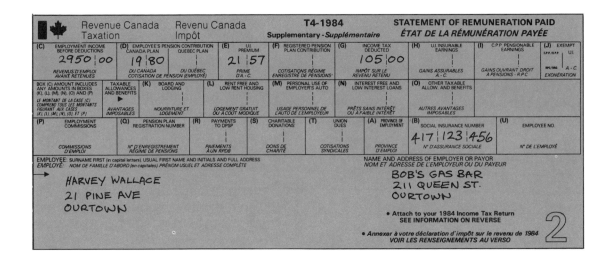

Case 2

Gina, born March 10, 1968, is a recent graduate of Hillside High School and is presently working at two jobs. Gina is a waitress at Minnie's Kitchen where she earned wages shown on the T4 slip below and also earned approximately $600 in tips. Gina also works on weekends as a gas station attendant at G and G Garage, and the T4 slip for this job is also shown below. Gina also attended night school for 4 months and paid $320 in tuition. Complete Gina's tax return.

Revenue Canada / Taxation — Revenu Canada / Impôt	T4-1984 Supplementary - Supplémentaire	STATEMENT OF REMUNERATION PAID / ÉTAT DE LA RÉMUNÉRATION PAYÉE

Slip 1 — Minnie's Kitchen

(C) EMPLOYMENT INCOME BEFORE DEDUCTIONS	(D) EMPLOYEE'S PENSION CONTRIBUTION CANADA PLAN / QUEBEC PLAN	(E) U.I. PREMIUM	(F) REGISTERED PENSION PLAN CONTRIBUTION	(G) INCOME TAX DEDUCTED	(H) U.I. INSURABLE EARNINGS	(I) C.P.P. PENSIONABLE EARNINGS	(J) EXEMPT
4340 00	45 70	61 82		210 00			

(B) SOCIAL INSURANCE NUMBER: 423 789 155

EMPLOYEE: GINA LEE

NAME AND ADDRESS OF EMPLOYER OR PAYOR: MINNIES KITCHEN

• Attach to your 1984 Income Tax Return — SEE INFORMATION ON REVERSE
• Annexer à votre déclaration d'impôt sur le revenu de 1984 — VOIR LES RENSEIGNEMENTS AU VERSO

Slip 2 — G and G Garage

(C) EMPLOYMENT INCOME BEFORE DEDUCTIONS	(D) EMPLOYEE'S PENSION CONTRIBUTION CANADA PLAN / QUEBEC PLAN	(E) U.I. PREMIUM	(F) REGISTERED PENSION PLAN CONTRIBUTION	(G) INCOME TAX DEDUCTED	(H) U.I. INSURABLE EARNINGS	(I) C.P.P. PENSIONABLE EARNINGS	(J) EXEMPT
1740 00		19 50		55 00			

(B) SOCIAL INSURANCE NUMBER: 423 789 155

EMPLOYEE: GINA LEE

NAME AND ADDRESS OF EMPLOYER OR PAYOR: G AND G GARAGE

• Attach to your 1984 Income Tax Return — SEE INFORMATION ON REVERSE
• Annexer à votre déclaration d'impôt sur le revenu de 1984 — VOIR LES RENSEIGNEMENTS AU VERSO

187

Case 3

Terry Banner is single and was born December 2, 1967. Terry works full-time as a salesman at Harper's Department Store earning both wages and commission. The T4 slip is shown below. In addition, Terry has receipts for $205 in allowable medical expenses and a receipt for a $130 donation to the United Appeal. Complete Terry's tax return.

Revenue Canada Taxation	Revenu Canada Impôt		T4-1984 Supplementary - Supplémentaire		STATEMENT OF REMUNERATION PAID ÉTAT DE LA RÉMUNÉRATION PAYÉE				
(C) EMPLOYMENT INCOME BEFORE DEDUCTIONS 17420.00	(D) EMPLOYEE'S PENSION CONTRIBUTION CANADA PLAN / QUEBEC PLAN 300.60	(E) U.I. PREMIUM 460.72	(F) REGISTERED PENSION PLAN CONTRIBUTION 340.00	(G) INCOME TAX DEDUCTED 1940.00	(H) U.I. INSURABLE EARNINGS	(I) C.P.P. PENSIONABLE EARNINGS	(J) EXEMPT
REVENUS D'EMPLOI AVANT RETENUES	DU CANADA / DU QUÉBEC COTISATION DE PENSION (EMPLOYÉ)	PRIME D'A.-C.	COTISATIONS RÉGIME ENREGISTRÉ DE PENSIONS	IMPÔT SUR LE REVENU RETENU	GAINS ASSURABLES A.-C.	GAINS OUVRANT DROIT À PENSIONS - R.P.C.	EXONÉRATION
BOX (C) AMOUNT INCLUDES ANY AMOUNTS IN BOXES (K), (L), (M), (N), (O) AND (P). LE MONTANT DE LA CASE (C) COMPREND TOUS LES MONTANTS FIGURANT AUX CASES (K), (L), (M), (N), (O), ET (P)	TAXABLE ALLOWANCES AND BENEFITS ► AVANTAGES IMPOSABLES	(K) BOARD AND LODGING NOURRITURE ET LOGEMENT	(L) RENT FREE AND LOW RENT HOUSING LOGEMENT GRATUIT OU À COÛT MODIQUE	(M) PERSONAL USE OF EMPLOYER'S AUTO USAGE PERSONNEL DE L'AUTO DE L'EMPLOYEUR	(N) INTEREST FREE AND LOW INTEREST LOANS PRÊTS SANS INTÉRÊT OU À FAIBLE INTÉRÊT	(O) OTHER TAXABLE ALLOW. AND BENEFITS AUTRES AVANTAGES IMPOSABLES	
(P) EMPLOYMENT COMMISSIONS 2500.00 COMMISSIONS D'EMPLOI	(Q) PENSION PLAN REGISTRATION NUMBER 2951X4 N° D'ENREGISTREMENT RÉGIME DE PENSIONS	(R) PAYMENTS TO DPSP PAIEMENTS À UN RPDB	(S) CHARITABLE DONATIONS DONS DE CHARITÉ	(T) UNION DUES 120.00 COTISATIONS SYNDICALES	(A) PROVINCE OF EMPLOYMENT PROVINCE D'EMPLOI	(B) SOCIAL INSURANCE NUMBER 464 504 349 N° D'ASSURANCE SOCIALE	(U) EMPLOYEE NO. N° DE L'EMPLOYÉ

EMPLOYEE: SURNAME FIRST (in capital letters), USUAL FIRST NAME AND INITIALS AND FULL ADDRESS
EMPLOYÉ: NOM DE FAMILLE D'ABORD (en capitales), PRÉNOM USUEL ET ADRESSE COMPLÈTE

→ TERRY BANNER

NAME AND ADDRESS OF EMPLOYER OR PAYOR
NOM ET ADRESSE DE L'EMPLOYEUR OU DU PAYEUR

HARPERS DEPT. STORE

• Attach to your 1984 Income Tax Return
SEE INFORMATION ON REVERSE

• Annexer à votre déclaration d'impôt sur le revenu de 1984
VOIR LES RENSEIGNEMENTS AU VERSO

2

Case 4

Pat McTavish, born May 3, 1964, recently graduated from college and now works as a computer programmer. The T4 slip is shown below. Pat attended college full-time for 5 months last year and paid $700 in tuition and $150 for textbooks. Interest amounting to $89 was earned from Pat's savings account. Pat also won $100 from a provincial lottery. Complete Pat's tax return.

Revenue Canada Taxation	Revenu Canada Impôt		T4-1984 Supplementary - Supplémentaire		STATEMENT OF REMUNERATION PAID ÉTAT DE LA RÉMUNÉRATION PAYÉE				
(C) EMPLOYMENT INCOME BEFORE DEDUCTIONS 13650.00	(D) EMPLOYEE'S PENSION CONTRIBUTION CANADA PLAN / QUEBEC PLAN 197.00	(E) U.I. PREMIUM 265.00	(F) REGISTERED PENSION PLAN CONTRIBUTION 205.00	(G) INCOME TAX DEDUCTED 2400.00	(H) U.I. INSURABLE EARNINGS	(I) C.P.P. PENSIONABLE EARNINGS	(J) EXEMPT
REVENUS D'EMPLOI AVANT RETENUES	DU CANADA / DU QUÉBEC COTISATION DE PENSION (EMPLOYÉ)	PRIME D'A.-C.	COTISATIONS RÉGIME ENREGISTRÉ DE PENSIONS	IMPÔT SUR LE REVENU RETENU	GAINS ASSURABLES A.-C.	GAINS OUVRANT DROIT À PENSIONS - R.P.C.	EXONÉRATION
BOX (C) AMOUNT INCLUDES ANY AMOUNTS IN BOXES (K), (L), (M), (N), (O) AND (P). LE MONTANT DE LA CASE (C) COMPREND TOUS LES MONTANTS FIGURANT AUX CASES (K), (L), (M), (N), (O), ET (P)	TAXABLE ALLOWANCES AND BENEFITS AVANTAGES IMPOSABLES	(K) BOARD AND LODGING NOURRITURE ET LOGEMENT	(L) RENT FREE AND LOW RENT HOUSING LOGEMENT GRATUIT OU À COÛT MODIQUE	(M) PERSONAL USE OF EMPLOYER'S AUTO USAGE PERSONNEL DE L'AUTO DE L'EMPLOYEUR	(N) INTEREST FREE AND LOW INTEREST LOANS PRÊTS SANS INTÉRÊT OU À FAIBLE INTÉRÊT	(O) OTHER TAXABLE ALLOW. AND BENEFITS AUTRES AVANTAGES IMPOSABLES	
(P) EMPLOYMENT COMMISSIONS COMMISSIONS D'EMPLOI	(Q) PENSION PLAN REGISTRATION NUMBER N° D'ENREGISTREMENT RÉGIME DE PENSIONS	(R) PAYMENTS TO DPSP PAIEMENTS À UN RPDB	(S) CHARITABLE DONATIONS DONS DE CHARITÉ	(T) UNION DUES COTISATIONS SYNDICALES	(A) PROVINCE OF EMPLOYMENT PROVINCE D'EMPLOI	(B) SOCIAL INSURANCE NUMBER 217 987 654 N° D'ASSURANCE SOCIALE	(U) EMPLOYEE NO. N° DE L'EMPLOYÉ

EMPLOYEE: SURNAME FIRST (in capital letters), USUAL FIRST NAME AND INITIALS AND FULL ADDRESS
EMPLOYÉ: NOM DE FAMILLE D'ABORD (en capitales), PRÉNOM USUEL ET ADRESSE COMPLÈTE

→ PAT McTAVISH

NAME AND ADDRESS OF EMPLOYER OR PAYOR
NOM ET ADRESSE DE L'EMPLOYEUR OU DU PAYEUR

CREATIVE COMPUTERS

• Attach to your 1984 Income Tax Return
SEE INFORMATION ON REVERSE

• Annexer à votre déclaration d'impôt sur le revenu de 1984
VOIR LES RENSEIGNEMENTS AU VERSO

2

Income Tax Consultant

Many taxpayers rely on tax consultants to help complete their tax returns. The tables in the tax guide book provide information about the tax payable on taxable income up to approximately $30 000. If the taxpayer's taxable income is above this amount you or a tax consultant will calculate the tax payable. Revenue Canada provides Schedule 1 for this purpose. A simplified Schedule 1 is used below.

Example 1

Determine the 1983 federal tax payable if a taxpayer's taxable income is $40 000.

The 1983 rates of Federal Income Tax are shown below. The rates for the present year can be found on the bottom of Schedule 1 in your tax guide.

1983 Rates of Federal Income Tax

Taxable Income	Tax	
$1,179 or less	6%	
1,179	$ 71 + 16% on next	$1,179
2,358	259 + 17% on next	2,358
4,716	660 + 18% on next	2,358
7,074	1,085 + 19% on next	4,716
$11,790	1,981 + 20% on next	4,716
16,506	2,924 + 23% on next	4,716
21,222	4,009 + 25% on next	11,790
33,012	6,956 + 30% on next	23,580
56,592	14,030 + 34% on remainder	

First, find the largest taxable income in the chart that is smaller than $40 000. This taxpayer is in the "tax bracket" associated with $33 012.

Basic Federal Tax
$$= \$6956 + 30\% \times (\$40\,000 - \$33\,012)$$
$$= \$6956 + 30\% \times \$6988$$
$$= \$6956 + \$2096.40$$
$$= \$9052.40$$

The taxpayer owes $9052.40 in basic federal tax. Often the federal government will give tax reductions. In 1983, the government offered a $200 reduction on this basic Federal Tax. The provincial tax owing will vary from province to province. It is a stated percentage of the basic federal tax (varying from 38% to 60%).

Exercise

1. Determine the 1983 Basic Federal Tax owing on each of the following taxable incomes.
   (a) $45 000
   (b) $72 000
   (c) $32 000

2. Repeat Question 1, except use the most recent tax rates.

3. Calculate the Basic Federal Tax on each of the following taxable incomes, using the most recent tax rates. Compare your answers to those given in the tax guide.

   (a) $23 014
   (b) $9000

Unit 10 Review

1. Classify the following as income or deduction.

   (a) $60 paid in Unemployment Insurance
   (b) $700 collected in Unemployment Insurance when temporarily out of work
   (c) $350 earned from tips as a waiter
   (d) $120 tuition fee for a night school course
   (e) $77 interest earned from a savings account
   (f) $250 paid to a company pension plan

2. Below is Teri's T4 slip from her employer. This was Teri's only source of income.

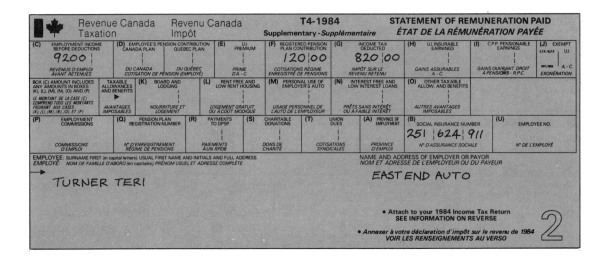

   (a) Calculate the Employment Expense Deduction.
   (b) Calculate Teri's Total Income.
   (c) Find the total of all deductions that are possible before determining Net Income.
   (d) What is Teri's Net Income?
   (e) Is Teri a dependant?
   (f) Determine Teri's income after deducting her Basic Personal Exemption.
   (g) If Teri had $130 in medical expenses and contributed $60 to a registered charity, determine her Medical/Charity Deduction.
   (h) Calculate Teri's Taxable Income.
   (i) Determine Teri's Total Tax Payable.
   (j) Determine any refund or balance due.

3. Complete a tax return for Ben Celari.

Ben was born October 6, 1967 and works full-time as a short-order cook at a local restaurant. As well as the income shown below, Ben earned $450 by sharing in the tips given to the waiters and waitresses. Ben also paid $240 tuition for a college-level course taken at night.

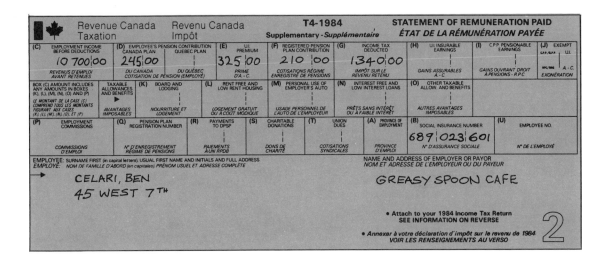

4. Paola Perelli is single and was born November 5, 1966. She presently works during the day as a car salesperson earning wages and commission, but often works on weekends as a part-time cab driver. The T4 slips for both jobs are shown below. In addition, Paola paid $370 in allowable medical expenses and made a $98 donation to a local charity. Complete Paola's tax return.

Revenue Canada Taxation	Revenu Canada Impôt			**T4-1984** Supplementary - *Supplémentaire*			**STATEMENT OF REMUNERATION PAID** *ÉTAT DE LA RÉMUNÉRATION PAYÉE*		

(C) EMPLOYMENT INCOME BEFORE DEDUCTIONS: 16 500 00
(D) EMPLOYEE'S PENSION CONTRIBUTION CANADA PLAN: 338 40 QUEBEC PLAN:
(E) U.I. PREMIUM: 508 56
(F) REGISTERED PENSION PLAN CONTRIBUTION: 700 00
(G) INCOME TAX DEDUCTED: 1890 00
(H) U.I. INSURABLE EARNINGS:
(I) C.P.P. PENSIONABLE EARNINGS:
(J) EXEMPT

(P) EMPLOYMENT COMMISSIONS: 3500.00
(T) UNION DUES: 400 00
(B) SOCIAL INSURANCE NUMBER: 901 522 391

EMPLOYEE: PERELLI, PAOLA
1313 KENT AVENUE
METROPOLIS

NAME AND ADDRESS OF EMPLOYER OR PAYOR: JIMMY OLSEN USED CARS

• Attach to your 1984 Income Tax Return SEE INFORMATION ON REVERSE
• Annexer à votre déclaration d'impôt sur le revenu de 1984 VOIR LES RENSEIGNEMENTS AU VERSO

2

Revenue Canada Taxation	Revenu Canada Impôt			**T4-1984** Supplementary - *Supplémentaire*			**STATEMENT OF REMUNERATION PAID** *ÉTAT DE LA RÉMUNÉRATION PAYÉE*		

(C) EMPLOYMENT INCOME BEFORE DEDUCTIONS: 5600 00
(D) EMPLOYEE'S PENSION CONTRIBUTION CANADA PLAN: 102 00 QUEBEC PLAN:
(E) U.I. PREMIUM: 130 00
(F) REGISTERED PENSION PLAN CONTRIBUTION:
(G) INCOME TAX DEDUCTED: 240 00
(H) U.I. INSURABLE EARNINGS:
(I) C.P.P. PENSIONABLE EARNINGS:
(J) EXEMPT

(B) SOCIAL INSURANCE NUMBER: 901 522 391

EMPLOYEE: PERELLI PAOLA

NAME AND ADDRESS OF EMPLOYER OR PAYOR: KRYPTON CAB CO. METROPOLIS

• Attach to your 1984 Income Tax Return SEE INFORMATION ON REVERSE
• Annexer à votre déclaration d'impôt sur le revenu de 1984 VOIR LES RENSEIGNEMENTS AU VERSO

2

Unit 11

Spending Money

Instalment Buying
Calculating the Instalment Payment
Calculating the True Interest Rate
Retail Buying
Unit 11 Review

Instalment Buying

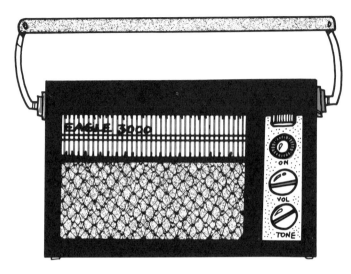

How much more than the cash price of $129.95 must you pay if you agree to buy the radio for $10 down plus $11.15/month for 12 months?

- Value of 12 monthly
  payments at $11.15 each
  is $11.15 × 12. $133.80
- Down payment   10.00
- Instalment price $143.80
- Cash price   129.95
- Difference $ 13.85

You would pay $13.85 more than the cash price.

Paying for an article on a regular monthly basis is *instalment buying*.

Purchasing by instalments costs more than paying in cash. The additional cost is called the *finance charge*.

The finance charge in the example above is $13.85.

Example 1

Chico buys a stereo that has a cash price of $935.00. He agrees to pay 10% down and $42.00/month for 24 months.

- Calculate the finance charge.

Value of 24 Instalment Payments is 24 × $42.	$1008.80
Down Payment is 10% of $935.00.	93.50
Instalment Price	$1101.50
Cash Price	935.00
Finance Charge	$ 166.50

- By what percent is the instalment price more than the cash price?

$$\frac{\text{Finance Charge}}{\text{Cash Price}} \times 100\%$$
$$= \frac{\$166.50}{\$935.00} \times 100\%$$
$$= 17.8\%$$

The finance charge on Chico's purchase would be $166.50.
The instalment price is 17.8% more than the cash price.

Use the following formulas to calculate instalment price and finance charge.

Instalment Price	=	Down Payment	+	Value of Instalment Payments

Finance Charge	=	Instalment Price	−	Cash Price

Exercise

A **1.** Which method of instalment buying would be the more expensive?
 • A small down payment with payments spread over 2 a
 • A large down payment with payments spread over 1 a
Explain.

2. Why might a company encourage you to buy an article by instalment?

3. State the instalment price in each case.

(a) $60 down, $10/week for 8 weeks
(b) $100 down, $50/month for 12 months

4. Calculate the instalment price and finance charge for each of the following.

Item	Cash Price	Instalment Terms
(a) Bicycle	$175	$25 down, $26.72/month for 6 months
(b) Radio	$240	$40 down, $18.38/month for 12 months
(c) Tape Recorder	$450	$100 down, $22.05/month for 18 months

5. A portable stereo can be purchased for $190 cash or pay $40 down and make 12 monthly payments of $13.65.

(a) Calculate the finance charge.
(b) By what percent is the instalment price more than the cash price?

6. Determine the missing information in each case.

Item	Cash Price	Finance Charge	Instalment Terms
(a) Portable Stereo	$190	$30	$10 down, ▢/month for 6 months
(b) Bicycle	$220	$25	$50 down, $39/month for ▢ months
(c) Guitar	$300	$48	$60 down, ▢/month for 18 months
(d) Television	$600	$102	$150 down $46/month for ▢ months

7. Brenda can buy a used motorcycle for $1500 cash or pay a down payment of 10% and make 24 monthly payments of $64.80.

(a) Calculate the finance charge.
(b) By what percent is the instalment price more than the cash price?

8. Paul can buy a Porta-Sound for $850 cash or pay a down payment of 20% and the balance in equal monthly payments of $38. How many months will it take him to pay for the Porta-Sound if the total instalment price is $930?

9. Sandra bought a set of drums for $800 by making a down payment of $80. The finance charge was 15% of the unpaid balance. Sandra paid the total of the unpaid balance and finance charge by making 24 equal monthly instalments. How much did she pay each month?

Calculating the Instalment Payment

For instalment purchases, the calculations needed to find the amount of each equal monthly payment can be very complicated. Yet some people, like salespeople or credit managers, work with these types of calculations every day. They make their work easier by using a table like the one on the opposite page.

Example 1

Let's see — that would be $3.97 a month.....

Calculate the amount of the monthly payment if $400 is financed for 18 months at an interest rate of $16\frac{1}{2}\%$/a.

In the table of monthly payments, look for $16\frac{1}{2}\%$/a, then find the row of figures corresponding to a term of 18 months.

24	4.78		24	4.90
30	3.95		30	4.06
6	17.35	$16\frac{1}{2}\%$	6	17.48
12	8.98		12	9.10
18	6.19		18	6.31
24	4.80		24	4.92
	3.97		30	4.09

The monthly payment of $6.31 would be for an amount of $100. For $400 the equal monthly payment is 4 times greater than for $100.

$$\text{Equal Monthly Payment} = \frac{\text{Amount Financed}}{100} \times \text{Value from Table}$$
$$= \frac{400}{100} \times \$6.31$$
$$= \$25.24$$

The instalment payment is $25.24/month for 18 months.

Example 2

• Calculate the monthly payment if $845 is financed for 24 months at 16.5%/a.

$$\text{Equal Monthly Payment} = \frac{\text{Amount Financed}}{100} \times \text{Value from Table}$$
$$= \frac{845}{100} \times \$4.92$$
$$= \$41.57$$

The instalment payment is $41.57/month for 24 months.

• What is the finance charge?

Instalment price is	
$41.57 × 24.	$997.68
Amount financed	
is $845.00.	845.00
Subtract.	$152.68

The finance charge on this instalment loan is $152.68.

Exercise

A 1. Use the table below to state the value of the equal monthly payment for each of the following.

Amount Financed	Instalment Terms
(a) $100	6 months at $12\frac{1}{2}\%$/a
(b) $100	18 months at 13%/a
(c) $200	12 months at 14.5%/a

B 2. Use the table below to calculate the equal monthly payment for each of the following. Calculate the finance charge in each case.

Amount Financed	Instalment Terms
(a) $400	6 months at 12%/a
(b) $850	12 months at $13\frac{1}{2}\%$/a
(c) $575	18 months at 15%/a
(d) $295	24 months at 16.5%/a
(e) $295	30 months at 18%/a
(f) $1250	24 months at 17.5%/a

Monthly Payment for Financing $100								
Interest Rate	Terms in Months	Monthly Payment	Interest Rate	Terms in Months	Monthly Payment	Interest Rate	Terms in Months	Monthly Payment
12%	6	17.25	$14\frac{1}{2}\%$	6	17.38	17%	6	17.50
	12	8.89		12	9.00		12	9.12
	18	6.10		18	6.21		18	6.33
	24	4.71		24	4.83		24	4.94
	30	3.87		30	3.99		30	4.11
$12\frac{1}{2}\%$	6	17.28	15%	6	17.40	$17\frac{1}{2}\%$	6	17.52
	12	8.91		12	9.03		12	9.14
	18	6.12		18	6.24		18	6.36
	24	4.73		24	4.85		24	4.97
	30	3.90		30	4.02		30	4.14
13%	6	17.30	$15\frac{1}{2}\%$	6	17.43	18%	6	17.55
	12	8.93		12	9.05		12	9.14
	18	6.15		18	9.39		18	6.38
	24	4.75		24	4.87		24	4.99
	30	3.92		30	4.04		30	4.16
$13\frac{1}{2}\%$	6	17.32	16%	6	17.45	$18\frac{1}{2}\%$	6	17.58
	12	8.96		12	9.07		12	9.19
	18	6.17		18	6.29		18	6.40
	24	4.78		24	4.90		24	5.01
	30	3.95		30	4.06		30	4.19
14%	6	17.35	$16\frac{1}{2}\%$	6	17.48	19%	6	17.60
	12	8.98		12	9.10		12	9.21
	18	6.19		18	6.31		18	6.43
	24	4.80		24	4.92		24	5.04
	30	3.97		30	4.09		30	4.21

Calculating the True Interest Rate

When you buy an article on the instalment plan, you are really borrowing money from the company selling you the article. You should be aware of the *true interest rate* when you buy under these conditions.

Here is a formula to approximate the true interest rate on an instalment purchase.

$$r = \frac{200NC}{P(n + 1)}\%$$

r is true interest rate per annum;
N is number of payment intervals per year;
C is finance charge;
P is principal (cash price minus down payment);
n is number of payments made.

Example 1

A TV set can be purchased for $550 cash or by paying $50 down and $31.20/month for 18 months. Calculate the true rate of interest being charged.

$N = 12$ payments per year
$C = (\$31.20 \times 18 + \$50) - \$550$
$\quad = \$61.60$
$P = \$550 - \$50$
$\quad = \$500$
$n = 18$ payments made

$r = \dfrac{200NC}{P(n + 1)}\%$
$\quad = \dfrac{200(12)(61.60)}{500(18 + 1)}\%$
$\quad = 15.56\%$

The true interest rate is about 15.6%.

Exercise

B **1.** Calculate the true interest rate on each instalment purchase.

	Cash Price of Article	Instalment Terms
(a)	$400	$100 down, $52.35/month for 6 months
(b)	$875	$50 down, $81.70/month for 12 months
(c)	$900	$90 down, $57.60/month for 18 months
(d)	$1500	$200 down, $54.75/month for 30 months

2. The Dubois family can purchase a personal computer for $895 cash or pay $50 down and make 18 monthly instalments of $54.30.
   (a) Calculate the finance charge.
   (b) Determine the true rate of interest charged.

3.

An electric guitar sells for $1599 cash or $100 down and 24 monthly instalments of $72.25. Determine the true rate of interest.

4. A motorcycle sells for $2800 cash or $300 down and 36 monthly instalments of $97.55. Determine the true rate of interest.

Retail Buying

When you spend money on things like recreation, entertainment, or clothing, performance or appearance may be deciding factors. Cost may also be a deciding factor.

Example 1

- Determine the total price including 8% sales tax.

Regular Price	$895.00
Discount	150.00
Net Price	$745.00
8% Sales Tax	59.60
Total Price	$804.60

- Calculate the rate of discount. The solution gives you a formula for finding rate of discount.

$$\text{Rate of Discount} = \frac{\text{Amount of Discount}}{\text{Regular Price}} \times 100\%$$

$$= \frac{150}{895} \times 100\%$$

$$= 16.8\%$$

The total price of the guitar is $804.60. The rate of discount is 16.8%.

Example 2

Two different video cassette recorders are offered by two dealers for the same cash price of $575, including sales tax, but under different instalment plans.

Dealer A: $75 down plus $46.20/month for 12 months

Dealer B: $80 down plus $32.70/month for 18 months

- Which dealer offers the lower instalment price?

Find the instalment price for buying from Dealer A.

Instalment payments are 12 × $46.20.	$554.40
Down Payment	75.00
Instalment Price	$629.40

Now find the instalment price for Dealer B.

Instalment payments are 18 × $32.70	$588.60
Down Payment	80.00
Instalment Price	$668.60

Dealer A has the lower instalment price.

- Which dealer offers the better true interest rate?

$$r = \frac{200NC}{P(n+1)}\%$$

Dealer A:

$$r = \frac{200 \times 12 \times 54.40}{500 \times 13}\%$$
$$\doteq 20\%$$

Dealer B:

$$r = \frac{200 \times 12 \times 93.60}{495 \times 19}\%$$
$$\doteq 23.9\%$$

Dealer A offers a lower true interest rate.

- Which is the better of the 2 instalment plans? Dealer A has the lower instalment price but requires larger monthly payments. Dealer B has the higher interest rate but offers the lower monthly instalment. Which one would you consider?

You might base your decision on a number of factors.

- amount you can afford each month
- service provided by each dealer
- reliability of the cassette recorder
- difference in instalment price
- true interest rate
- reputation of the brand name
- quality
- performance

Exercise

A **1.**

Would the store refund your money if the earphones on the portable radio didn't work?

2. What are some factors that might help in your decision when you are comparison shopping for a stereo set?

B **3.** An inflatable boat that regularly sells for $249.95 is offered for sale at a discount of $50.

(a) Calculate the rate of discount. (Do not include sales tax.)
(b) Determine the total price of the boat including 7% sales tax.

4.

Regularly $37.29
NOW 25% OFF

(a) What is the discount price?
(b) What is the total price including 9% sales tax?

5. Calculate the discount price on each of the following items.

   (a) A sweater, regularly priced at $45, is on sale for 30% off.
   (b) A bicycle, regularly priced at $129.98, is on sale for 28% off.

6. A portable stereo regularly priced at $475.00 is on sale for 15% off.

   (a) Calculate the discount price.
   (b) Use the table on page 197 to calculate the monthly payment if the discount price is financed for 12 months at 16%/a.

7. Calculate the rate of discount on each of the following items.

   (a) A tennis racket, regularly priced at $89.95, is on sale at a discount of $20.00.
   (b) A set of golf clubs, regularly priced at $198, is on sale at a discount of $40.00.
   (c) A $75 jacket is on sale at a discount of $20.00.

8. A record album, regularly priced at $10.95, is on sale at 2 for $7.95. What percent do you save by buying 2 albums at the sale price?

9. The subscription price of a music magazine is $25 for one year. A 2 a subscription is offered for $40 and a 3 a subscription is offered for $55.

   (a) What is the rate of discount if a 2 a subscription is purchased instead of two 1 a subscriptions?
   (b) What is the rate of discount if a 3 a subscription is purchased instead of three 1 a subscriptions?

10. The bus fare between two cities is $14.95 one way. A round-trip ticket costs $25. What is the rate of discount if a round-trip ticket is purchased instead of 2 one-way tickets?

11.

Sale Price $40⁷⁵

REGULARLY $50.00

Polyester crêpe knit
Russet, teal blue or cinnamon

(a) What is the amount of the discount?
(b) What is the rate of discount?

12.

2-Piece Suit
Regular Price — $175
Discount — 25%
5% off the discount price if you pay cash

Another store has a similar suit, regularly priced at $175, on sale for 30% off.

If you pay cash, which store has the better offer?

13. Two different television sets are offered by two dealers for the same cash price of $650, but different instalment plans.

Dealer A: $100 down plus
$34.90/month for 18 months
Dealer B: $50 down plus
$30.10/month for 24 months

(a) Which dealer has the lower instalment price?
(b) Which dealer offers the better true interest rate?
(c) Which dealer would you buy from? Why?

14. A set of 4 tires are offered by two dealers for the same cash price of $480, but under different instalment conditions.

Dealer A: $80 down plus
$37.40/month for 12 months
Dealer B: No money down plus
$44.50/month for 12 months

(a) Which dealer offers the lower instalment price?
(b) Which dealer offers the lower true interest rate?
(c) Which dealer would you buy from? Why?

15. A sailboat sells for $1200 cash. Two dealers offer the same sailboat with the following instalment plans.

Dealer X: 10% down payment plus
$53.90/month for 24 months
Dealer Y: 15% down payment plus
$41.45/month for 30 months

(a) Which dealer offers the lower instalment price?
(b) Which dealer offers the better true interest rate?
(c) Which dealer would you buy from? Why?

16. Use the table on page 197 to calculate the monthly payment on a sailboat selling for $950 if it is financed for 24 months at 18% per annum.

Unit 11 Review

1. Determine the missing information in each case.

	Item	Cash Price	Finance Charge	Instalment Terms
(a)	Sewing Machine	$350	$175	$☐ down, $40/month for 12 months
(b)	Drafting Board and Accessories	$550	$290	$200 down, $☐/month for 16 months
(c)	Turntable	$300	$100	$100 down, $25/month for ☐ months

2. Angelo bought a pair of used water skis for $150 by making a down payment of $100. For the next 6 months, he paid 20% of the balance each month. What was the finance charge?

3. Michael buys a cassette tape recorder that sells for a cash price of $535. He agrees to pay $50 down and $44.50/month for 12 months.

   (a) Determine the finance charge.
   (b) By what percent is the instalment price more than the cash price?

4. Calculate the instalment price and finance charge for each of the following.

	Item	Cash Price	Instalment Terms
(a)	Portable Radio	$685	$100 down, $37.35/month for 18 months
(b)	Sail Board	$990	15% down, $42.20/month for 24 months

5. Jacqueline can purchase a set of drums for $750 cash, or pay a down payment of 20% and the balance in equal monthly payments of $38.70. How many months will it take her to pay for the drums if the instalment price is $846.60?

6. Debra purchased a motocross bike for $350 and made a down payment of $50. The carrying charges were 18% of the unpaid balance. The total of the unpaid balance and carrying charges was paid by Debra in 12 equal monthly instalments. How much did she pay each month?

7. Use the table on page 197 to calculate the value of the equal monthly payment for each of the following. Calculate the carrying charges in each case.

Amount Financed	Instalment Terms
(a) $900	18 months at 15%/a
(b) $450	6 months at $13\frac{1}{2}$%/a
(c) $625	12 months at $14\frac{1}{2}$%/a
(d) $1200	24 months at 18%/a

8. Calculate the true interest rate on each of the following instalment purchase.

Cash Price of Item	Instalment Terms
(a) $500	$100 down, $36.80/month for 12 months
(b) $950	$60 down, $56.45/month for 18 months

9. A personal computer sells for $899 cash or $80 down and 24 monthly instalments of $40.30. Determine the true rate of interest.

10. A saxophone that regularly sells for $1250 is on sale at a discount of $150.

   (a) Calculate the rate of discount.
   (b) Determine the discount price of the saxophone including 9% sales tax.
   (c) What is the discount price if another store has the saxophone priced for the same amount but on sale for 16% off?
   (d) Use the table on page 197 to calculate the monthly payment if the discount price in part (b) is financed for 24 months at 16%/a.

11. Blank tapes regularly selling for $4.95 each, are on sale at 3 for $12. What is the rate of discount if you buy 3 tapes at the sale price?

12. A set of skis, regularly selling for $425, are on sale for $399. What is the rate of discount?

13. A snowmobile sells for $1700 cash. Two dealers offer the same snowmobile with the following instalment plans.

   Dealer A: $200 down plus $75.30/month for 24 months
   Dealer B: 15% down plus $63.75/month for 30 months

   (a) Which dealer offers the lower instalment price?
   (b) Which dealer offers the better true interest rate?
   (c) Which dealer would you buy from? Why?

Unit 12

The World of Finance: Calculating Interest

Borrowing at Simple Interest

Julie has already saved $400 towards a new stereo system. If she waits to save the rest of the money she needs, she won't be able to take advantage of the sale price.

Should she borrow money to be able to buy the stereo now?

Julie is facing the same problem that many consumers face. One way she can help herself to decide whether or not to borrow is by enquiring at a bank about making a loan.

The loans officer at the bank would have to ask Julie several questions to complete the loan application.

The loans officer will ask Julie whether she owns a car, furniture, or stocks or bonds. Assets like these form Julie's **collateral**.

The loans officer will ask Julie whether she has ever had a loan before, and whether she owes any money right now, or has credit cards in her name. Julie's answers will give the officer a sense of Julie's **credit rating**.

One of *Julie's* questions should be to ask what rate of interest is charged on the loan, and what the total amount of interest would be. In Canada, it is required that the lender *clearly* show the answer to both questions in the contract.

If Julie decides to borrow money at 14%/a to buy the stereo, she can calculate the interest due if she takes 8 months to pay the loan. Start by calculating how much she needs altogether.

Sale price + Sales tax
= $850 + 8% of $850
= $850 + $68
= $918

She already has saved $400.

$918 − $400 = $518

Calculate the interest on $518 by using the simple interest formula, $I = Prt$.

$$I = (518)(0.14)\left(\tfrac{8}{12}\right)$$
$$= 48.35$$

$P = 518$
$r = 14\%$ or 0.14
$t = \tfrac{8}{12}$ (12 months in a year)

Total interest on the loan would be $48.35.

How much can Julie save by borrowing the money to buy now?

Exercise

A 1. State as a decimal.

(a) 15%

(b) 8%

(c) 3.4%

(d) $20\frac{1}{2}$%

(e) 134.8%

(f) $\frac{1}{2}$%

2. State as a fraction of one year.

(a) 7 months

(b) 49 d

(c) 25 weeks

(d) 5.5 months

(e) 404 d

(f) 2.5 a

3. (a) What should a consumer do to obtain a credit rating?

(b) What would cause a person to have a bad credit rating?

(c) What do you have that you could use for collateral for a loan?

B 4. Calculate the simple interest for each of the following loans.

(a) $400 for 6 months at 8%/a

(b) $120 for 4 a at 19%/a

(c) $1000 for 9 months at 11%/a

(d) $500 for 73 d at 21%/a

(e) $340 for 5 months at 9%/a

(f) $7000 for 100 d at 6.5%/a

(g) $425 for 3 a at 8.5%/a

(h) $48 for 90 d at $11\frac{1}{4}$%/a

(i) $20 000 for 15 months at $18\frac{3}{4}$%/a

(j) $1560 for 17 weeks at $6\frac{3}{8}$%/a

5. Steve borrows $250 for one month from a finance company that charges an interest rate of 23%. What amount must he pay at the end of the month?

6. Pat can save $60 by buying a computer today for $540. Pat can borrow $540 for 4 months at 18%/a.

(a) How much simple interest must Pat pay on the loan?

(b) How much less is the simple interest than the $60 saving?

7. Sandy MacDonald owns a clothing store. By buying immediately, Sandy can obtain a line of men's suits for $8000 that would normally cost $8500. Sandy does not have the funds available, but can borrow $8000 for 120 d at 21.5%/a. Calculate the amount that must be repaid after 120 d. Should Sandy take advantage of the discount?

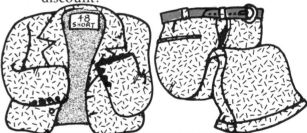

Project

1. There are 4 major lending institutions.
- chartered banks
- trust companies
- credit unions
- finance companies

Investigate the rate of interest that each institution charges on personal loans.

2. Investigate the services provided by the following institutions.
- Dun and Bradstreet
- Better Business Bureau

Finding the Amount of a Loan

Julie's loan for the stereo amounted to $518 for the principal and $48.35 for the simple interest, or a total of $566.35. **The amount** of the loan was $566.35.

$$A = P + I$$

If you borrow $200 at 14%/a, what amount is due after 56 d?

You can calculate the amount by calculating interest first, then adding the interest to the principal.

$$\begin{aligned} I &= Prt \\ &= (\$200)(0.14)(\tfrac{56}{365}) \\ &= \$4.30, \text{ to 2 decimal places} \end{aligned}$$

$$\begin{aligned} A &= P + I \\ &= \$200 + \$4.30 \\ &= \$204.30 \end{aligned}$$

The amount owing on the loan is $204.30.

You can develop a formula from the definition of amount.

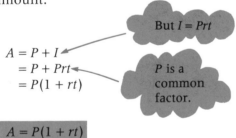

But $I = Prt$

$$\begin{aligned} A &= P + I \\ &= P + Prt \\ &= P(1 + rt) \end{aligned}$$

P is a common factor.

$$\boxed{A = P(1 + rt)}$$

Apply the formula to find the amount on the $200 loan described above.

$$\begin{aligned} A &= (200)[1 + (0.14)(\tfrac{56}{365})] \\ &= (200)(1.021\ 479) \\ &= \$204.30, \text{ to 2 decimal places} \end{aligned}$$

208

Example 1

If Meghan borrows $300 on April 22 and repays the loan on July 14 of the same year, for how many days is Meghan charged interest?

You can find the number of days by counting the number of days between April 22 and July 14, *including July 14*.

April	8 ← number of days left in April
May	31
June	30
July	14
	83

Interest will be charged on 83 d.

Another way to find the number of days is by using the *Days of the Year* table on page 456.

From the table, you read that April 22 is the 112th day. July 14 is the 195th day.
$$195 - 112 = 83$$

So interest will be charged on 83 d.

If the loan dates fall in different calendar years there is an extra step involved.

Example 2

Find the number of days between September 11, 1985 and May 27, 1986.
September 11 is the 254th day.
May 27 is the 147th day.

The number of days in 1985 = 365 − 254
$$= 114$$
The number of days in 1986 = 147
Total number of days = 261

114 + 147

There are 261 d between the 2 dates.

You can use the table to find the date on which a loan must be repaid.

Example 3

Lee's loan for $900 was taken out March 20 and is to be repaid in 63 d, when Lee is expecting a bonus to come through at work. Interest is 14%/a. Find the date the loan is due and the amount that must be repaid.

March 20 is the 79th day. 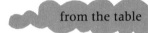 79 + 63
The loan will be repaid on the 142nd day.

The loan will be due on May 22.

from the table

Use the formula to find the amount to be repaid.

$$A = P(1 + rt)$$
$$= (\$900)[1 + (0.14)(\tfrac{63}{365})]$$
$$= \$921.75, \text{ to 2 decimal places}$$

The amount due on May 22 is $921.75.

The formula for amount can also be used to find the principal.

Example 4

Bill wants to borrow money to buy a computer. How much could Bill borrow today from a finance company that charges 23%/a, if he will have $950 in 150 d to repay the loan?

$$A = P(1 + rt)$$
$$\$950 = P[1 + (0.23)(\tfrac{150}{365})]$$
$$\$950 = P(1.094\ 521)$$
$$P = \tfrac{\$950}{1.094\ 521}$$
$$= \$867.96$$

Bill could afford to borrow $867.96.

Another way of solving Example 4 would be to rewrite the amount formula with P as the subject.

$$A = P(1 + rt)$$
$$P = \frac{A}{1 + rt}$$

When solving for principal in business situations, people prefer to use the formula in this form.

Use the formula to check the solution to Example 4.

Exercise

A 1. Find the number of the day for each of the following dates.

   (a) March 12   (c) December 25
   (b) August 30   (d) October 4

B 2. Calculate the amount due for each of the following.

   (a) $600 borrowed for 10 months at 17%/a
   (b) $30 borrowed for 4 a at $12\frac{1}{2}$%/a
   (c) $450 borrowed for 123 d at 11.7%/a
   (d) $12 000 borrowed for 400 d at $19\frac{1}{4}$%/a

3. Find the number of days between each of the following dates. All dates are in the same or successive years.

   (a) June 15 to October 8
   (b) February 16 to December 27
   (c) October 23 to April 16
   (d) September 12 to May 1
   (e) March 24 to January 1

4. Angela borrowed $630 on February 14 at 21%/a and repaid the loan on July 26 of the same year. How much did she repay?

5. Frank borrows $2000 and signs a note on August 5 agreeing to repay the loan on May 23 of the following year. If the interest is $16\frac{1}{4}$%/a, find the amount that Frank will pay on the due date.

6. A retailer borrows $7000 for 123 d on July 12. If interest is being charged at 17.4%/a, find the amount that must be repaid on the due date. What is the due date for the payment?

7. Sam took out a loan for $1400 on July 15 at $13\frac{1}{2}$%/a for 63 d.

   (a) What date is payment due?
   (b) What is the amount that must be repaid?
   (c) Sam could only pay $800 on the due date. The lender agreed that Sam could make the $800 payment and owe the balance until February 20, but with interest charged at a new rate of 15%/a. Find the amount to pay the loan on February 20.

8. Calculate the principal borrowed for each of the following.

   (a) Repay $1000 after 7 months at 15%/a
   (b) Repay $650 after 123 d at 12%/a
   (c) Repay $120 after 3 a at 9%/a
   (d) Repay $5890 after 430 d at 19.7%/a

9. What principal was borrowed on May 17 at 11%/a if $650 was paid on September 3 to clear the loan?

10. Flora is checking the accounts of a small business. She finds a receipt that shows that the company repaid $358 on February 16 for a loan taken out 78 d previously. The rate of interest charged was 14.2%/a.

    (a) What date was the loan taken out?
    (b) How much had the company borrowed on that date?

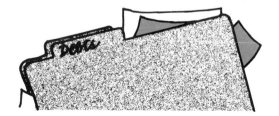

Applications of $I = Prt$

Nick deposited $300 in his savings account. After 5 months, the balance of the account was $310.63. Nick can check the rate of interest the bank was paying by using the formula for simple interest.

$$I = Prt$$
$$(\$10.63) = (\$300)r\left(\tfrac{5}{12}\right)$$
$$10.63 = 125r \longleftarrow \quad 300 \times \tfrac{5}{12}$$
$$r = \frac{\$10.63}{125}$$
$$= 0.085\ 04$$

The rate of interest paid is 8.5%, to the nearest tenth of a percent.

Another way to find the rate of interest is to rewrite the formula $I = Prt$, with r as the subject.

$$I = Prt$$
$$\frac{I}{Pt} = \frac{Prt}{Pt}$$
$$\frac{I}{Pt} = r \qquad \text{Divide both sides by } Pt.$$
$$r = \frac{I}{Pt}$$

Then substitute the known quantities into the resulting formula.

$$r = \frac{I}{Pt}$$
$$= \frac{\$10.63}{\$300 \times \tfrac{5}{12}}$$
$$= 0.085\ 04$$

The answer is identical to the one above.

Example 1

How many days will it take for $700 to earn $20 interest at 12.4%/a?

Substitute into the formula for simple interest.

$$I = Prt$$
$$\$20 = (\$700)(0.124)t$$
$$20 = 86.8t$$
$$t = 0.230\ 414$$

The unknown, t, is in years. To convert to days, multiply by 365.

$$0.230\ 414\ a = 0.230\ 414 \times 365\ d$$
$$\doteq 85\ d$$

Must be rounded *up* to nearest whole number.

The interest will be earned in 85 d.

The solution to Example 1 could have been found using the formula below.

$$t = \frac{I}{Pr}$$

How would you use the simple interest formula to determine the formula given for t?

Here are the variations of the simple interest formula.

- $I = Prt$
- $r = \dfrac{I}{Pt}$
- $t = \dfrac{I}{Pr}$
- $P = \dfrac{I}{rt}$

Below is a memory device for the formulas.

$$r = \frac{I}{p \times t}$$

Exercise

B **1.** Copy and complete the table.

	Principal	Interest	Rate/a	Time
(a)	$4200	▨	11%	56 d
(b)	$500	$20	▨	4 months
(c)	$6000	$550	▨	200 d
(d)	▨	$200	14%	2 a
(e)	▨	$45	6.5%	11 months
(f)	$240	$6.50	8.7%	▨
(g)	$980	$50	$20\frac{3}{4}$%	▨

2. A credit union charges 17%/a interest for most personal loans. How much money could you borrow for 8 months if the interest on the loan is to be $90?

3. Jennifer borrows $1100 from a trust company at an interest rate of 20.5%/a. How many days can Jennifer have the loan before the interest charged on the loan is at least $100?

4. Seventy days ago, Lise deposited $1200 in a new savings account, and today that account has a balance of $1224.32. What rate of interest is being credited to Lise's savings account?

5. Andy deposits $800 in a new savings account that pays 7% interest. How long must Andy leave the money in the account before he can withdraw $1000?

6. Dave had to borrow $300 to pay his rent but his credit rating was too poor to qualify for a bank loan. Instead, he had to borrow from a friend. If Dave borrowed the $300 for 40 d and paid $25 in interest, what rate of interest was he charged?

7. Ivy borrows $450 on March 12 at 15.8%/a interest. Ivy doesn't want to pay any more than $20 in interest.

   (a) How many days can Ivy wait before she repays the loan?
   (b) Assuming she waits until the last possible day to repay, on what date should payment be made?

8. Top Dollar Value stores offer credit terms for all purchases. In one month, Leslie made purchases of $430 and was charged $8 interest on the monthly instalment. What rate of interest was the store charging?

9. Gwen's bank pays 8%/a on a daily interest savings account. The portion of her bankbook shown below shows the deposit of interest on July 24.

DATE	ITEM	WDL	DEP	BALANCE
▬▬▬				567.25
JUL 24	INT		31.12	598.37

The balance of $567.25 was the amount in the account at the start of the interest period ending July 24. Find the date the previous balance was recorded.

10. A deposit of $500 earns interest at the rate of 9%/a for 60 d. How much more time would be needed to earn the same amount of interest if the $500 were invested at 7%/a instead of 9%/a?

Computing Interest

To calculate the period of time that an amount of money, invested at a given interest rate, will earn a specific amount of interest, you can use a calculator and the formula below.

$$t = \frac{I}{Pr}$$

But what if you want to find the period of time for several different investments? Using a computer and the program below can shorten your work.

```
NEW
10   REM ** FINDING T **
90   HOME
100  INPUT "ENTER THE PRINCIPAL.$";P
110  INPUT "ENTER THE ANNUAL INTEREST
       RATE.'; R

120  INPUT "ENTER THE INTEREST. $";I
130  REM ** CALCULATE T **
140  T = 365 * (I/(P*R)/100))
150  REM ** ROUND-UP VALUE OF T
160  T = INT(T + .9999)
170  REM ** OUTPUT ANSWERS **
180  HOME
190  PRINT "PRINCIPAL = $";P
200  PRINT "RATE=";R;"%"
210  PRINT "INTEREST = $";I
220  PRINT
230  PRINT "TIME PERIOD = "; T; "DAYS"
240  PRINT
250  PRINT "DO YOU WISH TO REPEAT THE
       PROGRAM (Y/N)?"
260  INPUT Z$
270  IF Z$ = "Y" THEN GOTO 90
280  PRINT "PROGRAM HAS ENDED."
290  END
```

Exercise

1. Use the given program to complete the table below.

Principal	Interest Rate	Interest	Time
$ 700	5.2%	$ 60	▨
$ 700	8.9%	$ 60	▨
$ 700	12 %	$ 60	▨
$ 700	15.75%	$ 60	▨
$2000	9.44%	$ 10	▨
$2000	9.44%	$100	▨

2. Change the program so that it will solve for the principal, given the formula below.

$$P = \frac{I}{R * T}$$

- Change line 100 to enter the time period in days.
- Change line 140 to
  P = I/((R/100)*(T/365)).
- Change line 160 to
  P = INT(100*P+.5)/100.
- Change lines 190 to 230 to give the proper output.

Use your program to complete the table.

Interest Rate	Interest	Time in Days	Principal
9.2%	$40	100	▨
9.2%	$40	188	▨
9.2%	$40	251	▨

Compound Interest

If you bought a $100 bond with compound interest at 12%, the *principal* of your investment would increase each year. The interest earned each year, or period, would be added to the principal, or **compounded into principal**.

How much would the bond be worth at the end of 3 a?

Calculate the amount at the end of year 1.
$$A = P(1 + rt)$$
$$= (\$100)[1 + (0.12)(1)]$$
$$= \$100(1.12)$$
$$= \$112$$

$1 amounts to $1.12 in 1 a.

This amount becomes the principal during year 2. Calculate the amount at the end of year 2.
$$A = P(1 + rt)$$
$$= (\$112)[1 + (0.12)(1)]$$
$$= \$112(1.12)$$
$$= \$125.44$$

Now use the principal of $125.44 to calculate the amount at the end of year 3.

$$A = P(1 + rt)$$
$$= (\$125.44)[1 + (0.12)(1)]$$
$$= \$125.44(1.12)$$
$$= \$140.49, \text{ to 2 decimal places}$$

The bond would be worth $140.49 after 3 a.

The calculations are summarized in the table.

Time	Amount	
Now	$100.00	
1 a	$112.00	× 1.12
2 a	$125.44	× 1.12
3 a	$140.49	× 1.12

Each amount can be calculated by multiplying the previous amount by 1.12. The multiplier 1.12 is the **growth factor**.

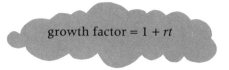

growth factor = $1 + rt$

Interest can be compounded semi-annually (every 6 months), quarterly (every 3 months), and monthly as well.

Example 1

Kim deposits $600 in a new account that pays 8%/a compounded semi-annually. Find the amount in Kim's account and the interest earned after 2 a.

The growth factor is $1 + rt$.
$$1 + rt = 1 + (0.08)\left(\tfrac{6}{12}\right)$$
$$= 1.04$$

The table summarizes the calculations.

Time	Amount = P × Growth Factor	Amount
Now		$600.00
6 months	$600.00(1.04)	$624.00
12 months	$624.00(1.04)	$648.96
18 months	$648.96(1.04)	$674.92
24 months	$674.92(1.04)	$701.92

The amount after 2 a will be $701.92. Interest earned is $701.92 − $600.00, or $101.92.

Exercise

A 1. State the growth factor for each given interest rate and period.

(a) 15%/a compounded annually
(b) 8%/a compounded semi-annually
(c) 12%/a compounded quarterly
(d) 6%/a compounded monthly

B 2. Find the amount owing after 4 a if $400 is borrowed at each of the following interest rates.

(a) 16%/a simple interest
(b) 16%/a compounded annually

3. Find the amount owing and the interest accumulated after 3 a if $8000 is borrowed at each of the following interest rates.

(a) 18% simple interest
(b) 18%/a compounded semi-annually

4. If $1200 is deposited in a savings account, find the amount on deposit after 2 a at each of the following interest rates.

(a) 10%/a simple interest
(b) 10%/a compounded annually
(c) 10%/a compounded semi-annually
(d) 10%/a compounded quarterly

5. (a) Find the amount after 5 months if $800 is invested at 9%/a simple interest.
(b) Find the amount after 5 months if $800 is invested at 9%/a compounded monthly.

6. Copy and complete the table.

	Principal	Rate	Time	Amount
(a)	$600	6%/a compounded semi-annually	3a	▨
(b)	$80	8%/a semi-annually	4a	▨
(c)	$210	14%/a quarterly	3a	▨
(d)	$1400	12%/a monthly	3 months	▨
(e)	$720	24%/a monthly	5 months	▨

7. Calculate the interest earned on a $400 deposit after 1 a for each of the following interest rates.

(a) 6%/a compounded annually
(b) 6%/a compounded semi-annually
(c) 6%/a compounded quarterly
(d) 6%/a compounded monthly

What conclusion would you make about the amount of interest earned as the frequency of compounding is increased?

The Compound Interest Formula

Jack has a goal of having $1500 for community college in 3 a.

He invests $1000 at 12%/a compounded monthly. How much will the investment be worth in 3 a?

In 3 a, with interest compounded monthly, there are 36 interest calculations altogether (one a month for three years). If you can find a pattern in the first several calculations, then maybe the pattern can be generalized to save you work.

Start by finding the growth factor for Jack's investment.

$$\text{growth factor} = 1 + rt$$
$$= 1 + (0.12)(\tfrac{1}{12})$$
$$= 1.01$$

Now start the first of the 36 required calculations.

- First month
  $$A = P \times \text{growth factor}$$
  $$= 1000(1.01)$$

- Second month
  $$A = P \times \text{growth factor}$$
  $$= 1000(1.01) \times (1.01)$$
  $$= 1000(1.01)^2$$

New principal

- Third month
  $$A = P \times \text{growth factor}$$
  $$= 1000(1.01)^2 \times (1.01)$$
  $$= 1000(1.01)^3$$

New Principal

Month	Amount
1	$1000(1.01)$
2	$1000(1.01)^2$
3	$1000(1.01)^3$
⋮	⋮

What is the pattern? What amount would you predict for the fourth month? for the fifth month?

After 36 months, $A = \$100(1.01)^{36}$
$$= \$1430.77$$

Jack will be short of his goal by $69.23.

The pattern can be generalized to give the *compound interest formula*.

$$A = P(1 + i)^n$$
n is the number of interest periods.
i is the interest rate *per period*.

Use $i = \tfrac{r}{N}$; r is the annual rate of interest;
N is the number of interest periods per year.

Example 1

An investment of $200 earns 20%/a compounded quarterly for 2 a. Write in the form $A = P(1 + i)^n$.
Start by finding n and i.

$$n = 4 \times 2$$
$$= 8$$

$$i = \tfrac{r}{N}$$

4 interest periods each year

$$= \tfrac{20\%}{4}$$
$$= 5\% \text{ or } 0.05$$

Now substitute for n and i.
$$A = P(1 + i)^n$$
$$= \$200(1 + 0.05)^8$$

When you apply the compound interest formula, there are two methods available for evaluating final answers: by using a calculator, or by using the tables on page 457. The example below shows each method.

Example 2

Find the amount and the interest earned if $300 is invested at 10%/a compounded semi-annually for 42 months.

Find the amount first.

$$A = P(1 + i)^n$$
$$= \$300(1.05)^7$$

$P = \$300$

$i = \dfrac{10\%}{2}$ or 5%

$n = \dfrac{42}{6}$ or 7

• Evaluate using a calculator.

1.05 $\boxed{y^x}$ $\boxed{7}$ $\boxed{=}$ $\boxed{\times}$ 300 $\boxed{=}$

$\boxed{422.13013}$

• Evaluate using tables. Read down the column under 5%.

n	4%	5%	6%
1	1.04000	1.05000	1.06000
2	1.08160	1.10250	1.12360
3	1.12486	1.15763	1.19102
4	1.16986	1.21551	1.26248
5	1.21665	1.27628	1.33823
6	1.26532	1.34010	1.41852
7	1.31593	1.40710	1.50363
8	1.36857	1.47746	1.59385
9	1.42331	1.55133	1.68948
10	1.48024	1.62889	1.79085

$$A = \$300(1.05)^7$$
$$= \$300(1.40710)$$
$$= \$422.13, \text{ to 2 decimal places}$$

Whether you use a calculator or the tables, the answer is $428.13, to 2 decimal places.

Calculate total interest by subtracting principal from amount.

$$\$422.13 - \$300 = \$122.13$$

The interest earned is $122.13.

Exercise

A 1. State the value of N, i, and n for each of the following.

   (a) 12%/a compounded semi-annually for 5 a
   (b) 12%/a compounded quarterly for 5 a
   (c) 12%/a compounded monthly for 5 a
   (d) 12%/a compounded annually for 5 a
   (e) 18%/a compounded quarterly for 3 a
   (f) 5%/a compounded semi-annually for 18 months
   (g) 10%/a compounded quarterly for 15 months
   (h) 6%/a compounded monthly for 3.5 a.

2. Use the tables or a calculator to evaluate.

   (a) $(1.05)^{20}$
   (b) $(1.08)^{12}$
   (c) $(1.045)^{44}$
   (d) $(1.1)^{37}$
   (e) $(1.005)^9$
   (f) $(1.075)^{48}$

B 3. For each investment, write A in the form $P(1 + i)^n$.

   (a) $30 is invested at 8%/a compounded quarterly for 6 a.
   (b) $200 is invested at 24%/a compounded monthly for 4 a.
   (c) $3000 is invested at 9%/a compounded semi-annually for 11 a.
   (d) $5 is invested at 13%/a compounded quarterly for 21 months.
   (e) $90 000 is invested at 9%/a compounded monthly for 20 months.

4. Evaluate the following using tables or a calculator.

(a) $20(1.04)^{15}$
(b) $700(1.085)^{23}$
(c) $340(1.015)^{45}$
(d) $32.76(1.065)^{33}$

5. Find the amount for each investment.

(a) $500 for 5 a at 14%/a compounded semi-annually
(b) $80 000 for 3 a at 6%/a compounded monthly
(c) $345 for 9 a at 22%/a compounded quarterly
(d) $56 for 18 months at 11%/a compounded semi-annually

6. Find the interest for each of the following investments.

(a) $700 invested at 12%/a compounded monthly for 3 a
(b) $150 invested at 18%/a compounded quarterly for 9 months
(c) $23 000 invested at 8%/a compounded annually for 15 a
(d) $90 invested at 9%/a compounded every 2 months for 2 a

7. Frank's parents invested $4000 by opening an account in his name when he was first born. The account paid interest at 5%/a compounded semi-annually.

(a) How much could Frank withdraw on his sixteenth birthday?
(b) How much of the withdrawal is interest?

8. Four years ago, Sarah purchased a $2000 savings bond for her education. If interest was paid at 12%/a compounded monthly, what amount will Sarah have today? How much interest did she earn?

9. Bill bought a $10 000 Canada Savings Bond that bears interest at 10%/a compounded semi-annually.

(a) Find the value of the bond in 6 a.
(b) Find the value of the bond in 7 a.
(c) How much interest will Bill earn from the bond during the seventh year?

10. Two competing banks offer different interest rates on savings accounts. One bank pays interest at 12%/a compounded monthly, and the other pays 12.5%/a compounded annually. If $100 is deposited at each bank today and is left for 4 a, which account pays more interest? How much more?

11. If $4000 is invested for 12 a, how much more interest will be earned at an interest of 14%/a compounded quarterly, than at 14%/a compounded annually?

12. Di bought a $2000 Canada Savings Bond 5 a ago that bears interest at 6%/a compounded monthly, and a $5000 Canada Savings Bond 2 a ago that bears interest at 10%/a compounded quarterly. If she cashes both bonds today, how much interest will she have earned altogether?

13. Archie wants to invest $1000 for 3 a. Which of the following rates accumulates the most amount of interest?

(a) 18%/a compounded monthly
(b) 18.4%/a compounded annually
(c) 23%/a simple interest

14. Tony opens a savings account by depositing $800 at 6%/a compounded monthly. After 1 a the rate is changed to 5%/a compounded semi-annually. How much will be in the account after 3 a?

15. One year ago, Paula opened a bank account by depositing $500 at 10%/a compounded monthly. Eight months ago, she withdrew $200. Three months ago she deposited $100. How much is in the account today?

Turning the Tables

How long will it take for the money in a savings account to double in value?

What interest rate has to be charged on a loan if the lender wants to triple the investment in 8 a?

Questions like these can be solved by using the Compound Interest Tables on pages 457 and 458.

Example 1

If $400 is deposited today at 10%/a compounded quarterly, how long will it take the deposit to double in value?

The $400 deposit has to grow to $800.

$$A = P(1 + i)^n$$
$$\$800 = \$400(1.025)^n$$
$$2 = (1.025)^n$$

n	$1\frac{1}{2}\%$	2%	$2\frac{1}{2}\%$
24	1.42950	1.60844	1.80873
25	1.45095	1.64061	1.85394
26	1.47271	1.67342	1.90029
27	1.49480	1.70689	1.94780
28	1.51722	1.74102	1.99650
29	1.53998	1.77584	2.04641
30	1.56308	1.77584	2.09757

Approximate n by looking under the 2.5% column of the tables.

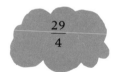

2 or greater

The approximate value of n is 29, which represents 29 quarterly intervals, since interest is being compounded quarterly.

$$\frac{29}{4}$$

The money will double in value in 7.25 a, or 7 a 3 months.

Example 2

What annual rate of interest has to be charged for a $400 investment to triple in value over 11 a if interest is compounded semi-annually?

$$A = P(1 + i)^n$$
$$\$1200 = \$400(1 + i)^{22}$$
$$3 = (1 + i)^{22}$$

n	4%	5%	6%
1	1.04000	1.05000	1.06000
19	2.10685	2.52695	3.02560
20	2.19112	2.65330	3.20714
21	2.27877	2.78596	3.39956
22	2.36992	2.92526	3.60354
23	2.46472	3.07152	3.81975
24	2.56330	3.22510	4.04893
25	2.66584	3.38635	4.29187

Approximate i by looking along the row where $n = 22$. The value of i lies between **5%** and **6%**.

A better approximation can be found by the method shown below.

Let 5% + x% be the interest rate to triple the investment. Create the table below.

Interest rate	$(1 + i)^{22}$
5%	2.925 26
5% + x%	3.000 00
6%	3.603 54

Take corresponding differences to create an equation.

$$\frac{(5\% + x\%) - 5\%}{6\% - 5\%} = \frac{3.000\ 00 - 2.925\ 26}{3.603\ 54 - 2.925\ 26}$$
$$\frac{x\%}{1\%} = \frac{0.074\ 74}{0.678\ 28}$$

Solve the equation.

$$x = \frac{0.074\ 74}{0.678\ 28}$$
$$= 0.110\ 190, \text{ to 6 decimals}$$

The value of i is 5.110 190% every 6 months.

The annual rate of interest is about 10.2% compounded semi-annually (nearest 0.1%).

Exercise

A 1. From the tables, state the value of n.

(a) $(1.03)^n = 2$ (d) $(1.045)^n = 3.5$
(b) $(1.08)^n = 6$ (e) $(1.015)^n = 1.8$
(c) $(1.05)^n = 1.4$ (f) $(1.1)^n = 5$

2. From the tables, find approximate values for i.

(a) $(l + i)^{15} = 2$ (d) $(l + i)^{10} = 1.2$
(b) $(l + i)^{36} = 3$ (e) $(l + i)^{25} = 3.1$
(c) $(l + i)^{20} = 1.5$

B 3. How long will it take \$500 to double in value at the following interest rates?

(a) 10%/a compounded annually
(b) 10%/a compounded semi-annually
(c) 12%/a compounded semi-annually
(d) 12%/a compounded quarterly
(e) 24%/a compounded quarterly
(f) 24%/a compounded monthly

4. How many years and months will it take \$2000 to triple in value if it is invested at the given interest rate?

(a) 6%/a compounded semi-annually
(b) 12%/a compounded semi-annually
(c) 18%/a compounded semi-annually

5. Joe deposits \$500 in a savings account that pays 10%/a compounded quarterly. How many years and months will Joe have to wait before he can close the account and use the money to buy a computer for \$800?

6. Approximate to find the value of i, to the nearest 0.1%.

(a) $(l + i)^{14} = 2$ (c) $(l + i)^{10} = 1.4$
(b) $(l + i)^{21} = 4$ (d) $(l + i)^{36} = 7.5$

7. What rate of interest compounded annually is needed to have \$700 double in value in 10 a?

8. A \$2000 savings bond that was bought 8 a ago is now worth \$4000. What rate of interest compounded quarterly was the bond earning?

9. Nicki needs to have \$1500 in 3 a for tuition and books at college. If she deposits \$1000 in a savings account today, what rate of interest compounded monthly is needed for Nicki to reach her goal?

Side Trip

There is a formula to calculate i, the interest rate per period.

$$i = \left(\frac{A}{P} \right)^{\frac{1}{n}} - 1$$

To find the rate of interest compounded quarterly that will allow \$100 to grow to \$250 in 6 a, use the formula.

$$i = \left(\frac{250}{100} \right)^{\frac{1}{24}} - 1$$
$$= (2.5)^{\frac{1}{24}} - 1$$

2.5 $\boxed{y^x}$ $\boxed{(}$ 1 $\boxed{\div}$ 24 $\boxed{)}$ $\boxed{=}$ $\boxed{-}$ 1 $\boxed{=}$

$$\boxed{0.037917}$$

$i = 0.038\ 917$, to 6 decimal places
So $4i = 0.155\ 668$

The annual rate is 15.6%, (to 0.1%).
Use the formula to check your answers to Questions 7 to 9 above.

Unit 12 Review

1. Find the number of the day for each of the following dates.

   (a) February 18
   (b) August 30
   (c) July 11
   (d) December 24

2. State the value of i and n for each of the following.

   (a) 14%/a compounded semi-annually for 5 a
   (b) 30%/a compounded quarterly for 8 a
   (c) 30%/a compounded monthly for 6 a
   (d) 6%/a compounded quarterly for 45 months
   (e) 12%/a compounded monthly for 9 a

3. Calculate the simple interest for each of the following.

   (a) $600 for 5 months at 7%/a
   (b) $1400 for 145 d at 16%/a
   (c) $56.10 for 20 d at 28%/a
   (d) $23 000 for 3 a at 11%/a
   (e) $150 for 8 weeks at 14.25%/a

4. A finance company charges simple interest at 30%/a on short-term loans. Find the interest charged on a loan of $450 for 18 d.

5. Find the number of days between each of the following dates. All dates are in the same or successive years.

   (a) April 2 to October 15
   (b) June 25 to February 17
   (c) April 26 to February 27

6. Jim can save $40 by buying a camera today for $310. To buy it today, he would have to borrow $310 for 5 months at 25%/a, simple interest.

   (a) How much simple interest would Jim have to pay on the loan?
   (b) How much will he save if he borrows the money to buy the camera today?

7. Calculate the amount at simple interest for each of the following.

   (a) $700 borrowed for 9 months at 19%
   (b) $1250 borrowed for 300 d at 15.6%
   (c) $300 borrowed at 15% on March 14 and repaid on July 11
   (d) $925 borrowed at 9.5% on November 23 and repaid on May 3

8. Harry borrowed $350 on June 11 and repaid the loan on December 14 of the same year. Simple interest is charged at 13%/a. Calculate the amount repaid.

9. To take advantage of a wholesaler's discount, a retailer borrows $3500 on October 24 for 170 d at 21.75%/a. Find the date that payment is due, and the amount owing.

10. Calculate the principal borrowed for each of the following simple interest loans.

   (a) Repay $650 after 5 months at 12%/a.
   (b) Repay $6000 after 320 d at 16%/a.
   (c) Repay $2140 after 2 a at 20.2%/a.

11. What sum was borrowed on September 21 at 8%/a if $1820 was paid on May 18 in the following year to pay off the loan?

12. Copy and complete the table.

	Principal	Interest	Rate/a	Time
(a)	$390	▨	6%	11 months
(b)	$910	▨	10.3%	77 d
(c)	▨	$32	9%	2 a
(d)	▨	$112	19%	68 d
(e)	$67	$13	▨	14 months
(f)	$3240	$120	▨	211 d
(g)	$400	$30	15%	▨
(h)	$80	$5	9%	▨

13. What sum of money could be borrowed for 4 months at a simple interest rate of 10%/a if the interest is to be $45 for the loan?

14. On March 8, Gerry borrowed $420. On September 12 of the same year, the loan was paid off with a payment of $428.50. What rate of simple interest was Gerry charged on the loan?

15. Alicia borrows $800 on September 15 for unexpected school expenses. The interest rate on the loan was 22%/a. What is the latest date that the loan can be repaid if Alicia doesn't want to pay more than $50 interest?

16. For each of the following, write the amount in the form $A = P(l + i)^n$.

   (a) $50 invested at 10%/a compounded semi-annually for 8 a
   (b) $85 invested at 6%/a compounded quarterly for 9 a
   (c) $3000 invested at 15%/a compounded monthly for 5 a
   (d) $20 invested at 17.5%/a compounded annually for 19 a
   (e) $5400 invested for 24 months at 14%/a compounded quarterly
   (f) $250 invested for 54 months at 11.4%/a compounded semi-annually
   (g) $90 000 invested for 20 a at 9%/a compounded monthly

17. Find the amount and the interest earned on each of the following.

   (a) $500 invested at 10%/a compounded semi-annually for 10 a
   (b) $500 invested at 10%/a compounded quarterly for 10 a
   (c) $500 invested at 10%/a compounded annually for 10 a
   (d) $7000 invested at 12%/a compounded monthly for 4.5 a
   (e) $75 invested for 30 months at 18%/a compounded quarterly

18. Donald invests $2500 for 2 a. Which of the following interest rates accumulates the greatest amount of interest?

   (a) 16%/a compounded quarterly
   (b) 16.6%/a compounded annually
   (c) 20.5%/a simple interest

19. If you borrow $600 for 27 months, how much more interest is charged if the interest rate is 18%/a compounded monthly rather than 18%/a compounded quarterly?

20. (a) Bill borrowed $2000 2 a ago at 10%/a compounded quarterly and had agreed to pay off the debt today. How much does Bill owe today?

   (b) Bill can only pay $1500 today. His lender agrees to accept the $1500 and accept the balance owing in 1 a, but the interest rate will be 16%/a compounded quarterly. What amount does Bill owe 1 a from now?

   (c) How much extra in interest will Bill pay by not having the necessary funds to pay off the loan today?

21. State the value of n using the compound interest tables.

   (a) $(1.06)^n = 2$ (c) $(1.035)^n = 3$
   (b) $(1.04)^n = 1.6$ (d) $(1.09)^n = 4.2$

22. How many years and months does it take to have $900 double in value at each of the following interest rates?

   (a) 8%/a compounded annually
   (b) 8%/a compounded semi-annually
   (c) 8%/a compounded quarterly

23. How many years and months would it take for $400 to increase to a value of $600 at 18%/a compounded monthly?

24. State an approximation for i using the compound interest tables.

   (a) $(1 + i)^{12} = 1.3$
   (b) $(1 + i)^{23} = 3$
   (c) $(1 + i)^{39} = 2.5$
   (d) $(1 + i)^5 = 1.35$

25. Approximate to find the value of i, to the nearest 0.1%.

   (a) $(1 + i)^{27} = 3$
   (b) $(1 + i)^{12} = 1.7$
   (c) $(1 + i)^{42} = 8$

Side Trip

Use a calculator with a power key to answer the following.

1. Find the value of a deposit of $100 after 60 a at each of the following interest rates.

   (a) 12%/a simple interest
   (b) 12%/a compounded annually
   (c) 12%/a compounded monthly

2. Find the amount in an account after 1 a if $100 is deposited today at each of the following interest rates.

   (a) 24%/a simple interest
   (b) 24%/a compounded monthly
   (c) 24%/a compounded daily (365 d/a)
   (d) 24%/a compounded hourly
   (e) 24%/a compounded each minute

Unit 13

The World of Finance: Saving Money

Banking Your Money
Comparing Simple and
Compound Interest
Amount of an Annuity
Present Value of an Amount
Present Value of an Annuity
Unit 13 Review

Banking Your Money

Maureen just received her first paycheque. Maureen knows that the best thing to do with her money is to make it grow, so she wants to put part of the cheque in a savings account where it will earn interest.

The interest rates and terms offered by different financial institutions can be confusing and are often hard to compare. Banks and trust companies offer a variety of plans: true savings accounts; daily interest with chequing privileges; chequing accounts; term deposits; and others.

Maureen asks herself the following questions before deciding on the type of account that is best for her.

• How often is the interest calculated?

Is interest calculated on the minimum daily, monthly, or semi-annual balance? Suppose that interest is calculated on the minimum semi-annual balance. If Maureen is depositing $100 on the first day of each month, then interest will be calculated on the first $100 deposit made—the last five deposits will not earn any interest in the first six months.

• How often is interest credited?

Is the interest credited and compounded into principal daily, monthly, or semi-annually? The more often that interest is compounded, the more quickly Maureen's principal will increase.

• Are there service charges?

What are some of the service charges for transferring money from one account to another? Can more than one or two withdrawals be made per month?

• What other fees are there?

Is there a fee charged for each cheque written or can I write cheques for free? Does a fee for cheques written depend on the minimum balance for the month?

• Who offers the best interest rate?

Do trust companies or credit unions offer better interest rates than banks?

- Is the account convenient for me?

True savings accounts pay higher interest rates, but Maureen would not be able to write cheques on the account. She has to decide whether that is convenient for her savings plans.

- How do I plan to save my money?

Maureen may be planning to hold her savings for a long time. If she is saving toward a large purchase, like a car, it would be a good idea for her to find out about term deposits or Canada Savings Bonds.

- What are the business hours?

Will the banking hours be convenient for me? If Maureen works during each weekday, she would probably want to open an account at an institution that had some evening or Saturday hours. She could also find out about banking machines.

Maureen decided to open a daily interest savings account at Cana-Bank, with interest compounded monthly. Maureen can't write cheques on the account, but she can make cash withdrawals. The account pays a higher interest rate than other accounts that have chequing privileges.

Example 1

Maureen's account pays interest at 8%/a, calculated daily. What is the interest for March 2?

CANA-BANK				
DATE	ITEM	WDL	DEP	BALANCE
FEB 24	DEP		50.00	605.10
MAR 2	DEP		100.00	705.10
MAR 2	WDL	300.00		405.10
MAR 2	DEP		210.00	615.10

The balance column in the bankbook shows a minimum daily balance of $405.10 on March 2. Calculate 8% interest on $405.10 for 1 d.

$I = Prt$
$= (\$405.10)(0.08)(\frac{1}{365})$
$= \$0.09$

$P = \$405.10$
$r = 8\%$
$= 0.08$
$t = \frac{1}{365}$

The interest earned on March 2 is $0.09.

Maureen is also interested in other types of savings accounts. For example, term deposits yield higher interest than other savings accounts. But they require a higher principal ($1000 or $2000) and a cash penalty is given if any withdrawals are made during the term of the agreement. The period of time for term deposits usually varies from 30 d to 5 a. Interest rate remains fixed during the term.

Example 2

Cana-Bank offers Guaranteed Investment Certificates with the following rates and terms.

Term	Rate
30 to 59 d	10%
60 to 89 d	10.25%
90 to 179 d	10.5%
180 to 364 d	10.75%
1 a	11%
5 a	12.5%
Minimum deposit $1000 *Interest compounded annually	

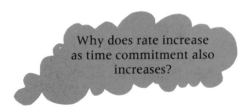

Why does rate increase as time commitment also increases?

What interest would you earn if you invested $1000 for 75 d?

Use the simple interest formula.
$$I = Prt$$
$$= (\$1000)(0.1025)(\tfrac{75}{365})$$
$$= \$21.06$$

At the end of 75 d you would earn $21.06 in interest.

Example 3

Calculate the interest earned on a 5 a investment of $3000 with Cana-Bank.

Since interest is compounded annually and the period is for more than 1 a, use the compound interest formula.

$$A = P(1 + i)^n$$
$$A = \$3000(1.125)^5$$
$$= \$3000(1.802\ 032)$$
$$= \$5406.10$$

From calculator

$A = ?$
$P = \$3000$
$i = 12\tfrac{1}{2}\%$
$= 0.125$
$n = 5$

At the end of 5 a, the investment has accumulated to $5406.10 and has earned $5406.10 − $5000, or $406.10 in interest.

Exercise

B 1. For each investment, calculate the interest earned during the given period.

   (a) $305.20 for 1 d, at 7%/a compounded daily
   (b) $925.40 for 1 d, at 8%/a compounded daily
   (c) $1030.90 for 1 month, at 9%/a compounded monthly
   (d) $540.50 for 1 month at $10\tfrac{1}{2}\%$/a compounded monthly
   (e) $1395.23 for 3 months at 12%/a compounded quarterly
   (f) $295.60 for 6 months, at 10%/a compounded semi-annually

2. Cana-Bank offers term deposits with the following rates and terms.

Term	Rate
30 to 59 d	9%
60 to 89 d	9.25%
90 to 179 d	9.5%
180 to 364 d	9.75%
1 a	10.25%
5 a	11.5%

(a) Calculate the interest earned on a 100 d deposit of $1000.

(b) Calculate the interest earned on a 250 d deposit of $5000.

(c) Calculate the interest earned on a 5 a deposit of $9000.

3. Calculate the interest earned on each term deposit. All interest is compounded annually.

	Amount	Term	Rate
(a)	$1000	85 d	10%
(b)	$2000	90 d	10.5%
(c)	$4000	10 a	11%
(d)	$1000	360 d	10.75%
(e)	$10 000	3 a	12%
(f)	$8000	5 a	12.5%
(g)	$3000	30 d	9.5%
(h)	$5000	5 a	13%
(i)	$6000	119 d	12%
(j)	$9000	2 a	11.75%

Project

1. Chartered banks, trust companies, and credit unions offer many features to meet the different needs of their customers. Visit one of these financial institutions and investigate the following items.

- chequing accounts
- chequing-savings accounts
- daily interest accounts
- true savings accounts
- term deposits
- Canada Savings Bonds
- service charges
- interest rates
- how interest is paid
- business hours

Use the questions that Maureen asked herself to help you decide on the type of account that would be best for you right now.

2. What are some of the differences between chartered banks, trust companies, and credit unions?

3. Why and how do banks, trust companies, and credit unions compete for your savings?

4. What financial institutions are available in your area?

5. Most banks and trust companies offer daily interest chequing accounts. Obtain some information from one of these financial institutions about these accounts and then answer the following questions.

(a) How are the service charges determined?

(b) What are the service charges if a minimum balance is not maintained?

(c) Is the interest applied to the full balance or only a portion of it?

(d) What are the record-keeping methods?

Comparing Simple and Compound Interest $

Graphing is one of the best ways of comparing different situations. The graph below shows the difference between investing $1000 at 12%/a simple interest and investing $1000 at 12%/a compounded annually.

Simple Interest: $A = P(1 + rt)$

Years	1	2	3	4	5	6	7	8	9	10	11	12	13
Amount	1120	1240	1360	1480	1600	1720	1840	1960	2080	2200	2320	2440	2560

Compound Interest: $A = P(1 + i)^n$

Years	1	2	3	4	5	6	7	8	9	10	11	12	13
Amount	1120	1254.93	1404.94	1573.34	1762.82	1973.82	2210.69	2475.96	2773.05	3105.85	3418.53	3895.28	4363.49

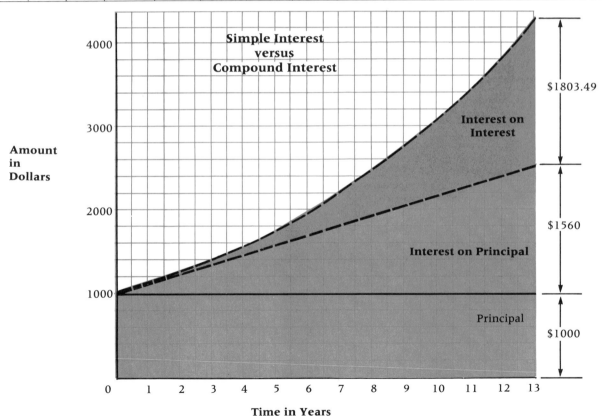

Exercise

B *Use the graph to answer the following questions.*

1. At the end of 13 a, what is the difference in the amount of interest earned between simple and compound interest?

2. About how many years does it take to double your money at 12%/a compounded annually?

3. About how many years does it take to earn four times the original principal if your money earns 12%/a compounded annually?

4. Estimate the number of years it would take to earn four times the original principal if your savings earn 12%/a simple interest. Use the formula below to check your answer.

$$t = \frac{A - P}{Pr}$$

   A is 4 times the original amount; *P* is the principal; *r* is the interest rate; *t* is the time in years.

5. Estimate the number of years it would take to earn eight times the original principal if your savings earn 12%/a compounded annually. Use a calculator and the formula below to check your answer.

$$A = P(1 + i)^n$$

   You may need to make several guesses for the value of *n* before finding a good estimate.

6. A $1000 investment for 12 a can earn:
   - 10%/a simple interest;
   - 10%/a compounded annually.
   Make tables of values and draw a graph like the one on page 230.

Use your graph from Question 6 to answer the following questions.

7. After 12 a what is the difference in the amount of interest earned?

8. About how many years does it take to double your money if it earns 10%/a simple interest? 10%/a compounded annually?

9. About how many years does it take to earn four times the original principal if your money earns 10%/a compounded annually?

10. Estimate the number of years it would take to earn four times the original principal if your money earns 10%/a simple interest. Use the formula given in Question 4 to check your answer.

Side Trip

You can estimate the time required for money to double by dividing 72 by the rate of interest. For example, if the rate is 6% compounded annually, then $1 becomes $2 in 72 ÷ 6, or 12 a.

How long would it take for money compounded annually to double at an interest rate of 8%? 9%? 10%? 12%? How do your last 2 answers compare to those for Questions 2 and 8?

Amount of an Annuity

Ben plans to invest the $500/a he receives from his grandfather. Ben invests the $500 at the end of each year for 4 a, so that he will have enough money to buy a motorcycle when he graduates from high school. The investment pays interest at the rate of 9%/a compounded annually. How much money will Ben have accumulated at the time he makes his last deposit, 4 a from now, if he does not make any withdrawals?

This sequence of regular deposits is an **annuity**. Ben's annuity of $500 can be represented on a *time diagram*.

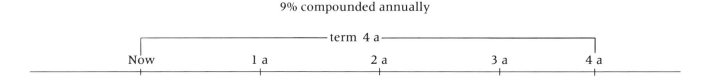

The deposits or payments of an annuity are made at the end of the year unless stated otherwise. In this case, Ben makes the first deposit 1 a from now and the last deposit 4 a from now. The payment interval is 1 a and the term of annuity is 4 a.

To calculate the amount in Ben's account, you must calculate the accumulated value of each deposit as follows.

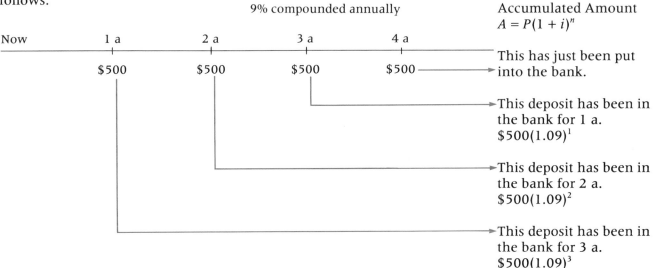

The first $500 deposit accumulates at compounded interest for 3 a, the second $500 accumulates for 2 a, and so on.

The amount in Ben's account is the sum of these accumulated amounts. The amount A of the annuity is calculated below.

$$A = \boxed{\begin{array}{c}\text{Value of}\\\text{Last Deposit}\end{array}} + \boxed{\begin{array}{c}\text{Value of}\\\text{Third Deposit}\end{array}} + \boxed{\begin{array}{c}\text{Value of}\\\text{Second Deposit}\end{array}} + \boxed{\begin{array}{c}\text{Value of}\\\text{First Deposit}\end{array}}$$

$$= \$500 + \$500(1.09) + \$500(1.09)^2 + \$500(1.09)^3$$
$$= \$500 + \$545 + \$594.05 + \$647.51$$
$$= \$2286.56$$

Ben has $2286.56 in his account at the end of 4 a. The interest earned is $2286.56 − (4 × $500), or $286.56.

Example 1

Maria plans to deposit $100 every six months for 3 a in an account that pays interest at the rate of 10%/a compounded semi-annually. How much money will she have in her account at the end of 3 a if she makes her first deposit 6 months from now?
Calculate the interest she earns.
Use a time diagram to organize your solution.

In this example the payment interval is 6 months and the term of the annuity is 3 a.

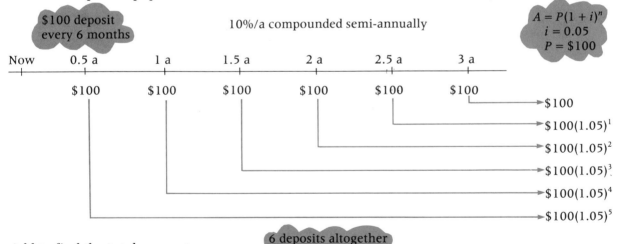

Add to find the total amount.

$$A = \$100 + \$100(1.05)^1 + \$100(1.05)^2 + \$100(1.05)^3 + \$100(1.05)^4 + \$100(1.05)^5$$
$$= \$100 + \$105.00 + \$110.25 + \$115.76 + \$121.55 + \$127.63$$
$$= \$680.19$$

Maria will have $680.19 in her account at the end of 3 a.

The interest earned is $680.19 − (6 × $100), or $80.19.

Exercise

B 1. In each case:
- copy and complete each diagram;
- write out the sum of the accumulated amounts;
- calculate the amount of the annuity;
- calculate the interest earned.

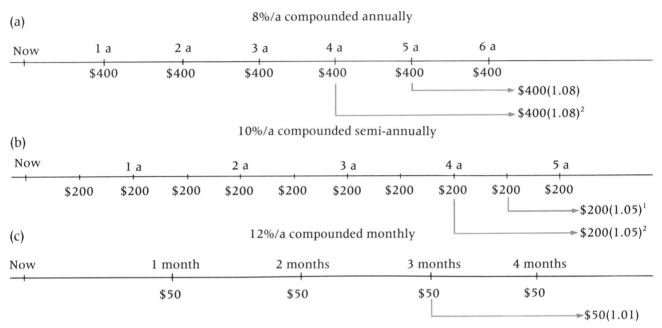

(a)

8%/a compounded annually

(b)

10%/a compounded semi-annually

(c)

12%/a compounded monthly

2. For each annuity in Question 1, what is the term of the annuity, the value of each payment, and the payment interval?

3. Draw a time diagram for each of the following. Calculate the amount of the annuity and the interest earned.

	Value of Each Payment	Payment Interval	Term of Annuity	Interest Rate
(a)	$2000	1 a	4 a	7%/a compounded annually
(b)	$500	6 months	3 a	18%/a compounded semi-annually
(c)	$300	1 month	6 months	12%/a compounded monthly

4. Ann is saving for a trip. She deposits $200 every 6 months for 4 a in an account earning 10%/a compounded semi-annually. How much will be in the account at the end of 4 a if she makes the first deposit 6 months from now? How much will the annuity earn?

234

Present Value of an Amount

Mario just won $1000 in a lottery. He wants to spend some of his winnings, but he also knows that he will need $1000 in 3 a to pay for his first year's college tuition.

How much should he invest today to have $1000 in 3 a, if a trust company will pay interest at 10%/a compounded annually?

Let x represent the amount he should invest today.
The time diagram below shows the amount, x, and its value, $1000, 3 a from now.

10%/a compounded annually

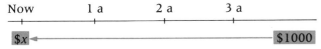

Mario wants $x to increase to $1000. You know $A = P(1 + i)^n$; substitute known values in the formula.

$$1000 = x(1.10)^3$$
$$x = \frac{1000}{(1.10)^3}$$
$$= 1000 \times \frac{1}{(1.10)^3}$$

$A = 1000$
$P = x$
$i = 10\%$ or 0.10
$n = 3$

Evaluate using a calculator or the table on pages 457 to 458.

$$x = 1000 \times 0.751\ 31$$
$$= 751.31$$

If Mario invests $751.31 now, he will have $1000 in 3 a.

There is a general formula for the value today, or **present value** (*PV*).

$$PV = \frac{F}{(1 + i)^n}$$

PV is present value;
F is future amount;
i is the interest rate per period;
n is the number of interest periods.

Example 1

What amount invested today will accumulate to $3000 5 a from now? The interest rate is 12%/a compounded semi-annually.

Make a time diagram.

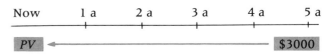

Apply the formula for present value.

$$PV = \frac{F}{(1 + i)^n}$$
$$= \frac{\$3000}{(1.06)^{10}}$$
$$= \$3000 \times \frac{1}{(1.06)^{10}}$$
$$= \$3000 \times 0.558\ 39$$
$$= \$1675.18$$

$P = \$3000$
$i = 0.06$
$n = 10$

If $1675.18 is invested today, it will accumulate to $3000 in 5 a.

Exercise

B 1. Evaluate each of the following.

(a) $\dfrac{1}{(1.07)^5}$ (d) $\dfrac{10}{(1.05)^{20}}$

(b) $\dfrac{1}{(1.035)^{10}}$ (e) $\dfrac{300}{(1.09)^{12}}$

(c) $\dfrac{2000}{(1.08)^{15}}$ (f) $\dfrac{455}{(1.07)^{22}}$

2. What is the future value, F, for each of the quantities in Question 1?

3. Calculate the present value, PV, for each of the following.

(a)

9%/a compounded annually

(b)

10%/a compounded semi-annually

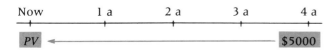

(c)

10%/a compounded quarterly

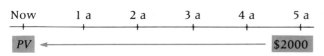

(d)

12%/a compounded monthly

4. Calculate the present value, PV, for each of the following.

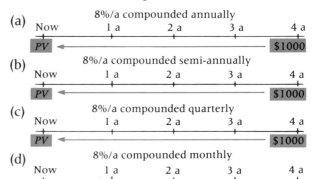

What significance does the compounding period have with respect to the present value?

5. Calculate the present value of each of the following future amounts.

(a) $3000 in 6 a at 10%/a compounded annually

(b) $400 in 4 a at 12%/a compounded semi-annually

(c) $600 in 5 a at 8%/a compounded quarterly

(d) $1200 in 3 a at 18%/a compounded monthly

6. Pat wants to have $5000 available in 5 a to be able to start a business. How much should Pat invest today in a term deposit that pays interest at 10%/a compounded annually?

7. What amount of money invested today is equivalent to a payment of $1000 2 a from now if money earns interest at 14%/a compounded semi-annually?

8. Jeff is planning to take a trip to Europe in 2 a. How much should he invest today at 12%/a compounded quarterly so that he will have $2000 for the trip?

Present Value of an Annuity

Albert has just inherited $10 000. He'd like to deposit enough money today so that he can withdraw $2000 at the end of each year for 5 a. His first withdrawal will be made 1 a from now. What is the least amount that Albert should invest today if a trust company will pay interest at 10%/a compounded annually?

Albert needs to calculate the present value of each $2000 withdrawal as follows. A time diagram can help to organize the solution.

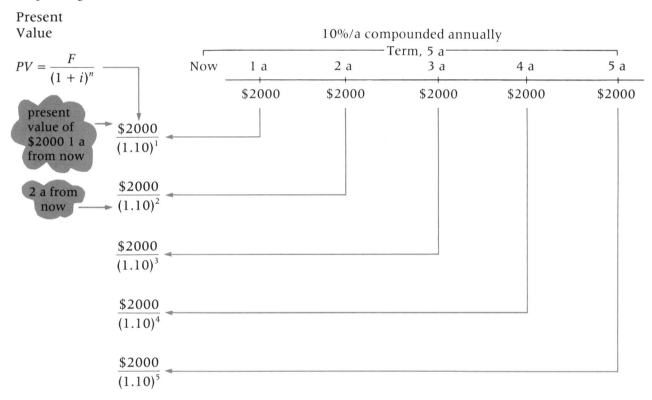

The amount, P, that must be invested now is the sum of the present value of each $2000 withdrawal.

$P = \dfrac{\$2000}{(1.10)^1} + \dfrac{\$2000}{(1.10)^2} + \dfrac{\$2000}{(1.10)^3} + \dfrac{\$2000}{(1.10)^4} + \dfrac{\$2000}{(1.10)^5}$

$= \$2000(0.909\ 09) + \$2000(0.826\ 45) + \$2000(0.751\ 31) + \$2000(0.683\ 01) + \$2000(0.620\ 92)$

$= \$1818.18 + \$1652.90 + \$1502.62 + \$1366.02 + \$1241.84$

$= \$7581.56$

The present value of the 5 regular withdrawals of $2000 is $7581.56. This present value is also referred to as the **present value of the annuity**.

Albert must invest $7581.56 today so that he can withdraw $2000 at the end of each year for the next 5 a.

The payment interval for this annuity is 1 a; the term of the annuity is 5 a.

Example 1

Kathy wants to buy a stereo today. She can afford to make payments of $100 at the end of each month for 4 months. How much can she borrow now at 18%/a compounded monthly to buy a stereo?

Make a time diagram to organize the solution.

18%/a compounded monthly $i = 1.5\%$

Now	1 month	2 months	3 months	4 months
	$100	$100	$100	$100

$$\frac{\$100}{(1.015)^1}$$

$$\frac{\$100}{(1.015)^2}$$

$$\frac{\$100}{(1.015)^3}$$

$$\frac{\$100}{(1.015)^4}$$

Calculate the sum of the present value of each $100 payment.

$$P = \frac{\$100}{(1.015)^1} + \frac{\$100}{(1.015)^2} + \frac{\$100}{(1.015)^3} + \frac{\$100}{(1.015)^4}$$

$$= \$100(0.985\ 22) + \$100(0.970\ 66) + \$100(0.956\ 32) + \$100(0.942\ 18)$$
$$= \$98.52 + \$97.07 + \$95.63 + \$94.22$$
$$= \$385.44$$

Kathy could borrow $385.44 now.

Exercise

B **1.** In each case:
   • copy and complete the diagram;
   • write the sum of the present values for each withdrawal.

(a)   10%/a compounded annually

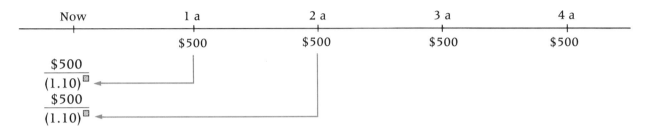

(b)   10%/a compounded semi-annually

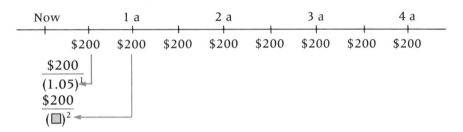

(c)   12%/a compounded quarterly

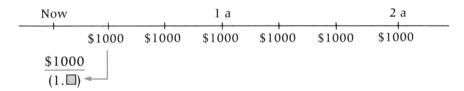

(d)   18%/a compounded monthly

Payment every month

2. In each case:
- copy and complete each time diagram;
- write the sum of the present values for each withdrawal;
- calculate the present value of each annuity by finding this sum.

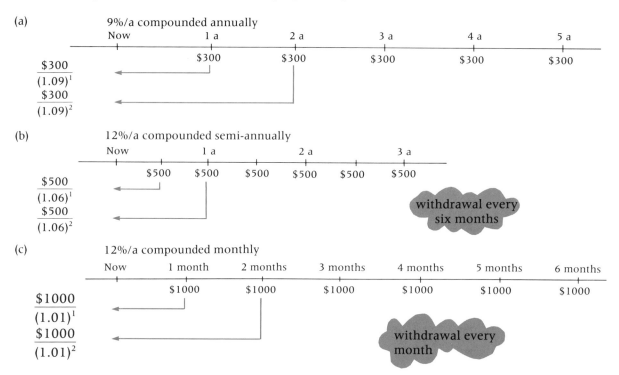

(a)

9%/a compounded annually

$\dfrac{\$300}{(1.09)^1}$

$\dfrac{\$300}{(1.09)^2}$

(b)

12%/a compounded semi-annually

$\dfrac{\$500}{(1.06)^1}$

$\dfrac{\$500}{(1.06)^2}$

withdrawal every six months

(c)

12%/a compounded monthly

$\dfrac{\$1000}{(1.01)^1}$

$\dfrac{\$1000}{(1.01)^2}$

withdrawal every month

3. Susan decides to deposit enough money now from her $100 000 lottery win so that she can withdraw $20 000 at the end of each year for 6 a. Her first withdrawal will be made 1 a from now. A bank will pay interest at 10%/a compounded annually.

(a) Draw a time diagram.
(b) Calculate the sum of the present values of each $20 000 withdrawal.
(c) What is the smallest amount that she can invest now at 10%/a compounded annually?
(d) How much money remains from her winnings for her to spend now?

4. Joe wants to borrow money to buy a car. What is the smallest amount that Joe can borrow today so that he can repay the loan in 5 regular monthly payments of $500? The first payment is due at the end of the month. The interest rate is 18%/a compounded monthly. (Draw a time diagram.)

240

Unit 13 Review

1. Calculate the interest in each case.

   (a) a minimum balance of $210.50 for 1 d, at 10%/a compounded daily
   (b) a minimum balance of $350.00 for 1 month, at 12%/a compounded monthly

2. Calculate the interest earned on each term deposit. All interest is compounded annually.

	Amount	Term	Rate
(a)	$1000	43 d	9%
(b)	$3000	95 d	9.5%
(c)	$4000	2 a	12%
(d)	$10 000	5 a	13.5%

3. An investment of $2000 over 12 a has interest calculated as:
   • 9% simple interest;
   • 9% interest compounded annually.

   (a) Make a table of values for each interest rate and make a graph to represent the situation.
   (b) In 12 a, what is the difference in the interest earned?
   (c) About how many years does it take to double your money for each interest rate?

4. Copy and complete each of the following time diagrams. In each case, calculate the amount of the annuity and the interest earned.

   (a)   9% compounded annually

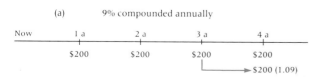

   (b)   10% compounded semi-annually

5. For each of the following draw a time diagram, then calculate the amount of the annuity and the interest earned.

   (a) an investment of $300 for a term of 5 a, with payment intervals of 1 a, at 8%/a compounded annually
   (b) an investment of $500 for a term of 4 a, with payment intervals of 6 months, at 10%/a compounded semi-annually
   (c) an investment of $100 for a term of 6 months, with payment intervals of 1 month, at 12% compounded monthly

6. Jerry saves money by depositing $200 at the end of each year in a credit union that pays interest at 10%/a compounded annually. How much does Jerry have in this account at the end of 6 a if the first deposit is made 1 a from now?

7. Michelle decides to deposit $10 in a new bank account at the end of each month for 5 months. The account pays interest at 12%/a compounded monthly. How much will Michelle have on deposit at the end of 5 months if she makes the first deposit 1 month from now?

8. Evaluate each of the following.

(a) $\dfrac{100}{(1.08)^5}$ (c) $\dfrac{300}{(1.09)^7}$

(b) $\dfrac{200}{(1.015)^{12}}$ (d) $\dfrac{10}{(1.06)^{15}}$

9. Calculate the present value, *PV*, for each of the following.

(a) 8%/a compounded annually

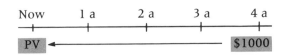

(b) 10%/a compounded semi-annually

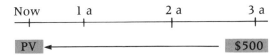

10. Calculate the present value for each of the following future amounts.

(a) $2000 in 5 a at 9%/a compounded annually
(b) $1000 in 3 a at 12%/a compounded semi-annually
(c) $4000 in 2 a at 12%/a compounded monthly

11. Janice wants to have $4500 available in 3 a so that she can pay for her college tuition. How much should she invest today in a term deposit that pays interest at 12%/a compounded annually?

12. Copy and complete each of the following time diagrams. In each case, calculate the present value of the annuity.

(a) 8%/a compounded annually

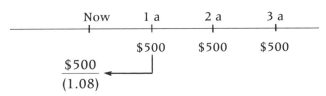

(b) 18%/a compounded monthly

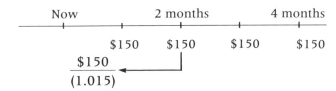

13. Calculate the present value of each of the following annuities. Draw a time diagram to organize your calculations.

(a) $1000 received at the end of each year for 5 a at 9%/a compounded annually
(b) $500 received at the end of each month for 6 months at 12%/a compounded monthly

14. Jeff received $10 000 from a sale of land. He wants to invest enough money today so that he can withdraw $2000 at the end of each year for 5 a. His first withdrawal will be made 1 a from now.

(a) What is the smallest amount that he must invest now at 10%/a compounded annually?
(b) How much is left that he can use towards buying a new stereo?

Unit 14

Cost of Transportation

Buying a Used Car

Most of us look forward to the sense of freedom and independence associated with driving our own car.

Before you make such a major purchase, though, you should check into the *costs* involved in owning a car.

Bennie wants to buy a used car. In addition to the price asked for the car, and insurance costs associated with driving it, Bennie must consider certain other costs.

- **sales tax**–based on the selling price of the car
- **licence and transfer fee**–usually a fixed amount, payable to the provincial transportation authority
- **certification fee**–an amount paid to a registered auto mechanic for determining the "roadworthiness" of a vehicle
- **repair costs**–work necessary to make the car legally safe for operation

The sales tax, transfer fee, and certification fee vary from province to province. Repair costs depend on the condition of the car itself.

Bennie buys a used car from a dealer. The car is priced at $3750, certified, with sales tax at 7% and a transfer fee of $5. No repair work is needed on the car.

What is the total cost to Bennie?

The calculation for total cost is shown below.

- Price $3750.00
- Sales Tax   262.50 ← $3750 × 0.07
- Transfer Fee   5.00

                    $4017.50

The total cost for the car is $4017.50.

If you're looking for a used car, you'll probably check the papers as well as enquiring at automobile dealerships.

d'Elegance 4 dr., fully loaded, silver, excel. cond. $6,600.	78 Mercury Zephyr 4 door, 4 cyl, 4 spd, P/S, P/B, 45,000 orig. mi. A-1, no rust. Cert. $1,675.
79 CAMARO Z28. Cert. New motor. Asking $8,500 or best offer. Call Frank, after 6 p.m.	78 Mustang, excel. cond., no rust. $2,900 neg. Cert. evgs.
79 Camaro, 6 cyl. P/S, P/B, 40,000 mi. mint, $4,500.	78 Mustang Ghia, 2 dr., 6 cyl., auto, p/s/b, AM/FM, excel. cond., $2,795. after 5:30.
79 Chev Caprice, white, clean. $3750. Cert. Must Sell	78 Peugeot ask $3,100 cert. or best offer. call 8-2 p.m.
79 Chrysler 5th Avenue, loaded, $5,600. Mint condition	78 Plymouth Sapporo, 5 spd., A1, no rust, cert. $3,300.
79 Cougar XR7, immac. cond., loaded, low mi. 1 owner.	78 Pontiac Catalina, 2 dr., auto. V8, P/S, P/B, AM/FM cassette, A-1. $2,250 cert
79 Dodge Omni 024 Sport, Rally rims, low mi., clean, radio, winterized, cert. $2,150.	78 VW Rabbit, Deluxe, 2 dr. stan., excellent cond., 61,000 mi., after 6.
79 EL CAMINO, excl. cond. reasonable, call after 4.	77 AMC station wagon, excel. cond. Certifiable. $800
79 Fairmont, $3200, 6 cyl. auto., A-1. Cert. -860	77 Aspen, 2 dr., p/s&b, radio, $1,200, cert.
79 Fiat Brava, 131, silver metallic with gold interior, 5 spd., stan., Pioneer KPX 9500 radio, sunroof, excel. cond. No winters. Ideal touring car. Cert. $4,200. Serious calls only. Days Angelo.	77 Buick Century, no rust, beautiful cond., cert. $1,800.
	77 Cadillac Seville, grey, excellent cond. $7500. Chatham

Margaret is buying a used car that has been advertised in the paper. She pays $2400 for the car, and there is 8% sales tax. The transfer fee is $9.50. Margaret agrees to pay for the brake repair ($85.32) as well as the mechanic's certification fee of $28.50. Find Margaret's total cost for the car.

- Price $2400.00
- Sales Tax   192.00 ← $2400 × 0.08
- Transfer Fee   9.50
- Brake Repairs   85.32
- Certification Fee   28.50

                    $2715.32

Margaret must pay a total of $2715.32 for the car.

Exercise

A 1. State as many reasons as possible why it might be better to buy a used car rather than a new car.

2. Discuss advantages and disadvantages for buying a used car from an authorized dealer rather than from an individual.

3. List some sources of information concerning each of the following.
   - prices of used cars
   - performance rating
   - history of ownership

B 4. Sally purchases a used car from a dealer. The car is priced at $3250, including certification, and the sales tax in that province is 10%. If the transfer fee is $6, determine how much Sally must pay for the car.

5. George buys a used car from his friend after agreeing to pay for certification of the car. The price of the car was $2300 and George paid for the following repairs.
   - new exhaust system $145.80
   - disc brake pads $ 23.40
   - tune-up $ 39.95

   The mechanic's fee for certification was $30 and there was a transfer fee of $5. If sales tax was 8%, what was the total amount that George paid for the car?

6. Danielle's father agrees to pay $2000 towards a car for her to use at college. Danielle finds just the car she is looking for: a used compact car priced at $2199. The seller agrees to pay for any repairs to have the car certified and Danielle agrees to pay the certification fee of $31.50. She also pays a transfer fee of $7.50 and sales tax of 6%.

   (a) What is the total cost of the car?
   (b) How much does Danielle have to pay?

7. Sam purchases a used car by answering a newspaper ad. The seller offers Sam a choice: pay $5000 plus sales tax (7%), certification fee ($30), and transfer fee ($8), with the seller paying for all repairs necessary for certification, *or* pay $4500 plus repairs, sales tax, certification fee, and transfer fee. Sam decides to go with the second option and pays for the following repairs.
   - bodywork, repainting $485.00
   - 2 new tires $184.00
   - brake shoes, universal joints $ 88.78

   How much would Sam have saved by taking the first offer?

Project

1. Enquire at a local service station and determine what major items on a car a mechanic must check to certify that the car is roadworthy.
2. Use newspaper ads to investigate the kind of used car you could purchase for $1500.

Buying a New Car

If you decide to buy a new car, some of the equipment will be *standard*, and some will be optional. The sticker price of the car is the **base price** plus the cost of any optional equipment.
Here is a typical list of standard and optional equipment on a new car.

Compact 4-door Sedan—Base Price $8761.00—Options List			
Standard Equipment		High Capacity Battery	
2.0 L 4-cylinder engine		Floor Console	
4-speed manual transmission		AM Radio (Fixed Antenna)	
Power Brakes		Vinyl Trim	
Fibreglass-Belted Radial B/Wall Tires		Deluxe Wheel Covers	
Optional Equipment		AM-FM ETR Radio with	
Transmission—Manual Overdrive	$100.00	① 4-Speaker Stereo System	$166.70
—3-speed Automatic	$483.95	② Item ①, plus Digital Display	$214.00
Power Door Locks	$153.80	③ Item ②, plus Cassette Tape Player	$334.45
Power Rear Lid Release	$ 49.45	④ Item ③, plus Seek and Scan	$549.55
6-way Power Seat (Driver)	$263.50	Special Handling Suspension	$ 37.65
Power Steering	$250.60	Wire Wheel Covers and Locks	$235.50
Power Windows	$318.35	Rallye Wheels with Trim Rings	$ 52.70
Air Conditioner	$765.70	Chromed Super Stock Wheels	$195.75
Plus Federal Excise Tax	$100.00	Pulse Windshield Wiper System	$ 61.30
Front Seat Armrest	$ 72.05	Steering Wheel—Custom Sport	$ 62.40
Luggage Carrier	$122.60	—Tilt-a-way	$128.00
Sunroof (tinted, removeable)	$367.80	Extended Warranty	
Custom Cloth Trim Interior	$306.50	A—36 months or 60 000 km	$375.00
Accent Body Stripes	$ 54.85	B—48 months or 80 000 km	$625.00

The options that Carrie Simms wants on her new car are automatic transmission, power steering, rallye wheels, AM-FM radio with 4-speaker stereo digital display and cassette tape player, and extended warranty plan A.

Determine the sticker price of Carrie's car. If Pre-Delivery Inspection (PDI) and freight total $356.80, and sales tax is 7%, what total amount does Carrie pay for the car?

• Base Price	$ 8 761.00
• Automatic Transmission	483.95
• Power Steering	250.60
• Rallye Wheels	52.70
• Radio Option	334.45
• Extended Warranty (A)	375.00
• PDI and Freight	356.80
Sticker Price	$10 614.50
• Sales Tax at 7%	743.02
Total	$11 357.52

Carrie must pay $11 357.52 for her new car.

Exercise

A 1. State as many reasons as possible why it might be better to purchase a new car rather than a used car.

2. Where can you find information to compare the value and performance of new cars?

B 3. Using the base price and Options List on the opposite page, calculate the sticker price in each case.
   (a) PDI and freight $289.75
       Manual overdrive
       Power windows
       Air conditioner
       Luggage carrier
       Accent body stripes
       Chromed super stock wheels
   (b) PDI and freight $401.62
       Automatic transmission
       Power door locks
       Power rear lid release
       6-way power seat
       Power steering
       Power windows
       Front seat armrest
       Sunroof
       Custom cloth trim interior
       AM-FM radio with item ④
       Wire wheel covers and locks
       Pulse wiper system
       Tilt-a-way steering wheel
   (c) PDI and freight $319.89
       Manual overdrive
       Sunroof
       Accent body stripes
       AM-FM radio with item ③
       Special handling suspension
       Chromed super stock wheels
       Custom sport steering wheel
       Extended warranty B

4. If sales tax is at 8%, calculate the total price of each car in Question 3.

5. Charles cannot spend more than $11 750 (including 6% sales tax) on a new car. There are two cars, with options as listed below, that Charles is interested in buying. Which car, if either, can he afford to buy?
   (a) PDI and freight $365.11
       Manual overdrive
       Power steering
       Air conditioning
       Accent body stripes
       AM-FM radio with item ④
       Wire wheel covers and locks
       Custom sport steering wheel
   (b) PDI and freight $342.78
       Sunroof
       Luggage carrier
       Custom cloth trim interior
       AM-FM radio with item ③
       Chromed super stock wheels
       Tilt-a-way steering wheel
       Continuous protection Plan A

6. Suppose that you want to buy a new car with base price and available options as shown on the opposite page. If PDI and freight total $390.46, what would the sticker price of *your* car be?

7. If PDI and freight total $379.29, what would be the sticker price of the most expensive car possible, using the options sheet opposite?

Project

Contact a local automobile dealership and price the car of your dreams!

Financing a Car

Whether you decide to buy a used car or a new car, you may find it necessary to pay for your purchase by *instalments*.

PROBABLY $325 A MONTH FOREVER!

Bette buys a used car from a dealer for a total price of $4350 plus sales tax at 7%. She makes a down payment of $1000 and agrees to make 24 monthly payments of $190 to clear the debt.

There are several questions that Bette should consider before she signs the contract with the dealer.

What is the total cash price?

> $4350 + 7% of $4350
> = $4350 + 304.50
> = $4654.50

What is the instalment price?
> Down payment + Instalment payments
> = $1000 + ($190 × 24)
> = $1000 + $4560
> = $5560

24 payments of $190 each

What is the finance charge?

> Instalment price − Cash price
> $5560 − $4654.50
> = $905.50

What is the interest rate being charged?

There is a formula that Bette can use to calculate the true interest rate of this instalment purchase.

$$r = \frac{200NC}{P(n + 1)} \%$$

r is the true interest rate per year;
N is the number of payment intervals per year;
C is the finance charge (total instalment price minus cash price);
P is the principal (cash price minus down payment);
n is the number of payments.
First find the values of the variables to substitute into the formula.

$N = 12$ ← *Payments are monthly, and there are 12 months/a.*

$C = \$905.50$

$P = $ Cash price − Down payment
$\quad = \$4654.50 - \$1000$
$\quad = \$3654.50$

$n = 24$ ← *total number of payments made*

Now substitute.
$$r = \frac{200NC}{P(n + 1)} \%$$
$$= \frac{(200)\,(12)\,(905.50)}{(3654.50)\,(24 + 1)} \%$$
$$= 23.8\%$$

The true rate of interest on the purchase is 23.8%.

Exercise

B 1. For each used car shown below, determine:
  - the cash price (sales tax is at 6%);
  - the instalment price;
  - the finance charge.

(a)

A GREAT BUY!
ONLY $3695 cash
AND IT'S YOURS!
(OR PAY $500 DOWN AND
$177.95/MONTH FOR
24 MONTHS)

(b)

EXCELLENT CONDITION
Drive it away for
only $4999⁰⁰
NO 1
OR PAY $800 DOWN
PLUS 36 MONTHLY
PAYMENTS OF $162.55

(c)

BUY OF THE WEEK
$2800⁰⁰ cash
or pay $287.26/month for
1 year — no money down!

(d)

JUST WHAT YOU'VE
BEEN LOOKING FOR!
$6250⁰⁰ CASH
OR $1000 DOWN PLUS $242.97
A MONTH FOR THREE YEARS —
ask for Louie.

2. Calculate the true interest rate for each part of Question 1.

3. Ruth buys a used car for $5200 with sales tax at 8%. She pays $2000 down, then pays off the rest of the debt by making 18 monthly payments of $246.21.

  (a) Determine the finance charge.
  (b) Calculate the true rate of interest Ruth is paying.

4. Judith purchases a new car whose sticker price is $8714.65, plus sales tax at 7%. She makes a down payment of 30% followed by 24 monthly payments of $313.90.

  (a) Calculate the finance charge.
  (b) What rate of interest is Judith paying?

5. José purchases a new car with the following options.
  - PDI and freight $345.09
  - Automatic transmission
  - Power steering
  - Sunroof
  - Radio option ③
  - Wire wheel covers and locks
  - Extended warranty A

  (a) Use the base price and Options List on page 246 to determine the total cash price of the car (5% tax).
  (b) If José puts $3800 down, and pays the remainder in 36 monthly payments of $270.57, calculate the true rate of interest he is paying.

Cost of Operating a Car

Once you have invested in an automobile, you will want to keep it running properly. Using and maintaining a car involve **operating expenses**. Operating expenses fall into 2 categories.

- *variable costs* like gasoline, oil, regular maintenance, and repairs
- *fixed costs* like licence fees, insurance, and depreciation

An automobile generally decreases in value as it gets older. This loss in value is **depreciation**. The chart below gives approximate depreciated values for a medium-priced automobile.

Age (Years)	Value after Depreciation (percent of original cost)
1	70%
2	56%
3	42%
4	33%
5	25%

If a car is purchased new for $11 500, then its value after 3 a would be about 42% of $11 500.

42% of $11 500 = $4830

How much does the value of the car drop in the fifth year?
Depreciation in the Fifth Year
= Value at Age 4 − Value at Age 5
= 33% − 25%
= 8%
So the value drops 8% of $11 500 or $920 during the fifth year.

Example 1

I'LL TAKE THAT ONE!

Jack uses his lottery winnings to purchase a new car for $18 560. During the first year of operation of his car, Jack keeps track of all expenses and summarizes them as below.

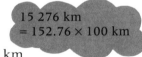

100% − 70% = 30%

Gas, oil, lubrication	$ 966.83
Licence fees	53.00
Insurance	2478.00
Depreciation (30% of $18 560)	5568.00
Total Expenses	9335.83

- What is Jack's average monthly cost of operating his car?

$9335.83 ÷ 12 = $778

- If Jack drove 15 276 km during the year, what was the operating cost per 100 km?

15 276 km = 152.76 × 100 km

($9335.83÷152.76)/100 km
= $61.11/100 km

The average monthly cost of operating Jack's car is $778.
The operating cost per 100 km is $61.11.

Example 2

Karen originally paid $9375 for her car when it was new. She has driven 12 600 km in the fourth year of owning the car. During the year she paid an average of 45¢/L for gasoline and the fuel consumption for her car was 7.8 L/100 km.

She also spent $78.43 for oil and lubrication, $865 for insurance, $48 for licence fees, and $316 for repairs. Find the cost per 100 km to operate her car during the fourth year of operation.

• Account for depreciation.

9% of $9375 = $843.75   42% − 33% = 9%

• Calculate fuel costs for the year.

$$\text{Fuel used} = \frac{7.8 \text{ L}}{100 \text{ km}} \times 12\ 600 \text{ km}$$
$$= 982.8 \text{ L}$$

$$\text{Fuel cost} = 982.8 \text{ L} \times \$0.45/\text{L}$$
$$= \$442.26$$

• Now find the total of depreciation and fuel costs together with the costs given for other expenses.

Depreciation	$ 843.75
Fuel cost	442.26
Oil and lubrication	78.43
Insurance	865.00
Licence	48.00
Repairs	316.00
Total costs	$2593.44

• Now divide total costs by 126 to find cost per 100 km.
$2593.44 ÷ 126 = $20.58

Karen has spent $20.58/100 km to operate her car during the fourth year.

Exercise

A 1. State reasons why the greatest depreciation for a car is during the first year.
   2. Why would some makes of cars depreciate at a different rate than others?
   3. What types of cars depreciate quickly? slowly?
   4. Name a car that might increase in value over time. Give reasons.
   5. Give reasons why a car might:
      • decrease in value;
      • increase in value.

B 6. Joe purchases a new car for $10 600. Using the table on the opposite page, determine each of the following.

   (a) Depreciated value after 2 a
   (b) The value it depreciates during the second year.
   (c) Its depreciated value at the end of 3 a; 4 a; 5 a.
   (d) The value it depreciates during the fourth year.

   7. For each of the following, determine
      • average monthly cost of operation;
      • operating cost per 100 km.
      All items are costs for 1 a.

Item \ Car	(a)	(b)	(c)	(d)
Gas, Oil, Lubrication	$619.28	$937.12	$748.92	$893.41
Insurance	$865	$1281	$986	$1192
Licence	$48	$63	$47	$53
Repairs	$55.16	—	$411.45	$214.65
Depreciation	$752	$1156	$960	$842
Distance Driven (km)	12678	16750	13473	14550

8. The figures below show expenses during the first year's operation of a car purchased new for $12 975.
   - Gas, oil, lubrication $1058.63
   - Insurance $1751.00
   - Licence fees $ 41.00

   The odometer reading is 14 762 km at the end of the year. Taking depreciation into account, calculate the following.

   (a) the average monthly operating cost
   (b) the cost per 100 km

9. In the third year of operation of her car, Sarah drives 13 941 km. On the average, she paid about $0.43/L for gasoline and her car's fuel consumption was 6.8 L/100 km. During the year, Sarah spent $92.38 for oil and lubrication, $836 for insurance, $48 for license fees, and $269.84 for repairs. If Sarah paid $9985 for her car when it was new, calculate the cost per 100 km to operate her car during the third year she owns it.

10. At the start of the fifth year of operation the odometer on Dwight's car read 87 456 km and 104 470 km at the end of the year. The cost of gasoline averaged 45¢/L throughout the year, and the car's average fuel consumption was 7.1 L/100 km.
    Dwight's other expenses for the year are listed below.
    - Oil and lubrication $ 101.68
    - Insurance $1260.00
    - Licence fees $ 63.00
    - Repairs $ 658.16

    If Dwight paid $8265 for his car when it was new, determine the cost per 100 km to operate it during the fifth year he owned it.

11. Pat's gasoline purchase and service record for the month of August is shown below.

Date	Cost	Litres	Odometer Readings (km)	
Aug. 3	$4.50	10.4	52 140	
Aug. 8	$13.00	29.6	52 570	
Aug. 10	Servicing	(oil, lube, filter, PCV valve)		
	$23.85			
Aug. 13	$17.00	39.9	53 044	
Aug. 18	$22.00	44.1	53 620	
Aug. 22	$20.00	40.1	54 107	
Aug. 26	$22.00	46.5	54 610	
Aug. 31	$12.00	27.3	54 921	

Pat also has annual costs of $1340.85 for insurance and $54 for licence fees.

If Pat paid $12 650 for the car when it was new (three years ago), calculate the cost per 100 km to operate the car during the month of August.

Project

1. Determine the approximate cost of each of the following by contacting the appropriate place of business.
   - Oil change
   - Tankful of gasoline
   - New set of spark plugs
   - Front wheel alignment
   - New set of tires
   - Windshield replacement
   - Brake job
   - Cost of one year's insurance on the car of your choice

2. Investigate the fuel consumption rating for several new cars. Use your figures to calculate fuel costs for driving each car 20 000 km. Use current fuel costs.

Maintaining a Car

Regular servicing of your car is excellent preventative maintenance: it will save you money in the long run!

The chart below shows items requiring regular attention, as well as frequency and costs for the service.

Item	Frequency	Typical Cost
Oil Change	3000 km or 2 months	$2.29/L
Oil Filter	6000 km (with every other oil change)	$3.99 + $1.50 labor
Lubrication	With each oil change	$4.25
PCV Valve	Every 9000 km or 6 months	$2.69
Air Filter	15 000 km	$6.15
Gas Filter	Every 9000 km or 6 months	$2.19 + $1.50 labor
Spark Plugs	Check every 10 000 km	$1.79 + $1.00 labor
Antifreeze	Check each fall	$9.49/4 L

Exercise

B **1.** Karen takes her car into a service station for servicing. Determine the total cost for the service items shown.
  - Oil change (4.5 L of oil)
  - Lubrication
  - PCV valve
  - Air filter

  All items are subject to sales tax of 8%

2. Determine the total cost for the service items listed below. There is a sales tax of 7% for all items, but the labor charges are not taxable.
  - Oil (4.5 L) and oil filter
  - Lubrication
  - Gas filter
  - Set of 6 spark plugs

3. Each fall, Arnie takes his car in for servicing to prepare for winter. A typical list of service items is shown below.
  - Oil (4.5 L) and oil filter
  - Lubrication
  - PCV valve
  - Gas filter
  - Spark plugs (set of 4)

  In addition to these items, Arnie had the brake fluid "topped up" for $0.75, bought a bottle of windshield-washer solution for $1.89, and replaced both wiper blades (on special at 2 for $7.98). On the recommendation of the mechanic, he also had the radiator flushed and tested ($17.95 for labor) and refilled with two 4 L containers of antifreeze. Calculate Arnie's total bill if the sales tax is 10%. (Labor is not taxable.)

Cost of Other Means of Transportation

Not everyone wants to own a car. There are situations where it is more economical to use other means of transportation.

Jodi travels by bus between her apartment and the college she attends. The one-way fare is $0.75 and she attends classes 5 d each week. Since she attends college for a total of 27 weeks, she calculates annual transportation costs to and from school as follows.

- Daily fare 2 × $0.75 = $1.50
- Weekly fare 5 × $1.50 = $7.50
- Annual fare, 27 weeks at $7.50/week
    27 × $7.50 = $202.50

Jodi's annual school transportation expense is $202.50.

Chris works the night shift at a meat-packing plant and must use a taxi to return home.
Taxi fare is made up of 2 parts.
- a fixed rate of $1.60
- a variable rate of $1.20/km

Chris lives 8.4 km from work. How much is the one-way taxi fare home?
    $1.60 + ($1.20 × 8.4)
    = $1.60 + $10.08
    = $11.68

The one-way fare is $11.68.

Tony decides to rent a car for one week's vacation. The rental agency quotes the following rates for a compact car.

- $160/week
- first 1000 km free
- 6¢/km for distances over 1000 km
- insurance included
- You only pay for the gas!

Tony estimates that he will travel about 2100 km during the week and he knows that gasoline costs about 48¢/L. Since the car has a fuel consumption of 5.8 L/100 km, Tony calculates his transportation expenses for the week as shown below.

- Calculate the cost for 2100 km.

    (2100 − 1000) km × $0.06/km
    = 1100 km × $0.06/km
    = $66

    > 1000 free kilometres

- Calculate fuel costs.

    Fuel required = 5.8 L/100 km × 2100 km
                  = 121.8 L
    Cost of fuel = 121.8 L × $0.48/L
                 = $58.46

- Now total the costs.

Basic weekly rate	$160.00
Cost for 2100 km	66.00
Fuel cost	58.46
	$284.46

Tony's transportation expenses for the week would be $284.46.

Exercise

A 1. State as many advantages and disadvantages as you can for each method of transportation.

(a) "shanks ponies" (walking)
(b) bicycle
(c) motorcycle
(d) taxi
(e) bus or subway
(f) train
(g) airplane
(h) automobile

Time?
Comfort?
Cost?

B 2. While attending a city high school, Grant uses the bus for transportation to and from school. He makes the return trip for 5 d each week for 30 weeks. In addition, he travels downtown by bus 43 times over the school year to see movies, attend sporting events, and to visit his girlfriend. If one-way student fare is $0.55, how much does Grant spend on bus transportation during the school year?

3. Ellen and 2 friends share equally in the expense of cab fare to and from work, 5 d each week. They live 11.2 km from work and cab fare is at a fixed rate of $1.75 plus a variable rate of $1.35/km. Determine Ellen's share of the weekly transportation expense.

$1.75/km... $1.35/km....divided by 3....

4. Ernie and 3 friends rent a full-size car for a weekend to visit some friends in a nearby city. The rate for the car is $36.95/d for each of the 3 d, with the first 100 km "free", and 8¢/km thereafter. The boys agree to pay an extra $5.50/d for total insurance coverage. When they return the car, they find they have driven a total of 673 km and spent $34.66 on gasoline. How much did the weekend transportation cost each boy?

5. Before entering college in the fall, Heidi and 2 of her friends plan a trip by car to Canada's east coast. They rent a compact car for the 3-week trip. In order to calculate each person's share of the transportation expense, they use the following information.

- Basic weekly rental, $162.50
- Distance rate 6¢/km (over 1000 km)
- Distance travelled, 3520 km
- Fuel consumption, 6.3 L/100 km
- Average fuel cost, $0.49/L

Determine each person's transportation expense.

Project

Plan a week's trip by car, then call a car rental agency to determine the week's transportation expenses using the car of your choice.

Comparing Transportation Costs

At times, you may have the option of choosing among several methods of transportation.

Geoff must travel to do business in another city. If he rents a car, his estimated costs are as follows.

• Basic rental rate for 2 d	
$2 \times \$38.25$	$ 76.50
• Distance rate	
(8.1¢/km over 1000 km)	
$(1183 - 1000)$ km $\times \$0.08$/km	14.82

Estimated distance driven

• Full insurance coverage	6.50
• Fuel costs	62.14
	$159.96

If Geoff chooses to travel by train, his expenses are as listed below.

• Return train fare	$125.60
• Cab fare	38.75
• Tips and gratuities	12.50
	$176.85

Compare the two methods of transportation by finding the difference in cost.

$$\$176.85 - \$159.96 = \$16.89$$

Geoff would save $16.89 by travelling by car.

But there may be other factors that affect Geoff's decision. For instance, if he travels by train, he'll be free to do other work as he travels. He'll arrive somewhat refreshed, having avoided the personal strain of driving through traffic.

Nancy has to decide whether to purchase a new car, required for her job as salesperson for a national clothing manufacturer, or whether to lease a car. She compares costs over an interval of 3 a.

Plan A: Purchase

Nancy estimates the following.
• Original cost (including tax), $12 850
• Distance driven annually, 25 000 km
• Annual fuel costs, $1225
• Annual maintenance and repairs, $500
• Annual insurance, licence fees, $800

She uses the estimates to calculate her expenses.

• Cost of depreciation	
58% after 3 a	$ 7 453
• Fuel costs	
$3 \times \$1225$	3 675
• Maintenance	
$3 \times \$500$	1 500
• Insurance, licence	
$3 \times \$800$	2 400
Total Purchase Cost	$15 028

Plan B: Lease

With a monthly lease rate of $348, Nancy calculates the following.

• Leasing costs for 3 a	
$\$348 \times 36$	$12 528
• Fuel costs	3 675
• Maintenance	1 500
Total Lease Cost	$17 703

Compare by subtracting.
$$\$17 703 - \$15 028 = \$2675$$

Nancy would save $2675 over the 3 a by purchasing rather than leasing.

What other considerations should Nancy take into account?

Exercise

A **1.** State what factors, other than cost, might affect a decision about the different types of transportation given in each case.

  (a) car or train
  (b) bus or car
  (c) train or airplane
  (d) bus or train
  (e) motorcycle or car

B **2.** Travel between 2 cities can be by car, train, or airplane. Compare the cost per 100 km for each method of transportation.

  (a) Automobile:
    • Distance travelled, 1285 km
    • Rental for 3 d at $27.50/d
    • Distance rate, 6.5¢/km over 1000 km
    • Fuel costs, $54.60

  (b) Train:
    • Distance travelled, 1104 km
    • Train fare, $155.70
    • Tips, $7.50

  (c) Airplane:
    • Distance travelled, 975 km
    • Air fare, $165

3. Cheryl estimates that she travels 180 km/week in the city.

  • If she travelled by taxi, she would make 18 trips averaging 10 km/trip. Taxi fare is a fixed charge of $1.70 plus a variable rate of $1.25/km.
  • Cheryl can rent a car for $200/week and estimates fuel costs at $9/week. She will also have parking fees of $35/week.

  How much can Cheryl save each week by renting a car rather than taking taxis?

4. Jim plans to visit his cousin for a few days. The return distance for the 1-week trip is 2340 km. Use the information below to determine which method of transportation would be most economical for Jim.

  (a) Car rental:
    • Basic weekly rate, $175.00
    • Full insurance coverage, $35.00
    • Distance rate, 6.5¢ over 1000 km
    • Fuel consumption, 6.4 L/100 km
    • Average fuel cost, $0.46/L
  (b) Airplane and taxi:
    • Return air fare, $209.80
    • Taxi, estimated 10 trips and total distance of 130 km
    • Taxi, $1.80 fixed rate plus $1.15/km
    • Tips, $12.50

5. Melanie compares the cost of leasing a car for 3 a with the cost of purchasing her own car. The car she has in mind is valued at $9000 including tax. Her estimated annual expenses are as listed.
  • Fuel costs $910
  • Maintenance, $390
  • Insurance and licence, $1050

Melanie drives about 23 000 km annually. If the monthly lease rate is $240, determine how much she would save over 3 a by purchasing rather than leasing an identical car.

Automobile Insurance

Even the best drivers may be involved in an accident, through no fault of their own. **Insurance** provides protection against unexpected financial loss in the event of an accident. By law, owners of automobiles are required to have certain types of insurance on their vehicles.

Generally speaking, there are 2 categories of insurance.

Protection for Others
(Also called third-party liability insurance)

- *Public liability insurance* protects the owner against loss due to damages claimed by people who are injured (or killed) in an accident involving the insured automobile.
- *Property damage insurance* protects the owner against loss due to claims from an accident in which another person's property is damaged by the insured automobile.

Protection for the Owner

- *Medical insurance* pays the medical or funeral expenses of a person riding in the insured automobile when it was involved in an accident.
- *Collision insurance* pays for damages to the insured automobile.
- *Comprehensive insurance* pays for damage to the insured automobile resulting from items other than collision. Items such as fire, theft, wind damage, and vandalism are in this category.

With collision and comprehensive insurance, there is usually a *deductible* amount that is paid by the owner, and the insurance company pays the rest. A common deductible amount is $100; the less the deductible amount, the greater the cost of the insurance.

The charts below show some typical annual premiums (cost for 1 a) for various types of insurance.

Automobile: New '84 Firebird	Driver—Age 19			
	No Previous Driving Experience		3 a Driving Experience or Driver Training	
Type of Insurance	Male	Female	Male	Female
$500 000 Public Liability Medical Collision ($100 deductible) Comprehensive ($25 deductible)	$1033 22 1546 147	$ 455 22 773 147	$ 716 22 1104 147	$ 317 22 552 147
Total Annual Premium	$2748	$1397	$1989	$1038

Automobile: Used '78 Camaro	Driver—Age 19			
	No Previous Driving Experience		3 a Driving Experience or Driver Training	
Type of Insurance	Male	Female	Male	Female
$500 000 Public Liability Medical Collision ($100 deductible) Comprehensive ($25 deductible)	$1033 22 631 71	$ 455 22 317 71	$ 716 22 451 71	$ 317 22 266 71
Total Annual Premium	$1757	$ 865	$1260	$ 676

Exercise

1. In each case, calculate the difference in annual premiums for a male and female driver.
   (a) Total annual premium for an '84 Firebird; no previous driving experience
   (b) Collision insurance on an '84 Firebird; driver training
   (c) Collision and comprehensive insurance on a '78 Camaro; 3 a driving experience

2. Calculate the difference in annual premium in each case, for a new '84 Firebird and a used '78 Camaro.
   (a) Total annual premium for a male with no previous driving experience
   (b) $500 000 public liability for a female with driver training
   (c) Collision, medical, comprehensive for a male with 3 a driving experience

Project

Contact a local insurance agent and determine what annual premium *you* would have to pay to drive a new car (valued at, say, $10 000) for the following insurance coverage.
- $100 000 public liability
- medical
- collision ($200 deductible)
- comprehensive ($100 deductible)

Unit 14 Review

1. Yolande purchases a used car by answering a newspaper ad. The car is priced at $3850, with sales tax at 7%. The transfer fee is $8. Yolande agrees to pay for repairs of $145 as well as the mechanic's certification fee of $32.50. Determine Yolande's total cost for the car.

2. Gregory purchases a used car from a friend, having agreed to pay expenses involved in having the car certified. The repairs involved were as follows.
   - Universal joints $38.50
   - Body work $80.00
   - New tires $260.00
   - Brakes $89.95

   The mechanic's certification fee was $35, and there was a transfer fee of $7.50. If the price of the car was $2900, plus 8% sales tax, calculate Gregory's total cost for the car.

Use the Options List on page 246 in questions 3, 4, and 5.

3. Calculate the sticker price of the car with each set of options listed.
   (a) PDI and freight, $319.75
   Automatic transmission
   Power door locks
   Power steering
   Sunroof
   Accent body stripes
   AM-FM radio with item ②
   Pulse wiper system

   (b) PDI and freight, $289.50
   Manual overdrive
   Power rear lid release
   6-way power seat
   Air conditioner
   Front seat armrest
   Luggage carrier
   AM-FM radio with item ①
   Rallye wheels
   Tilt-a-way steering wheel
   Extended warranty B

   (c) PDI and freight, $340.25
   Sunroof
   Custom cloth interior
   AM-FM radio with item ④
   Special handling suspension
   Wire wheel covers and locks
   Custom sport steering wheel

4. Which set of options is the more expensive and by how much?
   (a) Automatic transmission
   Power door locks
   Air conditioner
   Accent body stripes
   AM-FM radio with item ③
   Chromed super stock wheels
   Extended warranty B

   (b) Manual overdrive
   6-way power seat
   Sunroof
   Custom cloth interior
   AM-FM radio with item ④
   Wire wheel covers and locks
   Extended warranty A

5. Calculate the total cash price, including 7% sales tax, of a car with the following options.

    PDI and freight, $337.30
    Automatic transmission
    Power door locks
    Power rear lid release
    6-way power seat
    Power steering
    Power windows
    Air conditioner
    Front seat armrest
    Custom cloth interior
    AM-FM radio with item ④
    Wire wheel covers and locks
    Pulse wiper system
    Tilt-a-way steering wheel
    Extended warranty B

6. For each used car shown, determine:
   - the cash price (sales tax is at 8%);
   - the instalment price;
   - the finance charge;
   - the true interest rate.

(a)

OR PAY $1000 DOWN PLUS 24 MONTHLY PAYMENTS OF $255.

YOURS for only... $5395!

(b)

DRIVE ME AWAY FOR ONLY $6250!

OR make 36 easy monthly payments of $290

*NO MONEY DOWN

7. Arlene buys a new car whose sticker price is $10 563.90, plus sales tax at 6%. She makes a down payment of 25%, and agrees to make 36 monthly payments of $361.38.
   (a) Calculate the finance charge.
   (b) What interest rate is Arlene paying?

8. In each case, determine:
   - average monthly cost of operation;
   - operating cost per 100 km.

   All items are given on an annual basis.

Item \ Car	(a)	(b)	(c)	(d)
Gas, Oil Lubrication	$856.21	$716.30	$1009.42	$917.85
Insurance	$1163	$975	$2163	$1500
Licence	$48	$53	$37	$63
Repairs	$316.72	$104.50	—	$409.11
Depreciation	$2012	$1408	$2953	$1675
Distance Driven (km)	15050	17612	19600	14283

9. During the third year of operation of her car, Dianne drives 18 520 km. The cost of gasoline averaged 51¢/L for that year, and the car's average fuel consumption was 6.9 L/100 km. Dianne's other expenses for the year are listed below.
   - oil, lubrication $114.73
   - insurance $968.40
   - licence fee $ 48.00
   - repairs $473.82

If Dianne paid $9565 for her car when it was new, determine the cost/100 km to operate it during the third year she owns it.

10. Sherri and a friend share cab fare to and from work 5 d each week. The girls live 9.8 km from work, and cab fare is at a fixed rate of $1.60 plus a variable rate of $1.35/km. Calculate Sherri's weekly transportation costs to and from work.

11. Gary and 2 friends rent a compact car for weekend travel. The rental rate is $27.50/d, plus 6.4¢/km over 100 km driven. The boys also pay an extra $4.50/d for full insurance coverage. In the 3 d they have the car, they drive a total of 514 km, and spend $18.45 on gasoline. How much did Gary pay as his share of the total expenses?

12. Compute the transportation cost in each case.

   (a) Automobile:
      • Distance driven, 278 km
      • Rental rate, $38.50/d
      • Distance rate, 8.3¢/km over 100 km
      • Fuel costs, $14.50
   (b) Bus and Taxi:
      • Bus fare, $19.50
      • Taxi (15.8 km one way) return trip at $1.75 + $1.20/km

13. Bev drives a distance of 1642 km in one week. The average price of gasoline on the trip is 48¢/L. Use the information below to determine how much money Bev would save by renting a compact rather than a full-size car.

   (a) Compact Car Rental:
      • Basic rate $160/week
      • 6¢/km over 1000 km
      • Fuel consumption 5.9 L/100 km
   (b) Full-size Car Rental:
      • Basic rate $225/week
      • 8¢/km over 1000 km
      • Fuel consumption 10.3 L/100 km

14. Tony compares the cost of purchasing a car with the cost of leasing an identical car over a period of 3 a. The car of his choice is valued at $8500, plus tax at 8%. Tony's estimated annual expenses are as follows.
   • Fuel costs $ 850
   • Maintenance $ 500
   • Insurance and licence $1000

   Tony drives about 20 000 km/a. If the monthly lease rate is $265, calculate how much Tony would save over 3 a by purchasing rather than leasing a car.

15. Account for the differences in insurance premiums for public liability and collision on the basis of each of the following.
   (a) driving experience
   (b) male or female driver

Unit 15

Running a Business

Markup
Margin
Markdown
Trade Discounts
Equivalent Discounts
Real Estate Agent
Unit 15 Review

Markup

Terry has started a new business selling audio equipment.

One style of cassette recorder costs Terry $120 to purchase. The store sells it for $180. The difference between Terry's *cost price* and the *selling price* is **markup**.

For the cassette recorder, the markup is $180 − $120, or $60.

There is a simple relationship between cost price, selling price, and markup.

> Markup = Selling Price − Cost Price
> or   Cost Price + Markup = Selling Price
> $$C + M = S$$

For retailers like Terry, the markup has to be high enough to cover the cost of running the business, and also to ensure an adequate profit. However, the retailer must also keep markup at a reasonable level to be competitive with other retailers selling similar goods.

Markup can also be expressed as a percent. The *rate of markup* is expressed as a percent of the *cost* price.

> $$\text{Rate of Markup} = \frac{\text{Markup}}{\text{Cost Price}} \times 100\%$$

What is the rate of markup on the cassette recorder?

$$\text{Rate of Markup} = \frac{\$60}{\$120} \times 100\%$$
$$= 50\%$$

Terry's rate of markup on the recorder was 50% of the cost price.

The cost price is the *base* of the calculation.

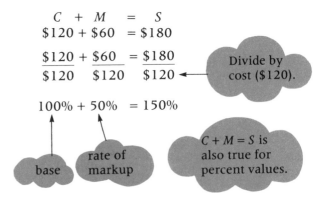

$$C + M = S$$
$$\$120 + \$60 = \$180$$

$$\frac{\$120}{\$120} + \frac{\$60}{\$120} = \frac{\$180}{\$120}$$

Divide by cost ($120).

$$100\% + 50\% = 150\%$$

base   rate of markup

$C + M = S$ is also true for percent values.

Example 1

Find the markup and the selling price of a turntable that costs $160 if Terry uses a rate of markup of 90%.

$$\begin{aligned}
\text{Markup} &= \text{Rate of Markup} \times \text{Cost Price} \\
&= 90\% \times \$160.00 \\
&= 0.9 \times \$160.00 \\
&= \$144.00
\end{aligned}$$

$$\begin{aligned}
\text{Selling Price} &= \text{Cost} + \text{Markup} \\
&= \$160.00 + \$144.00 \\
&= \$304.00
\end{aligned}$$

You could also use a chart to solve the problem. This approach provides a general procedure that can be applied to all markup problems.

The *base* of the calculation is the cost price.

Cost + Markup = Selling Price

	Dollar Value	Percent
C	$160	100% ← base
+ M	+ M	+ 90%
S	S	190% ← 100% + 90%

If M is the markup, a ratio can be written using the known quantities in the chart.

$$\frac{\$160}{\$M} = \frac{100\%}{90\%}$$

$$\frac{160}{M} = \frac{10}{9}$$
$$1440 = 10M$$
$$M = 144$$

The markup (M) is $144 and the selling price (S) is $160 + $144, or $304.

Example 2

A cassette tape that cost the retailer $2.10 is sold for $4.65. What is the rate of markup?

	Dollar Value	Percent
C	$2.10	100% ← base
+ M	+ $2.55	+ M%
S	$4.65	S%

($4.65 − $2.10 → $2.55)

Let M% be the rate of markup.

$$\frac{\$2.10}{\$2.55} = \frac{100\%}{M\%}$$
$$2.10M = 255$$
$$M = 121.428\ 57$$

The rate of markup is 121.4%, to 1 decimal.

Using a chart to organize information will help you to simplify difficult problems.

Example 3

George owns a computer store and marks up all merchandise 130%. If a computer is selling for $940, find the cost price of the computer.

BUT MOM – IT'S ALWAYS A 130% MARKUP!!

MODEL T-12 THIS SIDE UP

	Dollar Value	Percent
C	C	100% ← base
+ M	+ M	+ 130%
S	$940	230%

Let the cost price of the computer be $C.

$$\frac{\$C}{\$940} = \frac{100\%}{230\%}$$

$$\frac{C}{940} = \frac{10}{23}$$
$$23C = 9400$$
$$C = 408.70, \text{ to 2 decimal places}$$

The cost price of the computer is $408.70.

Exercise

A **1.** State the missing information.

	Cost	Markup	Selling Price
(a)	$65.00	$ 15.00	▢
(b)	$40.00	▢	$47.00
(c)	▢	$ 12.00	$58.00
(d)	$ 4.50	$ 0.80	▢
(e)	$13.25	▢	$17.00
(f)	▢	$100.00	$930.00

2. State the missing information.

	Cost	Rate of Markup	Selling Price
(a)	$ 40	50%	▢
(b)	$200	10%	▢
(c)	$400	100%	▢
(d)	$ 60	200%	▢
(e)	100%	30%	▢
(f)	100%	▢	190%
(g)	▢	150%	▢

B **3.** Copy and complete the table.

	Cost	Markup	Rate of Markup	Selling Price
(a)	$ 75.00	$15.00	▢	▢
(b)	$120.00	$48.00	▢	▢
(c)	$ 70.00	▢	▢	$ 84.00
(d)	$ 35.20	▢	▢	$ 57.50
(e)	$ 80.00	▢	20%	▢
(f)	$ 3.60	▢	125%	▢
(g)	▢	$45.00	▢	$300.00
(h)	▢	$23.20	▢	$ 94.50
(i)	▢	$15.00	40%	▢
(j)	▢	$62.50	65%	▢
(k)	▢	▢	30%	$ 10.00
(l)	▢	▢	42%	$160.00
(m)	$520.00	▢	28%	▢
(n)	$ 78.50	▢	▢	$119.99
(o)	▢	▢	33%	$240.00

4. Pete's Hardware pays $3.65 for a screwdriver and sells it for $4.95. Find the markup and the rate of markup.

5. The cost to bake a loaf of bread at a bakery is $0.37. If the selling price of a loaf is $1.29, find the rate of markup.

6. Sav-more Department Store received a shipment of rocking chairs priced at $125.00 each. If the chairs are marked up 62%, find the selling price of each rocking chair.

7. A service station receives a shipment of batteries priced at $26.75 each. Find the markup and the selling price if the rate of markup is 42.5%.

8. The cost of manufacturing a hockey stick is $4.75. Find the manufacturer's selling price if the rate of markup is 180%.

9. A retailer marks up all blouses from a certain manufacturer at the rate of 95% of the cost price. If the markup on a blouse is $12.45, find the cost price and the selling price of the blouse.

10. The selling price of a baseball glove is $46.95. Find the cost price of the glove if the rate of markup is 140%.

11. Paula's House of Tennis marks up all tennis equipment 82%. Determine the markup on a tennis racket that sells for $39.95. What is the cost price?

Margin

In Terry's Sound Shop, a pair of headphones sells for $60. Terry's cost to purchase the headphones from the manufacturer was $45. A retailer's **margin** is the amount that is subtracted from selling price to give the cost price.

The headphones have a margin of $60 − $45, or $15.

> Selling Price − Margin = Cost
> $$S - M = C$$

The markup on the headphones is also $15.

Margin and markup are two different names for the *same* quantity. The use of margin or markup depends on the view taken by the retailer. An amount *added* to cost price is known as markup. An amount *subtracted* from selling price is known as margin.

However, the *rate of margin* is not the same as the rate of markup. The base of the calculation to determine rate of margin is the selling price.

> $$\text{Rate of Margin} = \frac{\text{Margin}}{\text{Selling Price}} \times 100\%$$

What is the rate of margin for the headphones in Terry's store?

> $$\text{Rate of Margin} = \frac{\$15}{\$60} \times 100\%$$
> $$= 25\%$$

The rate of margin is 25%.

The selling price is the base of the calculation.

Selling Price	− Margin	= Cost Price
$60	− $15	= $45
$\frac{\$60}{\$60}$	$\frac{\$15}{\$60}$	$\frac{\$45}{\$60}$
100%	− 25%	= 75%

Divide by selling price ($60).

Example 1

A pair of skis from The Ski Den sells for $240. The shop has found that a margin of 40% is required to cover all expenses and earn a reasonable profit. Determine the margin and the cost price of the skis.

Use a chart similar to the ones used for the markup problems. This time, the chart is based on the margin formula.
Selling price is the base of the calculation.

Selling Price − Margin = Cost Price

	Dollar Value	Percent
S	$240	100%
− M	− $ M	− 40%
C	$ C	60%

base

Let $M represent the retailer's margin.

$$\frac{\$240}{\$M} = \frac{100\%}{40\%}$$

$$\frac{\$240}{M} = \frac{5}{2}$$

$$480 = 5M$$

$$96 = M$$

The margin is $96 and the cost price is $240 − $96, or $144.

267

Even though the margin and markup have the same value, the *rate of margin* and *rate of markup* may have very different values.
Markup is based on cost price.
Margin is based on selling price.

Example 2

Determine the rate of margin if an album that sells for $10.99 costs the retailer $5.96.

Selling Price − Margin = Cost Price

	Dollar Value	Percent
S	$10.99	100% ← base
$- M$	$− 5.03$	$− M\%$
C	$ 5.96	$C\%$

Let $M\%$ represent the rate of margin.

$$\frac{\$10.99}{\$5.03} = \frac{100\%}{M\%}$$
$$10.99M = 503$$
$$M = 45.8, \text{ to 1 decimal place}$$

The rate of margin is 45.8%.

Compare this to the rate of markup.

Cost Price + Markup = Selling Price

	Dollar Value	Percent
C	$ 5.96	100% ← Cost is base.
$+ M$	$+ 5.03$	$+ M\%$
S	$10.99	$S\%$

Let $M\%$ represent the rate of markup.

$$\frac{\$5.96}{\$5.03} = \frac{100\%}{M\%}$$
$$5.96 M = 503$$
$$M = 84.4\%$$

The rate of markup is 84.4%.

Example 3

Betty's Boutique operates on a margin of 44%. Find the selling price of a sweater that has a cost price of $26.

Selling Price − Margin = Cost Price

	Dollar Value	Percent
S	$$S	100%
$- M$	$− M	$− 44\%$
C	$26	56%

Let $$S$ be the selling price of the seater.

$$\frac{\$S}{\$26} = \frac{100\%}{56\%}$$
$$56S = 2600$$
$$S = 46.43, \text{ to 2 decimal places}$$

The selling price of the sweater is $46.43.

Exercise

A **1.** State the missing information.

	Selling Price	Margin	Cost Price
(a)	$55.00	$10.00	▣
(b)	▣	$25.00	$100.00
(c)	$ 2.50	▣	$ 1.00
(d)	$32.00	$18.00	▣

2. State the missing quantity.

	Selling Price.	Rate of Margin	Cost Price
(a)	$ 60.00	10%	$▣
(b)	$200.00	50%	$▣
(c)	100%	30%	▣%
(d)	▣%	25%	▣%
(e)	▣%	▣%	65%

B **3.** Determine the values missing from the table below.

	Selling Price	Margin	Rate of Margin	Cost Price
(a)	$ 40.00	$ 10.00	▣	▣
(b)	$ 340.00	$ 68.00	▣	▣
(c)	$ 64.00	▣	45%	▣
(d)	$ 130.00	▣	70%	▣
(e)	$ 80.00	▣	▣	$ 50.00
(f)	$ 2.40	▣	▣	$ 1.00
(g)	▣	$ 70.00	15%	▣
(h)	▣	$165.50	40%	▣
(i)	▣	$ 36.00	▣	$ 90.00
(j)	▣	$ 6.50	▣	$ 4.00
(k)	▣	▣	32%	$400.00
(l)	▣	▣	20%	$ 12.50
(m)	$ 75.00	$ 30.00	▣	▣
(n)	$2000.00	▣	15%	▣
(o)	$ 9.40	▣	▣	$ 6.15
(p)	▣	$ 0.85	60%	▣
(q)	▣	$360.00	▣	$920.00
(r)	▣	▣	44%	$ 29.59

4. A department store sells calculators for $35 each. Determine the store's margin and rate of margin if the calculators cost $21 each.

5. Elm trees sell for $76 each at Nancy's Nursery. Determine the rate of margin if the trees were purchased for $40 each.

6. Jack's Jewellery Store sells necklaces for $65.50 each. Jack works on a margin of 36%. Find the margin and the cost price of the necklace.

7. Find the cost price of a computer that sells for $780, if the store operates on a margin of 53%.

8. Tony wants a margin of 19% on all merchandise sold. If an item has a margin of $24.00, determine the cost price and the selling price of the item.

9. The margin on a ten-speed bike is $95, and the rate of margin is 60%. Find the selling price of the bike.

10. A retailer's cost price for a football is $44.60. Find the selling price of the football if the retailer uses a rate of margin of 23%.

11. Determine the rate of margin and the rate of markup for each item.
  (a) A meal at Bob's Restaurant costs $3.60 to prepare and is sold for $5.50.
  (b) A dozen Straight-Flite golf balls cost the retailer $11.25, and are sold for $25.00.

12. George's House of Lamps uses a rate of margin of 66%. Find the margin if the cost of a table lamp to the retailer is $52.45.

Markdown

Retailers often put their goods on sale. These markdowns allow the retailer to clear seasonal, discontinued, or slow-moving items.

The cassette recorders at Terry's Sound Shop that are priced at $180 have not been selling as fast as Terry hoped. Terry offers a price reduction of $30 on each recorder.

The price after the reduction, $180 − $30, or $150, is the sale price or discount price.

> Markdown = Selling Price − Discount Price
>
> Selling Price − Markdown = Discount Price
> $$S - M = D$$

The rate of markdown is *based* on selling price.

> $$\text{Rate of Markdown} = \frac{\text{Markdown}}{\text{Selling Price}} \times 100\%$$
> Markdown = Rate of Markdown × Selling Price

What is the rate of markdown on the recorder?
Rate of markdown is $\frac{\$30}{\$180} \times 100\%$, or 16.7%, to 1 decimal place.

Example 1

Find the markdown and the discount price of a pair of jeans, normally selling for $39.00, that is marked down at the rate of 30%.

$$\text{Markdown} = \text{Rate} \times \text{Selling Price}$$
$$= 0.30 \times \$39.00$$
$$= \$11.70$$

The markdown is $11.70, and the discount price is $39.00 − $11.70, or $27.30.

You could also solve by using the chart method.

Selling Price − Markdown = Discount Price

	Dollar Value	Percent
S	$39.00	100%
$- M$	$-$ \$M	$-$ 30%
D	$D	70%

Let $M represent the markdown.

$$\frac{\$39.00}{\$M} = \frac{100\%}{30\%}$$
$$117 = 10M$$
$$11.70 = M$$

The markdown is $11.70.

Example 2

A shirt goes on sale for 33% off the regular price. If the discount price is $16.20, find the regular price of the shirt.

Use the chart method.

Selling Price − Markdown = Discount

	Dollar Value	Percent
S	$S	100%
$- M$	$-$ \$M	$-$ 33%
D	$16.20	67%

Let $S represent the regular selling price of the shirt.

$$\frac{\$S}{\$16.20} = \frac{100\%}{67\%}$$
$$67S = 1620$$
$$S = 24.18, \text{ to 2 decimal places}$$

The regular price of the shirt is $24.18.

Exercise

A 1. State some reasons that a retailer would offer a markdown.

2. Why would a retailer sell a few items below the store's own cost price? (This is known as a "loss leader.")

3. State the missing information.

	Selling Price	Markdown	Discount Price
(a)	$55.00	$ 12.00	▨
(b)	$12.00	▨	$ 9.00
(c)	▨	$170.00	$800.00

B 4. Copy and complete the table.

	Selling Price	Markdown	Rate of Markdown	Discount Price
(a)	$ 400.00	$ 80.00	▨	▨
(b)	$ 16.50	$ 9.00	▨	▨
(c)	$ 64.00	▨	25%	▨
(d)	$ 39.95	▨	12%	▨
(e)	$ 94.00	▨	▨	$ 56.40
(f)	$ 3.55	▨	▨	$ 2.99
(g)	▨	$ 8.00	30%	▨
(h)	▨	$150.00	24%	▨
(i)	▨	$ 45.50	▨	$ 75.00
(j)	▨	$630.00	▨	$520.00
(k)	▨	▨	45%	$300.00
(l)	▨	▨	66%	$ 49.95
(m)	$2400.00	▨	50%	▨
(n)	$ 42.25	▨	▨	$ 29.95
(o)	▨	$725.00	28%	▨
(p)	▨	▨	60%	$ 54.36

5. During a special at Fred's Fried Chicken the $10.99 bucket of chicken is on sale for $7.99. Find the markdown and the rate of markdown.

6. Rosie's Furniture Warehouse is offering 35% off all merchandise in the store. Tony buys a refrigerator regularly priced at $825 and a stove regularly priced at $929. What did Tony pay in total after the discount?

7. A used-car dealer claims all car prices have been "slashed" by at least 15% for one day only. The price on a 1982 Firebird was decreased from $8765.99 to $7188.99. Is the dealer's claim true for the Firebird?

8. Mike's Men's Wear is offering a sale on end-of-season fashions. Find the rate of markdown given on each item.
   (a) A $149.00 sports jacket on sale for $99.00
   (b) A $29.00 shirt on sale at 2 for $32.50
   (c) A $45.50 pair of pants on sale for $29.95

9. Fiona's Fine Women's Apparel has a special on all sweaters that regularly sell for $29.00 each.

BUY ONE SWEATER AND GET THE SECOND ONE FOR $5.00!

   Find the rate of markdown if a customer buys 2 sweaters.

10. Lois can save $9.90 if she buys a calculator on sale today at a store that is offering 30% off the regular price. Find the sale price and the regular price of the calculator.

11. Flowers by Francis is going out of business. To clear stock quickly, all plants have been marked down 60%. Find the amount saved, or the markdown, on each of the following plants, given the indicated discount prices.
    (a) Scheflerras on sale for $8.95
    (b) Cut roses reduced to $2.55 each

Trade Discounts

Terry is ordering a pair of Excel-Tone speakers for a customer. Excel-Tone, like many manufacturers, gives retailers catalogues that describe and illustrate the features of each product. For each product, there is a price at which the manufacturer recommends the product be sold, the **list price**. Terry can show the customer the catalogue and the list price before ordering the speakers.

The price that Terry will pay for the speakers is not shown in the catalogue. Instead, Terry has a booklet of trade discounts, usually stated as percents, from which Terry can calculate the net price.

> Trade Discount = List Price − Net Price
>
> List Price − Trade Discount = Net Price
>
> $$L - D = N$$

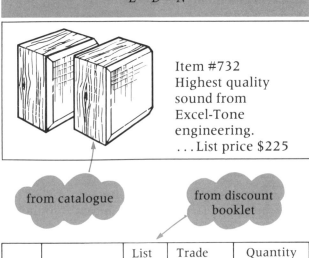

Item #732
Highest quality sound from Excel-Tone engineering.
...List price $225

from catalogue

from discount booklet

Item	Description	List Price	Trade Discount	Quantity Disc. 24
732	Speakers	$225	30%	10%

If Terry orders one pair of speakers, the net price can be calculated as follows.

List Price	$225.00
Trade Discount	− 67.50
Net Price	$157.50

0.3 × $225

Terry's net price is $157.50.

The table in the discount booklet also indicates a *quantity discount*. If Terry orders 24 or more pairs of speakers, there is an additional discount of 10%.

List Price	$225.00
Trade Discount	− 67.50
	$157.50
Quantity Discount	− 15.75
Net Price	$141.75

10% of $157.50

On an order of 24 or more, Terry's net price is $141.75 on each pair of speakers.

Excel-Tone offered a series of discounts, or a **chain discount**, of 30% and 10%. Many manufacturers offer an additional *bonus* discount to valued retailers that buy large volumes of merchandise over the years. An example of such a chain discount is given below.

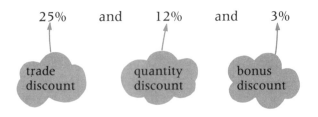

25% and 12% and 3%

trade discount   quantity discount   bonus discount

Each discount is deducted successively.

Example 1

Excel-Tone's suggested list price on a turntable is $125.50. Find the net price if Terry qualifies for a chain discount of 40%, 10%, and 2%.

List Price	$125.50
Trade Discount (40%)	− 50.20
	$ 75.30
Quantity Discount (10%)	− 7.53
	$ 67.77
Bonus Discount (2%)	− 1.36
Net Price	$ 66.41

The net price of the turntable is $66.41.

Exercise

A **1.** Why would a manufacturer offer a quantity discount?

2. Why would a manufacturer offer a bonus discount?

3. What advantages do large, established retail businesses have over newly-established small businesses when ordering directly from the manufacturer?

B **4.** Calculate the net price for each item in the table.

	List Price	Trade Discount	Quantity Discount	Bonus Discount
(a)	$540.00	55%	—	—
(b)	$300.00	40%	10%	—
(c)	$ 68.75	30%	15%	—
(d)	$145.50	35%	12%	2%
(e)	$ 49.99	25%	9%	3%
(f)	$467.85	45%	8%	1%

5. Paula wants to order some binders for her shop, Paper Thin Stationery. The supplier offers a trade discount of 35%, and a quantity discount of 7% if 25 or more are ordered. Find the net price per binder for each order below.

(a) 15 binders listed at $5.60 each
(b) 35 binders listed at $7.95 each

6. Mary is a buyer for a large department store and has the choice of two suppliers to order a shipment of hammers. Both suppliers list the price of the hammer at $29.50 each.

   • Supplier X offers discounts of 40% and 10%.
   • Supplier Y offers discounts of 45% and 5%.

   If Mary's store qualifies for all discounts, which supplier offers the better deal?

7. A tennis racket is listed at $45.00.

   (a) Find the net price after discounts of 30%, 10%, and 5%.
   (b) Find the net price after discounts of 35% and 10%.
   (c) Find the net price after a trade discount of 45%.
   (d) Are the 3 discounts above equivalent? If not, which is the best and which is the worst for a retailer?
   (e) One supplier offers a 25% trade discount and a second supplier offers discounts of 20% and 5%. Use the results of parts (a), (b), and (c) to find which discount would be better for the retailer.

8. A shirt is listed at $39.49.

   (a) Find the net price after discounts of 25% and 15%.
   (b) Find the net price after discounts of 15% and 25%.
   (c) Does the order of the discounts have any effect on the net price?

9. Frank owns The Light House. He has the choice of ordering lamps from a manufacturer that has a list price of $59.49 and offers discounts of 60%, 5%, and 2%, or ordering from another manufacturer that has a list price of $62.50 and offers discounts of 55%, 10%, and 4%. Which supplier gives the lower net price?

10. Two suppliers sell identical chairs.

   Supplier A

List Price	Trade Discount	Quantity Discount 80	Bonus Discount
$255	40%	10%	1%

   Supplier B

List Price	Trade Discount	Quantity Discount 20	Bonus Discount
$255	33%	16%	5%

   (a) Calculate the net price of the chair from each supplier if a retailer orders 80 chairs and qualifies for the bonus discount. Which supplier gives the better deal?
   (b) Calculate the net price of the chair from each supplier if a retailer orders 100 chairs but does not qualify for the bonus discount. Which supplier gives the better deal?
   (c) Calculate the net price of the chair from each supplier if the retailer orders 45 chairs but does not qualify for the bonus discount. Which supplier gives the better deal?
   (d) Calculate the net price of the chair from each supplier if a retailer orders 15 chairs but does not qualify for the bonus discount. Which supplier gives the better deal?

Equivalent Discounts

Terry must calculate the net price on a stereo stand that lists for $85.00 and is offered with a trade discount of 35%. The method used in the last section involved multiplying to find discount and then subtracting.

List Price $85.00
Trade Discount   −   29.75 ← 0.35 × 85
Net Price $55.25

But the net price can be found in one step. Subtract the discount percent from 100% to get the **complement** of the trade discount. The complement of 35% is 100% − 35%, or 65%.

Find the net price of the stereo stand by multiplying the list price by the complement of the trade discount.

Net Price = $85.00 × 65% ← complement of 35%
= $55.25

The use of complements can also be extended to chain discounts.

Example 1

Find the net price if discounts of 30% and 5% are given on a $400 amplifier.

Start by finding the complements.
100% − 30% = 70%
100% − 5%   = 95%

Then multiply.
Net Price = $400 × 70% × 95%
= $400 × 0.7 × 0.95
= $266.00

The net price on the amplifier is $266.00

You could check this answer by calculating as below.

List Price $400.00
Trade Discount   −   120.00
                              $280.00
Quantity Discount   −   14.00
Net Price $266.00

Both methods give a net price of $266.00.

When comparing chain discounts from different suppliers, a retailer can express the chain discount as a single equivalent discount.

Look at Example 1. The list price of $400 was reduced $400 − $266, or $134, by discounts of 30% and 5%.
To find the single discount, calculate as below.

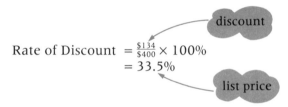

Rate of Discount $= \frac{\$134}{\$400} \times 100\%$
$= 33.5\%$

Another way to find the rate is to use the product of the complements.

70% × 95% = 0.7 × 0.95
= 0.665
= 66.5%

Then subtract the product from 100%.

100% − 66.5% = 33.5%.

This is the same rate as found above.

> Single discount
> = 100% − (Product of Complements)

Example 2

Find the single discount that is equivalent to the chain discount of 25%, 10%, and 2%.
Use the answer to find the net price of a $65 portable radio, subject to the chain discounts.

$$\begin{aligned}
\text{Single Discount} &= 100\% - (75\% \times 90\% \times 98\%) \\
&= 100\% - (0.75 \times 0.9 \times 0.98) \\
&= 100\% - 66.2\% \text{ (to 1 decimal)} \\
&= 33.8\%
\end{aligned}$$

The chain discount is equivalent to a single discount of 33.8%.

To find the net price of the radio, multiply the list price by the complement of the single discount.

$$\begin{aligned}
\text{Net Price} &= \$65.00 \times (100\% - 33.8\%) \\
&= \$65.00 \times 66.2\% \\
&= \$43.03
\end{aligned}$$

The list price of the radio is $43.03.

Example 3

Excel-Tone manufactures a car speaker system that lists for $210.00 and is offered with a trade discount of 30%. A competitor offers the same quality speaker at a net price of $130.00. What further discount must Excel-Tone offer to have the same net price as their competitor?

$$\begin{aligned}
\text{Price after Trade Discount} \\
= \$210.00 \times 70\% \\
= \$147.00
\end{aligned}$$

To match the competitor, Excel-Tone must drop the price a further $147.00 − $130.00, or $17.00.

$$\begin{aligned}
\text{Rate of Discount} &= \tfrac{\$17.00}{\$147.00} \times 100\% \\
&= 11.6\%, \text{ to 1 decimal place}
\end{aligned}$$

Excel-Tone would have to offer a further discount of 11.6% to remain competitive.

OUR BEST MODEL — PLAYS ONLY TOP 40!!

Exercise

A 1. State the complement of each.

(a) 40% (d) 55%
(b) 15% (e) 92%
(c) 25% (f) 83%

B 2. Find the net price of each.

	List Price	Discounts
(a)	$ 80.00	34%
(b)	$ 45.50	18%
(c)	$ 200.00	45% and 5%
(d)	$ 44.00	20% and 15%
(e)	$ 360.00	33% and 6%
(f)	$ 75.00	24%, 12%, and 5%
(g)	$ 645.45	60%, 15%, and 5%
(h)	$2440.00	54%, 14%, and 3%

3. Find the single equivalent discount for each series of discounts.

(a) 30% and 8%
(b) 47% and 9%
(c) 21% and 3.4%
(d) 55%, 11%, and 2.5%
(e) 42%, 37%, and 6%
(f) 33%, 12%, and 1.5%

4. Using the single equivalent discount, find which discount is best for the retailer.

	Supplier A	Supplier B
(a)	25% and 10%	30% and 5%
(b)	45% and 12%	48% and 8%
(c)	30% and 9%	25% and 15%
(d)	20%, 10%, 5%	25%, 5%, 3%
(e)	25%, 8%, 3%	28%, 5%, 2%
(f)	36% and 12%	32%, 15%, 5%

5. Fine furniture offers discounts of 35%, 14%, and 3% on all wood products.

(a) Find the single discount that is equivalent to the chain discount.
(b) Use your answer from part (a) to find the net price for each of the following.
  • $510.00 rocking chair
  • $1464.00 pine bed
  • $288.00 coffee table

6. Clear-View Auto Glass manufactures a style of windshield that sells for $360 with a trade discount of 25%. A competitor sells an equivalent windshield for $250. What further rate of discount should Clear-View offer to be competitive?

7. A supplier offers trade discounts of 35% on all merchandise. What further discount is necessary for each of the following so that an article listed at $56.50 has the indicated net price?

(a) $35.00
(b) $30.00
(c) $36.00

Real Estate Agent

A real estate agent works with home buyers to help them find the home they can afford. But the agent also works with the home seller by advertising the home and bringing potential buyers to view the home.

The agency charges a commission to the seller based on the selling price of the home.

Selling Price − Commission = Owner's Receipts

$$SP - C = OR$$

Example 1

An agency charges a commission of 5%. Find the selling price of a house if the owners want to receive $52 000 for their house.

Make a table similar to the ones you used to solve problems involving markup or margin.

$SP - C = OR$

	Percent	Dollar Value
SP	100%	$ SP
$- C$	− 5%	− $ C
OR	95%	$52 000

Write an equation from the table.

$$\frac{100\%}{95\%} = \frac{SP}{\$52\,000}$$

$$SP = \$54\,736.84$$

The house must be sold for about $54 740. The real estate agent should advise the owners to list the house at a price higher than $54 740 to allow room for bargaining with potential buyers.

Exercise

1. Here are some typical advertisements from a real estate paper. If the real estate agent can sell the house for the asking price, how much commission would the agent earn on each sale?

(a)

Beautiful bungalow with 3 bedrooms, Fireplace, newly renovated basement. Asking $78,000.

Agent's rate of commission is 5%.

(b)

A quiet corner of your own. This ranch-style house has 4 bedrooms, 2 baths. $96,000.

Agent's rate of commission is 5.5%.

(c)

Lakefront property in cottage country. Lot 125 m by 150 m. Asking $32,999.

Agent's rate of commission is 6%.

2. Determine the selling price necessary for the owners to receive each of the following amounts at the indicated commission rates.
   (a) Receive $44 000, with 6% commission.
   (b) Receive $68 000, with 4.5% commission.

3. Determine the selling price of each of the following homes for the agent to receive the indicated commission. The rate of commission is 6%.
   (a) $4000
   (b) $2830

4. A real estate agent suggests that a home be listed at 12% higher than the desired selling price. Determine the list price of a home if the owner wishes to receive $56 000, and must pay 5% commission to the agent.

Unit 15 Review

1. Find the missing information.

	Cost	Markup	Selling Price
(a)	$ 70.00	$15.00	▨
(b)	$130.00	▨	$210.00
(c)	▨	$ 2.50	$ 4.50

	Selling Price	Margin	Cost
(d)	$95.00	$10.00	▨
(e)	$58.00	▨	$40.00
(f)	▨	$30.00	$20.00

	Selling Price	Markdown	Discount Price
(g)	$720.00	$100.00	▨
(h)	$ 0.75	▨	$ 0.35
(i)	▨	$ 9.00	$19.00

2. Determine the complement of each.
   (a) 15%   (b) 45%   (c) 62%   (d) 99%

3. Copy and complete each table.

	Cost	Markup	Rate of Markup	Selling Price
(a)	$ 80.00	$ 22.00	▨	▨
(b)	$150.00	▨	20%	▨
(c)	$ 9.00	▨	▨	$ 12.00
(d)	▨	$ 46.25	12.5%	▨
(e)	▨	▨	45%	$144.25
(f)	▨	$520.00	▨	$915.00

	Selling Price	Margin	Rate of margin	Cost Price
(g)	$ 62.00	$24.00	▨	▨
(h)	$ 420.00	▨	27%	▨
(i)	$1400.00	▨	▨	$910.00
(j)	▨	$ 2.40	32%	▨
(k)	▨	$72.80	▨	$166.68
(l)	▨	▨	16.25%	$ 49.95

	Selling Price	Markdown	Rate of Markdown	Discount Price
(m)	$ 94.00	$ 7.20	▨	▨
(n)	$ 312.00	▨	22%	▨
(o)	$1420.50	▨	▨	$867.77
(p)	▨	$99.40	10%	▨
(q)	▨	▨	45%	$ 29.49
(r)	▨	$3.24	▨	$2.99

4. Joe's Pizzeria sells Kool Kola for $0.65. Kool Kola costs $0.40 from the supplier.

   (a) What is the markup?
   (b) What is the rate of markup?
   (c) What is the margin?
   (d) What is the rate of margin?

5. Fran purchased several pairs of jeans for her boutique and paid $19.90 per pair. Fran sells the jeans at $44.99 per pair.

   (a) Calculate the rate of markup.
   (b) Calculate the rate of margin.

6. Tom's Taco Hut is offering a Tuesday special. The regular $3.49 taco is on special for $2.99. What is the markdown? What is the rate of markdown?

7. Jane works at a service station. She marks up the price of all tires 35% from the cost price. Find the markup and selling price of a steel-belted radial purchased at a cost price of $66.40.

8. Sam's Sports sells on a margin of 21%. Find the margin and cost price of a fishing rod selling for $52.95.

9. The House of Handbags is offering a "get-acquainted" sale. If you buy 3 handbags, you don't pay for the least expensive one. Find the rate of markdown for each of the following.

(a) Buy 3 bags priced at $24.50, $32.20, and $19.70.
(b) Buy 3 bags priced at $32.00, $34.50, and $14.20.

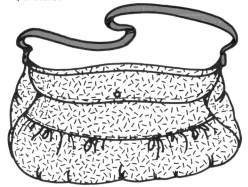

10. Find the rate of markdown if Flic Pens, that regularly sell for $0.49 each, are on sale at 2 for $0.65.

11. Claire marks up the price of all belts in her store by 43%. Find the cost price and the selling price of a belt that has been marked up by $4.26.

12. A florist sells on a margin of 26%. If the retailer's margin on a floral arrangement is $7.42, find the cost price and selling price.

13. The selling price of a baseball bat is $21.25. Find the cost price if the rate of markup is 120%.

14. A retailer's cost price for a squash racket is $42.25. Find the selling price if the retailer uses a rate of margin of 20%.

15. Calculate the net price if the retailer receives all indicated discounts for each of the following.

	List Price	Discounts
(a)	$ 39.95	30%
(b)	$ 17.75	40% and 15%
(c)	$ 185.00	65% and 6.5%
(d)	$ 6.45	33% and 5%
(e)	$ 411.00	31%, 8% and 2%
(f)	$1521.80	43%, 12.5%, and 1.5%

16. Find the single discount that is equivalent to each of the following chain discounts.

(a) 32% and 4%
(b) 50%, 9%, and 3%
(c) 66%, 15%, and 1%

17. Which of the following chain discounts is best for the retailer?

(a) 35% and 10%
(b) 38% and 9%
(c) 25%, 15%, and 10%
(d) 30%, 14%, and 4%

18. Find the net price of each of the following articles if all are subject to discounts of 62%, 11%, and 2%.

(a) List price of a TV set is $388.00.
(b) List price of a video cassette recorder is $649.95.
(c) List price of a microwave oven is $529.99.

19. High-Tech Computers manufactures a disk drive that lists for $299.50, and offers discounts of 25% and 10%. A competitor sells the equivalent disk drive for the net price of $196.50. What third bonus discount is needed for High-Tech to be competitive?

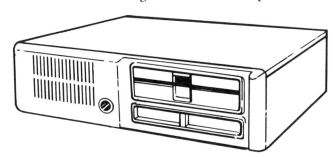

20. Copy and complete the table.

	Cost Price	Selling Price	Markup/ Margin	Rate of Markup	Rate of Margin	Markdown	Rate of Markdown	Discount Price
(a)	$ 84.00	$120.00	☐	☐	☐			
(b)	$ 25.00	☐	$ 7.50	☐	☐			
(c)	☐	$440.00	$120.00	☐	☐			
(d)	$ 36.50	$ 55.20	☐	☐	☐	$ 5.20	☐	☐
(e)	$ 821.40	☐	$740.00	☐	☐	$225.00	☐	☐
(f)	☐	$ 5.49	$ 3.60	☐	☐	☐	20%	☐
(g)	$ 250.00	$395.00	☐	☐	☐	☐	15%	☐
(h)	$ 340.00	☐	☐	50%	☐	☐	25%	☐
(i)	☐	$ 75.00	☐	☐	25%	☐	☐	$ 70.00
(j)	$1400.00	☐	☐	70%	☐	☐	☐	$2000.00
(k)	☐	☐	$ 60.00	☐	30%	☐	12%	☐
(l)	☐	☐	$ 4.29	45%	☐	☐	33%	☐
(m)	$ 92.40	☐	☐	☐	20%	$ 5.00	☐	☐

Summary of Units 9 to 15

Unit 9   Earning Money

What you have learned to do	For review, see page...
• Calculate gross pay in situations involving overtime, tips, bonus pay, or commission	158, 160
• Calculate straight commission or step commission	160
• Read the tables of deductions for C.P.P., U.I., and income tax	163
• Calculate net earnings after all deductions	162-164
• Read information about earnings from graphs	166
• Compare earnings by reading information from graphs representing 2 simultaneous situations	169
• Read hourly rate or rate of commission from the slope of a graph	166, 169

Unit 10   Calculating Income Tax

What you have learned to do	For review, see page...
• Read the information from a T4 slip	177
• Identify the 4 main sections of a tax return form	178
• Read information from a General Tax Guide	177-179
• Complete the *Calculation of Total Income* section of an income tax return form	180
• Complete the *Calculation of Taxable Income* section of an income tax return form	181, 183
• Calculate net income	180-181, 183
• Calculate income tax payable, then calculate refund or balance due	183-185
• Complete a tax return form for given cases	186-188

Unit 11   Spending Money

What you have learned to do	For review, see page...
• Calculate instalment price and finance charge on an instalment purchase	194
• Calculate the regular instalment payment to be made for a given purchase	196
• Calculate the true rate of interest on a given instalment plan	198
• Calculate discount and rate of discount	199-200
• Compare the terms of 2 different instalment plans	200

Unit 12   The World of Finance: Calculating Interest

What you have learned to do	For review, see page...
• Calculate simple interest	206
• Calculate the amount of a loan	208-209
• Read from the *Days of the Year* table to simplify finding the number of days	208-209
• Apply the formula for amount to find principal	209
• Apply the simple interest formula to find I, P, r or t	211
• Find the growth factor in a compound interest situation	214
• Calculate compound interest using the growth factor and a table of calculations	214
• Calculate amount of an investment earning compound interest	214
• Apply the compound interest formula to calculate compound interest of the amount of an investment	216-217
• Evaluate final answers, after applying compound interest formula, by using a calculator or tables	217
• Find the rate of interest needed for a given investment to earn a set amount of interest	220

Unit 13   The World of Finance: Saving Money

What you have learned to do	For review, see page...
• Identify the types of questions to ask before opening an account	226-227
• Calculate the interest earned on an account	227
• Calculate interest earned on a Guaranteed Investment Certificate or other types of term deposits	228
• Compare simple and compound interest on an investment	230
• Make a time diagram for an annuity	232
• Calculate the amount of an annuity	232-233
• Make a time diagram to represent a situation in which present value is to be found	235
• Calculate the present value of a given amount	235
• Calculate the present value of an annuity	237-238

Unit 14   Cost of Transportation

What you have learned to do   **For review, see page...**

- Identify the costs associated with buying a used car   244
- Calculate the total cost involved in buying a used car   244
- Read an options list for a new car   246
- Identify the costs involved in buying a new car   246
- Calculate the total cost of a new car   246
- Calculate instalment price and finance charge for financing a car   248
- Calculate the true rate of interest on an instalment plan for buying a
  car   248
- Calculate depreciation costs of a car   250
- Calculate the cost of operating a car, including depreciation   250-251
- Calculate the costs involved in maintaining a car   253
- Compare methods of transportation   254-256
- Read tables specifying insurance rates   258-259

Unit 15   Running a Business

What you have learned to do   **For review, see page...**

- Calculate the markup on a given item   264-265
- Calculate the rate of markup   264-265
- Solve for selling price or cost price in situations involving markup   264-265
- Calculate the margin on a given item   267-268
- Differentiate between margin and markup   268
- Calculate rate of margin   267-268
- Solve for selling price or cost price in situations involving margin   267-268
- Calculate markdown on a given item   270
- Calculate rate of markdown   270
- Solve for selling price or discount in situations involving markdown   270
- Calculate the trade discount due to a retailer for a given order   272-273
- Calculate chain discounts on retailer's order   272-273
- Use the complement of a percentage to calculate net price   275-276
- Use the complement to solve problems involving chain discounts   275-276
- Find the single discount equivalent to a chain discount   276

Units 9 to 15 Review

Unit 9 *Earning Money*

1. In each case, calculate total wages. Overtime is 1.5 times the regular rate.

	Regular Hours Worked	Regular Hourly Rate	Overtime Hours Worked
(a)	35.5	$ 9.00	4
(b)	40	$ 6.60	6.5
(c)	36	$12.45	3.5
(d)	32.5	$ 8.21	1.5

2. Morag works as a waitress. In addition to her regular pay of $4.20/h for a 36 h week, Morag keeps 70% of all tips she receives. Calculate her gross pay for a week in which she received $84.55 in tips.

3. Al works in a plant assembling stereo receivers. His base pay is $11.25/h for a 40 h week, and Al also receives a bonus of $0.375 for every receiver assembled in excess of 110 in 1 d. Use the information in the table to calculate Al's gross pay for the week.

Day of the Week	M	T	W	T	F
Receivers Assembled	126	95	142	112	133

4. Calculate each value missing from the table.

	Rate of Commission	Amount of Sales	Commission Earned
(a)	9%	$2110	▨
(b)	6.25%	$ 842.50	▨
(c)	10.5%	▨	$ 92.40
(d)	▨	$3420	$165.00

5. Step commission on sales is calculated as follows:
   - 4% on the first $1500;
   - 5.5% on the next $3500;
   - 7.2% on sales over $5000.

   Calculate the total commission for the given sales.

   (a) $1245 (c) $4817.44 (e) $6347.40
   (b) $3420 (d) $5211   (f) $9921.24

6. Dianne is paid $387.00 weekly, plus commission of 3.5% on sales. In 1 week the value of her sales was $3820. If Dianne has a net claim code 2 and her other deductions, in addition to C.P.P., U.I., and income tax, total $22.25, calculate her net pay for the week.

7. Bob earns $320/week, plus a step commission of 2.5% on the first $4000 of sales, and 4% on sales over $4000. Bob has deductions for life insurance ($4.50), charities ($7.50), and Canada Savings Bonds ($21.00). If Bob has net claim code 3, and his sales for the week total $4820, calculate his net pay for the week.

8. Seema earns a guaranteed weekly salary plus step commission based on sales. The graph shows possible earnings.

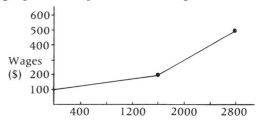

   (a) What weekly salary is guaranteed?
   (b) What sales will give Seema wages of $200? $400? $500?
   (c) Calculate the slopes of *AB* and *BC*. What rate of commission does Seema receive on sales up to $1600? over $1600?

9. Complete a tax return for William Harris. Will was born October 31, 1968, and works part-time as salesman at a local sporting goods store. He's a student at Forest Heights Collegiate and received the T4 slip below from his employer.

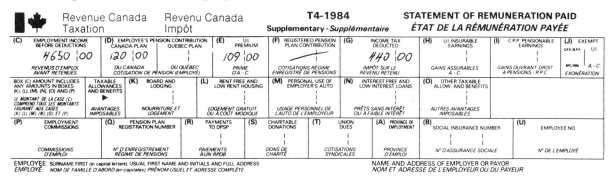

→ Harris, William
  364 Bevan Drive

→ Evans Sporting Goods

10. Claudia Ramage, born March 2, 1962, works full-time as a reporter for a local newspaper. Claudia's T4 slip is shown below. In addition, Claudia has receipts for $410 in allowable medical expenses, has paid $190 in tuition for a night school course, has donated $140 to the Cancer Society, and paid $320 in union dues.
    Complete Claudia's tax return.

<table>
<tr><th colspan="2">Revenue Canada
Taxation</th><th>Revenu Canada
Impôt</th><th colspan="2">T4-1984
Supplementary - Supplémentaire</th><th colspan="4">STATEMENT OF REMUNERATION PAID
ÉTAT DE LA RÉMUNÉRATION PAYÉE</th></tr>
</table>

(C) EMPLOYMENT INCOME BEFORE DEDUCTIONS	(D) EMPLOYEE'S PENSION CONTRIBUTION CANADA PLAN	QUEBEC PLAN	(E) U.I. PREMIUM	(F) REGISTERED PENSION PLAN CONTRIBUTION	(G) INCOME TAX DEDUCTED	(H) U.I. INSURABLE EARNINGS	(I) C.P.P. PENSIONABLE EARNINGS	(J) EXEMPT C.P.P/R.P.P. / U.I.
19,340 00	320 00		385 00	820 00	240 00			
REVENUS D'EMPLOI AVANT RETENUES	DU CANADA COTISATION DE PENSION (EMPLOYÉ)	DU QUÉBEC	PRIME D'A.-C.	COTISATIONS RÉGIME ENREGISTRÉ DE PENSIONS	IMPÔT SUR LE REVENU RETENU	GAINS ASSURABLES A.-C.	GAINS OUVRANT DROIT À PENSION - R.P.C.	EXONÉRATION

BOX (C) AMOUNT INCLUDES ANY AMOUNTS IN BOXES (K), (L), (M), (N), (O) AND (P)	TAXABLE ALLOWANCES AND BENEFITS	(K) BOARD AND LODGING	(L) RENT FREE AND LOW RENT HOUSING	(M) PERSONAL USE OF EMPLOYER'S AUTO	(N) INTEREST FREE AND LOW INTEREST LOANS	(O) OTHER TAXABLE ALLOW. AND BENEFITS	
LE MONTANT DE LA CASE (C) COMPREND TOUS LES MONTANTS FIGURANT AUX CASES (K), (L), (M), (N), (O), ET (P)	AVANTAGES IMPOSABLES	NOURRITURE ET LOGEMENT	LOGEMENT GRATUIT OU À COÛT MODIQUE	USAGE PERSONNEL DE L'AUTO DE L'EMPLOYEUR	PRÊTS SANS INTÉRÊT OU À FAIBLE INTÉRÊT	AUTRES AVANTAGES IMPOSABLES	

(P) EMPLOYMENT COMMISSIONS	(Q) PENSION PLAN REGISTRATION NUMBER	(R) PAYMENTS TO DPSP	(S) CHARITABLE DONATIONS	(T) UNION DUES	(A) PROVINCE OF EMPLOYMENT	(B) SOCIAL INSURANCE NUMBER	(U) EMPLOYEE NO.
COMMISSIONS D'EMPLOI	N° D'ENREGISTREMENT RÉGIME DE PENSIONS	PAIEMENTS À UN RPDB	DONS DE CHARITÉ	COTISATIONS SYNDICALES	PROVINCE D'EMPLOI	N° D'ASSURANCE SOCIALE	N° DE L'EMPLOYÉ

EMPLOYEE: SURNAME FIRST (in capital letters) USUAL FIRST NAME AND INITIALS AND FULL ADDRESS
EMPLOYÉ: NOM DE FAMILLE D'ABORD (en capitales) PRÉNOM USUEL ET ADRESSE COMPLÈTE

NAME AND ADDRESS OF EMPLOYER OR PAYOR
NOM ET ADRESSE DE L'EMPLOYEUR OU DU PAYEUR

→ Ramage, Claudia
  255 Fischer Drive

→ Vawterloo Voice

• Attach to your 1984 Income Tax Return
SEE INFORMATION ON REVERSE

• Annexer à votre déclaration d'impôt sur le revenu de 1984
VOIR LES RENSEIGNEMENTS AU VERSO

2

11. Vickie buys a new pair of speakers for her band. The speakers sell for a cash price of $1240, and Vickie agrees to pay $150 down and $104.50/month for 12 months.

   (a) Determine the finance charge.
   (b) By what percent is the instalment price more than the cash price?

12. Calculate the instalment price and finance charge for each of the following.

	Item	Cash Price	Instalment Terms
(a)	Personal Computer	$895	$100 down; $62/month for 15 months
(b)	Drums	$1310	20% down; $52.50/month for 24 months

13. Joshua can purchase a guitar for $830 cash or pay a down payment of 15% and the balance in equal monthly payments of $49.50. How many months will it take him to pay for the guitar if the instalment price is $916.50?

14. Use the table on page 197 to calculate the value of the equal monthly payment for each of the following. Calculate the carrying charges in each case.

	Amount Financed	Instalment Terms
(a)	$1500	24 months at 17%/a
(b)	$750	18 months at 12%/a
(c)	$8440	30 months at 14%/a

15. Calculate the true interest rate on each of the following instalment purchases.

	Cash Price of Item	Instalment Terms
(a)	$625	$50 down; $58/month for 12 months
(b)	$1200	$300 down; $35/month for 30 months

16. A squash racket, regularly selling for $45.90, is on sale for $36.99.

   (a) Calculate the rate of discount.
   (b) Determine the discount price of the racket, including 7% sales tax.

17. Baseball caps, regularly selling for $8.95 each, are on sale at 2 for $11.50. What is the rate of discount if you buy 2 caps at the sale price?

Unit 12   *Calculating Interest*

18. Calculate the simple interest for each of the following.

   (a) $800 for 7 months at 11%/a
   (b) $1300 for 210 d at 9.4%/a
   (c) $7800 for 2 a at 7%/a

19. Scotty is charged 17%/a simple interest on a loan. If Scotty borrows $450 on May 3, how much interest does he owe on August 17?

20. Calculate the amount at simple interest for each of the following.

(a) $850 borrowed for 7 months at 12%/a
(b) $1120 borrowed for 83 d at 14%/a
(c) $200 borrowed on October 25 and repaid on March 11, with interest rate 15%/a

21. Copy and complete the table.

	Principal	Interest	Rate/a	Time
(a)	$450	▢	5%	9 months
(b)	▢	$17	8%	92 d
(c)	▢	$120	9%	2 a
(d)	$400	$25	▢	7 months
(e)	$725	$95	▢	310 d
(f)	$50	$8	7%	▢
(g)	$1145	$175	13%	▢

22. On March 10, Sarah borrowed $286 from the Faraday Finance Company. On August 22 of the same year, the loan was repaid with a payment of $305.50. What rate of simple interest was Sarah charged on the loan?

23. Find the amount and the interest earned on each of the following.

(a) $300 invested at 8%/a compounded semi-annually for 3 a
(b) $880 invested at 6%/a compounded quarterly for 5 a
(c) $4500 invested at 6%/a compounded monthly for 4.5 a

24. Henri invests $1100 for 4 a. Which of the following interest rates accumulates the greatest amount of interest?

(a) 12%/a compounded monthly
(b) 13%/a compounded quarterly
(c) 15%/a simple interest

25. State the value of N using the compound interest tables.

(a) $(1.07)^N = 2.1$
(b) $(1.04)^N = 3$

26. How many years and months does it take for $500 to triple in value at each of the following interest rates?

(a) 9%/a compounded annually
(b) 12%/a compounded quarterly

27. Approximate the value of i, to the nearest 0.1%.

(a) $(1 + i)^{30} = 5$
(b) $(1 + i)^{44} = 2.4$

Unit 13 *Saving Money*

28. Copy and complete each of the following time diagrams. In each case, calculate the amount of the annuity and the interest earned.

(a)   7% compounded annually

Now   1 a   2 a   3 a   4 a   5 a

$100 $100 $100 $100 $100

(b)   9% compounded semi-annually

Now   1 a   2 a

$350 $350 $350 $350

29. For each of the following, draw a time diagram, then calculate the amount of the annuity and the interest earned.

   (a) An investment of $200 for a term of 18 months, with payment intervals of 3 months, earns interest at 8%/a compounded quarterly.

   (b) An investment of $40 for a term of 5 months, with payment intervals of 1 month, earns interest at 12%/a compounded monthly.

30. Frieda decides to deposit $30 at the end of each month for 7 months. The account pays interest at 6%/a compounded monthly. How much does Frieda have on deposit after 7 months if she makes the first deposit in 1 month?

31. Calculate the present value, *PV*, for each of the following.

   (a)   5% compounded annually

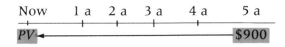

   (b)   11% compounded semi-annually

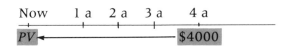

32. Brian wants to have $3000 saved in 2 a. How much should he invest today in a term deposit that pays 10%/a compounded semi-annually? 9%/a compounded monthly?

33. Copy and complete each of the following time diagrams. In each case, calculate the present value of the annuity.

   (a)   6%/a compounded annually

Now	1 a	2 a	3 a	4 a
	$300	$300	$300	$300

$300 ← 1.06

   (b)   6%/a compounded monthly

0	1 month				5 months
	$50	$50	$50	$50	$50

$50 ← 1.005

34. Calculate the present value of each of the following annuities. Draw a time diagram to organize your calculations.

   (a) $1600 received at the end of each year for 3 a at 11%/a compounded annually

   (b) $800 received at the end of every 6 months for 3 a at 11%/a compounded semi-annually

Unit 14   *Cost of Transportation*

35. Terry purchases a used car and agrees to pay for the following repairs to have the car certified.

   • emergency brake cable $ 19.50
   • 2 new tires $118.00
   • exhaust system $138.75
   • body work $ 84.30

The certification fee was $32, and the transfer fee was $8.50. If the price of the car was $3150 plus 7% sales tax, calculate Terry's total cost for the car.

Use the Options List on page 246 to help you answer Questions 35, 36, and 37.

36. Calculate the sticker price of the car with each set of options listed.

(a) PDI and freight $345
Power door locks
6-way power seat
Air conditioner
Accent body stripes
AM-FM radio with item ④
Wire wheel covers and locks

(b) PDI and freight $327.45
3-speed automatic transmission
Power steering
Luggage carrier
AM-FM radio with item ③
Special handling suspension
Chromed super stock wheels

37. Which set of options is the more expensive and by how much?

(a) Manual overdrive transmission
Power windows
Front seat armrest
Sunroof
Accent body stripes
Special handling suspension

(b) Automatic transmission
Power steering
Luggage carrier
AM-FM radio with item ①
Rallye wheels with trim rings
Tilt-a-way steering wheel

38. Calculate the total cash price, including 8% sales tax, of a car with the following options.

PDI and freight $403.95
Automatic transmission
Air conditioning
Sunroof
Accent body stripes
AM-FM radio with item ②
Special handling suspension
Custom sport steering wheel
Warranty plan B

39. For the used car shown, determine:
• cash price (sales tax is at 9%);
• instalment price;
• finance charge;
• true interest rate.

A great buy for only $4295!
or $1100 down plus
24 monthly payments of only $180.00

40. Annual operating expenses for an automobile include the following items

• Gas, oil, lubrication	$ 968.43
• Insurance	$1245.00
• Licence	$ 60.00
• Repairs	$ 583.90
• Depreciation	$1475.00

If the car is driven 1850 km during the year, determine

(a) the average monthly cost of operation
(b) operating cost per 100 km

41. During the fourth year of operation of her car, Janice drives 19 000 km. The cost of gasoline averaged 50.8¢/L for that year, and the car's average fuel consumption was 7.1 L/100 km. Janice's other expenses for the year are listed below.

    • Oil, lubrication $ 130.90
    • Insurance $1052.00
    • Licence $ 54.00
    • Repairs $ 379.85

    If Janice paid $10 150 for her car when it was new, calculate the cost per 100 km to operate it during the fourth year she owns it.

42. Shannon and 3 friends rent a compact car for the weekend. They pay $28/d, plus 6.2¢/km over 100 km driven, as well as $5/d for full insurance coverage. In the 3 d they have the car, they drive 608 km, and spend $25.50 on gasoline. What was Shannon's share of the total expense of weekend transportation?

43. Darren travels by taxi to and from work 5 d each week. Taxi fare is at a fixed rate of $1.50 plus a variable rate of $1.30/km. If Darren lives 8.6 km from work and shares transportation expenses with 2 other employees who live in the same apartment building, find his weekly cost of transportation.

Unit 15   *Running a Business*

44. Steve's Sound Shop sells cassette tapes for $7.59 that are purchased from the supplier at $3.99.

    (a) What is the markup?
    (b) What is the rate of markup?
    (c) What is the margin?
    (d) What is the rate of margin?

45. Margo sells items in her boutique at a margin of 24%. Find the margin and cost price of a dress selling for $95.49.

46. Reggie marks up the price of all video cassette recorders in his store by 70%. Find the cost price and the selling price of a VCR that has been marked up by $285.

47. A retailer's cost price for a bicycle is $105. Find the selling price if the retailer uses a rate of margin of 15%.

48. Find the rate of markdown if graph paper, regularly selling at $1.49/pad, is on sale at 3 for $2.89.

49. Calculate the net price if the retailer receives all the indicated discounts for each of the following.

	List Price	Discounts
(a)	$ 49.95	40% and 6%
(b)	$ 35.49	30% and 5%
(c)	$420	20%, 7%, and 1.5%

50. Find the single discount that is equivalent to each of the following chain discounts.

    (a) 25% and 9%
    (b) 30%, 8%, 2.5%
    (c) 45%, $12\frac{1}{2}$%, $3\frac{1}{4}$%

51. Find the net price of a car stereo that is subject to discounts of 35%, 14%, and 4.2% if the list price of the stereo is $329.95.

Unit 16

Statistics

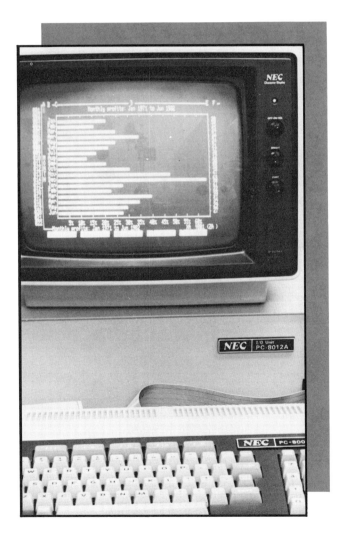

Collecting Data

"Statistical thinking will one day be as necessary for efficient citizenship as the ability to read and write."

H.G. Wells

When you open a newspaper or turn on a radio, you're often presented with statistical information.

The field of statistics involves:
• collecting numerical information (data);
• organizing and analysing the information;
• making decisions based on the information.

There are many techniques that can be used to collect data. Some are described here.

1. Conducting an Experiment

Vitamins Improve Grades
Tests conducted by Dr. Harris have shown a link between daily use of vitamins and student performance

A scientist wants to find out whether taking a multi-vitamin each day will improve a student's marks. To collect data, the scientist uses 2 groups of 100 high school students. One group is given vitamins to take daily. The other group takes no vitamins: this is the **control group**, and it provides the scientist with a standard of comparison. After several months the scientist will compare the student grades from each group to see whether there is any difference in performance between the 2 groups.

2. Re-examine Past Data

Student Marks Affected by Semestering?
When marks of graduating students in semestered schools were compared to marks of students before semestering was implemented, researchers found th

Terry's school recently became semestered. Terry wants to know whether semestering has had any effect on students' grades. Data can be collected from past records of students at the school before and after semestering was introduced. The data can be analysed to determine if there is any noticeable difference in performance that can be related to semestering.

3. Choosing a Sample

> **Canadians Will Re-elect Government**
> A recent poll taken by our paper indicates
> that if an election were held today, the
> present government would

Political polls are often taken to see how Canadians would vote. Since it isn't practical to ask every Canadian voter, a small group called a **sample** is chosen to represent the **population**. Sample surveys can be very reliable—*if* the sample accurately represents the population. If every person in the population has an equal opportunity to be selected for the sample, then the sample is said to be **unbiased**.

Conclusions from a survey should be restricted to the sample chosen. A reporter who asks 25 people in downtown Ottawa their opinion on who will win the next federal election, should not make conclusions about how *all* Canadians will vote. The reporter's survey was not taken across Canada, so not all Canadians had an equal opportunity to be selected.

AND WHAT DO **YOU** THINK, SIR?

Exercise

A 1. State what method you would use to collect data to answer the following questions.

   (a) Has the percentage of students that drop out before grade 12 increased since 1970?
   (b) Does a program of regular physical exercise make workers more productive?
   (c) Who will be elected mayor in the next city election?
   (d) Does eating an apple every day really keep the doctor away?
   (e) How many students in your town have part-time jobs?
   (f) Can mandatory seatbelt legislation reduce the number of traffic fatalities?
   (g) How many damaged eggs can be expected in a day's production?

2. Joan is conducting a survey of students at her high school to find out how much students earn from part-time jobs. Joan doesn't want to survey everyone, so she decides to ask a sample of 50 students. Suggest some methods Joan could use to select an unbiased sample.

3. A scientist is studying the effects of a special diet on student grades. Why is a control group necessary?

4. Ten years ago, City Council increased the speed limit on the road in front of George's house. George wants to know if traffic accidents have also increased. He examines the records of accidents on the road for 10 a before and 10 a after the speed limit was changed, and concludes that accidents have increased 20% *due to the speed limit change*. Is this necessarily a valid conclusion? What other factors should George consider? What are some problems that can arise by drawing conclusions from past records?

5. Rosie works on the school paper and wants to know how many students like the cafeteria food. Rosie selects 2 students at random. One student enjoys the food and the other prefers to bring sandwiches made at home. Based on that survey, Rosie writes an article "50% of Students Dislike Cafeteria Food." Comment on Rosie's conclusion.

6. A brand-name toothpaste advertises that, "2 out of 3 Dentists Recommend Dent-Paste to Their Patients." What other information would you like to have before accepting the claim?

Project

Look through newspapers and magazines to find 2 examples of each of the 3 techniques of collecting data.

Side Trip

Workers at wildlife parks can estimate the number of a certain species that are in the park by capturing and tagging a few of the animals in one year. The following year, another sample is captured and the number of tagged animals in the sample is counted.

You can simulate this **capture-recapture** method of estimating wildlife populations by conducting the following experiment, which will lead you to a method of estimating the number of marbles in a jar.

You will need a jar with an unknown large number of marbles in it. Or use pennies, buttons, or even paper clips.

Select 10 marbles from the jar and mark them. Use a felt-tip marker or a bit of paint.

Return the marbles to the jar and mix all the marbles *thoroughly*.

Randomly select 20 marbles and count the number of marbles that are marked. Now you can perform a calculation to estimate the number, t, in the jar.

Suppose m is the number of marked marbles in your second sample.

$$\frac{10}{t} = \frac{m}{20}$$

number marked — compared to total

Solve for t, the total number of marbles in the jar.

Make the estimate more and more accurate by repeating the experiment.

Making Predictions

The results of a sample survey can be used to make predictions.
In a sample survey of 150 car owners, 27 have red cars. You can find the **relative frequency** of red cars as a percent of the total sample.

$\frac{27}{150} \times 100\% = 18\%$ Relative frequency is 18%.

In a population of 3400 car owners, how many would you expect to have red cars? Use the relative frequency to make a prediction.

$18\% \times 3400 = 612$

The accuracy of the prediction of 612 red cars depends on how well the sample was chosen.

Example 1

Pat wants to publish a newspaper at school but needs to predict how many students would buy the paper. Pat conducts a survey with an unbiased survey of 70 students. In the sample survey, 46 students stated that they would buy a school paper. How many papers can Pat expect to sell if there are 1166 students in the school?

Calculate relative frequency.

$\frac{46}{70} \times 100\% = 65.7\%$, to 1 decimal

Multiply by total population.

$65.7\% \times 1166 = 766$, nearest whole number

Pat could expect to have 766 students buying the paper.

Exercise

B 1. (a) An inspector of computer software inspected 80 diskettes at random and found that 3 were flawed. Find the relative frequency of damaged diskettes. If 9000 diskettes were produced, how many can the manufacturer expect to be returned as damaged?
   (b) How could the inspector ensure that the selection of diskettes was random?

2. (a) An unbiased telephone survey of 800 households showed that 56 used Sudsy Soap and 47 used Bubbles Soap. Estimate the number of boxes of Sudsy Soap and Bubbles Soap in a population of 3.2 million households.
   (b) How would you conduct a survey of households to ensure an unbiased sample?

3. Last year a game warden captured and tagged 50 deer. This year, the warden captures 140 deer and discovers that 8 are tagged. Calculate the estimated deer population, P, of the park by using a ratio like the one below.
   $\frac{50}{P} = \frac{8}{140}$

4. (a) Survey your class and then predict the number of blonde students in the school.
   (b) Why is your survey biased?

5. (a) By surveying your class, predict the number of Canadians that part their hair on the right side of their head.
   (b) Why is your survey biased?

Organizing Data

Joan is on Student Council and she wants to find out how much money students spend at the school cafeteria. She decides to record the amount spent by the first 70 students through the cafeteria line. Here is the data Joan collected.

$2.35	$1.20	$1.60	$2.15	$1.00	$3.24	$1.88
$2.35	$1.10	$1.59	$1.85	$2.05	$3.55	$2.00
$1.40	$1.62	$2.80	$1.75	$1.60	$3.65	$2.35
$2.95	$0.60	$2.20	$1.95	$3.05	$2.15	$2.85
$1.50	$1.99	$2.88	$1.70	$1.59	$2.60	$3.50
$2.60	$1.75	$1.95	$0.90	$3.70	$0.95	$1.85
$2.05	$2.00	$1.68	$3.09	$1.99	$3.25	$1.40
$2.09	$1.00	$2.95	$1.80	$2.90	$0.75	$2.20
$1.10	$1.05	$3.00	$1.90	$2.65	$2.45	$1.80
$1.95	$2.10	$2.88	$2.55	$1.60	$2.70	$1.55

The amounts **range** from $0.60 to $3.70. To make the information useful, Joan groups the data into smaller ranges, or **classes**. It's usually best to have about 10 classes. Joan will use 8 classes.

She finds the **interval** for each class by using the formula below.

$$\text{Interval} = \frac{\text{Largest Value} - \text{Smallest Value}}{\text{Number of Classes}}$$
$$= \frac{\$3.70 - \$0.60}{8}$$
$$= \$0.39, \text{ to 2 decimals}$$

Joan selects an interval of $0.40.

Now Joan can use the data to make a frequency table.

Amount Spent	Tally	Frequency
$0.60 to $1.00	III	3
$1.00 to $1.40	HHT I	6
$1.40 to $1.80	HHT HHT IIII	14
$1.80 to $2.20	HHT HHT HHT HHT	20
$2.20 to $2.60	HHT II	7
$2.60 to $3.00	HHT HHT I	11
$3.00 to $3.40	HHT	5
$3.40 to $3.80	IIII	4

The graph below shows the frequency distribution.

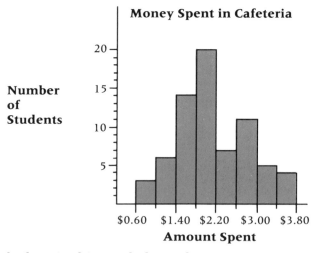

$1.80 to $2.20 includes all values from $1.80 up but *not* including $2.20. If x is a value in the interval, then $\$1.80 \leq x < \$2.20$.

Money Spent in Cafeteria

Number of Students

Amount Spent

The bars in this graph do not have spaces between them. The graph is a **histogram**.

It is easy to see from the histogram that the amount spent by most students was between $1.80 and $2.19.

How would you find the number of students who spent less than $2.60? The answer is not easy to find on the histogram. But Joan can make another graph, based on a table of *cumulative* frequencies.

Amount Spent	Frequency	Cumulative Frequency
$0.60 to $1.00	3	3
$1.00 to $1.40	6	9
$1.40 to $1.80	14	23
$1.80 to $2.20	20	43
$2.20 to $2.60	7	50
$2.60 to $3.00	11	61
$3.00 to $3.40	5	66
$3.40 to $3.80	4	70

You can make a cumulative frequency graph by plotting the cumulative frequency against the middle value of each interval.

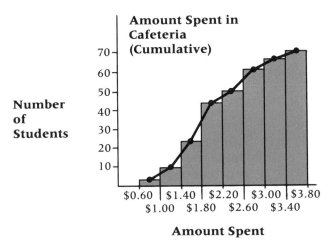

The graph shows that 60 students spent less than $2.60.

Joan also wants to look at the *percentage* of students in each class. She makes a **relative frequency table**.

Amount Spent	Frequency	Relative Frequency
$0.60 to $1.00	3	4.3%
$1.00 to $1.40	6	8.6%
$1.40 to $1.80	14	20.0%
$1.80 to $2.20	20	28.6%
$2.20 to $2.60	7	10.0%
$2.60 to $3.00	11	15.7%
$3.00 to $3.40	5	7.1%
$3.40 to $3.80	4	5.7%
Totals	70	100%

She uses the table to make a histogram.

$\frac{3}{70} \times 100\%$ $\frac{14}{70} \times 100\%$

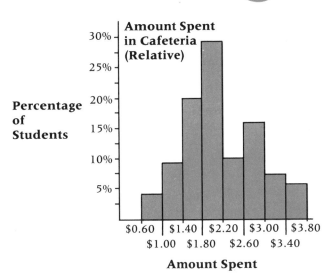

Compare this graph to the graph on the opposite page.

Exercise

A 1. In her survey Joan recorded the amount spent by the first 70 students in the cafeteria line. Discuss possible reasons why Joan's survey could be biased. Suggest ways that Joan could have made her sample less biased.

2. State the range for each set of data.

(a) 18, 43, 17, 9, 11, 25
(b) 354, 276, 320, 173, 299, 345

3. A manufacturer of dishwashers claims, "Nine out of ten of our dishwashers made in the last twelve years are still running." A histogram of the manufacturer's sales for the 12 a period is given below.

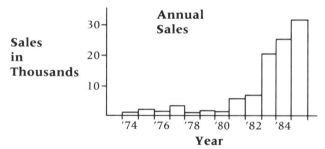

Comment on the manufacturer's claim, in view of the sales graph.

4. What interval would you use for each class?

(a) Wages range from $40 to $100 and 12 classes are to be used.
(b) Marks range from 30 to 80 and 10 classes are to be used.
(c) Heights range from 90 cm to 130 cm and 8 classes are to be used.
(d) Ages range from 7 a to 50 a and 9 classes are to be used.

5. The 3 graphs below represent the same data.

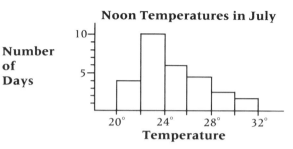

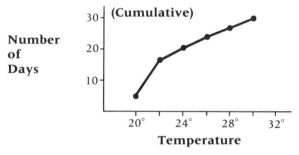

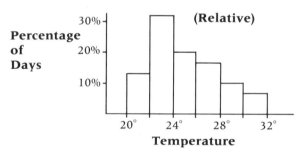

(a) State the second most common interval of July noon temperature.
(b) State the percentage of the days in July that have noon temperatures between 20°C and 22°C.
(c) State the number of days in July that have noon temperatures below 26°C.
(d) State the percentage of July days that have noon temperatures below 24°C.
(e) State the number of days in July that have noon temperatures above 28°C.

B **6.** In a traffic study, the speeds of 60 cars travelling on a stretch of highway were recorded.

Speed (km/h)	Frequency	Cumulative Frequency	Relative Frequency
30 to 40	4		
40 to 50	11		
50 to 60	24		
60 to 70	16		
70 to 80	3		
80 to 90	2		

(a) Copy and complete the table.
(b) Draw the frequency distribution histogram.
(c) Draw the cumulative frequency graph.
(d) Draw the relative frequency histogram.
(e) If the speed limit is 60 km/h, how many drivers were driving below the speed limit? What percentage were driving below the speed limit?

7. Here is a list of the Mathematics marks of 80 grade 11 students.

57	66	89	92	34	61	72	81
45	50	65	45	78	90	55	69
72	62	81	30	83	59	60	77
72	64	58	48	88	72	79	66
92	87	52	75	80	61	42	76
68	54	68	63	53	77	65	84
72	50	58	62	74	83	62	61
86	72	65	68	74	60	74	96
64	61	73	79	79	57	66	68
75	46	80	51	83	67	42	91

(a) Find the range of the marks.
(b) Find an interval that will divide the data into 7 classes.
(c) Tally the data to make a frequency distribution table.
(d) Make a frequency distribution histogram.
(e) Extend your table to include a cumulative frequency graph.
(f) How many students had marks above 60?

8. A survey of 60 students with part-time jobs gave the following hourly rates for the sample.

$2.76	$5.65	$3.85	$3.80	$2.95
$2.85	$2.70	$3.60	$4.20	$3.05
$5.70	$2.90	$3.00	$5.45	$2.75
$3.30	$2.60	$2.50	$3.80	$4.30
$4.70	$2.90	$5.85	$3.90	$2.70
$2.55	$3.05	$2.60	$4.10	$3.60
$3.90	$2.95	$5.10	$3.75	$4.45
$2.70	$3.90	$4.40	$2.90	$3.45
$2.00	$3.35	$2.95	$2.60	$5.60
$3.40	$3.30	$4.25	$3.80	$2.65
$5.25	$3.70	$2.90	$4.05	$5.40
$4.05	$5.30	$3.70	$3.40	$4.35

(a) Tally the data in intervals of $0.50 (starting from $2.00) to make a frequency distribution table.
(b) Make a frequency distribution histogram.
(c) Extend the table in part (a) to calculate the relative frequencies and make a relative frequency histogram.

9. Use the same data as in Question 8 to do the following.

(a) Make a frequency distribution table using intervals of $1.00 (starting at $2.00).
(b) Make a frequency distribution histogram.
(c) Compare your answer in part (b) to your answer in part (b) of Question 8. What information has been lost by regrouping the data?

Project

1. Pick a sport like hockey, baseball, or football. Collect data on the number of points scored by the winning team and the number of points scored by the losing team. Data should be collected from at least 50 games. Make a frequency table and a frequency distribution histogram for both sets of data.

2. The most frequently used letters in the English language are A, E, H, I, N, O, R, S, and T, but not in that order. Start a frequency distribution table with 10 rows as shown below.

Letter	Tally	Frequency
A		
E		
H		
I		
N		
O		
R		
S		
T		

Now select several different types of reading material (not less than 2 pages) and tally all the occurrences of each letter in the table. Find the relative frequencies for each of the 9 letters and make a relative frequency histogram. What is the correct order of most frequent occurrence for the 9 letters? How could this information be useful in devising a strategy for playing a game like "Hangman"?

Mean, Median, and Mode

Frank collected data on 2 brands of headlights used on his fleet of 13 taxis. To find which brand is better, he compiled a list of the number of months the headlights were used before needing to be replaced.

Brand A	Brand B
15	11
13	8
13	16
16	10
15	9
11	42
15	
Total, 98	Total, 96

To measure the durability of the headlights, Frank can compare data to an *average* value. But average is a general term that has several different meanings. In statistics, there are 3 types of averages, as described below. One way to compare the durability of the headlights is to calculate the **mean** life of a headlight.

$$\text{Mean} = \frac{\text{Sum of the Data}}{\text{Number of Data}}$$

What is the mean life expectancy of the headlights, using Frank's data?

Brand A:
Mean $= \frac{98}{7}$
$= 14$

Brand B:
Mean $= \frac{96}{6}$
$= 16$

If you base your judgement only on the mean, the better headlight appears to be Brand B.

The mean is the value that most people associate with average. However, the mean can be affected by extreme values. What value caused Brand B to have such a high mean?

Another statistical average is found by listing the data in order from least to greatest and finding the figure in the middle. This figure is the **median**.

Brand A: 11   13   13   15   15   15   16
Brand B: 8   9   10 | 11   16   42

The median for Brand A is 15. The median for Brand B is (10 + 11) ÷ 2, or 10.5.
This indicates that at least half of Brand A headlights give at least 15 months' service, as compared to 10.5 months' service for Brand B.

If you base your judgement on the median, the better headlight appears to be Brand A.

> The median is the middle item when the data are arranged from least to greatest. If there is an even number of items in the data, then the median is the average of the 2 middle items.

You can also evaluate performance by considering which number occurs the most often for each brand. This value is the **mode**.

The mode for Brand A is 15 months (since it occurs more often than any other value in the list). Brand B does not have a mode. This seems to indicate that Brand A is better on the basis of *more consistent* performance.

> The mode is the most frequently occurring item in the data. If every number occurs only once, then there is no mode.

The table summarizes the 3 values to represent the data.

	Brand A	Brand B
Mean	14	16
Median	15	10.5
Mode	15	None

Example 1

At a golf driving range, Fran records the lengths of her last 8 drives.

190 m   165 m   210 m   165 m
200 m   180 m   195 m   205 m

• Find the mean, median, and mode for the data.

Use the formula for mean.

$$\text{Mean} = \frac{190+165+210+165+200+180+195+205}{8}$$
$$= \frac{1510}{8}$$
$$= 188.75$$

To find the median, arrange the numbers from least to greatest.

165   165   180   190 | 195   200   205   210

$$\text{Median} = \frac{190 + 195}{2}$$
$$= 192.5$$

Since 165 appears twice, the mode is 165.

• If Fran drives the ball once more, what length of drive would it take to increase the mean to 190 m?

The total distance necessary to have a mean of 190 m after 9 drives is 190 m × 9, or 1710 m. The total distance on the first 8 drives was 1510 m.
Fran must drive 1710 m − 1510 m, or 200 m, on the last drive.

Exercise

A 1. State the median and mode for each set of data.

(a) 5, 8, 8, 12, 15, 23, 35
(b) 4, 4, 9, 13, 13, 27
(c) 15, 21, 32, 45, 52, 63, 79, 85
(d) 8, 21, 35, 42, 56, 56, 64, 78, 89, 95

2. State the mean, median, and mode for each set of data.

(a) 2, 10, 15
(b) 1, 2, 7, 8, 9, 9
(c) 4, 5, 5, 6
(d) 1, 1, 1, 1, 1, 1, 1, 1, 1, 91

3. Why would an importer of footwear be more likely to consider the mode of shoe sizes rather than the mean or median size, when placing an order?

4. Why is the following newspaper clipping misleading?

WANTED: Computer Repairman
Work in small office with average salary of $34 000. You're a technically-minded individual with experience in working with computers.

The company's calculation was based on the mean of the salaries in the office. Here is a summary of those salaries.
• Custodian: $20 000
• Keypunch operator: $22 000
• Secretary: $23 000
• Computer operator: $25 000
• President of company: $120 000

B 5. During April, the eight salespeople at Harry's Used Car Lot sold 5, 10, 7, 9, 11, 41, 5, and 8 cars respectively.

(a) Find the mean, median, and mode for the car sales.
(b) When Harry looked at the monthly figures, he said, "It was a bad month! Most of my salespeople sold just 5 cars."
What value was Harry using? Do you think it was a fair assessment of the monthly sales? Why or why not?
(c) Harry looked at the figures again and said, "Seven of my salespeople can't have worked hard enough this month: their sales are below the monthly sales average." Comment on Harry's assessment of the data.
(d) Which of the mean, median, and mode best represent the car sales data for April?

6. Find the mean, median, and mode for each set of data.

(a) 19, 16, 14, 23, 45, 32, 19, 28, 41, 36
(b) 9.4, 5.7, 4.9, 2.8, 8.0, 4.9, 3.5, 6.6, 7.8, 9.5, 7.4, 6.9, 4.9
(c) 53, 75, 84, 95, 47, 73, 75, 93, 82, 64, 82, 66, 59, 88, 72, 90

7. Leslie got the following scores after 6 games of ten-pin bowling.
201, 187, 198, 212, 168, 167

(a) Find the mean and median scores.
(b) Leslie played 2 more games and scored 152 and 186. Find the mean and median score for all 8 games.
(c) What score would Leslie need on the ninth game to get a mean score of 188?

8. Two Math classes got the same test. The first class has 18 students and the mean result was 70.5. The second class has 33 students and the class mean was 64. Calculate the mean of the test, based on the results of all 51 students.

9. A consumers' group is testing the life expectancy, in hours, of 3 brands of lightbulbs. Their findings are listed below.

Lightbulb A: 450h, 320 h, 210 h, 190 h, 500 h, 380 h, 500
Lightbulb B: 580 h, 710 h, 370 h, 540 h 410 h, 450 h, 440 h
Lightbulb C: 90 h, 505 h, 190 h, 520 h, 120 h, 500 h, 515 h

(a) Calculate the mean, median, and mode for each lightbulb.
(b) After the testing, each manufacturer claimed, "Our lightbulbs last an average of 500 h." On what average value was each manufacturer basing this claim?
(c) From which manufacturer would you purchase lightbulbs? Why?

Calculating Mean, Median, and Mode of Large Sets of Data

Stan works on the social committee at school. He wants to find the mean, median, and mode of the ages of students that attend a school dance.

Stan takes a poll of 150 people at the dance, but the data is too disorganized to find the answer quickly.

One way Stan can organize the data is to make a frequency table.

Age	Frequency
14	20
15	51
16	37
17	20
18	14
19	8

From the table, Stan can quickly find that the mode is 15. Could he simplify the data further to find the median without ordering all the numbers, and to find the mean without adding 150 numbers?

Stan could add 2 columns to the table.

Age	Frequency	Cumulative Frequency	Product Age × Frequency
14	20	20	14 × 20 = 280
15	51	71	15 × 51 = 765
16	37	108	16 × 37 = 592
17	20	128	17 × 20 = 340
18	14	142	18 × 14 = 252
19	8	150	19 × 8 = 152

to find mode   to find median   to find mean

To find the median in the list of 150 numbers find the average of the 75th and 76th numbers when arranged in order.

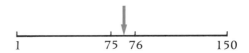

Look at the cumulative frequency column in the table: both the 75th and 76th numbers are in the row corresponding to an age of 16. The median age of students at the dance was 16.

Find the mean by dividing the total of the values in the last column by the total number of students at the dance.

$$\text{Mean} = \frac{280+765+592+340+252+152}{150}$$

$$= 15.9, \text{ to 1 decimal place}$$

The mean age of the students was 15.9 a.

Exercise

A 1. The table shows the number of children, classified by age, attending 2 summer camps.

Camp Blackfly

Age	Frequency	Cumulative Frequency
4	7	7
5	8	15
6	10	25
7	3	28

Camp Tippicanoe

Age	Frequency	Cumulative Frequency
4	6	6
5	5	11
6	7	18
7	9	27

(a) State the mode of the children's ages for each camp.
(b) State the median age for each camp.

2. The numbers below represent the number of items in a set of data. If the data have been arranged in ascending order, state the number of the items that would give the median.

(a) 25 (d) 32
(b) 100 (e) 54
(c) 45 (f) 63

B 3. Sam tries to predict the outcome of hockey games. To help with the predictions, Sam collected data about the number of goals scored by the winning team in each of the last 120 games.

Goals	Frequency
1	5
2	9
3	14
4	29
5	26
6	24
7	10
8	3

Extend the table to include the cumulative frequency and product columns. Use the data to find the mean, median, and mode for goals scored per game.

...GOALS PER... FREQUENCY... MEDIAN....

Calculating Mean, Median, and Mode from Grouped Data

The times of 85 racers at the Red Mountain Ski Meet are given in the table, grouped in intervals of 3 s. Find the mean, median, and mode of the racing times.

Time (seconds)	Frequency
15 to 18	4
18 to 21	14
21 to 24	27
24 to 27	31
27 to 30	9

With grouped data, there is no single value to multiply by the frequency to get a product. The *least biased* value that can represent the class is the average of the upper and lower bounds of the class. This is the class value.

Time (s)	Class Value	Frequency	Cumulative Frequency	Product Class Value × Frequency
15 to 18	16.5	4	4	66
18 to 21	19.5	14	18	273
21 to 24	22.5	27	45	607.5
24 to 27	25.5	31	76	790.5
27 to 30	28.5	9	85	256.5

$19.5 \times 14 = 273$

Since 31 is the greatest frequency, the mode is between 24 s and 27 s.

The median is the time of the racer that finished 43rd.

The median time is between 21 s and 24 s.

$$\text{Mean} = \frac{66 + 273 + 607.5 + 790.5 + 256.5}{85}$$
$$= 23.5 \text{ s, to 1 decimal place}$$

The mean has been calculated from data grouped in intervals. This is a **weighted mean**.

Exercise

A 1. Given the following data, state the missing information.

Height (m)	Class Height	Frequency	Cumulative Frequency	Product
20 to 40	▢	2	▢	▢
40 to 60	▢	4	▢	▢
60 to 80	▢	▢	11	▢

B 2. The table below contains a summary of the Science marks for 145 Grade 11 students. Make a table in your notebook that also includes columns for Class Value, Cumulative Frequency, and Product. Then find the mean, median, and mode of the data.

Mark	Frequency
30 to 40	5
40 to 50	11
50 to 60	23
60 to 70	35
70 to 80	44
80 to 90	21
90 to 100	6

3. A manufacturer of portable lanterns is experimenting with a new battery. The number of hours that the battery is operational is recorded. The table shows the data recorded.

Hours	Frequency
0 to 3	36
3 to 6	10
6 to 9	6
9 to 12	10
12 to 15	9
15 to 18	15
18 to 21	20
21 to 24	38

(a) Extend the table to find the mean, median, and mode.
(b) Draw the frequency distribution histogram. Statisticians call this a "Bathtub Distribution" because of the shape of the histogram.

4. The participants' times in seconds for one lap in the Dusty Road Motocross are given below.

34.8	44.9	52.6	40.8	39.1
37.8	50.7	55.2	43.3	37.0
48.6	54.8	33.1	37.9	42.6
55.2	50.9	34.3	35.8	47.0
46.8	38.0	52.2	51.8	36.0
45.1	42.8	37.0	35.9	53.1
35.4	38.2	41.9	51.4	36.6
42.2	32.4	38.9	46.2	54.9
37.8	43.3	34.0	54.8	39.5

Construct a frequency distribution table for the given data. Use 8 classes, with the first interval being 32 to 35. Find the class that contains the mode, and calculate the mean and median.

Interpreting Graphs

People in business deal with a large quantity of data every day. To save time, managers prefer to see data presented in graphical form, rather than tables of figures.

Many businesses that use computers have graphics software that can display statistical data in graph form. Many of these graphs have become very sophisticated.

One of the most common types of graphs used by businesses is the bar graph.

The bar graph below has been made from the frequency table shown.

Method	Frequency
Car	92
Bike	113
Bus	77
Walk	124

Methods of Travel to School

A bar graph is similar to a histogram, except that the bars do not touch. This often indicates that the *order* of the bars is not important.
The bar graph above can be misleading because of the vertical scale used. At first glance, it looks as if 4 or 5 times as many people walk to school as take the bus.

Here is the same graph with the vertical scale starting at zero.

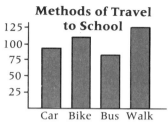

The visual distortion has been eliminated. But what advantage does the first graph have over the one above?

Comparison bar graphs can be used to show more than 2 sets of data at once.

Frequency polygons can also be used instead of histograms if you want to display data from several sources at once.

Weekly Sales of TV's in 1984

Total Sales	Toronto Store	Montreal Store
0 to 10	15	32
11 to 20	25	8
21 to 30	9	7
31 to 40	3	5

The frequency polygon below represents the data in the table above.

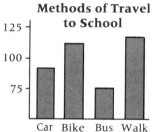

Weekly TV Sales

310

Circle graphs and horizontal bar graphs are another way to present data in graphical form. The two graphs below show the same results of a provincial political poll.

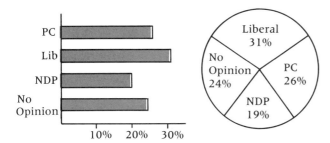

Which do you think represents the data best? Why?

By taking different perspectives of the circle graph, distortions can cause misleading impressions.
A different view of the previous circle graph is shown below.

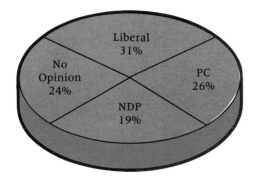

Which party benefits from the distortion?

Exercise

A **1.** Student Council surveyed 200 high school students with a variety of questions. State whether a bar graph or a histogram would best illustrate a frequency table for each of the following questions.

   (a) What is your height?
   (b) What's your favorite subject?
   (c) How much time do you spend on homework each night?
   (d) Male or female?
   (e) What country were you born in?
   (f) What is your mass?
   (g) What was your average in English last term?
   (h) What make of car would you most like to drive?

2. How has the following data been distorted?
   (a)

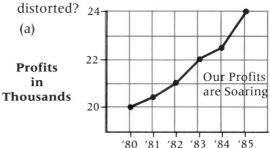

   (b)

A large slice of your municipal tax dollar goes to social services.

(c) The shrinking Canadian dollar

1959–$1.00

1964–$0.93

1968–$0.90

1975–$0.70

1984–$0.42

(d) We may be the number 2 paper in town, but we are catching up!

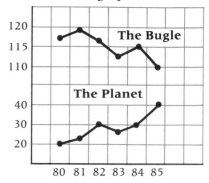

Total Subscribers in Thousands

The Bugle

The Planet

120
115
110
40
30
20

80 81 82 83 84 85

B **3.** The table gives sales data collected during 1 week in July.

Drink Brand	Store P	Store Q
Kool Kola	95	63
Bubbly Kola	88	72
Lime-Up	56	24
Orange-Aide	31	35
Cool-Pop	67	77

Draw a comparison bar graph of total sales.

4. The table gives the number of calls received at a police station during 1 d.

Time	Number
24:00 to 03:00	63
03:00 to 06:00	17
06:00 to 09:00	25
09:00 to 12:00	10
12:00 to 15:00	7
15:00 to 18:00	34
18:00 to 21:00	16
21:00 to 24:00	42

(a) Make a frequency polygon to illustrate the data.

(b) Give reasons for a large number of calls being received in the 4 most active times.

Finding the Curve of Best Fit

In business, graphs are used not just to display what has already happened, but also as an aid in predicting what might happen in the future. Using graphs to make predictions is a part of **trend analysis**.

Example 1

The Widget Manufacturing Company collected the following data on monthly sales during 6 months of the year.

Month	Total Sales
January	48
February	57
May	68
June	76
July	79
September	91

Make a frequency polygon to represent the data.

The data appears to have a fairly steady upward trend. You can find a curve (in this case it's a straight line) that reasonably approximates the data. This is the **curve of best fit**.

You can use the curve of best fit to predict future sales. For November, if the trend continues, sales of 102 widgets are likely. This prediction is obtained by **extrapolation** by extending the graph beyond the measured data to obtain new data.

The sales for March were not recorded in the table above. But by using the curve of best fit, you can see that sales of about 60 widgets in March were likely.

This method of finding additional information within the bounds of the original data is **interpolation**.

Exercise

B **1.** The graph compares the sales of 3 different brands of soap produced by the same manufacturer.

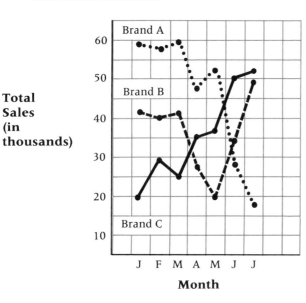

(a) What brand had the most total sales in March? May? June?

(b) State the approximate difference in sales between Brand B and Brand C in May.

(c) In what month did Brand A first sell less than 50 000 units?

(d) Which line graph could best be approximated as a straight line?

(e) If trends from May to July continue, which brand will have the highest sales in August?

(f) State a prediction of sales for each brand in August.

2. The table gives sales data for 2 types of paper sold by A-Z Stationery.

Month	Paper A	Paper B
February	21	64
March	23	58
April	32	47
July	42	27
September	54	16
October	55	6

(a) On 2 separate graphs, make frequency polygons to illustrate the data.

(b) Each frequency polygon can be approximated by a straight line. Draw the curve of best fit for each graph.

(c) Use the curve of best fit to predict sales for each type of paper in May; June; August; November; December.

(d) Extrapolating information from a graph can be misleading. Why?

3. Sammy's Sound Shop collected data on the weekly sales of a new rock album.

Time	Frequency
Week 1	28
Week 2	54
Week 3	68
Week 4	81
Week 5	93
Week 6	102
Week 7	101
Week 8	89
Week 9	78
Week 10	64

(a) Make a frequency polygon to represent the data.

(b) Draw the curve of best fit for the graph.

(c) Predict album sales in Week 11 and Week 12.

4. Agnes collected data on the number of family members in all the households in a community. The histogram displays the data she collected.

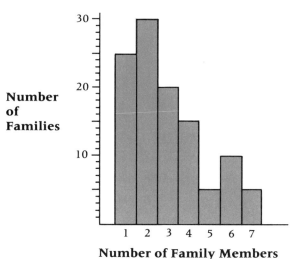

Number of Family Members

(a) Read data from the graph to copy and complete the table.

Family Size	Frequency
1	
2	
3	
4	
5	
6	
7	
8	

(b) Extend the table to include columns showing cumulative frequency and product.

(c) Find the mean, median, and mode for the data.

(d) What does the data suggest about the type of community that Agnes was studying?

5. Find the mean, median, and mode for the data displayed by each of the following graphs.

(a)

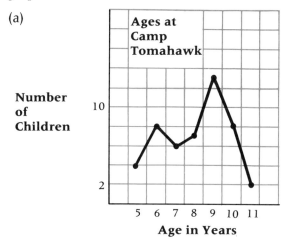

Age in Years

(b)

Wage Intervals

You first have to find the class value or "class wage."

315

Cumulative and Moving Averages

The histogram displays total sales of cassette recorders at Ron's Stereo for a seven month period.

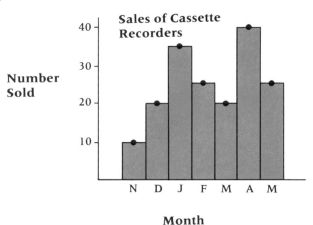

Sales of Cassette Recorders

Number Sold

Month

Ron can use the graph to quickly spot the good and bad sales months. But, as owner of the store, Ron is also interested in seeing sales trends as well as sales volume.

One way to see trends is by looking at the **cumulative average**.

$$\text{Cumulative Average} = \frac{\text{Cumulative Frequency}}{\text{Number of Months}}$$

Month	Frequency	Cumulative Frequency	Cumulative Average
November	10	10	10
December	20	30	15
January	35	65	21.7
February	25	90	22.5
March	20	110	22
April	40	150	25
May	25	175	25

The cumulative average can be graphed as a frequency polygon super-imposed on the histogram.

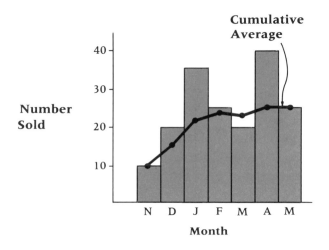

Cumulative Average

Number Sold

Month

The graph points out that even though monthly sales fluctuate, Ron can probably expect average monthly sales of about 20 to 25 units for the near future.

Another way for Ron to look at the data is to restrict each average to a 3 month period. The table summarizes the calculations involved.

Month	Frequency	3 Month Average	
Nov	10	—	
Dec	20	—	$\dfrac{20 + 25 + 35}{3}$
Jan	35	21.7	
Feb	25	26.7	
Mar	20	26.7	$\dfrac{25 + 20 + 40}{3}$
Apr	40	28.3	
May	25	28.3	

Each calculation gives a **moving average**. Ron can use the table to make a graph showing the moving average.

Exercise

B 1. Hani's Bike Bazaar recorded the number of monthly bike sales.

Feb	10	Jun	50
Mar	30	Jul	40
Apr	20	Aug	60
May	40		

(a) Construct a histogram to represent the data.
(b) Copy the above table and add columns to calculate Cumulative Frequency and Cumulative Average.
(c) Draw the frequency polygon to represent Cumulative Average on your graph from part (a).
(d) Does the graph indicate an upward or downward trend in monthly sales? What monthly sales can Hani expect for the next few months?
(e) Add a column to your table from part (b) to calculate 2-month moving average.
(f) Draw the frequency polygon to represent 2-month moving average on the same graph as part (a).

2. The annual sales at Betty's Sporting Goods were recorded for 6 a.

1980	$55 000	1983	$25 000
1981	$70 000	1984	$40 000
1982	$45 000	1985	$30 000

(a) Construct a frequency polygon to represent annual sales.
(b) Draw a table to aid in calculating the cumulative averages.
(c) Draw the frequency polygon to represent Cumulative Average.
(d) What annual sales could be expected for 1986?

3. The total monthly auto sales at Brown and Brown Car Sales are listed below.

Mar	152	Aug	137
Apr	63	Sep	204
May	48	Oct	171
Jun	76	Nov	218
Jul	160		

(a) Construct the frequency polygon to represent the data.
(b) Calculate the 2-month moving average.
(c) Calculate the 3-month moving average.
(d) Draw the 2-month and 3-month moving average on your graph from part (a).

4. The histogram represents the monthly sales of stereo receivers.

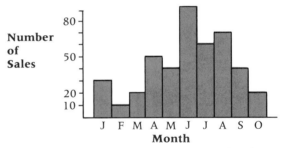

(a) Redraw the graph in your notebook.
(b) Use the graph to complete a table with the following headings.

Month	Sales	Cumulative Frequency	Cumulative Average	3-Month Moving Average

(c) Use the data from the graph to draw frequency polygons to represent cumulative averages and 3-month moving averages on your graph from part (a).

Unit 16 Review

1. State why each of the following surveys is biased.

   (a) To predict if the city residents want a dome stadium, 300 spectators at a football game are polled on a cold and rainy November day.

   (b) To predict the number of students at school that will attend a school dance, Pat polls 20 students from home room.

2. Use the bar graph to answer the questions below.

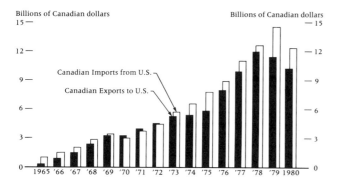

   (a) What year did Canada import the most automotive products?

   (b) State the highest number of automotive products exported to the U.S.

   (c) During what years did Canadian exports exceed imports?

3. State the range for each set of data.

   (a) 82, 57, 81, 94, 74

   (b) 124, 192, 211, 102, 201, 166

   (c) 4.5, 3.7, 8.9, 7.4, 2.8, 4.2

4. State the mean, median, and mode for each set of data.

   (a) 2, 3, 5, 10, 10

   (b) 1, 1, 2, 8, 8

   (c) 4, 5, 8, 11

5. Use the graph to answer the questions.

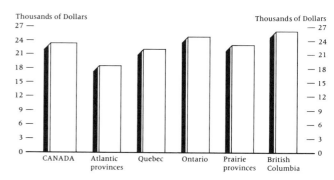

   (a) Which regions are above the Canadian average family income?

   (b) State the difference in mean family income between the Atlantic Provinces and Ontario.

   (c) The median family income for the year was $17 000. Give a reason for the median value being lower than the mean value.
   Which do you think best represents the average family income?

6. An inspector at a garment industry passed 57 of the 65 shirts that were inspected for flaws. How many shirts can the company expect to be flawless in a shipment of 1250 shirts?

7. A survey was taken of 50 full-time workers at various industries. Each worker was asked to report weekly earnings for the previous week. The data is listed below.

$590 $610 $311 $465 $310 $370
$455 $640 $520 $470 $625 $555
$460 $340 $460 $605 $340 $515
$490 $430 $460 $480 $565 $325
$570 $345 $540 $495 $645 $465
$530 $395 $385 $505 $475 $625
$475 $630 $455 $305 $515 $335
$575 $510 $485 $330 $635 $520
$320 $545

(a) What is the range of the data?
(b) Find an interval that will divide the data into 7 classes.
(c) Tally the data to make a frequency table. Start the first interval at $300.
(d) Make a frequency distribution histogram.
(e) Extend the frequency table to include a cumulative frequency column and make a cumulative frequency graph.
(f) Extend the table to include a relative frequency column and make a relative frequency histogram.

8. Find the mean, median, and mode of each set of data.

(a) 28, 15, 21, 37, 42, 19, 27, 45, 16, 22, 39
(b) 63, 85, 56, 94, 82, 56, 77, 71, 84, 60, 91, 83, 75, 85, 81, 47
(c) 2, 9, 1, 8, 10, 3, 2, 9, 5, 2, 10, 1, 8, 6, 2, 10, 7

9. Leslie had the following golf scores during June.
84, 79, 79, 81, 96, 79, 80

(a) Find the mean, median, and mode of the golf scores.
(b) If Leslie's best and worst scores are ignored, find the mean, median, and mode. Which value changed?
(c) What score will Leslie need on the next round of golf to have a mean of 81 for all 8 games?

10. Data was collected on the number of days it took for 170 letters to be delivered between 2 Canadian cities.

Days to Deliver	Frequency
1	20
2	24
3	40
4	35
5	30
6	10
7	5
8	4
9	2

Extend the table to include the cumulative frequency and product columns. Use the data to find the mean, median, and mode.

11. Terry surveyed 90 students to find data on the number of hours worked at part-time jobs.

Number of Hours Worked	Frequency
0 to 3	24
3 to 6	5
6 to 9	12
9 to 12	16
12 to 15	19
15 to 18	8
18 to 21	4
21 to 24	2

Make a table that includes columns for class value, cumulative frequency, and product. Calculate the mean, median, and mode.

12. The table summarizes the 9 major causes of forest fires in Canada, from a sample of 7777 fires.

Cause	Frequency
Recreation	1600
Lightning	2141
Settlement	732
Woods Operations	591
Railways	494
Incendiary	405
Miscellaneous	1133
Other Industry	312
Unknown	369

Construct a relative frequency bar graph to display the data.

13. Joe has kept records of his gross wages for 7 of the last 9 a.

Year	Gross Wage (in thousands)
1977	$11.2
1978	$13.1
1979	$17.1
1981	$20.0
1982	$24.4
1984	$28.7
1985	$32.4

(a) Draw the frequency polygon to represent the data.
(b) The data can be approximated by a straight line. Draw the curve of best fit.
(c) Use the curve of best fit to predict Joe's gross wages in 1980; 1983; 1987.

Unit 17

Geometric Figures and Their Properties

A Summary of Basic Geometric Terms

A fashion designer has to be familiar with the various patterns and sewing techniques of the trade. A mechanic needs adequate knowledge of the use of tools for auto repair. For similar reasons, a student of mathematics should recognize the following terms used in geometry.

Angles

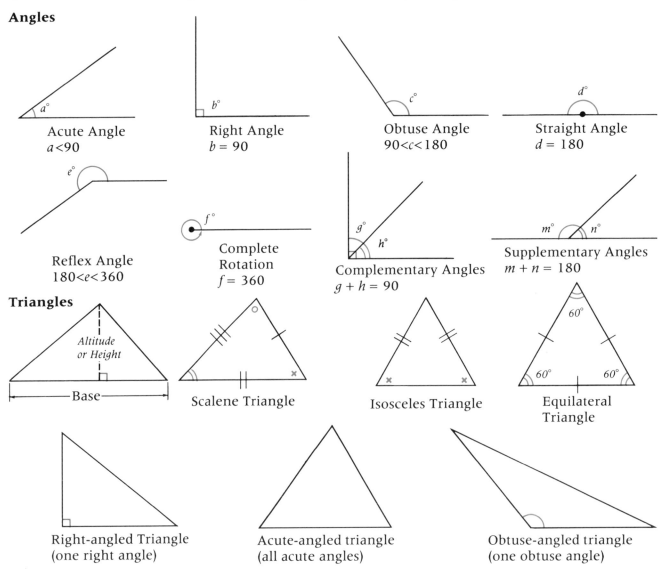

Acute Angle
$a < 90$

Right Angle
$b = 90$

Obtuse Angle
$90 < c < 180$

Straight Angle
$d = 180$

Reflex Angle
$180 < e < 360$

Complete Rotation
$f = 360$

Complementary Angles
$g + h = 90$

Supplementary Angles
$m + n = 180$

Triangles

Altitude or Height

Base

Scalene Triangle

Isosceles Triangle

Equilateral Triangle

Right-angled Triangle
(one right angle)

Acute-angled triangle
(all acute angles)

Obtuse-angled triangle
(one obtuse angle)

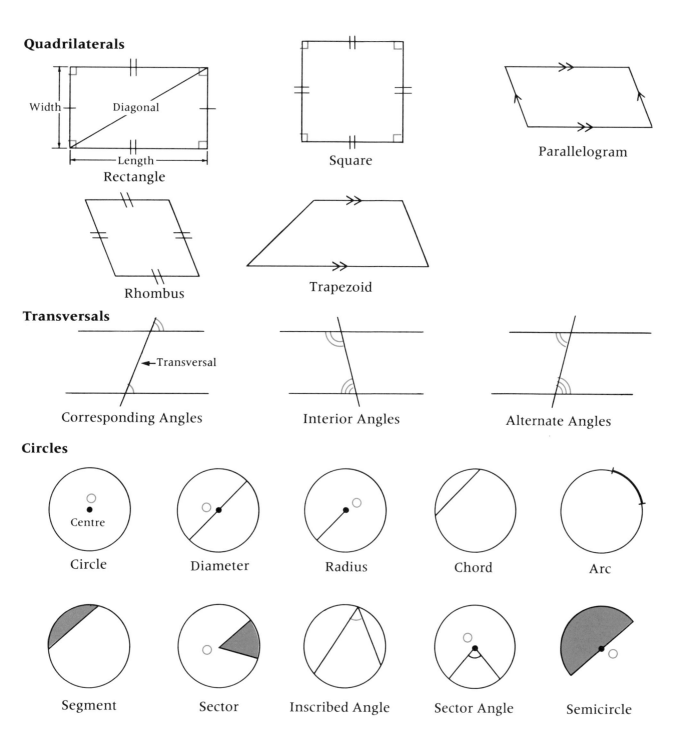

Quadrilaterals

Rectangle

Width · Diagonal · Length

Square

Parallelogram

Rhombus

Trapezoid

Transversals

Corresponding Angles — Transversal

Interior Angles

Alternate Angles

Circles

Circle · Centre

Diameter

Radius

Chord

Arc

Segment

Sector

Inscribed Angle

Sector Angle

Semicircle

Basic Angle Properties

Here is a summary of the basic angle properties.

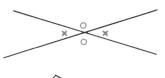

Opposite angles are equal.

The angle sum of any triangle is 180°.
$a + b + c = 180$

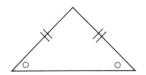

The base angles of an isosceles triangle are equal.

Each angle in an equilateral triangle is 60°.

When a transversal crosses 2 parallel lines, corresponding and alternate angles are equal. Interior angles are supplementary.

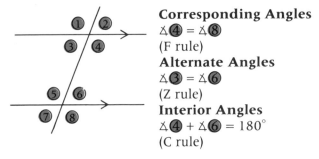

Corresponding Angles
$\angle④ = \angle⑧$
(F rule)
Alternate Angles
$\angle③ = \angle⑥$
(Z rule)
Interior Angles
$\angle④ + \angle⑥ = 180°$
(C rule)

Name other pairs of corresponding, alternate, and interior angles.

You can use these facts to solve for angles in geometric diagrams.

Example 1

A flower planter is being built so that the sides form a regular pentagon.

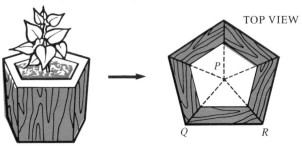

TOP VIEW

What angle of cut should the carpenter use for each side of the planter?

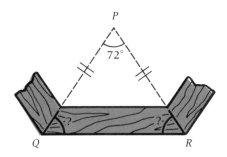

To find $\angle PQR$, first find $\angle QPR$.

If P is the centre, then the angle at P for 1 section is one fifth of a full rotation.

$$\tfrac{360°}{5} = 72°$$

But the angle sum of $\triangle PQR$ is 180°.
$$\angle Q + \angle R = 108°$$
And $\triangle PQR$ is isosceles.
$$\angle Q = \angle R = 54°$$
The angle of cut should be **54°**

Example 2

Find the value of each variable.

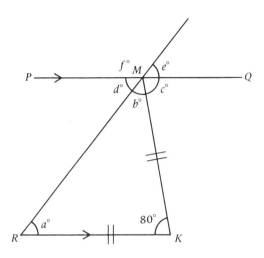

The angle sum of $\triangle MRK$ is $180°$.

Since $k = 80°$ then $a + b = 100$.

$\triangle MRK$ is an isosceles triangle.
So $a = b = 50$

PQ is parallel to RK; apply the properties of parallel lines and transversals.

$c = 80$
$d = a = 50$
$e = a = 50$

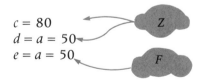

PM is a straight line.

$f + e = 180$
$\quad\ f = 130$

Exercise

A 1. State the value of each variable.

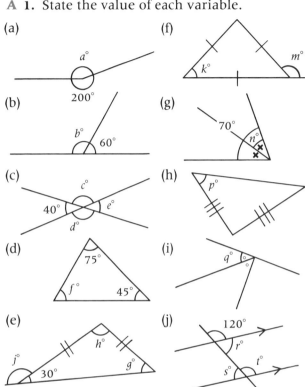

(a)

$a°$

$200°$

(b)

$b°$ $60°$

(c)

$40°$ $c°$ $e°$
$d°$

(d)

$75°$

$f°$ $45°$

(e)

$j°$ $30°$ $h°$ $g°$

(f)

$k°$ $m°$

(g)

$70°$ $n°$

(h)

$p°$

(i)

$q°$

(j)

$120°$ $r°$
$s°$ $t°$

B 2. Explain how you could determine the size of each marked angle without climbing the stairs.

3. A carpenter uses a wooden brace to support a vertical wall frame. What angle does the brace make with the wall?

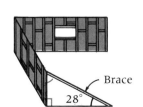

Brace

$28°$

325

4. A wagon wheel has 12 spokes regularly spaced around the perimeter of the wheel. Determine the central angle at the hub of the wheel, between 2 adjacent spokes.

5. Determine the value of each variable.

(a)

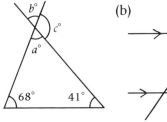

(b)

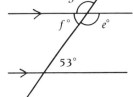

(c)   (d)

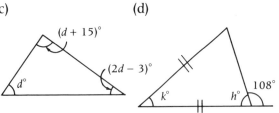

6. Calculate the angle between 2 adjacent sides of the stop sign.

7. A 1983 penny is in the form of a 12-sided polygon. Calculate the angle between 2 adjacent sides.

8. Calculate the value of each variable.

(a)

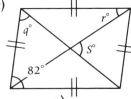

(b)

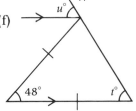

(c)

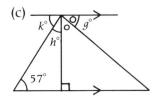

(d)

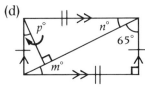

(e)

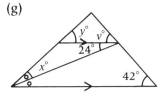

(f)

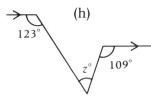

(g)

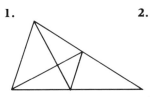

(h)

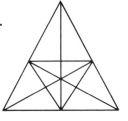

Angle Properties of Circles

Here is a summary of the angle properties for circles.

- The perpendicular bisector of any chord passes through the centre of the circle.

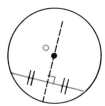

- Inscribed angles standing on the same chord or arc are equal.

- A sector angle is double an inscribed angle drawn on the same chord or arc.

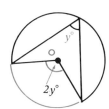

- An angle inscribed in a semicircle is a right angle.

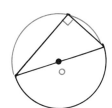

- The opposite angles of an inscribed quadrilateral add to 180°.

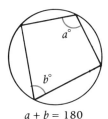

$a + b = 180$

Example 1

Find the value of each marked angle.

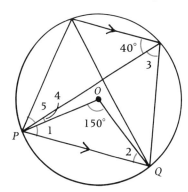

Segments OP and OQ are equal because they are both radii. So $\triangle OPQ$ is isosceles.

$$\angle 1 + \angle 2 = 30°$$

$$\angle 1 = \angle 2 = 15°$$

Chord PQ subtends a sector angle of 150° as well as $\angle 3$.

$$\angle 3 = \tfrac{1}{2}(150°)$$
$$= 75°$$

Apply the Z rule for parallel lines and transversals.

$$\angle 1 + \angle 4 = 40°$$
$$\angle 4 = 40° - 15°$$
$$= 25°$$

$\angle 1 = 15°$

Now apply the property that opposite angles of inscribed quadrilaterals add to 180°.

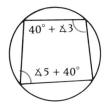

$$(40° + \angle 3) + (\angle 1 + \angle 4 + \angle 5) = 180°$$
$$40° + 75° + 15° + 25° + \angle 5 = 180°$$
$$\angle 5 = 25°$$

327

Exercise

A 1. How could you use the set square to locate the centre of a given circle?

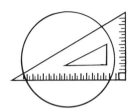

2. State the value of each variable.

(a)
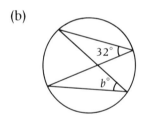

(e)
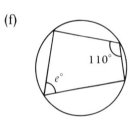

(b)
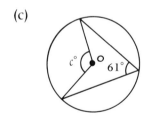

(f)
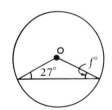

(c)
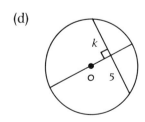

(g)

(d)
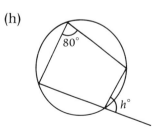

(h)

B 3. Find the value of each variable.

(a)
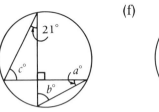

(f)
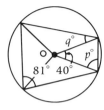

(b)
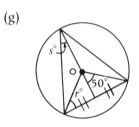

(g)
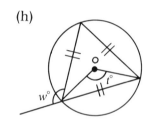

(c)
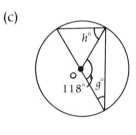

(h)
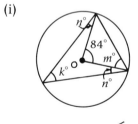

(d)
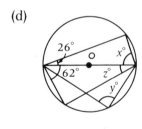

(i)

(e)
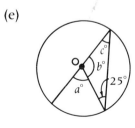

(j)
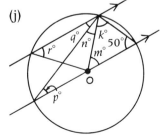

(c)
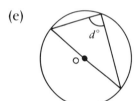

328

Applying the Law of Pythagoras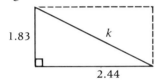

Pat is building a patio fence from sections with dimensions as shown below.

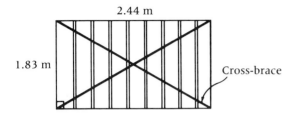

How long would the cross-brace be? Use the Law of Pythagoras to find the length.

Let the length of the brace be k metres.

$$k^2 = 1.83^2 + 2.44^2$$
$$= 3.3487 + 5.9636$$
$$= 9.3025$$
$$k = \sqrt{9.3025}$$
$$\doteq 3.05$$

The cross-brace should be about 3.05 m long.

The Law of Pythagoras is used to find missing lengths in right-angled triangles.

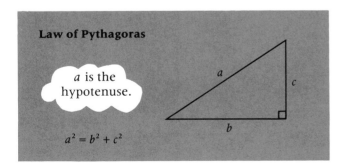

Law of Pythagoras

a is the hypotenuse.

$$a^2 = b^2 + c^2$$

Example 1

Find the value of the variable.

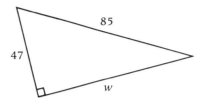

The hypotenuse is 85.

$$85^2 = w^2 + 47^2$$
$$7225 = w^2 + 2209$$
$$5016 = w^2$$
$$w = \sqrt{5016}$$
$$= 71, \text{ to the nearest whole number}$$

Example 2

Rita is making a square kerchief as part of a costume for the school play.

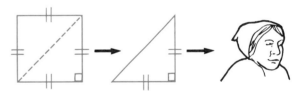

The diagonal length must be at least 96 cm to be able to be tied around the performer's head. What dimensions should Rita use for the fabric?

Let each side be r centimetres in length.

$$96^2 = r^2 + r^2$$
$$9216 = 2r^2$$
$$4608 = r^2$$
$$r = \sqrt{4608}$$
$$\doteq 67.88$$

Rita has to make the kerchief 68 cm square.

Exercise

A 1. For each right-angled triangle, name the hypotenuse and state the equation relating the sides.

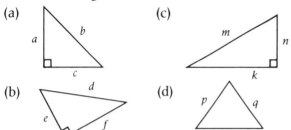

(a)

(c)

(b)

(d)

2. If possible, state an equation you would use to find k in each case.

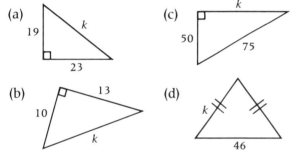

(a)

(c)

(b)

(d)

B 3. For each part of Question 2, calculate the value of k, correct to the nearest whole number.

4. Determine the value of each variable, correct to 1 decimal place.

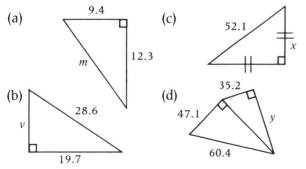

(a)

(c)

(b)

(d)

5. The diagram shows the relative positions of 3 pulleys in a car engine.

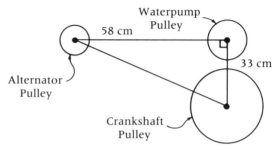

Calculate the distance between the centre of the alternator pulley and the centre of the crankshaft pulley, correct to 1 decimal place.

6. Calculate the indicated horizontal distance for the wheelchair ramp, correct to 1 decimal place.

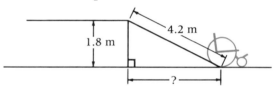

7. A tablecloth is 218 cm by 218 cm. Calculate the diagonal length of the tablecloth, correct to the nearest centimetre.

8. Solve for y in each case, correct to 1 decimal place.

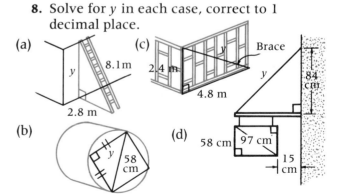

(a)

(c)

(b)

(d)

9. The door on the back of a station wagon opens to provide a rectangular opening with dimensions as given. Show that a sheet of plywood 244 cm long and 122 cm wide can fit into the back of the station wagon.

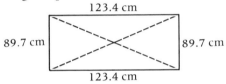

10. Sheila works in a car repair shop. To check if the frame of a car is properly aligned, Sheila determines whether the diagonal measurements are the same by using a tape measure.

123.4 cm

89.7 cm   89.7 cm

123.4 cm

For the frame with the dimensions shown, what should be the correct diagonal distance? Give your answer to 1 decimal place.

11. Calculate the total length of the car wheel ramp as shown.

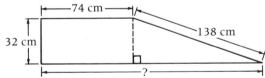

12. Allowing 65 cm for the overhang, calculate the length of the rafter shown. Give your answer to the nearest centimetre.

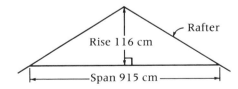

13. Traffic marker cones have dimensions as shown. Calculate the diameter of the cone, correct to 1 decimal place.

14. Determine the dimensions of the largest square cake that will just fit inside a round cake tin 31 cm in diameter. Give your answer correct to the nearest centimetre.

15. A stage platform is made of box sections like the one shown. A steel rod is used as a diagonal brace to ensure that the box section remains square.

(a) Using the dimensions given, calculate the length of the floor diagonal, *DB*, to the nearest centimetre.

(b) What is the length of the steel rod *AD*, correct to the nearest centimetre?

331

Side Trip

1. Railroad tracks are put in place with a small gap between adjacent sections of track to allow for expansion in very hot weather.

Suppose that a continuous piece of track the length of 2 city blocks (about 0.35 km) is laid in mid-winter. In summer, the temperature rises and causes an increase of 2 cm in the length of the tracks. If the ends of the tracks are fixed in position, this increase in length will cause the track to bow upward, as shown in diagram ①. To simplify the problem, consider *AB* and *BC* as straight-line segments, as shown in diagram ②.

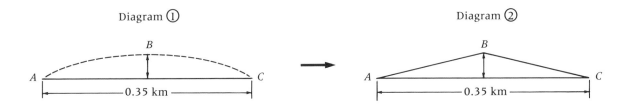

How high will the centre of the track rise? Enough to place your hand under it? To crawl under it? To walk under it?

To answer this question (and the answer will surprise you!) use diagram ② and apply the Law of Pythagoras.

2. The quadrilaterals numbered ① through ⑨ are perfect squares. If each side of square ① measures 8 units, and each side of square ② measures 7 units, find the width (*AB*) and length (*AD*) of rectangle *ABCD*.

Is *AKLM* a square?

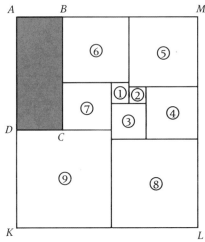

Congruent Triangles

Assembly lines produce items that are identical.

Items that are identical in shape and size are **congruent**.

Two congruent triangles have corresponding sides and corresponding angles equal.

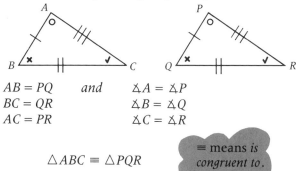

$$AB = PQ \quad and \quad \angle A = \angle P$$
$$BC = QR \qquad\qquad \angle B = \angle Q$$
$$AC = PR \qquad\qquad \angle C = \angle R$$

$$\triangle ABC \equiv \triangle PQR$$

≡ means *is congruent to*.

There are 6 correspondences (3 sides, 3 angles) in congruent triangles.

What if you only know that some of the corresponding sides and corresponding angles are equal?

The following activities show that in some cases, congruence is determined by only 3 special correspondences.

Activity 1

Construct at least 4 triangles with sides of 2.5 cm, 3 cm, and 4 cm.
One way to do the constructions is with ruler and compasses. Another way is by cutting 3 strips of paper with the given lengths, arranging the strips to form a triangle, then marking the corners and drawing in the sides.

Here are a few possible constructions done with ruler and compasses.

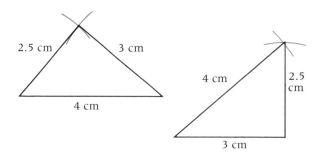

Are the triangles different? Check by tracing and cutting out 1 triangle, and then fitting it onto the other triangles. What conclusion can you make?

If the 3 sides of one triangle are equal to 3 sides of another triangle, then the triangles are congruent. This is a condition for congruence called **SSS** (Side; Side; Side).

Activity 2

Construct at least 4 triangles with sides of 3 cm and 4 cm that contain an angle of 45°.

Some possible constructions are given below.

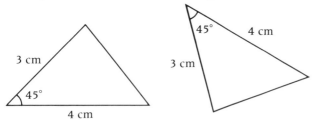

Check whether the triangles are congruent by tracing and cutting out 1 triangle and fitting it on top of the other triangles you have drawn. What conclusion can you make?

> If 2 sides and the contained angle in a triangle are equal to 2 sides and the contained angle in another triangle, then the triangles are congruent. This condition for congruence is called **SAS** (Side; Angle; Side).

Activity 3

Construct at least 4 triangles with 1 side 3 cm long, and the angles formed at the ends of the side 40° and 65°.
Check whether the triangles are congruent by tracing and cutting out 1 triangle and fitting it on top of the other triangles you have drawn.

What conclusion can you make?

> If 2 angles and the contained side of a triangle are equal to the corresponding angles and side of another triangle, then the triangles are congruent. This condition for congruence is called **ASA** (Angle; Side; Angle).

Exercise

A 1. Look around you and state several examples of congruent objects.

2. From the triangles below, select pairs of congruent triangles. For each pair of triangles, name pairs or corresponding sides and angles.

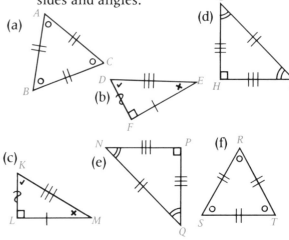

3. State why the triangles in each pair are not necessarily congruent.

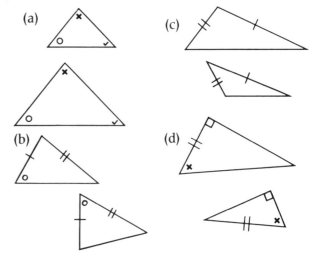

4. In each diagram below:
- select 2 congruent triangles;
- state the reason for congruence (SSS, SAS, ASA);
- name 3 pairs of equal sides;
- name 3 pairs of equal angles.

(a)

(c)

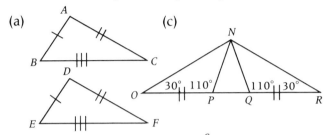

(b)

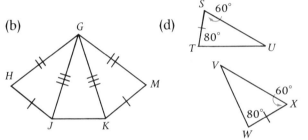

(d)

5. Is it possible to draw a triangle whose sides are 2 cm, 2 cm, and 1 cm? What kind of triangle is it?

6. Is it possible to draw a triangle whose sides are 2 cm, 3 cm, and 6 cm? Explain.

7. Is it always possible to construct a triangle if you are given 2 sides and the contained angle?

8. Why are △ABC and △DEF not congruent?

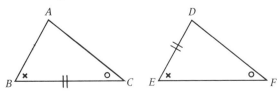

B **9.** Select pairs of triangles that are congruent and give reasons why they are congruent.

(a) (c)

(b) (d)

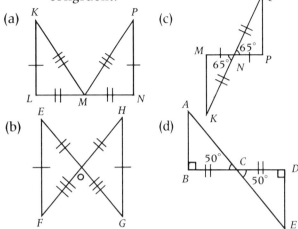

10. Side GJ is common to both △GHJ and △GKJ.

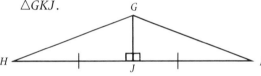

(a) Show that △GHJ and △GKJ are congruent triangles.
(b) List the 6 correspondences for the two triangles.

11. Side MP is common to both △MNP and △PQM.

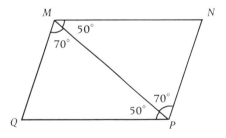

(a) Show that △MNP ≡ △PQM.
(b) List the 6 correspondences for the two triangles.

335

Proving Triangles Congruent

For 2 triangles to be congruent, one of the following sets of conditions must be true.

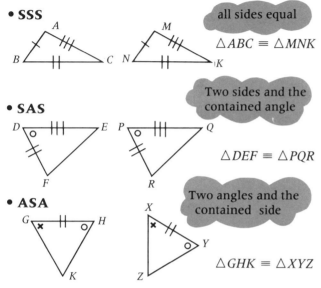

- **SSS**

  all sides equal

  $\triangle ABC \equiv \triangle MNK$

- **SAS**

  Two sides and the contained angle

  $\triangle DEF \equiv \triangle PQR$

- **ASA**

  Two angles and the contained side

  $\triangle GHK \equiv \triangle XYZ$

You can use these conditions for congruence to help you to prove that triangles are congruent.

Example 1

Prove that $\triangle ABC \equiv \triangle DEF$ and list corresponding equal angles.

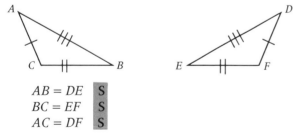

$$
\begin{aligned}
AB &= DE \quad \text{S}\\
BC &= EF \quad \text{S}\\
AC &= DF \quad \text{S}
\end{aligned}
$$

By SSS, $\triangle ABC \equiv \triangle DEF$

This means that $\angle A = \angle D$,
$\qquad\qquad\quad \angle C = \angle F$,
and $\angle B = \angle E$.

Example 2

Prove $\triangle MPQ \equiv \triangle SRQ$.

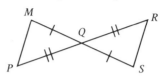

Opposite angles at Q are equal, so mark on your diagram that $\angle MQP = \angle SQR$.

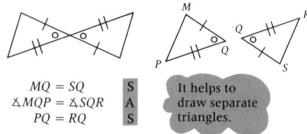

$$
\begin{aligned}
MQ &= SQ \quad &\text{S}\\
\angle MQP &= \angle SQR \quad &\text{A}\\
PQ &= RQ \quad &\text{S}
\end{aligned}
$$

It helps to draw separate triangles.

By SAS, $\triangle MPQ \equiv \triangle SRQ$

Sometimes proving triangles congruent is the first step in finding an unknown side or angle.

Example 3

Find x and y.

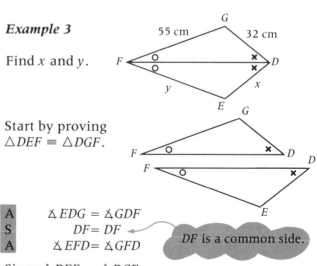

Start by proving $\triangle DEF \equiv \triangle DGF$.

$$
\begin{aligned}
\text{A} \quad & \angle EDG = \angle GDF\\
\text{S} \quad & DF = DF\\
\text{A} \quad & \angle EFD = \angle GFD
\end{aligned}
$$

DF is a common side.

Since $\triangle DEF \equiv \triangle DGF$,
then $DG = DE$ so $x = 32$ cm.
and $FG = FE$, so $y = 55$ cm.

Example 4

Rosemarie is building a kite. She starts by placing 2 lightweight pieces of wood at right angles to each other, with the shorter piece being bisected as shown.

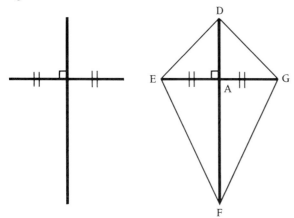

She covers the cross-piece with a large sheet of paper. The wood divides the paper into 4 triangles, as shown above. Prove that △DEA and △DGA are congruent. Draw 2 separate triangles to help you see the solution.

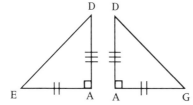

DA is a common side; DA = DA.

$$DA = DA$$
$$\angle DAE = \angle DAG$$
$$EA = GA$$

S
A
S

By SAS, △DEA ≡ △DGA

How would you prove that △EAF ≡ △GAF?

Exercise

A 1. State the value of each unknown.

(a)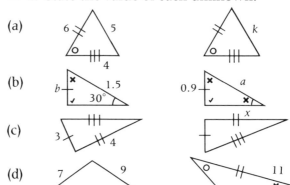

(b)

(c)

(d)

B 2. Prove that △PQR ≡ △PSR.

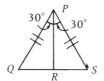

3. In each diagram:
  • prove 2 triangles congruent;
  • find the values of x and y.

(a) (b) (c) (d) (e) (f)

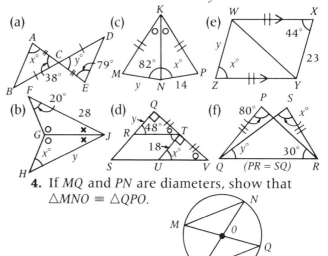

4. If MQ and PN are diameters, show that △MNO ≡ △QPO.

5. Prove that $\triangle ABD \equiv \triangle CDB$.

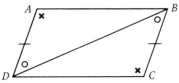

6. Prove that $\triangle KRW \equiv \triangle VRW$, and then find the value of x.

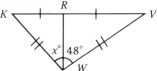

Side Trip

Follow the steps outlined below to make an interesting geometric figure, a hexaflexagon. Start with a strip of paper that is at least 6 times longer than it is wide.

1. Fold the strip to find the centre line at one end.

2. Fold the strip again so that B falls on the centre line and makes a crease through A. What kind of triangle is $\triangle ABC$?

3. Fold the strip back so that the crease CD falls along CB. What kind of triangle is $\triangle CDA$? Continue folding back and forth until 10 equilateral triangles have been formed. Cut off the excess of the strip as well as the first right-angled triangle, $\triangle ABC$.

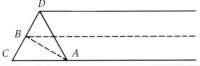

4. Place the strip as shown and number the triangles accordingly.

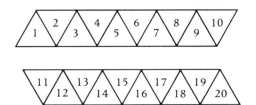

5. Turn the strip over and continue numbering. Be sure that triangle 11 is behind triangle 1. If you want to color the triangles or draw designs on them, do that in this step.

6. To fold the hexaflexagon, hold the strip with triangle 1 at your left. Fold triangle 1 over triangle 2. Then fold triangle 15 on triangle 14 and triangle 8 on triangle 7. If your folding now gives you the arrangements shown, glue triangle 1 to 10. If you do not have this arrangement, recheck the directions given.

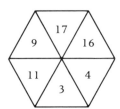 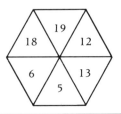

Unit 17 Review

1. Name each quadrilateral.

(a)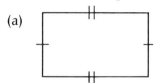

(c)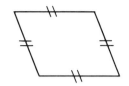

(b)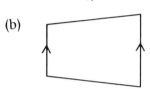

(d)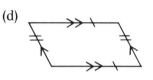

2. Name the item shown in color in each diagram.

(a)

(d)

(b)

(e)

(c)

(f)

3. State the value of each variable.

(a)

(b)

(c)

50° m°
n°

(f)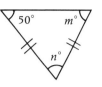

w°

(d)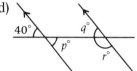

40° q°
p°
r°

(g)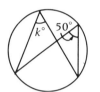

v° 60°
y°

(e)

k° 50°

(h)

t°
75°

4. For each right-angled triangle, name the hypotenuse and state the equation relating the sides.

(a)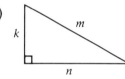

k m
n

(b)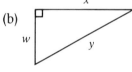

x
w y

5. In each diagram:
- name 2 congruent triangles;
- state the reason for congruence;
- name 3 pairs of equal sides;
- name 3 pairs of equal angles.

(a)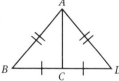

A
B C D

(c)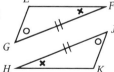

M R
N Q
P

(b)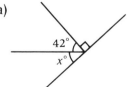

E F
G J
H K

(d)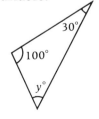

S T
W V

339

6. Calculate the value of each variable.

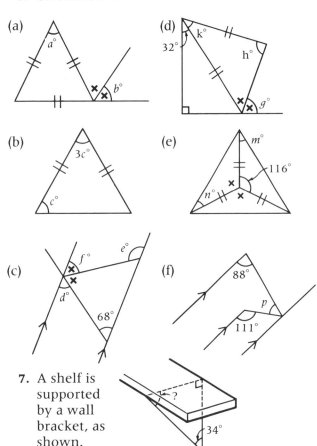

(a)

(b)

(c)

(d)

(e)

(f)

7. A shelf is supported by a wall bracket, as shown.

Determine the angle between the shelf and the longest side of the bracket.

8. The wheel valve on a water line has 9 spokes equally spaced around the hub. Determine the angle at the hub between adjacent spokes.

9. Calculate the angle between 2 adjacent sides of a regular 15-sided polygon.

10. Calculate the value of each variable.

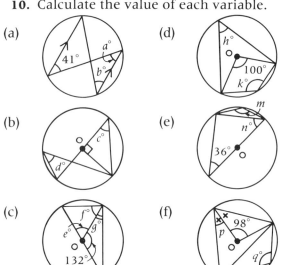

(a)

(b)

(c)

(d)

(e)

(f)

11. Calculate the value of each variable, correct to the nearest whole number.

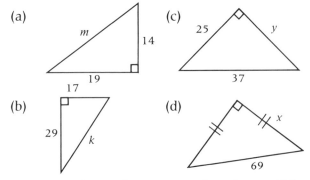

(a)

(b)

(c)

(d)

12. A roadway slopes upward as shown. What horizontal distance does a car travel if it does 530 m along the road?

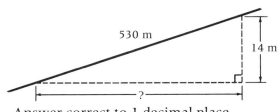

530 m

14 m

?

Answer correct to 1 decimal place.

340

13. Solve for *k* in each case, correct to 1 decimal place.

(a)
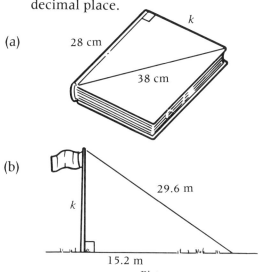

(b)
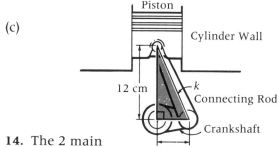

(c)
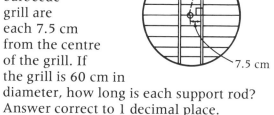

14. The 2 main support rods for a barbecue grill are each 7.5 cm from the centre of the grill. If the grill is 60 cm in diameter, how long is each support rod? Answer correct to 1 decimal place.

15. As a building inspector, Jill has to determine whether the corners of a foundation are square. Jill checks by measuring to see that the diagonals are equal in length.

If each foundation shown has square corners, what diagonal measurement should Jill find? Answer correct to the nearest centimetre.

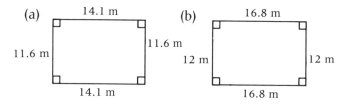

16. Determine the rise of the roof shown.

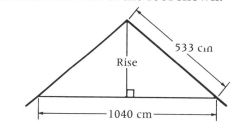

Answer correct to the nearest centimetre.

17. A sheet of paper measures 20 cm by 32 cm. How much greater is its perimeter than the length of its diagonal? Answer correct to 1 decimal place.

18. Sandy swims diagonally across a swimming pool while Rick walks around the side.

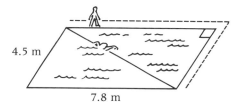

How much shorter is Sandy's swim than Rick's walk? Answer correct to 1 decimal place.

341

19. A rectangular bin for storing lengths of welding rods is constructed with dimensions as shown.

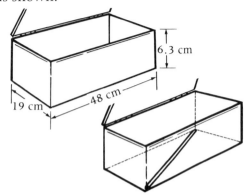

6.3 cm

48 cm

19 cm

(a) Calculate the length of the longest piece of welding rod that can lie flat on the bottom of the box (to the nearest cm).

(b) Determine the length, to the nearest centimetre, of the longest piece of welding rod that can be placed within the box and still allow the lid to close.

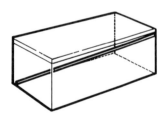

20. A sewing box has inside dimensions as shown.

34 cm

15 cm

22 cm

Calculate (to the nearest centimetre) the length of the longest knitting needle that will just fit inside the box, and still allow the lid to close.

21. Show that $\triangle PQS \equiv \triangle RQS$.

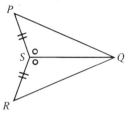

22. In each diagram:
   • prove 2 triangles congruent;
   • find the values of x and y.

(a)

(c)

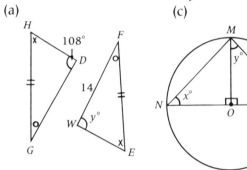

H x 108°   F

14

W $y°$

G E

M

$y°$

N $x°$ K

O

(b)

(d)

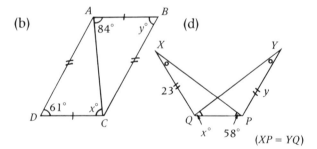

A   B

84° $y°$

X

23

y

D   61° $x°$ C

Q $x°$ 58°   P

$(XP = YQ)$

23. Show that $\triangle MVN \equiv \triangle NTK$.

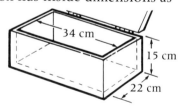

M   N   K

V

T

W

Unit 18

Perimeter, Area, and Volume

Perimeter

Lori's Youth Group collects newspapers to raise funds for a summer camp for disabled children. After the papers are collected, they are stacked in bundles like the one shown. Lori's job is to tie each bundle with strong cord.

She allows 20 cm to tie the knot, and calculates the length of string needed to tie each bundle as follows.

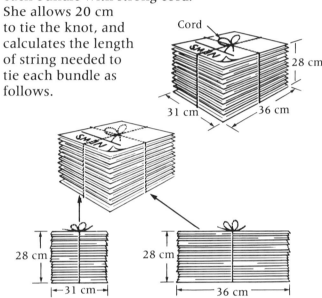

Length of String
= 2 × (31 + 28)
= 2 × (59)
= 118 cm

Length of String
= 2 × (36 + 28)
= 2 × (64)
= 128 cm

The length of string needed to tie each bundle of papers is 118 + 128 + 20 or 266 cm.

for the knot

To find the length of string needed for each bundle, Lori calculated the distance around a rectangle or the **perimeter** of a rectangle.

Some common figures and their perimeter formulas are given in the table below.

Figure		Perimeter Formula
Triangle		$P = a + b + c$
Rectangle		$P = 2 \times (l + w)$
Square		$P = 4s$
Circle		$C = \pi d$ or $C = 2\pi r$

The perimeter of a circle is called its circumference.

Example 1

Henry works for a home heating company. He must determine the length of strapping needed to hold a heating pipe in place.

The diameter of the pipe is 20 cm, so its radius is 10 cm. The strapping around the pipe forms a half circle from A to B to C.

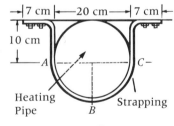

$\frac{1}{2} \times \pi d = \frac{1}{2} \times \pi \times 20$
$\doteq 31.4$ cm

$\pi = 3.1415926\ldots$

The total length of strapping needed is 7 + 10 + 31.4 + 10 + 7 or 65.4 cm.

The Law of Pythagoras may be needed to calculate a length before perimeter can be determined.

Example 2

As a landscape artist, Sherri designs and calculates the cost of landscape plantings.

For one garden area of an office complex shown below, she must determine the cost of a border planting of rose bushes.

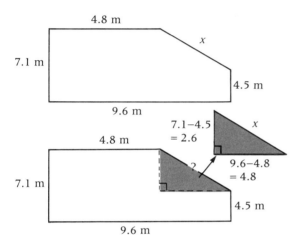

Let x metres represent the missing dimension.

$$x^2 = 2.6^2 + 4.8^2$$
$$= 6.76 + 23.04$$
$$= 29.8$$
$$x = \sqrt{29.8}$$
$$\doteq 5.5$$

Add the dimensions to find the perimeter.
$$4.8 + 7.1 + 9.6 + 4.5 + 5.5 = 31.5$$
The perimeter is 31.5 m.
The border planting requires 2 rose bushes per metre. The number of bushes needed is 2×31.5 or 63.

If each rose bush costs \$2.95, the border planting costs $63 \times \$2.95$ or \$185.85.

Exercise

A **1.** State the perimeter of each figure.

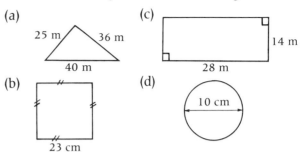

B **2.** Calculate the perimeter of each figure.

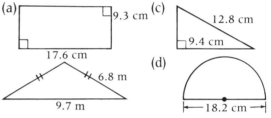

3. Determine any missing dimensions, then calculate the perimeter of each figure.

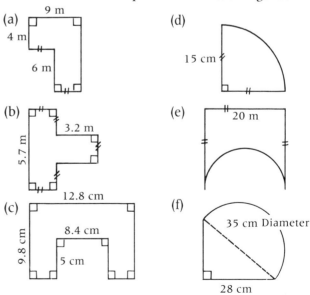

4. Cement curbing is placed around 3 sides of a rectangular parking lot, as shown. If the curbing costs $12.95/m, determine the cost of the curbing for the the lots.

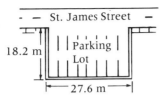

St. James Street

18.2 m

Parking Lot

27.6 m

5. The edges of a rectangular piece of canvas are to be reinforced with sash cord. If a loop of length 22 cm is left at each corner, how much sash cord is required?

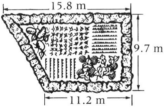

386 cm

291 cm

6. Mr. Wilson plants a hedge around his backyard, as shown, to keep Dennis and Ruff from getting into his strawberry patch.

(a) Calculate the perimeter of Mr. Wilson's garden (to the nearest metre).

15.8 m

9.7 m

11.2 m

(b) If the cost of planting is $4.50/m, determine the cost of the hedge.

7. In laying out nets, a fishing boat travels in a circular path 1.2 km in diameter. What length of net does the boat let out in making one such circuit? (Give your answer correct to 2 decimal places.)

8. Two pulleys, each 14 cm in diameter, are connected by a belt as shown. If the distance between the centres of the pulleys is 29 cm, calculate the length of the pulley to the nearest centimetre.

Belt

29 cm

9. A rectangular play area measuring 8.2 m by 11.6 m is to be fenced in using fencing costing $7.50/m. A gate 1 m wide and costing $55 is placed in the middle of one side of the enclosure. Calculate the total cost of materials for enclosing the play area.

10. Calculate the length of strapping needed to support a heating pipe 24 cm in diameter, as shown.

9 cm

Pipe

9 cm

11. Calculate the length of weatherstripping required for this doorway. Only the sides and the top arch require weatherstripping. (Give your answer to the nearest centimetre.)

Circular Arch

250 cm

88 cm

12. A rectangular apartment courtyard is fenced off into 6 identical enclosures, as show. If 96.3 m of fencing is used, determine the dimensions of each enclosure.

23.4 m

Plane Area

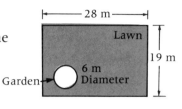

— 28 m —
Lawn
19 m
Garden → ○ 6 m Diameter

Myron must determine the quantity of bulk fertilizer to buy for a lawn with the dimensions shown.

First, he does two separate area calculations.

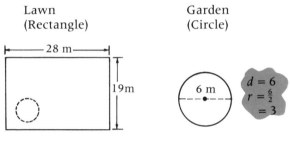

| Lawn (Rectangle) | Garden (Circle) |

— 28 m —
19 m

6 m
$d = 6$
$r = \frac{6}{2}$
$= 3$

Area = lw
= 28×19
= 532
The area is 532 m².

Area = πr^2
$\doteq 3.14 \times 3^2$
= 3.14×9
= 28.26
The area is 28.26 m².

Next, he subtracts to find the area of the lawn.

$$532 - 28.26 = 503.74$$

The area to be fertilized is about 504 m². If 1 kg of fertilizer treats 9 m² of lawn, how much fertilizer should he purchase?

$$\frac{\text{Area to be covered (m}^2)}{\text{Coverage (kg/m}^2)} = \frac{504}{9}$$
$$= 56$$

He should buy 56 kg of fertilizer.

To solve his problem, Myron had to work with area. Problems involving area often involve covering a surface. Units for area are square units such as m², cm², and km².

Some of the most commonly used area formulas are given in this table.

Figure		Area Formula
Rectangle or square	l · w	$A = lw$
Circle	r	$A = \pi r^2$
Triangle	h · b	$A = \frac{1}{2}\,bh$
Parallelogram or rhombus	h · b	$A = bh$
Trapezoid	a · h · b	$A = \frac{1}{2}\,h(a + b)$

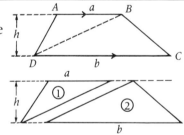

The formula for the area of a trapezoid can be obtained by considering the trapezoid as two triangles.

The area of the trapezoid is Area ① + Area ②.

Area ① + Area ② = $\frac{1}{2}\,ah + \frac{1}{2}\,bh$
$= \frac{1}{2}\,h\,a + \frac{1}{2}\,h\,b$
$= \frac{1}{2}\,h(a + b)$

$\frac{1}{2}h$ is a common factor.

The formula for the area of a parallelogram can be found in a similar fashion.

. . . Try it yourself!

Example 1

Darlene is in charge of a road repair crew that must repair a section of roadway with the given dimensions.

It costs $16/m² for material and labor. Darlene calculates the cost of the repair as follows:

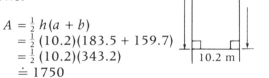

$$A = \tfrac{1}{2} h(a + b)$$
$$= \tfrac{1}{2}(10.2)(183.5 + 159.7)$$
$$= \tfrac{1}{2}(10.2)(343.2)$$
$$\doteq 1750$$

The area to be repaired is 1750 m².
$$\text{Cost} = \text{Area}(m^2) \times \text{Unit Cost } (\$/m^2)$$
$$= 1750 \times 16$$
$$= 28\ 000$$
It costs $28 000 to repair the road.

Areas of non-standard figures can be found by separating the given figure into standard figures whose area formulas are known.

Example 2

Find the area of the shaded region.
$$\text{Shaded Area} = \left(\begin{array}{c}\text{Area of}\\ \text{Square}\end{array}\right) - \left(\begin{array}{c}\text{Area of}\\ \tfrac{1}{4}\text{ Circle}\end{array}\right)$$

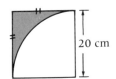

Shaded Area
$$= (lw) - (\tfrac{1}{4}\pi r^2)$$
$$\doteq (20 \times 20) - (0.25 \times 3.14 \times 20^2)$$
$$= 400 - (0.25 \times 3.14 \times 400)$$
$$= 400 - 314$$
$$= 86$$

The area of the shaded region is 86 cm².

Exercise

A 1. For each figure, state
  • its area formula
  • the area, with proper units.

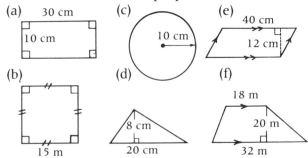

B 2. Calculate the area of each figure, to the nearest whole number.

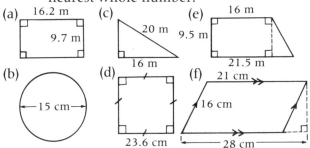

3. Determine the area of each piece of sheet metal to the nearest whole number.

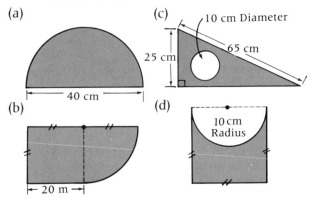

4. In trying to locate a disabled ship, a Search and Rescue helicopter flies a circular path 5 km in diameter. What area (correct to 1 decimal place) is enclosed by the helicopter's path?

5. A 12-slice pizza is 32 cm in diameter. If Enzo eats 4 slices of pizza, what area of pizza does he eat correct to the nearest whole number?

6. A type of tomato plant requires an area of 1.4 m² per plant for proper growth. How many plants should be placed in a garden 3.6 m wide and 5.3 m long?

7. Calculate the area of Charlie Brown's kite.

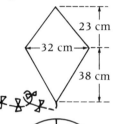

8. Calculate the area of the window shown. Give your answer correct to the nearest whole number.

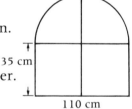

9. A lawn has dimensions as shown.

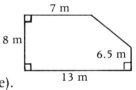

(a) Calculate the area of the lawn (to 1 decimal place).
(b) What quantity of fertilizer (nearest kilogram) is needed to fertilize the lawn if 1 kg of fertilizer treats 6 m² of lawn?
(c) Find the cost of fertilizing the lawn if 1 kg of fertilizer costs $1.49.

10. A rectangular room contains a carpet measuring 4.2 m by 2.9 m. There is a border of bare floor 0.6 m wide all around the carpet.

(a) Calculate the area of the carpet (to 2 decimals).
(b) Calculate the total area of the floor.
(c) Determine the area of the bare floor around the carpet.

11. A piece of sheet metal has an area of 453.75 cm². If its length is 27.5 cm, calculate its width.

12. The area of a circle is 132.7 cm². Determine its radius correct to 1 decimal place.

13. The end of a barn is to be painted and has dimensions as shown.

(a) Calculate the area to be painted.
(b) One can of paint covers 16 m² and costs $19.95. Determine the cost of painting the end of the barn.

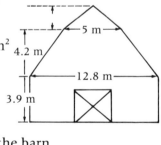

14. Calculate the area of oak veneer needed to cover the face of the mantle clock shown.

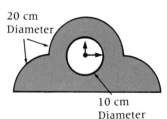

Surface Area

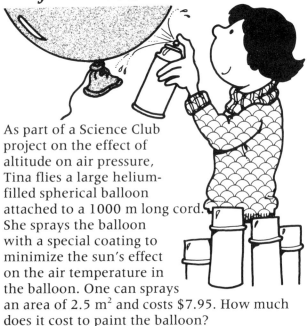

As part of a Science Club project on the effect of altitude on air pressure, Tina flies a large helium-filled spherical balloon attached to a 1000 m long cord. She sprays the balloon with a special coating to minimize the sun's effect on the air temperature in the balloon. One can sprays an area of 2.5 m² and costs $7.95. How much does it cost to paint the balloon?

Tina uses a formula to calculate the surface area of the balloon.

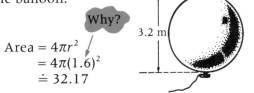

Why?

$$\text{Area} = 4\pi r^2$$
$$= 4\pi(1.6)^2$$
$$\doteq 32.17$$

The area to be painted is 32.17 m².

$$\text{Number of Cans} = \frac{\text{Total Area to be Covered}}{\text{Area Covered by 1 Can}}$$
$$= \frac{32.17}{2.5}$$
$$\doteq 12.87$$

Tina buys 13 cans.

$$\begin{array}{l}\text{Total}\\\text{Cost}\end{array} = (\text{Number of cans}) \times (\text{Cost of 1 Can})$$
$$= 13 \times 7.95$$
$$= 103.35$$

It costs $103.35 to paint the balloon.

Area formulas for some common 3-dimensional figures are shown in this table.

Figure		Area Formula
Sphere		$A = 4\pi r^2$
Cone		$A = \pi rs$ (Side only—not bottom)
Cylinder		$A = 2\pi rh$ (Side only—not top or bottom)
Pyramid		$A = 2sb$ (All 4 sides, but not the bottom)

Area problems often require more than one formula.

Example 1

Determine the exposed surface area of the oil storage tank with dimensions as shown.

- Find the area of the top of the tank.
$$A = \pi r^2$$
$$= \pi(9)^2$$
$$\doteq 254$$
The top is a circle.

The area of the top is about 254 m².

- Find the area of the curved side.
$$A = 2\pi rh$$
$$= 2\pi(9)(10)$$
$$\doteq 565$$
The side of a cylinder.

The area of the side is about 565 m².
The exposed surface area of the tank is about 254 + 565 or 819 m².

Example 2

An observatory is in the form of a cylinder topped by a hemispherical dome with dimensions as shown.

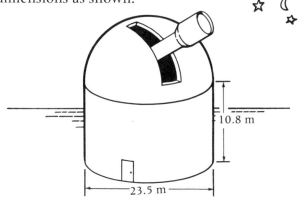

The exterior of the building is to be sand-blasted at a cost of $15/m². If the combined area of all windows and doors (not to be sand-blasted) is 38.7 m², determine the cost of sand-blasting the exterior of the observatory.

Find the area of the dome. The dome is half a sphere.

$$A = \frac{1}{2}(4\pi r^2)$$
$$= 2\pi r^2$$
$$= 2\pi(11.75)^2$$
$$\doteq 867.5$$

$r = \frac{23.5}{2}$
$= 11.75$

The area of the dome is 867.5 m².

Find the area of the side of the building.

$$A = 2\pi rh \qquad \text{cylinder}$$
$$= 2\pi(11.75)(10.8)$$
$$\doteq 797.3$$

The area of the side is 797.3 m².
The total area to be sand-blasted is
$(867.5 + 797.3 - 38.7)$m² or 1626.1 m².

windows, doors

The cost of sand-blasting the building is
1626.1 m² × $15/m² or about $24 392.

Exercise

A 1. To determine the *total* surface area of each object,
   • state the different shapes involved;
   • state the formula(s) that would be required.

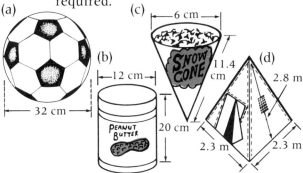

(a)

(b) 12 cm

(c) 6 cm, SNOW CONE 11.4 cm, 20 cm

(d) 2.8 m, 2.3 m, 2.3 m

PEANUT BUTTER

32 cm

B 2. Calculate the total surface area of each object in Question 1, correct to the nearest whole number.

3. The paper label from a tin of apple juice is cut as illustrated and laid flat on a table. What is the area of the label? Answer to the nearest whole number.

11.8 cm, 21 cm, APPLE JUICE, Cut

4. Determine the surface area of the outside of the paper cup to one decimal place.

7 cm, 12 cm

5. How much material is needed to cover a volleyball 28 cm in diameter?

preston Volleyball

351

6. A lawn roller has the dimensions shown. What area of lawn is covered by 1 rotation of the drum?

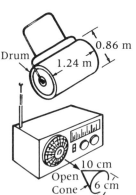

Drum
0.86 m
1.24 m

7. John makes cones for speakers in radio-cassette players. What is the surface area of 1 cone?

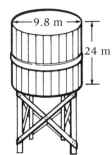

Open Cone
10 cm
6 cm

8. Pat works for the Wunkote Painting Company. One can of paint costs $25.98 and covers 30 m². If two coats of paint are needed to cover the water tower shown, what is Pat's cost for paint for the tower? (The bottom of the tower will not be painted.)

9.8 m
24 m

9. Calculate the exposed surface area of the traffic marker cone shown here. Use the Law of Pythagoras to first calculate *s*.

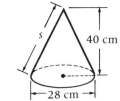

s
40 cm
28 cm

10. A gasoline storage tank consists of a cylindrical body and hemispherical end-sections. Calculate the area to be tar-coated before the tank is buried in the ground.

5.1 m
PROPANE GAS
2.1 m

A hemisphere is half a sphere.

11. A metal centre-punch is in the form of a hemisphere on top of a cone, as shown. Using the given dimensions, calculate the total exposed surface area, correct to the nearest whole number.

1.5 cm
12.5 cm

12. Phil plans to have a metal paperweight plated with various precious metals, as shown. Calculate Phil's cost for having the weight plated.

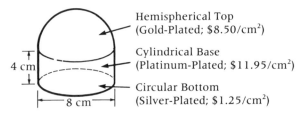

Hemispherical Top (Gold-Plated; $8.50/cm²)
Cylindrical Base (Platinum-Plated; $11.95/cm²)
Circular Bottom (Silver-Plated; $1.25/cm²)
4 cm
8 cm

13. (a) Calculate the total exposed surface area of the barbell.
    (b) What is the cost of chrome-plating the barbell if plating costs $0.07/cm²?

Hemisphere
3.2 cm
12.4 cm
16 cm

14. A metal stand for use in a circus is formed from the bottom part of a cone. What area of leather is needed to cover the side and top of the stand?

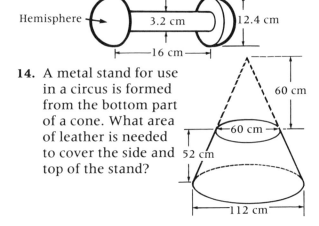

60 cm
60 cm
52 cm
112 cm

Volume

A circular above-ground swimming pool is 6.2 m in diameter and has a constant depth of 1.4 m. What quantity of water is required to fill the pool?

To find the volume of the pool, use the formula for volume of a cylinder.

$$V = \pi r^2 h$$
$$= \pi(3.1)^2(1.4)$$
$$\doteq 42.3$$

The volume of the pool is about 42.3 kL.

If the area of a cross section is constant, you can use another formula to calculate volume.

Volume = $\boxed{\text{Area of Cross Section}}$ × $\boxed{\text{Height (or thickness)}}$

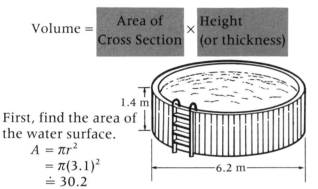

First, find the area of the water surface.

$$A = \pi r^2$$
$$= \pi(3.1)^2$$
$$\doteq 30.2$$

The area of the water surface is about 30.2 m².

square units

The volume is area times depth.

$$V = 30.2 \times 1.4$$
$$= 42.28$$

The volume of water needed to fill the pool is about 42.3 m³ or 42.3 kL.

cubic units

The volume formulas for several common figures are given in the table.

Figure		Volume Formula
Rectangular Solid		$V = lwh$
Sphere		$V = \frac{4}{3}\pi r^3$
Cone		$V = \frac{1}{3}\pi r^2 h$
Cylinder		$V = \pi r^2 h$
Pyramid		$V = \frac{1}{3}b^2 h$

Example 1

A manufacturer produces bowling balls made of a special plastic compound. If each ball is 15.2 cm in diameter, how much material is needed for 2500 bowling balls?

$$V = \frac{4}{3}\pi r^3$$
$$= \frac{4}{3}\pi(7.6)^3$$
$$\doteq 1838.8$$

$r = \frac{15.2}{2}$
$= 7.6$

One ball uses 1838.8 cm³ of material. Multiply to find the volume for 2500 balls.

$$1838.8 \times 2500 = 4\,597\,000$$

$4\,597\,000$ cm³ $= 4.597$ m³

About 4.6 m³ of material is needed for 2500 bowling balls.

Example 2

Gina is a design engineer for a bridge construction firm. One of her design projects involves constructing 3 reinforced concrete piers with the given dimensions. Each pier rests on a rectangular footing as shown.

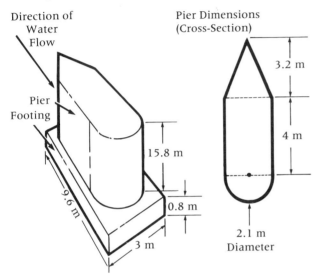

Reinforced concrete costs about $95/m³. Determine the approximate cost to build the 3 piers.

First, find the volume of each footing.
$$V = lwh$$
$$= 9.6 \times 3 \times 0.8$$
$$= 23.04$$
The volume of each footing is 23.04 m³.

Next, find the volume of each pier.

Volume
$$= \text{Area of Section} \times \text{Height}$$
$$= [\, \triangle + \square + \triangledown \,] \times \text{Height}$$
$$= [\tfrac{1}{2}bh + lw + \tfrac{1}{2}\pi r^2] \times \text{Height}$$
$$= [\tfrac{1}{2}(2.1)(3.2) + 4(2.1) + \tfrac{1}{2}\pi(1.05)^2] \times (15.8)$$
$$= [3.36 + 8.4 + 1.73] \times 15.8$$
$$\doteq 213.14$$

The volume of each pier is about 213.14 m³.

The total volume of one pier and footing is 23.04 + 213.14 or 236.18 m³.
The total cost for three piers and footings is 236.18 × $95 × 3 or about $67 300.

Example 3

A cylindrical casting has a volume of 500 cm³. If its height is 6.2 cm, calculate its radius to 1 decimal place.

Since $V = \pi r^2 h$
$$500 = \pi r^2(6.2)$$
$$\frac{500}{6.2} = r^2$$
$$25.67 = r^2$$
$$r = \sqrt{25.67}$$
$$r \doteq 5.1$$

The radius of the casting is about 5.1 cm.

Exercise

A 1. State the volume of each object shown.

Area is 70 cm²

3 cm

2. State the formula used to determine the volume of each object.

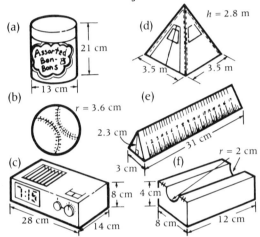

(a) 21 cm, Assorted Bon-Bons, 13 cm

(b) r = 3.6 cm

(c) 7:15, 28 cm, 8 cm, 14 cm

(d) h = 2.8 m, 3.5 m, 3.5 m

(e) 2.3 cm, 31 cm, 3 cm

(f) r = 2 cm, 4 cm, 8 cm, 12 cm

B 3. Calculate the volume of each object shown in Question 2.

4. Each object shown has a volume of 300 cm³. Determine the missing dimension for each one.

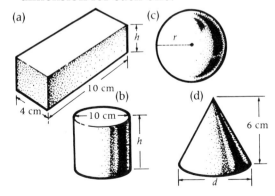

(a) h, 10 cm, 4 cm

(b) 10 cm, h

(c) r

(d) 6 cm, d

5. Calculate the volume of the hot water tank to the nearest litre.

1 L = 1000 cm³

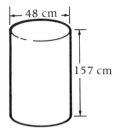

48 cm

157 cm

6. A classroom is 9.2 m long, 7.8 m wide, and 3.3 m high. For health reasons, there must be at least 5 m³ of air per student in the room. How many students can safely use the room?

7. A spherical weather balloon 15.2 m in diameter is filled with helium. Each tank of helium provides 30 m³ of gas and costs $19.75. What is the cost of filling the balloon with helium?

8. Charles uses a lawn roller in the spring and follows the manufacturer's instructions to fill the tank only $\frac{2}{3}$ full. How many litres of water does Charles put in the tank?

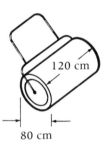

120 cm

80 cm

9. Calculate the volume of each metal casting to the nearest whole number.

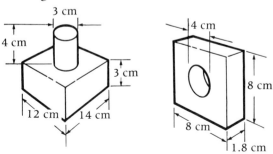

3 cm, 4 cm, 3 cm, 12 cm, 14 cm

4 cm, 8 cm, 8 cm, 1.8 cm

10. A window planter had a trapezoidal cross-section as shown. If the planter is filled to the top with soil, how many cubic metres of soil will the planter hold? Answer correct to 3 decimal places.

30 cm

21 cm

14 cm   52 cm

11. A block of metal used for rolling coins has the dimensions shown. Determine its volume.

2 cm

4 cm

1.8 cm   10 cm

12. The diagram gives the dimensions of a grain hopper in the form of a cylinder on top of a cone.
    (a) If only the conical portion is filled, how much grain is in the hopper?
    (b) How much grain is needed to completely fill the hopper?

5.6 m

8.2 m

CO-OP
GRAIN

4.9 m

13. A waste container has dimensions shown. If only 80% of the container is filled with waste, how much waste is there in the container? Answer in cubic metres, correct to 2 decimals.

Hemisphere

Litter Bin

PUSH

FEED ME! I'M HUNGRY

TRASH

1.4 m

60 cm

14. The gas envelope in a hot-air balloon is in the form of a hemisphere on top of a cone. What volume of gas will the balloon hold?

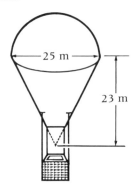

25 m

23 m

15. An hourglass has the dimensions shown.
    (a) One-half of the hourglass is filled with sand to 1.5 cm from the centre. How much sand is required to fill the bottom cone?
    (b) When the hourglass is turned over, the sand flows from the upper half at a rate of 200 mm^3/s. How many minutes does it take for the upper half to empty into the bottom half?

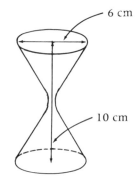

6 cm

10 cm

Measurement Problems

You can use the following checklist to help you solve perimeter, area, and volume problems.

- Decide on an appropriate type of measurement.

Perimeter: the distance around an object

Area: covering the surface of an object

Volume: "filling" a 3-dimensional object

- If necessary, make a diagram showing important information (shape, dimensions, and units).

- Choose an appropriate formula(s) for the figure(s) involved.

- Use proper units.

Perimeter: linear units (cm, m, km)
Area: square units (cm², m²)
Volume: cubic units (cm³, m³, L)

- Make calculations carefully. Use a calculator if it's helpful.

- Make a final statement, including proper units.

The following table gives a summary of the various formulas covered in this unit.

Figure	Formula		
	Perimeter	Area	Volume
Triangle	$P = a + b + c$	$A = \frac{1}{2}bh$	
Rectangle	$P = 2l + 2w$	$A = lw$	
Circle	$C = \pi d$	$A = \pi r^2$	
Parallelogram		$A = bh$	
Trapezoid		$A = \frac{1}{2}h\,(a + b)$	
Sphere		$A = 4\pi r^2$	$V = \frac{4}{3}\pi r^3$
Cone		$A = \pi rs$ (side)	$V = \frac{1}{3}\pi r^2 h$
Cylinder		$A = 2\pi rh$ (side)	$V = \pi r^2 h$
Pyramid		$A = 2sb$ (sides)	$V = \frac{1}{3}b^2 h$

Example 1

A town's reservoir is in the shape of a spherical container with a radius of 7.6 m.

- If one can of paint covers 20 m² and costs $24.95, calculate the cost of paint for the reservoir.

First, find the surface area of the reservoir.

$A = 4\pi r^2$
$\quad = 4\pi(7.6)^2$
$\quad \doteq 725.8$

The surface area is 725.8 m².

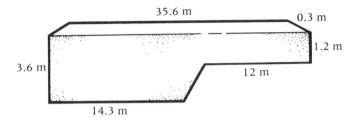

Next, determine how many cans of paint are needed.

$$\frac{\text{Number}}{\text{of Cans}} = \frac{\text{Total Area}}{\text{Coverage per Can}}$$
$$= \frac{725.8}{20}$$
$$= 36.29$$

37 cans are needed.

The cost of the paint is 37 × $24.95 or $923.15.

- Determine the capacity of the reservoir in kilolitres.

$V = \frac{4}{3}\pi r^3$
$\quad = \frac{4}{3}\pi(7.6)^3$
$\quad \doteq 1839$

1 kL = 1000 L

The capacity is 1839 m³ or 1.839 kL.

Example 2

If concrete costs $75/m³, determine the cost of pouring a section of retaining wall with the dimensions shown.

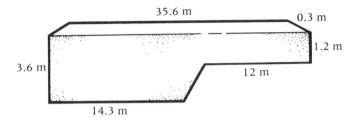

You need to know the volume of the wall before you can determine the cost. Since the wall is a non-standard shape, consider it in two separate parts.

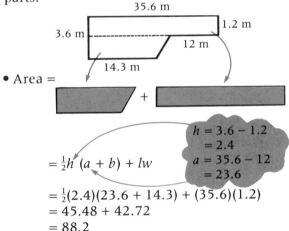

- Area =

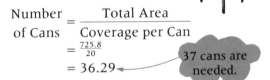

$h = 3.6 - 1.2$
$\quad = 2.4$
$a = 35.6 - 12$
$\quad = 23.6$

$= \frac{1}{2}h\,(a + b) + lw$
$= \frac{1}{2}(2.4)(23.6 + 14.3) + (35.6)(1.2)$
$= 45.48 + 42.72$
$= 88.2$

The area of both parts is 88.2 m².

- Volume = (Area)(Thickness)
  $\quad = (88.2)(0.30)$
  $\quad = 26.46$

The volume is 26.46 m³.

- Cost = (Total Volume)(Unit Cost)
  $\quad = (26.46)(75)$
  $\quad = 1984.50$

The concrete costs $1984.50.

Exercise

B 1. Calculate the length of a baseboard strip to go around a room 5.3 m long and 3.8 m wide. There are 2 doorways (not requiring the strip) each 0.8 m wide.

2. An oil spill fans out from a crippled tanker to form an oil slick with radius 2.7 km. Determine the area of the oil slick. Give your answer to the nearest square kilometre.

3. Fire fighters pump water from a water tanker at the rate of 8.5 L/s. If the tanker was full when they started pumping, how many minutes will it take until the tanker is half-full?

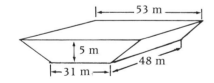

4. An excavation for the foundation of an apartment building is trapezoidal in cross-section with the dimensions shown below.

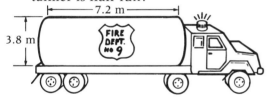

(a) Jill operates a front-end loader that holds 3 m³ of earth. What is the least number of loads required to dig the foundation?

(b) Dump trucks with a capacity of 12 m³ are used to haul away the earth that Jill removes. If she can load one truck every 5 min, how many hours will it take to haul away the earth?

5. During a paper drive, bundles of papers are tied with cord as shown.

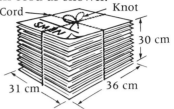

If 18 cm of cord is used to tie the knot, calculate the length of cord needed to tie one bundle of papers.

6. A square piece of sheet metal is 80 cm by 80 cm. What is the area of the largest circle that can be cut from the sheet metal? Answer to the nearest whole number.

7. An air deflector placed over an air vent has the dimensions shown. Calculate the total area of the material used to make the air deflector. Give your answer to the nearest square centimetre.

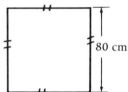

8. At a high school graduation, 275 students received diplomas wrapped with a ribbon, as shown. If 20 cm is used to tie each bow, how much ribbon was needed to tie all the diplomas? Answer in metres, correct to 1 decimal place.

9. A large plastic display sign is in the form of a semicircle, and has an area of 8 m². What is the radius of the sign, correct to 2 decimals?

10. A rectangular piece of land, with the dimensions shown, has a roadway 25 m wide built across it.

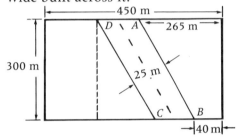

(a) What length of fencing is needed for the distance from *A* to *B* and *C* to *D*?

(b) What area of land was used for the roadway?

11. A grain storage bin in the shape of a rectangular solid is 12.3 m long, 8.1 m wide, and 2.7 m deep. How many kilolitres of grain will the bin hold when it is 65% full? Answer to the nearest whole number.

12. Cattle feed is stored in a concrete silo with inside dimensions as shown.

(a) If the silo is 80% full, how much feed is in it?

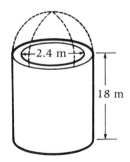

(b) If the walls of the silo are 0.3 m thick, calculate the volume of concrete used to make the silo. Answer to the nearest cubic metre.

(c) If concrete costs $72/m³, calculate the cost of concrete for the silo.

13. A metal paperweight has the dimensions shown.

(a) Calculate the volume of the paperweight. (Answer to the nearest whole number.)

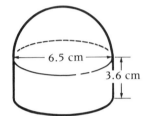

(b) If the metal used to make the paperweight has a density of 3.6 g/cm³, determine the total mass of the paperweight.

14. A wooden soup bowl has a hemispherical shape, and dimensions as shown.

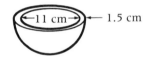

(a) How much soup will the bowl hold?

(b) If the bowl is totally immersed in water to wash it, calculate the total wetted surface area (nearest whole number).

15. The volume of a human body can be estimated by considering it as several different shapes. Using the values shown here, determine the volume of this body.

Arms: Cylinder 9 cm Diameter 60 cm Long
Sphere: 26 cm Diameter 8 cm High
Trunk: 45 cm × 19 cm × 40 cm
Legs: Cylinder 15 cm Diameter 90 cm Long
Neck: Cylinder 13 cm Diameter 8 cm High

Take some approximate measurements and determine the volume of *your* body!

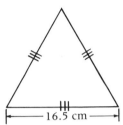

Problem-Solving in Geometry

1. Calculate the area of the equilateral triangle shown.

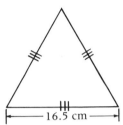

2. An ordinary sheet of notepaper measures 21.6 cm wide and 27.9 cm long. Draw 1 diagonal line from one corner of the paper to the opposite corner.
   (a) Into what 2 congruent geometric figures does the diagonal split the sheet of paper?
   (b) Use the Law of Pythagoras to calculate the length of the diagonal, correct to 1 decimal place.
   (c) Check your calculation in part (b) by measuring the diagonal with a ruler.
   (d) Roll the sheet of notepaper into a cylinder, taping the edges together as indicated in the diagram.

   Name the figure formed by the diagonal line.

3. A can of paint with the dimensions shown has a spiral line drawn on the label as indicated. Calculate the length of the spiral, to the nearest centimetre.

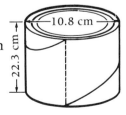

4. An oil storage tank is in the form of a large cylinder. Access to the top of the tank is by means of a ramp that spirals for 2 complete circuits of the tank, as shown.

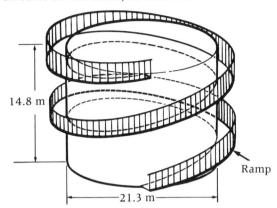

Determine the length of the ramp, to the nearest metre.

5. Determine the length of the side of a cube with the same volume as a sphere 10 cm in diameter.

6. How many tennis balls, each 7 cm in diameter, can be packed into a box measuring 14 cm by 21 cm by 35 cm?

7. A standard container of popcorn sells for $1.50.

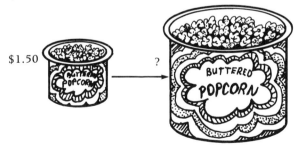

If the diameter and height of the container are each doubled, what should be the price of the large-size container of popcorn?

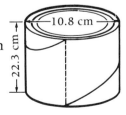

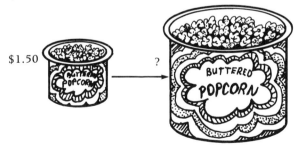

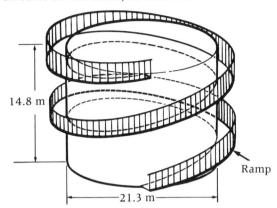

361

8. Pressure on a surface is given by

$$P = \frac{M}{A}$$

M is mass (kilograms); A is area (square centimetre).

Which of the following creates the greatest pressure?

(a) truck   (b) bicycle   (c) shoe heel

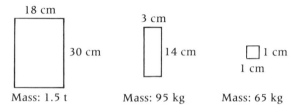

Mass: 1.5 t   Mass: 95 kg   Mass: 65 kg

9. A box in the form of a cube measures 20 cm to the side.

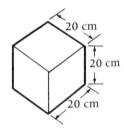

Determine the greatest volume of a sphere, cylinder, or cone that will fit inside the box.

10. How can the area of the figure shown be split up into 4 identical pieces (all equal in area and shape) and each with the same shape as the original figure?

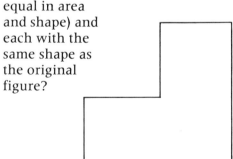

11. The dimensions of an in-ground swimming pool are shown in the diagram below.

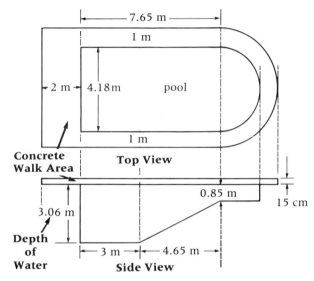

(a) If concrete costs $74.50/m³, calculate the cost of concrete for the walk area, to the nearest dollar.

(b) Determine the volume of water the pool will hold in kilolitres, correct to 1 decimal place.

(c) If the pool were filled at the rate of 0.95 kL/h, how many hours would it take to fill it?

(d) Calculate the surface area of the plastic pool liner in square metres, correct to 1 decimal place.

Unit 18 Review

1. Calculate the perimeter and area of each figure.

(a)

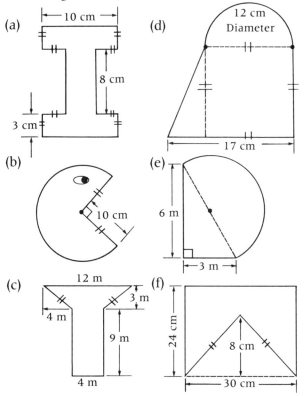

(b)

(c)

2. The track of an all-terrain vehicle runs on 2 wheels, each 0.8 m in diameter, as shown.

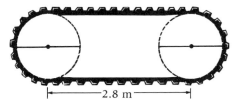

Determine the length of the track, correct to 1 decimal place.

3. The diagram shows the dimensions of a transformer core. If there are 2600 windings around the outside of the core, find the length of wire used in the winding, correct to the nearest metre.

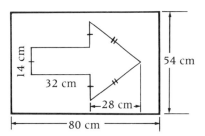

4. A room 6.1 m long, 4.8 m wide, and 2.8 m high is to be wallpapered on all 4 walls. If 7.5 m² of the room are doors and windows, what area of wallspace will be covered?

5. The dimensions of an arrow painted on a roadway sign are as shown.

(a) Calculate the area of the painted arrow.
(b) Determine the area of the sign that is not taken up by the arrow.
(c) Find the perimeter of the arrow.
(d) How much greater is the perimeter of the sign than the perimeter of the arrow?

363

6. A circular above-ground swimming pool is surrounded by a cedar deck, as shown.

   (a) Calculate the area of the surface of the pool.
   (b) Calculate the area of the deck.
   (c) If the cedar deck costs \$33.71/m to install, determine the cost of installing the deck, correct to the nearest dollar.

6.5 m | 2 m

Pool

Deck

7. Calculate the total surface area of a ball-bearing that is 0.88 cm in diameter. (Give your answer correct to 2 decimal places.)

8. Determine the surface area of the top and sides of the piston shown, to the nearest whole number.

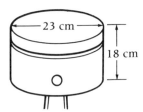

23 cm

18 cm

9. A metal lamp shade is in the shape of a cone, as shown. Calculate the outside area of the lamp shade, correct to 1 decimal place.

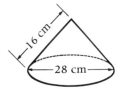

16 cm

28 cm

10. Pat's tent is in the form of a square-base pyramid with the dimensions shown.

    (a) Determine the amount of canvas used for the tent, including the floor.
    (b) If a strong wind collapses Pat's tent completely, what volume of air is forced out of the tent?

2 m

2.5 m   3 m

11. Gerda works for a company that installs air-conditioning systems. For one installation, Gerda must connect the square pipe on the right to a round pipe on the left.

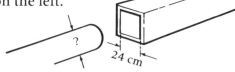

?   24 cm

If the two pipes must have the same cross-sectional area, determine the diameter of the round pipe, correct to the nearest centimetre.

12. In a scientific experiment, a balloon 20 m in diameter is filled with helium and spray-painted with a reflective coating.

    (a) Calculate the total area to be spray-painted.
    (b) If 1 can of spray-paint covers 25 m², how many cans are required to paint the balloon?
    (c) Determine the total cost of paint if 1 can costs \$18.95.
    (d) How many kilolitres of helium does the balloon contain when inflated to a diameter of 20 m?

13. Sand spills from a conveyor belt into a conical pile with dimensions as shown.

    (a) What area of the surface of the pile will get wet during a rainstorm?
    (b) What is the volume of sand in the pile?
    (c) If sand has a mass of 1200 kg/m³, determine the number of tonnes of sand in the pile.   1 t = 1000 kg

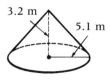

3.2 m

5.1 m

14. A cylindrical oil storage tank is 24 m in diameter and 10 m high.
  (a) What volume of oil can be stored in the tank, (to the nearest kilolitre)?
  (b) If one can of paint covers 70 m² and costs $50, what will it cost to apply 2 coats of paint to the top and side of the tank?

15. Determine the volume of each casting, to the nearest whole number.

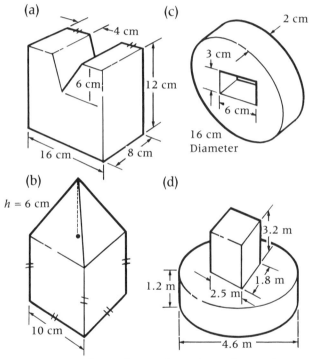

(a)

4 cm
6 cm
12 cm
16 cm
8 cm

(b)

h = 6 cm
10 cm

(c)

2 cm
3 cm
6 cm
16 cm
Diameter

(d)

3.2 m
1.8 m
1.2 m
2.5 m
4.6 m

16. Using the information given for each shape, determine each missing dimension.

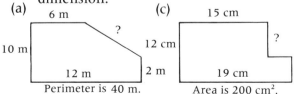

(a)

6 m
?
10 m
12 m
Perimeter is 40 m.

(c)

15 cm
12 cm
?
2 m
19 cm
Area is 200 cm².

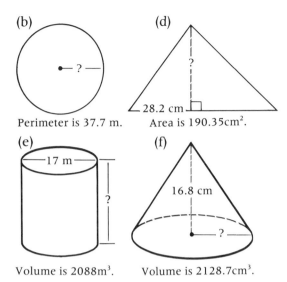

(b)

? ─

Perimeter is 37.7 m.

(d)

?
28.2 cm
Area is 190.35cm².

(e)

17 m
?

Volume is 2088m³.

(f)

16.8 cm
?

Volume is 2128.7cm³.

17. A watering trough has the dimensions shown.

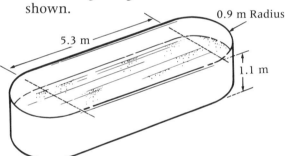

0.9 m Radius
5.3 m
1.1 m

If the trough is filled to a depth of 0.8 m, how many litres of water does it contain?

18. Aaron is a lumberjack in northern British Columbia. He eats at least 2.5 L of beef stew for dinner each night. One can of stew has the dimensions shown. If Aaron eats the contents of the tin, will he be satisfied?

14 cm
HOME STYLE BEEF STEW CHUNKY
17 cm

19. An A-frame cottage has dimensions as shown. If each person must have at least 12 m³ of air for safety reasons, how many people can safely sleep in the cottage?

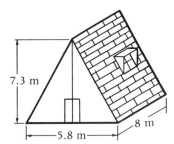

7.3 m

5.8 m

8 m

20. A sporting goods manufacturer produces hockey pucks with the dimensions shown.

How many cubic metres of material are required to make 2 500 000 pucks?

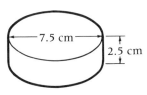

7.5 cm

2.5 cm

21. A sump pump reservoir has dimensions as shown. Before draining, a full reservoir has water to a level 7 cm from the top. During draining, the water level drops to within 3 cm of the bottom of the reservoir. If the reservoir is drained a total of 18 times on average each day, how much water would be used in 1 a? Give your answer in kilolitres, correct to 2 decimals.

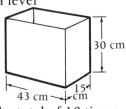

30 cm

43 cm

15 cm

22. A new sports complex contains a track area as shown.

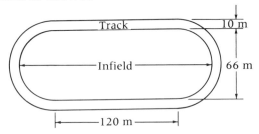

Track

Infield

10 m

66 m

120 m

(a) The inside and outside edges of the track are to be lined with a plastic curbing costing \$2.65/m. Calculate the total cost of the curbing.
(b) The infield area is to be covered with sod at a cost of \$1.25/m². Determine the total cost of covering the infield.
(c) The base for the track consists of a layer of crushed stone 25 cm deep. Calculate the cost of the base at \$22/m³ for crushed stone.
(d) The track surface will be a composition material costing \$4.50/m². What is the total cost of surfacing the track?

23. A rocket consists of a cylindrical body and conical nose section as shown.

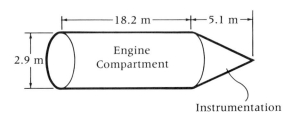

18.2 m

5.1 m

Engine Compartment

2.9 m

Instrumentation

(a) If 80% of the volume of the engine compartment is taken up by fuel, what volume of fuel does the rocket contain?
(b) What volume is available for instrumentation?

Unit 19

Ratio, Proportion, and Rate

Proportions with Two-Term Ratios

Susan is doing an Environmental Studies project for Geography class. She learns that, for the average person, the ratio of the amount of water used for showering to the amount of water that person used daily is $2:5$.

She determines that a person showering once each day uses an average of about 80 L of water. On the average, how much water is used daily?

Let x litres be the total used daily.

$$\overset{\text{showers}}{2:5} = \overset{}{80:x}$$
$$\underset{\text{total}}{x}$$

This equation, stating that one ratio is equal to another, is a **proportion**.

The ratios involved here are 2-term ratios. The proportion can be expressed in 2 different ways.

$$80:x = 2:5 \qquad \text{or} \qquad \frac{80}{x} \times \frac{2}{5}$$

When 2 ratios are equal, the numbers indicated by the arrows must have equal products.
$$2 \times x = 80 \times 5$$
$$2x = 400$$
$$x = 200$$

So a person, on the average, uses about 200 L of water daily.

A ratio in lowest terms contains whole numbers only (no fractions or decimals) and the numbers have no factors in common.

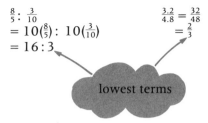

$$\frac{8}{5}:\frac{3}{10}$$
$$= 10\left(\tfrac{8}{5}\right):10\left(\tfrac{3}{10}\right)$$
$$= 16:3$$

$$\frac{3.2}{4.8} = \frac{32}{48}$$
$$= \frac{2}{3}$$

lowest terms

Example 1

Check whether each of the following pairs of ratios forms a proportion.

$$\frac{5}{9}, \frac{8}{15} \qquad\qquad 3:5, \ 42:70$$

Consider the products of the numbers indicated by the arrows below.

$$\frac{5}{9} \times \frac{8}{15} \qquad\qquad 3:5 , 42:70$$

$5 \times 15 = 75$ $3 \times 70 = 210$
$9 \times 8 = 72$ $5 \times 42 = 210$

Unequal products; *not* a proportion!

Equal products; this *is* a proportion.
$3:5 = 42:70$

Example 2

Bill and Terry form a partnership, in which they invest their money in the ratio $3:5$ respectively. How much should each receive from a profit of $7200?
The total profit should be shared in the same ratio as their investments.
Let the amount of profit received by Bill be $3k$; the amount received by Terry is $5k$.

$$3k + 5k = 7200$$
$$8k = 7200$$
$$k = 900$$

total profit

Bill receives $3 \times 900, or $2700.
Terry receives $5 \times 900, or $4500.

Exercise

A **1.** State which of the following pairs of ratios form a proportion.

(a) $\frac{5}{9}, \frac{6}{11}$

(b) $\frac{7}{2}, \frac{21}{6}$

(c) $4:5, 12:15$

(d) $\frac{3}{4}, \frac{4}{5}$

(e) $5:2, 25:10$

(f) $\frac{16}{3}, \frac{11}{2}$

2. State in lowest terms.

(a) $9:6$

(b) $\frac{15}{3}$

(c) $\frac{8}{48}$

(d) $1.5:3$

(e) $\frac{1}{2}:\frac{3}{2}$

(f) $32:48$

(g) $0.7:1.9$

(h) $\frac{40}{100}$

3. State the value of each variable.

(a) $\frac{5}{9} = \frac{10}{m}$

(b) $12:4 = 30:k$

(c) $\frac{6}{5} = \frac{r}{25}$

(d) $3:2 = a:14$

(e) $\frac{5}{s} = \frac{15}{6}$

(f) $c:6 = 6:18$

B **4.** Solve for each variable.

(a) $\frac{15}{8} = \frac{t}{7}$

(b) $4:7 = 11:m$

(c) $\frac{r+8}{12} = \frac{7}{6}$

(d) $\frac{5.8}{6} = \frac{b}{12}$

(e) $7:9.2 = C:1.8$

(f) $\frac{43}{p+3} = \frac{11}{p-1}$

5. An electronic timer-circuit costs \$28.50 to manufacture. The ratio of selling price to cost price is $3.65:1.72$. What is the selling price of the circuit?

6. In a certain automobile engine, the ratio of engine (crankshaft) speed to alternator pulley speed is $21:8$. When the crankshaft speed is 798 r/min, what is the alternator pulley speed?

7. The dimensions of 2 rectangles are as shown.

For rectangles ① and ② determine the ratio of their widths; lengths; perimeters; areas.

8. Two circles have diameters 8 cm and 10 cm. What is the ratio of their areas?

9. The ratio of the number of teeth on Gear A to the number of teeth on Gear B is $9:4$. If the total number of teeth on both gears is 169, how many teeth are there on each gear?

10. The ratio of the cost of a baseball bat to the cost of a glove is $7:9$. The total cost is \$50.40. Determine the cost of each.

Side Trip

Two cans of oil on a shelf have the same height. What is the diameter of the larger can, correct to 1 decimal place?

369

Proportions with Three-Term Ratios

At his family's cottage, Jim is faced with the problem of adapting an old gear system so that it can be used to haul their boat from the water up to the boat-house.

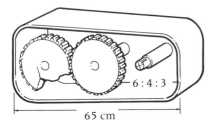

The gear drive shafts are intact, and the housing is not damaged, but one of the gears is badly damaged, and the third gear is missing.

From his shop work at school, Jim knows a formula relating gear diameter (D) to number of teeth (T).

$$D_1 : D_2 : D_3 = T_1 : T_2 : T_3$$

Jim also observes that the housing is a bit longer than 65 cm and has $6 : 4 : 3$ stamped inside it. He suspects that the numbers $6 : 4 : 3$ give the gear ratio. He wants to find the number of teeth needed in gears 1 and 3. The first step is to find the gear diameters. Let the diameters be $6k$, $4k$, and $3k$ centimetres, respectively.

$$6k + 4k + 3k = 65$$
$$13k = 65$$
$$k = 5$$

$6k = 30$
$4k = 20$
$3k = 15$

So the gear diameters are 30 cm, 20 cm, and 15 cm. (Jim's suspicions are confirmed!)

Jim finds by counting that gear 2 has 100 teeth. He uses the proportion relating diameters and number of teeth.

$$D_1 : D_2 : D_3 = T_1 : T_2 : T_3$$

This can be rewritten as follows.

$$\frac{D_1}{T_1} = \frac{D_2}{T_2} = \frac{D_3}{T_3}$$

$$\frac{30}{T_1} = \frac{20}{100} = \frac{15}{T_3}$$

From this, you can write 2 equations.

$$\frac{30}{T_1} = \frac{20}{100} \qquad \frac{15}{T_3} = \frac{20}{100}$$

$$T_1 = 150 \qquad T_3 = 75$$

Gear 1 has 150 teeth and gear 3 has 75 teeth.

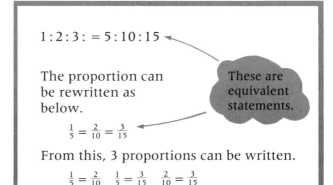

$$1 : 2 : 3 : = 5 : 10 : 15$$

The proportion can be rewritten as below.

These are equivalent statements.

$$\frac{1}{5} = \frac{2}{10} = \frac{3}{15}$$

From this, 3 proportions can be written.

$$\frac{1}{5} = \frac{2}{10} \qquad \frac{1}{5} = \frac{3}{15} \qquad \frac{2}{10} = \frac{3}{15}$$

Example 1

Determine the missing terms.

$$5:19:k = 8:m:20$$

Rewrite the statement.

$$\frac{5}{8} = \frac{19}{m} = \frac{k}{20}$$

Use the ratio $\frac{5}{8}$ in each of 2 equations. Solve for m and k.

$$\frac{5}{8} = \frac{19}{m}$$

$$5m = 152$$
$$m = 30.4$$

$$\frac{5}{8} = \frac{k}{20}$$

$$8k = 100$$
$$k = 12.5$$

Example 2

For a balanced ecological system, an aquarium should have tropical fish, snails, and scavengers in the ratio of $6:2:3$. If the total number of creatures in an aquarium is to be 55, how many fish, snails, and scavengers should there be?

Suppose there are $6y$ fish, $2y$ snails, and $3y$ scavengers.

$$6y + 2y + 3y = 55$$
$$11y = 55$$
$$y = 5$$

$$6y = 30$$
$$2y = 10$$
$$3y = 15$$

There should be 30 fish, 10 snails, and 15 scavengers in the aquarium.

Exercise

A **1.** In each case, determine the factor that multiplies the first ratio to give the second.

(a) $2:5:7 = 6:15:21$
(b) $1:3:4 = 5:15:20$
(c) $8:5:7 = 16:10:14$
(d) $0.2:1.3:4.5 = 4:26:90$
(e) $12:15:6 = 4:5:2$

2. True or false?

(a) $5:4:12 = 10:8:24$
(b) $4:8:12 = 1:2:4$
(c) $8:5:6 = 24:15:12$
(d) $35:50:75 = 7:10:15$
(e) $\frac{4}{5} = \frac{20}{25} = \frac{32}{40}$
(f) $\frac{9}{6} = \frac{2}{3} = \frac{12}{18}$
(g) $\frac{7.5}{2.5} = \frac{3}{15} = \frac{21}{7}$

B **3.** Determine the value of each variable.

(a) $\frac{4}{9} = \frac{x}{45} = \frac{28}{y+3}$
(b) $\frac{m}{8} = \frac{7}{11} = \frac{13}{k}$
(c) $\frac{4.8}{2.1} = \frac{r}{56} = \frac{s}{5}$
(d) $16:9 = a:5 = 28:b$
(e) $7:p:12 = 15:8:q$
(f) $(r+1):25:7.5 = 6:5:t$
(g) $w+1:5:6 = 7:8:4-x$

4. A length of pipe is to be cut in the ratio $7:4:5$. If the length of the first section is 91 cm, what are the lengths of the other two sections?

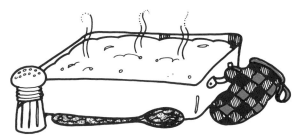

5. A batch of lasagna contains cheese, noodles, and ground beef in the ratio 3:8:4. If the amount of cheese is 2.7 kg, determine the following.

    (a) The amount of noodles and ground beef.
    (b) The total mass of the batch of lasagna.

6. A sampling of trees in a woodlot gives the ratio of maple to oak to evergreen trees as 20:3:11. If there are 5610 trees in the woodlot, how many are there of each type?

7. During one hockey season Sam, Arnold, and Ed scored goals in the ratio 4:6:5. If they scored a total of 285 goals, how many did each player score?

8. A certain alloy contains tin, lead, and silver in the ratio 12:8:3.

    (a) Find the quantity of tin and lead in a piece of alloy containing 90 g of silver.
    (b) Determine the quantity of each substance in 12.5 kg of the alloy.

9. In a waste recycling program, the ratio of paper to metal to glass collected is 5.1:3.4:4.5. In one week, the total amount of waste collected was 46.8 t. How much of each material was collected?

10. Three people share a lottery prize in the ratio 5:3:2. If the person winning the most money received $42 580, how much did each of the other 2 people receive?

11. A fertilizer mix contains nitrogen, potassium, and phosphorous in the ratio 12:5:7.

    (a) If a bag of fertilizer contains 15 kg of nitrogen, how much potassium and phosphorous does it contain?
    (b) How much of each ingredient would there be in a 42 kg bag of fertilizer?

12. A lake contains only bass, pickerel, and perch. In a sampling of fish from the lake, there are 14 bass, 51 perch, and 25 pickerel. If the total number of fish in the lake is 18 000, how many of each type of fish should there be in the lake?

Rates

Reggie is shopping for food for a party.

Which is the better buy?

To decide, Reggie calculates the unit cost for each brand of peanuts.

Brand	Cost	Quantity	Unit Cost
Grandma's	$2.19	500 g	$\frac{\$2.19}{500 \text{ g}} = 0.438$¢/g
Old South	$3.15	750 g	$\frac{3.15}{750 \text{ g}} = 0.420$¢/g

Old South brand is the better buy.
Calculating unit cost involves comparing items that are measured in different units; it involves working with **rates**.

Example 1

Find the price of 750 g of Grandma's peanuts.

Multiply by unit cost.
$$750 \text{ g} \times 0.438¢/\text{g} = \$3.29$$

The price is $3.29.

Example 2

How many grams of Old South peanuts can Reggie buy for $5?

$$\frac{\$5.00}{0.420/\text{g}} = \frac{500¢}{0.420¢/\text{g}}$$
$$\doteq 1190 \text{ g}$$

Reggie could buy 1190 g of Old South peanuts.

Example 2

Arlene jogs 8 km daily in preparation for a 10 km race. Her average time for the 8 km distance is 32 min. Use the formula for rate of speed to answer the questions below.

$$S = \frac{D}{t}$$

S is rate of speed;
D is distance;
t is time.

• What is Arlene's daily jogging rate?

$$S = \frac{D}{t}$$
$$= \frac{8 \text{ km}}{32 \text{ min}} \qquad = 0.25 \text{ km/min}$$

Her daily jogging rate is 0.25 km/min.

• At this rate, what should her time for the 10 km race be?

$$S = \frac{D}{t}$$
$$0.25 = \frac{10}{t}$$
$$t = 40$$

Her time should be 40 min.

• At this rate, how far could she run in 50 min?

$$S = \frac{D}{t}$$
$$0.25 = \frac{D}{50}$$
$$D = 12.5$$

In 50 min, she could run 12.5 km.

Example 3

A conical water reservoir, full of water, has the dimensions shown. It is drained during a dry spell at the rate of 18 m³/h. How long will it take to empty the reservoir?

— 30 m —

8 m

Use the dimensions given to calculate volume first.

$V = \frac{1}{3}\pi r^2 h$
$= \frac{1}{3}\pi(15)^2(8)$
$\doteq 1885$

$r = 15$
$h = 8$

Now find the time using the rate formula.

Rate = $\dfrac{\text{Volume}}{\text{Time}}$

$18 = \dfrac{1885}{T}$

$18T = 1885$

$T = 104.7$

It will take about 105 h to empty the reservoir.

Exercise

A 1. In comparison buying, what factors other than unit cost might affect your decision to purchase a particular brand of goods?

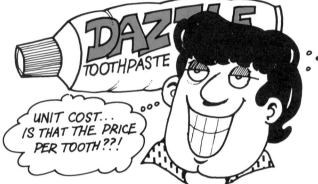

UNIT COST... IS THAT THE PRICE PER TOOTH??!

B 2. Calculate the unit cost in each case.

	Brand	Cost	Quantity	Unit Cost
(a)	A	$1.98	50 g	☐ ¢/g
(b)	B	$25	18 g	☐ $/g
(c)	C	$3.49	75 g	☐ ¢/g
(d)	D	$1.65	3 L	☐ ¢/L
(e)	E	$7.99	450 g	☐ ¢/g

3. "Dazzler" toothpaste is on special at $1.29 for a 100 mL tube. But Andy prefers the taste of his regular brand toothpaste, so he buys it at $2.25 for a 150 mL tube. How much more per millilitre did Andy's preference cost him?

4. A 10 kg bag of fertilizer sells for $12.99.

   (a) What is its unit cost in dollars per kilogram?
   (b) What should be the price of a 25 kg bag of fertilizer?
   (c) How much fertilizer should you be able to buy for $40?

5. Cathy earns $314 for working 40 h and Chris earns $303.75 for working 37.5 h. Who earns the greater rate per hour? By how much?

6. Fuel consumption figures for 3 automobiles are given in the table.

Make of Car	Amount of Fuel Used (L)	Distance Driven (km)
Zippo-6	1047.9	13 265
Cruiser-4	844.6	15 640
Zoom-B	1310	12 970

   (a) For each car, determine the rate of fuel consumption in litres per 100 km.
   (b) Determine the amount of fuel used by each car on a trip of 8000 km.
   (c) If fuel cost 51.8¢/L, calculate the fuel costs for each car for a trip of 5000 km.

7. The primary winding on a transformer has 8.5 turns per centimetre.

   (a) How many turns are there on the winding if it is 12 cm long?
   (b) If each turn uses 7.2 cm of wire, what is the total length of wire on the primary winding?
   (c) If the ratio of primary to secondary turns is 1 : 19, how many turns are on the secondary winding?

8. The world's tropical forest reserves of 935 000 000 ha are being depleted at the rate of 15 000 000 ha/a. Without replenishment, how many years will it be until only half of the reserves remain?

9. A new spherical water reservoir is to be filled with water. If the reservoir is 15 m in diameter, calculate the rate (cubic metres per hour) at which water must be pumped into it to fill in 9 d.

10. Each Canadian accounts for about 2 kg of garbage each day. At this rate:
   • What would be the annual garbage production per person?
   • Determine the annual garbage production for a city with a population of 500 000 people.
   • Calculate the total annual garbage produced in Canada if its population is 25 000 000 people.

11. Karen is a pharmacist. She receives a prescription calling for 50 mg of medication. The label on the bottle of the drug shows that 60 cm³ of solution contains 250 mg of medication. How much solution should Karen measure out to fill the prescription?

Applying Ratios in Photography

In photography, correct exposure of the film depends on the amount of light entering the camera through its lens.

The sizes of the adjustable lens openings are called **f-stops**.

$$\text{f-stop} = \frac{\text{Focal Length of Lens}}{\text{Diameter of Lens Opening}}$$

The camera shown above has a lens with focal length of 50 mm. When its lens opening is set at a diameter of 12.5 mm, the f-stop can be calculated from the formula.

$$\text{f-stop} = \frac{50}{12.5}$$
$$= 4$$

The f-stop is 4.

This is often written as f/4.

Exercise

1. A camera has a lens with a focal length of 150 mm.
   Calculate the f-stop for each given lens diameter opening.
   Give your answers in parts (a) and (b) to 1 decimal place, all others to the nearest whole number.

   (a) 42.9 mm   (d) 13.6 mm
   (b) 26.8 mm   (e) 9.4 mm
   (c) 18.8 mm   (f) 6.8 mm

2. Determine, to the nearest whole number, the focal length of a camera lens if a setting of f/5.6 results in a lens opening diameter of 24.1 mm.

3. A telephoto lens has a focal length of 200 mm. What will the diameter of the lens opening be for an f-stop of f/16?

Unit 19 Review

1. Which of the following pairs of ratios form a proportion?

   (a) $\frac{8}{3}, \frac{16}{6}$ (c) $\frac{17}{5}, \frac{10}{3}$

   (b) $7:5, 18:13$ (d) $8:20, 6:15$

2. Reduce to lowest terms

   (a) $15:6$ (c) $1\frac{1}{4}:\frac{3}{8}$

   (b) $\frac{18}{32}$ (d) $\frac{4.8}{6.4}$

3. Determine the value of each variable.

   (a) $\frac{7}{4} = \frac{x}{8}$

   (b) $5:6 = 45:m$

   (c) $\frac{17}{k} = \frac{51}{9}$

   (d) $\frac{3}{5}:r = \frac{4}{7}:\frac{5}{6}$

   (e) $\frac{p}{4.1} = \frac{6.3}{7.5}$

   (f) $5.8:3.2 = w:1.9$

   (g) $\frac{a+1}{a} = \frac{5}{4}$

   (h) $(r+1):9 = (r-3):5$

   (i) $7:9 = (m-1):(m+6)$

   (j) $\frac{12}{36} = \frac{7}{m} = \frac{n}{51}$

   (k) $3:7:y = k:2:5$

   (l) $6.3:a:1.4 = 1.8:4.2:b$

4. The rear-axle ratio for a car is given below.

   $$\frac{\text{number of teeth on ring gear}}{\text{number of teeth on pinion gear}}$$

   (expressed in colon form to 2 decimals, with denominator 1). Find the rear axle ratio for each gear combination.

	Number of Teeth on Ring Gear	Number of Teeth on Pinion Gear
(a)	68	17
(b)	64	15
(c)	77	22
(d)	60	18
(e)	75	18

5. The compression ratio of an engine is the ratio given below.

   Maximum Volume : Minimum Volume

   (expressed in colon form to 1 decimal with second term 1). If the maximum volume is 639 cm³ and the minimum volume is 72.5 cm³, calculate the compression ratio for the engine.

6. A hockey stick and helmet together cost $51.30. The ratio of the cost of the stick to the cost of the helmet is $7:20$. Determine the cost of each item.

7. Two spheres have diameters of 10 cm and 20 cm respectively. What is the ratio of the following.

   (a) their radii
   (b) their surface areas
   (c) their volumes

8. Three people share a lottery prize in the ratio 5 : 3 : 2. If the person winning the most money received $15 200, how much did each of the other two people receive?

9. A barbeque sauce mixture consists of ketchup, brown sugar, and spices in the ratio of 10 : 7 : 1. Determine the quantity of each ingredient in 829 g of sauce.

10. Ernie can type 808 words in 16 min. Ralph can type 1104 words in 23 min.
    (a) Who is the faster typist?
    (b) If they started typing together, what would be the difference in the number of words typed after 10 min?

11. Calculate the unit cost in each case.

Product	Cost	Quantity	Unit Cost
A	$97.35	15 kg	$☐/kg
B	$1.80	250 g	¢☐/g
C	$4.79	2.8 kg	$☐/kg
D	$6.95	750 ml	¢☐/ml
E	$5.85	4 L	$☐/L

12. A furnace fan moves about 3.2 m³ of air per minute. If the approximate dimensions for the living area of the house are 10 m by 13 m by 3 m, how many minutes will it take to totally change the air in the house? (Answer to the nearest minute.)

13. A chunk of cheddar cheese with mass 1.15 kg costs $8.29.
    (a) What is its unit cost in dollars per kilogram?
    (b) What should be the price of a 0.84 kg piece of cheese?
    (c) How many kilograms of cheese can you buy for $12?

14. In 1980, it was estimated that the world's tropical rain forest covered about 1 billion (1,000,000,000) hectares. A 1982 study by two United Nations agencies estimated that about 7,500,000 ha are lost each year to agriculture or logging. At this rate, with no replenishment, in about how many years will the rain forests disappear?

Unit 20

Variation

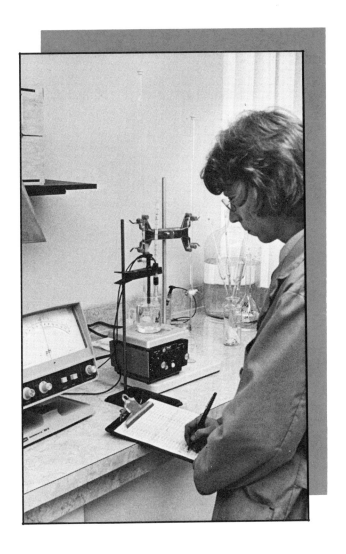

Direct Variation

Jackie drives a transport truck for All-Country Trucking.

The table of values shows the relationship between the number of litres (N) of diesel fuel required to fill the fuel tank and the cost (C) of the fuel in dollars.

N	100	150	400	300
C	50	75	200	150

The table of values can be used to graph the relationship.

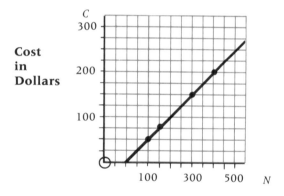

Cost in Dollars

Number of Litres

The graph clearly shows that, as the number of litres of fuel increases, the cost also increases.

The relationship between the cost, C, and the number of litres, N, can be written as a proportion.

$$\frac{C}{N} = \frac{50}{100} = \frac{75}{150} = \frac{200}{400} = \frac{150}{300}$$

or $\frac{C}{N} = \frac{1}{2}$

In this relationship the value of $\frac{C}{N}$ never changes: $\frac{C}{N}$ is a **constant value**, $\frac{1}{2}$ in this case. This value is the slope of the graph, and represents the cost per litre ($0.5).

The relationship between C and N can be written in the following forms.
$\frac{C}{N} = k$, or $C = kN$, where k is a constant
For this relationship, $k = \frac{1}{2}$, so $C = \frac{1}{2} N$.

This formula can be used to find the cost of 345 L of fuel.

Substitute $N = 345$ in the formula.
$$C = \frac{1}{2} N$$
$$= \frac{1}{2}(345)$$
$$= 172.50$$

The cost is $172.50.

The relationship between C and N can also be written as a proportion.

$$\frac{C_1}{N_1} = \frac{1}{2} \text{ and } \frac{C_2}{N_2} = \frac{1}{2}$$

(N_1, C_1) and (N_2, C_2) are points on the graph.

So $\frac{C_1}{N_1} = \frac{C_2}{N_2}$

Use this proportion to find the cost of 345 L of fuel.

Choose values of C_1 and N_1 from a point on the graph.

$$C_1 = 50, N_1 = 100; C_2 = ?, N_2 = 345$$

$$\frac{50}{100} = \frac{C_2}{345}$$

$$100\,C_2 = 50 \times 345$$

$$C_2 = \frac{50 \times 345}{100}$$

$$= 172.50.$$

The cost is \$172.50.

C increases as N increases: another way of saying this is that
C is **directly proportional** to N,
or C **varies directly** as N.

$$C \propto N$$

C varies directly as N.

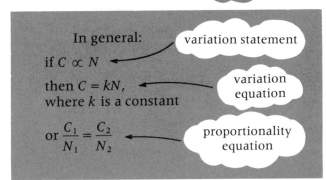

In general: variation statement

if $C \propto N$

then $C = kN$,   variation equation
where k is a constant

or $\frac{C_1}{N_1} = \frac{C_2}{N_2}$ proportionality equation

Example 1

In the table, y varies directly as x.

x	5	7	b
y	a	28	14

Complete the table.

• **Using a variation equation**

Since y varies directly as x, then $y = kx$, where k is a constant.

To find k, use the values $x = 7$ and $y = 28$ from the table.

$$(28) = k(7)$$
$$k = 4$$

The equation is $y = 4x$. Use the equation to complete the table.

x	5	7	3.5
y	20	28	14

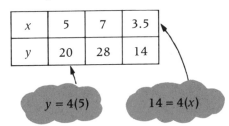

$y = 4(5)$ $14 = 4(x)$

• **Using a proportion**

Since x varies directly as y, you can write the proportion below.

$$\frac{x_1}{y_1} = \frac{x_2}{y_2}$$

Solve for a in the table.

$$\frac{5}{a} = \frac{7}{28}$$
$$7a = 5 \times 28$$
$$a = 20$$

Solve for b in the table.

$$\frac{b}{14} = \frac{7}{28}$$
$$28b = 7 \times 14$$
$$b = 3.5$$

Example 2

The voltage in an electric circuit varies directly as the current. A current of 10.4 A flows when the voltage is 90 V.
Find the voltage when the current is 14.3 A.

Let V represent the voltage, in volts.
Let I represent the current, in amperes.
Make a table to organize the information.

V	90	v
I	10.4	14.3

• **Using a variation equation**

$V \propto I$, so $V = kI$, k is a constant
Substitute $V = 90$ and $I = 10.4$.

$$90 = 10.4k$$
$$k \doteq 8.65$$

The formula is $V = 8.65 \, I$.

Let $I = 14.3$ and solve for V.

$$V = 8.65 \times 14.3$$
$$= 123.75$$

The voltage is about 124 A.

• **Using a proportion**

$V \propto I$, so $\dfrac{V_1}{I_1} = \dfrac{V_2}{I_2}$

Write an equation to find v.

$$\frac{90}{10.4} = \frac{V}{14.3}$$
$$10.4 \, V = 90 \times 14.3$$
$$V = 123.75$$

The voltage is about 124 A.

Exercise

A 1. For each of the following:
   • state a variation equation using the constant k;
   • state a proportion.

(a) a varies directly as b.
(b) w varies directly as t.
(c) $x \propto y$
(d) $t \propto w$
(e) The total cost ($\$C$) of record albums varies directly as the number (n) of albums purchased.
(f) At a given speed, the distance (d) that a car travels varies directly as the amount (a) of gasoline consumed.
(g) The length (L) of stretch in a spring varies directly as the mass (M) attached to it.
(h) The wage (W) a student earns varies directly as the number (N) of hours worked.
(i) The electric resistance of a wire (R) varies directly as its length (L).
(j) The circumference of a circle varies directly as its diameter.

B 2. Solve for each variable.

(a) $\dfrac{3}{4} = \dfrac{x}{28}$

(b) $\dfrac{9}{a} = \dfrac{108}{48}$

(c) $\dfrac{b}{9} = \dfrac{15}{30}$

(d) $\dfrac{7}{3} = \dfrac{20}{q}$

(e) $\dfrac{y}{15} = \dfrac{7}{80}$

(f) $\dfrac{8.3}{2.7} = \dfrac{t}{15}$

3. In each case, substitute the given values and then solve for k, correct to 1 decimal place.

(a) $y = kx$; $x = 7$, $y = 21$
(b) $a = kt$; $a = 9$, $t = 15$
(c) $w = ks$; $w = 12$, $s = 21$
(d) $q = km$; $q = 9.3$, $m = 4.5$

4. Given that m varies directly as w, answer each of the following.

(a) Write the variation statement and the variation equation using k as the constant.
(b) If $m = 25$ when $w = 10$, find k.
(c) Write an equation using the value for k found in part (b).
(d) Use the equation from part (c) to find m when $w = 5$; when $w = 9.5$.
    Find w when $m = 10$; when $m = 35$.

5. Given that $s \propto p$, answer the following.

(a) Write the proportion relating s and p.
(b) Complete the following table.

s	8	16	12	☐
p	☐	22	☐	55

6. (a) Given that $b \propto w$ and that $b = 8$ when $w = 4$, find b when $w = 9$.

(b) Given that A varies directly as X and that $A = 10$ when $X = 4$, find X when $A = 25$.
(c) Given that h varies directly as t and that $h = 9.3$ when $t = 2.5$, find h when $t = 5.5$.

7. The cost of catering the banquet for the soccer house league varies directly as the number of people attending.

(a) Write the variation statement and variation equation.
(b) For 80 people the cost is \$960. Find the value of the constant k.
(c) What is the cost for 120 people?
(d) Draw a graph of number of people versus cost.
(e) What is the slope of the graph?
(f) What does the slope represent in this situation?

8. In a lightning storm the time interval between seeing the flash and hearing the thunder varies directly as the distance between you and the storm.

(a) Write an equation to represent this variation statement.
(b) For thunder from lightning that is 4 km away, the time to reach you is 12 s. Find the value of the constant k.
(c) Calculate the times for the sound of thunder to reach you from lightning that is 2 km away; 3.4 km away; 7 km away.
(d) Draw a graph of time versus distance. In this situation, what does slope represent?

9. The circumference of a circle varies directly as the diameter.

   (a) Write an equation to represent the variation statement.
   (b) For a circumference of 12.56 cm the diameter is 4 cm. Find the value of the constant k.
   (c) What is the circumference of a circle with diameter 9 cm?
   (d) Find the diameter of the circle when the circumference is 18.84 cm.

10. Water pressure varies directly as its depth.

    (a) Write an equation to represent the variation statement.
    (b) For a depth of 3 m the pressure is 130 kPa. Find the value of the constant k.
    (c) What is the pressure at a depth of 14 m?
    (d) Draw a graph of depth versus pressure.
    (e) What is the slope of the graph?

11. The voltage in an electric circuit varies directly as the current.

    (a) Write an equation to represent the variation statement.
    (b) For a current of 8 A. the voltage is 18 V. Find the value of the constant k.
    (c) What is the voltage for a current of 12 A?
    (d) Draw a graph showing current, I amperes, versus voltage, V volts.

12. Tax on a property varies directly as the assessment.

    (a) Write an equation to represent the variation statement.
    (b) For a property tax of $1080, the assessment is $7200. Find the value of the constant k.
    (c) What is the tax on a property assessed at $9500?
    (d) What is the assessment on a property whose tax is $1245?

13. The mass of a substance varies directly as its volume.

    (a) Write an equation to represent the variation statement.
    (b) For a mass of 200 g, the volume is 170 cm^3. Find the value of the constant k.
    (c) What is the mass of the substance with volume 595 cm^3?
    (d) Find the volume of the substance when the mass is 595 g.

14. The mass of a metal rod varies directly as its length. The mass of a rod 6 cm long is 51 g. Find the mass of a rod 100 cm long.

Partial Variation

Al wants to rent a car.

The total charge for renting a car consists of 2 parts.
- a fixed cost (the daily charge)
- a charge per kilometre (varies directly as the distance driven)

This type of relationship, involving both a fixed part and a variable part, is known as **partial variation**.

You can write an equation to represent the total cost (C) of renting a car from SKE for driving a given distance (d kilometres).

$$C = 0.08d + 12$$

Here is a table of values and graph for the equation.

d	50	100
C	16	20

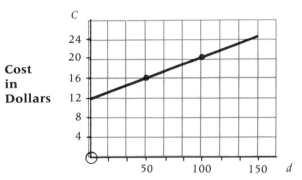

Distance in Kilometres

Compare the equation of this graph to the general form of an equation, $y = mx + b$.

$$C = 0.08d + 12$$
$$y = mx + b$$

The slope of the line is 0.08.
But the cost per kilometre is $0.08: in this situation, the slope of the line represents cost per kilometre.

The next example shows you how to find the fixed quantity and the variable quantity in partial variation.

Example 1

The cost (C) of printing a school yearbook consists of a fixed cost (F) and a variable cost that varies directly as the number (N) of yearbooks printed.

- Write the equation relating F, C, and N using the constant k.

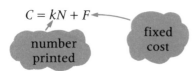

$$C = kN + F$$

number printed

fixed cost

- Find k and F, given that the cost for 500 yearbooks is $5400, and the cost for 900 yearbooks is $9400.

Substitute the given values in the equation above.

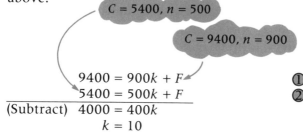

$C = 5400, n = 500$

$C = 9400, n = 900$

$$9400 = 900k + F \qquad ①$$
$$5400 = 500k + F \qquad ②$$
$$\text{(Subtract)} \quad 4000 = 400k$$
$$k = 10$$

Substitute $k = 10$ in equation ①.

$$9400 = 900(10) + F$$
$$F = 400$$

So the cost equation is $C = 10N + 400$.

The cost of printing 750 books would be $10 \times \$750 + \$400$, or $7900.

Exercise

A 1. The equation below represents a situation of partial variation.

$$C = 5t + 35$$

   (a) State the value of the fixed quantity.
   (b) What part of the equation involves the variable quantity?
   (c) What is the slope of the line represented by the equation?

2. For each of the following, state an equation for total cost.

   (a) The total cost (C) of a sports banquet is $500 for the room plus $6.50/person.
   (b) The total cost (C) of repairing a TV set is $25 for the service call plus $27/h labor charge.

3. For each of the following, state an equation using the constant k.

   (a) The annual cost (C) of operating a car consists of a fixed cost (F) and a variable part that varies directly as the number (N) of kilometres driven.
   (b) A salesperson's annual income (I) consists of a fixed cost (F) and a variable part that varies directly as the total sales (S).

B 4. The total cost (C) of renting a computer is $10/d plus a fixed cost of $25.

   (a) Write an equation that relates the total cost (C) and the time (t days).
   (b) What is the cost of renting the computer for 7 d?

5. As a salesperson, Sandy receives a fixed salary of $800/month plus 10% commission on sales.

   (a) Write an equation that relates Sandy's total income (I) for 1 month and total sales (S) for 1 month.
   (b) What is Sandy's income if sales for the month total $9700?

6. The total cost (C) of manufacturing widgets consists of a fixed cost (F) and a variable part that varies directly as the number (n) of widgets produced.

   (a) Write an equation relating C, F, and n using the constant k.
   (b) Determine k, if the total cost of producing 100 widgets is $620 and the fixed cost, F, is $120.
   (c) What is the equation relating C and n?
   (d) What is the total cost of manufacturing 1000 widgets?

7. The total cost (C) of an annual fashion award dinner consists of a fixed amount (F) and a variable part that varies directly as the number of guests (N).

   (a) Write an equation relating C, F, and N using the constant k.
   (b) Determine the value of k and F if for 150 guests the cost is $950 and for 200 guests the cost is $1250.
   (c) What is the equation relating C and N?
   (d) What does the value of k represent in this situation?
   (e) What is the total cost for 500 guests?

8. The cost (C) of operating a water slide consists of a fixed amount (F) and a variable part that varies directly as the number of days (t) the slide is operating.

   (a) Write an equation relating C, F, and t using the constant k.
   (b) Determine the value of k and F if for 5 d the cost is $1050 and for 12 d the cost is $2450.
   (c) What is the equation relating C and t?
   (d) What does the value of k represent in this situation?
   (e) What is the total cost of operating the slide for 20 d?

9. The total pressure (kiloPascals) on a skindiver's body is 100 kPa at the surface plus 10 kPa/m for every 1 m increase in depth.

   (a) Write an equation that relates the total pressure and the increase in depth (d metres).
   (b) What is the total pressure on a skindiver who is 14 m below the surface?

10. The annual operating cost (C) of driving a car depends on a fixed amount (F) (including insurance, depreciation, and licences) and a variable amount that depends on the distance (d kilometres) that the car is driven.

    (a) Write an equation relating C, F, and d using the constant k.
    (b) Determine the value of k and F if for 10 000 km the cost is $3800 and for 20 000 km the cost is $4500.
    (c) What is the equation relating C and d?
    (d) Draw a graph that represents the equation found in part (b).

Inverse Variation

Suppose you do an experiment to measure the length and width of a rectangle where the area is fixed at 12 cm². Listed below are some of the measurements you might obtain.

$A = 12 \text{ cm}^2$

Length (L) of Rectangle	Width (W) of Rectangle
1 cm	12 cm
2 cm	6 cm
3 cm	4 cm
4 cm	3 cm
6 cm	2 cm
12 cm	1 cm

The results of this experiment can be drawn on a graph.

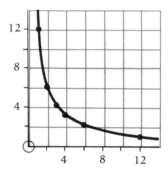

As the length of the rectangle increases, the width decreases.
There is a relationship between the length L and the width W.

$$1 \times 12 = 12$$
$$3 \times 4 = 12$$
$$6 \times 2 = 12$$

or $L \times W = 12$

W *decreases* as L *increases*: another way of saying this is that W **varies inversely** as L, or W is **inversely proportional** to L. This inverse variation is written as below.

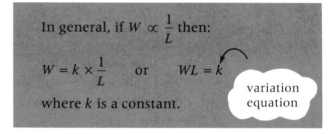

$$W \propto \frac{1}{L}$$

W varies inversely as L.

In general, if $W \propto \dfrac{1}{L}$ then:

$$W = k \times \frac{1}{L} \quad \text{or} \quad WL = k$$

where k is a constant.

variation equation

Example 1

Given that A varies inversely as W when $A = 5$ and $W = 7$, answer the following.

• Write an equation relating A and W using the constant k.

$$A \propto \frac{1}{W}$$
$$AW = k, \text{ where } k \text{ is a constant}$$

• Find k.

Substitute $A = 5$ and $W = 7$ in the general equation from above.

$$AW = k$$
$$(5)(7) = k$$
$$k = 35$$

The equation is $AW = 35$.

• Determine A when $W = 12$.
$$A(12) = 35$$
$$A = \frac{35}{12}$$
$$A \doteq 2.9$$

Example 2

A jet travelling at an average speed of 400 km/h takes 7.5 h to fly from one city to another. The time (t hours) required for the flight is inversely proportional to the speed (s kilometres per hour). How long will the jet take to fly the same distance if it travels at an average speed of 800 km/h?

Since $t \propto \dfrac{1}{s}$ then $ts = k$ (k constant)

Substitute $t = 7.5$ and $s = 400$ in the equation $ts = k$ to find the value of k.

$$k = (400)(7.5)$$
$$= 3000$$

The equation is $st = 3000$.
Now substitute $s = 800$ in the equation.

$$800t = 3000$$
$$t = 3.75$$

The time required is 3.75 h.

Here are 2 important properties related to inverse variation.
• The quantities change in different directions.
• The product of the quantities is a constant.

Exercise

A 1. State each of the following as an equation using the constant k.

(a) $m \propto$ (c) L varies inversely as t.
(b) $q \propto$ (d) I varies inversely as R.

B 2. Calculate the value of the constant for each of the following situations that represent inverse variation. Graph each relation.

(a)

I	2	4	20	12.5
R	50	25	5	8

(b)

P	100	200	4	3
V	12	6	300	400

(c)

L	15	10	5	4
W	2	3	6	7.5

3. For each of the following inverse variations, copy and complete the table.

(a) $a \propto \dfrac{1}{b}$

a	2	▨	8	▨
b	10	4	▨	9.2

(b) T varies inversely as S.

Time (T)	4	8	6	▨
Speed (S)	▨	120	▨	48

(c) T varies inversely as P.

Time (T)	15	3	40	▨
Pressure (P)	▨	210	▨	600

389

4. The current (I amperes) in an electrical circuit varies inversely with the resistance (R ohms) in the circuit.

   (a) Write the equation relating I and R using the constant k.
   (b) In a circuit of given voltage, the current is 2 A when the resistance is 40 Ω. Determine k.
   (c) What is the equation relating I and R?
   (d) Determine the resistance in the circuit when the current is 5 A.
   (e) Determine the current in the circuit when the resistance is 50 000 Ω.

5. The time (t minutes) required to plane a particular metal plate varies inversely as the width (w centimetres) of the cutting tool.

   (a) Write the equation relating t and w, using the constant k.
   (b) It takes 18 min to plane the metal plate with a cutting tool 0.02 cm wide. Determine k.
   (c) What is the equation relating t and w?
   (d) How wide a cutting tool do you need to plane the plate in 12 min?
   (e) How much time is required to plane a metal plate with a cutting tool 0.05 cm wide?

6. When 2 gears mesh, the speed of rotation (s) varies inversely as the number of teeth (n).

   (a) Write the equation relating s and n, using the constant k.
   (b) A gear with 18 teeth has a speed of 540 revolutions per minute. Determine k.
   (c) Determine the number of teeth on a gear turning at 360 revolutions per minute if it is meshing with an 18-tooth gear.

7. The time (t hours) required to travel between 2 cities varies inversely as the average speed (s kilometres per hour).

   (a) Write the equation relating t and s, using the constant k.
   (b) At a speed of 80 km/h, the trip takes 4 h. Find k.
   (c) How long will it take at 90 km/h? 100 km/h?
   (d) Calculate the average speed if the trip takes 3 h; 5 h; 4.5 h.
   (e) Draw a graph of this relationship.

8. If a string is under constant tension, its rate of vibration (v) varies inversely as its length (L centimetres).

   (a) Write the equation relating v and L, using the constant k.
   (b) A bass guitar string, 15 cm long, has a frequency of 5000 Hz (hertz). Find k.
   (c) If the tension is the same, what length of string will have a frequency of 4000 Hz? 6000 Hz?

Combined Variation

Some formulas combine both direct and inverse variation. For example, $V = \frac{kT}{P}$ can be rewritten as $V = k(T)(\frac{1}{P})$. This formula combines 2 variations: V varies directly as T *and* inversely as P.

Example 1

The volume (V millilitres) of a mass of gas varies directly as its absolute temperature (T degrees Kelvin) and inversely as the pressure (P Pascals) applied to it.

- Find an equation or formula relating V, T, and P using k as a constant.

Since $V \propto T$ and $V \propto \dfrac{1}{P}$, the formula is a combined variation.

That is, $V = k(T)\left(\dfrac{1}{P}\right)$ or $V = k\dfrac{T}{P}$

k is a constant.

- Find the value of k, given that a gas occupies a volume of 200 mL when the temperature is 300° k and the pressure is 900 Pa.

$$V = k\frac{T}{P}$$
$$(200) = \frac{k(300)}{(900)}$$
$$200 = \frac{k}{3}$$
$$k = 600$$

$V = 200$
$T = 300$
$P = 900$

- What is the equation relating V, T, and P?

$$V = \frac{600T}{P}$$

- Calculate the volume of the same gas when the temperature is 400° k and the pressure is 800 Pa.

$$V = \frac{600 \times 400}{800}$$
$$V = 300$$

$V = ?$
$T = 400$
$P = 800$

The volume of gas is 300 mL.

Exercise

A 1. State each of the following as an equation using the constant k.

(a) $x \propto y,\ x \propto \dfrac{1}{w}$

(b) s varies directly as t and inversely as r.

(c) The number of people needed to do a job varies directly as the amount of work to be done and inversely as the time in which it must be done.

(d) Centrifugal force varies directly as the square of the speed of a moving object and inversely as the radius of its circular path.

(e) The pressure needed to force water through a pipe varies directly as the square of the water's speed and inversely as the pipe's diameter.

B 2. Given that $x \propto y$ and $x \propto \frac{1}{w}$, answer the following.

(a) Write an equation relating $x, y,$ and w using the constant k.

(b) Determine k if $x = 10$, $y = 15$, and $w = 3$.

(c) What is the equation relating x, y, and w?

(d) Determine x if $y = 7$ and $w = 6$.

(e) Determine y if $x = 12$ and $w = 7$.

(f) Determine w if $y = 12$ and $x = 6$.

3. Given that $r \propto s^2$ and $r \propto \frac{1}{t}$, answer the following.

(a) Write an equation relating r, s^2 and t using the constant k.

(b) Determine k if $s = 5$ when $t = 4$ and $r = 50$.

(c) What is the equation relating r, s^2, and t?

(d) Determine r if $s = 16$ and $t = 8$.

4. The number of people (n) needed to do a job varies directly as the amount of work (w) to be done and inversely as the time (t hours) in which it must be done. If 12 students can pick 360 boxes of strawberries in 5 h, how many students are needed to pick 720 boxes in 6 h?

5. Ohm's Law states that the number of amperes of electric current (I amperes) varies directly as the measure of the potential difference (E in volts) and inversely as the measure of the resistance (R in ohms). From an experiment it is found that 110 V of potential difference and 220 Ω of resistance cause 0.5 A of electricity to flow. How many amperes of electricity flow if 120 V of potential difference is combined with 100 Ω of resistance?

6. The number (n) of vibrations per second of a stretched wire varies directly as the square root of the tension (T in Newtons) applied and inversely as the length (L in centimetres). A wire 70 cm long, which has a tension of 64 N, vibrates 180 times per second. Calculate the number of vibrations per second if the length is reduced to 50 cm and the tension is increased to 121 N.

Problem Solving: Making a List

A useful strategy for finding the number of solutions to a problem is to make a list.

Use an organized approach when making a list, so that you do not miss any items.

Example 1

How many ways can you receive change for 50¢ if at least one coin must be a quarter?

List the possibilities.

2 quarters
1 quarter, 2 dimes, 1 nickel
1 quarter, 2 dimes, 5 pennies
1 quarter, 1 dime, 3 nickels
1 quarter, 1 dime, 2 nickels, 5 pennies
1 quarter, 1 dime, 1 nickel, 10 pennies
1 quarter, 1 dime, 15 pennies
1 quarter, 1 nickel, 20 pennies
1 quarter, 2 nickels, 15 pennies
1 quarter, 3 nickels, 10 pennies
1 quarter, 4 nickels, 5 pennies
1 quarter, 5 nickels
1 quarter, 25 pennies

There are 13 ways of receiving change for 50¢, if at least one coin is a quarter.

Exercise

1. How many ways could you receive change for 25¢ if at least one coin is a nickel?

2. How many ways could you receive change for 50¢ if at least one coin is a dime and one coin is a nickel?

3. Paper plates can be bought in packages of 30 or 50. Terry bought 11 packages and received 410 plates. How many packages of 50 did Terry buy?

Side Trip

Three dimes and two quarters are arranged in a row.

Rearrange the coins so that they appear as shown. Follow the 2 rules given below.

1. A dime and the adjacent quarter *must* be moved together.

2. The dime or quarter may not be interchanged.

What are the least number of moves necessary to rearrange these coins?

Unit 20 Review

1. For each of the following, write a variation equation using the constant k.

   (a) x varies directly as y.
   (b) q varies inversely as t.
   (c) f varies directly as m and inversely as a.
   (d) The acceleration (a) of an object varies directly as the force (F) applied to it.
   (e) The value (V) of a car varies inversely as its age (t).
   (f) At a given speed, the distance (d) that a car travels varies directly as the amount (a) of gasoline consumed.

2. Calculate the value of the constant for each of the following situations that represent direct variation. Graph each relation and determine the slope of the graph.

   (a)

n	5	7	9
C	20	28	36

   (b)

W	3	5	7
A	18	30	42

3. Given that A varies directly as B, answer the following questions.

   (a) Write the variation equation using k as the constant.
   (b) If $A = 15$ when $B = 3$, find k.
   (c) Write the equation using the value for k found in part (b).
   (d) Use the equation from part (c) to find A when $B = 4$; when $B = 6.3$. Find B when $A = 45$; when $A = 12.5$.

4. Given that $p \propto w$ and that $p = 35$ when $w = 5$, find p when $w = 9$.

5. At a given speed the amount of gasoline (n litres) used by a car varies directly as the distance (d kilometres) travelled. Lisa uses 16 L of gasoline for a trip of 192 km. How many litres of gasoline would she use for a trip of 360 km?

6. The increase in length (L centimetres) of a spring varies directly as the mass (M kilograms) attached to it. A mass of 38 kg will stretch the spring 2.85 cm. What mass is required to stretch the spring 7.2 cm?

7. The acceleration of an object varies directly as the force applied to it. An acceleration of 25 m/s^2 is produced by a force of 125 N. What force will produce an acceleration of 15 m/s^2?

8. The distance (D kilometres) that a car travels at uniform speed varies directly as the time (T hours) taken to travel that distance. A car travels 180 km in 4 h.

   (a) How far will the car travel in 6 h?
   (b) Draw a graph of this relation.
   (c) What is the slope of the graph of this relation and what does the slope represent in this situation?

9. The total cost (C) of printing the school newspaper involves a fixed cost of $20 for overhead plus 15¢ per copy.

   (a) Write an equation that relates the total cost and the number of copies (n) printed.
   (b) What is the cost of printing 1500 newspapers?

10. The annual cost (C) of operating an automobile consists of a fixed amount (F) and a variable part that varies directly as the number (n) of kilometres travelled.

    (a) Write an equation relating C, F, and n using the constant k.
    (b) Determine k if the annual cost is $3200, the fixed cost is $1000, and the distance is 11 000 km.
    (c) What is the cost of driving 24 000 km in 1 a?

11. The total cost (C) of sending the school soccer team to an out-of-town tournament consists of a fixed amount (F) and a variable part that varies directly as the number (N) of players and coaches who make the trip.

    (a) Write the equation relating C, F, and N using the constant k.
    (b) Determine values for k and F if for 10 people the cost is $650 and for 15 people the cost is $775.
    (c) What is the equation relating C and N?
    (d) What does the value of k represent in this situation?
    (e) What is the cost for sending 21 people to the tournament?

12. The cost (C) of manufacturing wooden boxes consists of a fixed amount (F) and a variable part that varies directly as the volume (V cubic metres).

    (a) Write the equation relating C, F, and N using the constant k.
    (b) Determine values for k and F if a box of volume 4 m^3 costs $58 and a box of volume 7 m^3 costs $64.
    (c) What is the cost of manufacturing a wooden box with a volume of 11 m^3?

13. Calculate the value of the constant for each of the following situations that represent inverse variation. Graph each relation.

    (a)

M	5	10	25	20
t	40	20	8	10

    (b)

T	6	9	36	24
S	12	8	2	3

14. The time (t hours) required to complete a journey varies inversely as the speed (s kilometres per hour).

    (a) Write the equation relating t and s using the constant k.
    (b) It takes 5 h to complete the journey at 65 km/h. Find k.
    (c) How long would it take to complete the journey at 90 km/h?

15. The time (t minutes) required to cook food in a pressure cooker varies inversely as the pressure (P kiloPascals). It takes 25 min to cook a certain food at a pressure of 128 kPa. How long would it take to cook the food at 200 kPa?

16. The value (V) of a pipe organ varies inversely as its age (t years). The organ was worth $4260 after 2 a. Find its value after 8 a.

17. In an automobile engine, the volume (V in cubic centimetres) of air in a cylinder varies inversely as the pressure (P kilopascals). In testing his car, Jim finds that the pressure is 80 kPa when the volume is 70 cm^3. Find the pressure when the volume is 100 cm^3.

18. The current (I amperes) in an electric circuit varies inversely with the resistance (R ohms) in the circuit.

 (a) If a current of 24 A flows when the resistance is 840 Ω, find the resistance when the current is 18 A.
 (b) If the current is 4.5 A when the resistance is 40 Ω, find the current when the resistance is 100 Ω.

19. Given that $a \propto t$ and $A \propto \frac{1}{w}$, answer the following.

 (a) Write an equation relating $A, t,$ and W using the constant k.
 (b) Determine k if $t = 8$, $w = 4$, and $A = 30$.
 (c) What is the equation relating $A, t,$ and W?
 (d) Determine A if $t = 9$ and $w = 5$.

20. The number of people (n) needed to do a job varies directly as the amount of work (w) to be done and inversely as the time (t hours) in which it must be done. If 12 laborers can build a concrete curb 150 m long in 3 h, how fast can 8 laborers build a similar concrete curb 200 m long?

21. The volume (V millilitres) of a mass of gas varies directly as its absolute temperature (T degrees Kelvin) and inversely as the pressure (P pascals) applied to it. A particular gas occupies a volume of 48 mL when the temperature is 300° k and the pressure is 800 Pa. Calculate the volume of this gas after the pressure has been decreased to 640 Pa and the temperature increased to 400° k.

Unit 21

Trigonometry

Using Similar Triangles

When Ken returned from his trip to the Rockies, he had some of his photos enlarged.

In the enlarged photo, sizes are different but shapes are the same.

In geometry, figures that have the same shape but different sizes are **similar** figures.

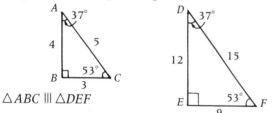

is similar to

Quadrilateral *KLMN* ⫴ Quadrilateral *PQRS*
The length of the sides of *KLMN* are twice the length of the sides of *PQRS*. That is, the ratio of lengths of corresponding sides is 2:1.

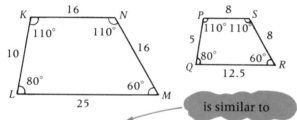

△*ABC* ⫴ △*DEF*

For triangles to be similar, corresponding angles must be equal.

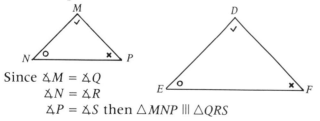

Since $\angle M = \angle Q$
$\angle N = \angle R$
$\angle P = \angle S$ then △*MNP* ⫴ △*QRS*

398

Since △*MNP* ⫴ △*QRS*, then pairs of corresponding sides are proportional.

$$\frac{MN}{QR} = \frac{NP}{RS} = \frac{MP}{QS}$$

Danny's summer employer asked him to find the amount of rope needed to raise a flag on the flagpole outside an office building. The exact height of the flagpole was unknown. Danny used his knowledge of similar triangles to find the height of the flagpole.

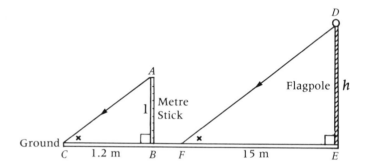

On a sunny day, he found the length of the shadow cast by a metre stick and by the flagpole.

Since the sun's rays are parallel, equal angles are formed with the rays and the ground.

$\angle C = \angle F$
Also $\angle B = \angle E$
$= 90°$
Then $\angle A = \angle D$

$\angle B$ and $\angle E$ are right angles.

Since all corresponding angles are equal, the triangles are similar.

△*ABC* ⫴ △*DEF*

Since the triangles are similar, the ratios of corresponding sides are equal.

$$\frac{h}{1} = \frac{15}{1.2}$$
$$1.2h = 15$$
$$h = \frac{15}{1.2}$$
$$h = 12.5$$

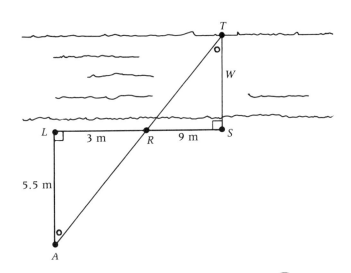

The rope must go up and back down.

Danny would need (12.5×2) m or 25 m of rope to raise the flag.

Let w metres represent the width of the river.

$$\frac{w}{5.5} = \frac{9}{3}$$
$$3w = 9 \times 5.5$$
$$w = \frac{9 \times 5.5}{3}$$
$$w = 16.5$$

The river is 16.5 m wide.

Example 1

To find the distance across a river, Lori and Amy set up stakes at S, R, L, and A as shown. They put A and R in line with a tree at T across the river. Then they calculated the width of the river using the measurements shown.

Since: $\angle ARL = \angle TRS$
$\angle ALR = \angle TSR$
$\angle LAR = \angle STR$,

both right angles

the triangles are similar.

$\triangle ALR \parallel\!\parallel \triangle RST$

Example 2

Determine the value of x.

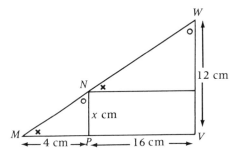

Draw 2 separate triangles.

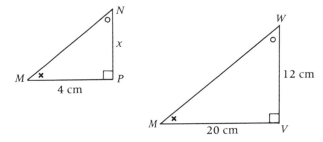

Since $\triangle MNP \parallel\!\parallel \triangle MWV$, corresponding sides are proportional.

$$\frac{x}{12} = \frac{4}{20}$$
$$20x = 48$$
$$x = 2.4$$

The value of x is 2.4 cm.

Exercise

A **1.** State pairs of corresponding sides and corresponding angles in each of the following pairs of similar triangles.

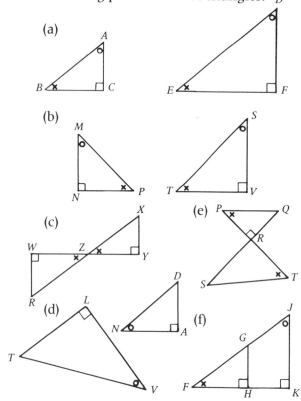

(a)

(b)

(c)

(d)

(e)

(f)

2. State the equal ratios for each pair of similar triangles in Question 1.

B **3.** Use similar triangles to find the unknown side in each of the following.

(a)

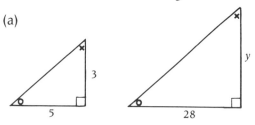

(b)

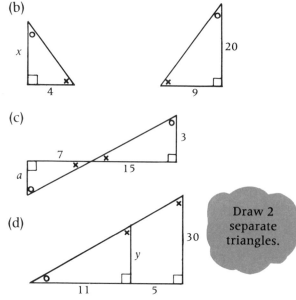

(c)

(d)

> Draw 2 separate triangles.

4. A pole 3 m high casts a 4 m shadow. A nearby tree casts a 15 m shadow. What is the height of the tree?

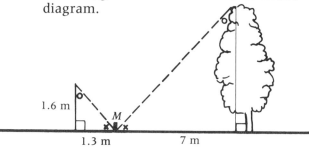

5. To find the height of a tree, Susan places a mirror on the ground and stands where she can see the reflection of the tree top in the mirror. Determine the height of the tree, given the measurements in the diagram.

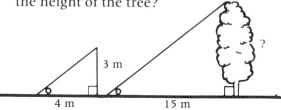

400

6. A ladder is placed with its foot 2 m from a wall. The ladder touches the top of a 2 m fence that is 1.5 m from the wall. How high up the wall does the ladder reach?

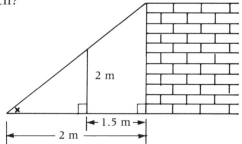

7. A student, 1.8 m tall, casts a 4 m shadow at the same time that a tower casts a 16 m shadow. Determine the height of the tower.

8. Two students, Phil and Alfredo, take measurements as shown in order to determine the width of a river. Find the width of the river.

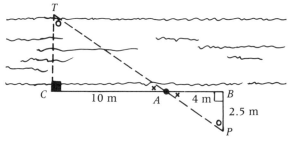

9. Use the measurements shown on the diagram to determine the approximate length of the pond to the nearest metre.

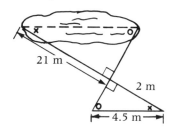

10. A guy wire supports a vertical pole as shown.

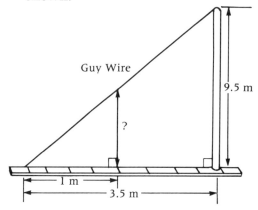

Using the dimensions given, calculate the clearance at the edge of the sidewalk away from the pole, correct to 2 decimal places.

Side Trip

A mining company has a straight tunnel dug at an angle of 15° with the level surface of the ground. At a point 500 m from the surface entrance to the tunnel, a vertical ventilation shaft is drilled to meet the tunnel at R. How deep is the shaft?

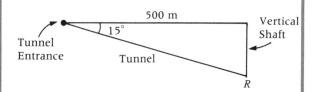

Make a scale drawing using a scale of 1 cm to 100 m.

An Activity with Similar Right Triangles

The activity questions make use of the new vocabulary outlined below.

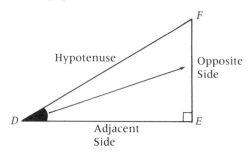

In △*DEF*,
DF is the hypotenuse.
With respect to ∡*D*;
EF is the opposite side;
DE is the adjacent side.

1. Name the hypotenuse and also name the opposite and adjacent sides for each indicated angle (∡).

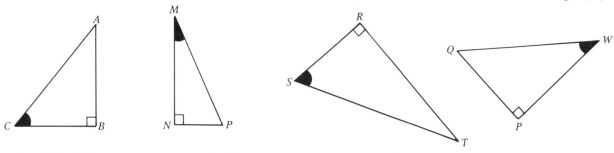

2. Each of the following right triangles has one angle equal to 75°.

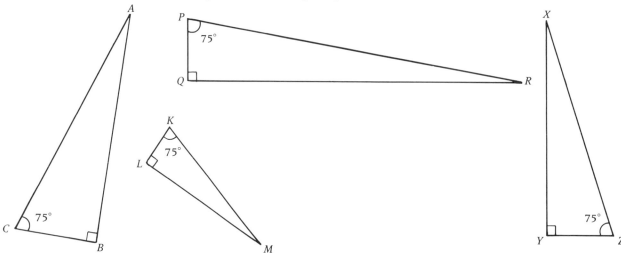

(a) Copy and complete the table below by measuring the side required.

Triangle	Side Opposite 75° Angle		Side Adjacent to 75° Angle		Ratio of $\dfrac{\text{Opposite Side}}{\text{Adjacent Side}}$	Ratio in Decimal Form
	Name	Measure	Name	Measure		
△ABC						
△PQR						
△KLM						
△XYZ						

(b) How are the ratios in the last column related?

3. (a) Draw 4 similar *right* triangles with one angle of 30°.
   (b) Complete a table like the one in Question 2 for each triangle.
   (c) How are the ratios in the last column related?

4. Repeat Question 3 for right triangles with one angle in each triangle equal to 45°.

5. If the measure of one angle of a right triangle is kept the same, then what can you conclude about the following ratio?

   $\dfrac{\text{The length of the side opposite to the angle}}{\text{The length of the side adjacent to the angle}}$

Summary

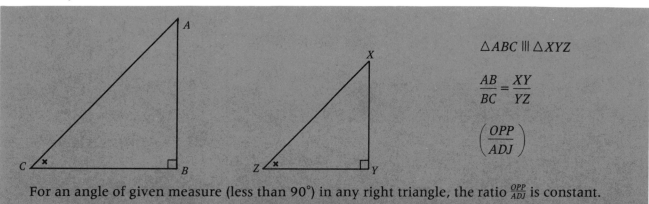

$$\triangle ABC \; ||| \; \triangle XYZ$$

$$\frac{AB}{BC} = \frac{XY}{YZ}$$

$$\left(\frac{OPP}{ADJ} \right)$$

For an angle of given measure (less than 90°) in any right triangle, the ratio $\frac{OPP}{ADJ}$ is constant.

6. Draw each of the following right triangles.

   (a) $\triangle ABC$ with $\angle B = 90°$, $BC = 10$ cm, $\angle C = 10°$
   (b) $\triangle DEF$ with $\angle E = 90°$, $EF = 10$ cm, $\angle F = 20°$
   (c) $\triangle GHK$ with $\angle H = 90°$, $HK = 10$ cm, $\angle K = 30°$
   (d) $\triangle MNP$ with $\angle N = 90°$, $NP = 10$ cm, $\angle P = 40°$
   (e) $\triangle RST$ with $\angle S = 90°$, $ST = 10$ cm, $\angle T = 50°$
   (f) $\triangle UVW$ with $\angle V = 90°$, $VW = 10$ cm, $\angle W = 60°$
   (g) $\triangle XYZ$ with $\angle Y = 90°$, $YZ = 10$ cm, $\angle Z = 70°$
   (h) $\triangle KLM$ with $\angle L = 90°$, $LM = 10$ cm, $\angle M = 80°$

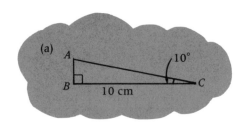

(a)

7. Copy and complete the following table. Use the triangles in Question 6 to obtain the information for each column.

Triangle	Given Angle	Side Opposite Given Angle		Side Adjacent to Given Angle		Ratio of $\dfrac{\text{Opposite Side}}{\text{Adjacent Side}}$	Ratio in Decimal Form
		Name	Measure	Name	Measure		
$\triangle ABC$	$10°$	AB	1.8 cm	BC	10 cm	$\frac{1.8}{10}$	0.18

8. As the measure of one angle of a right triangle increases, how does the ratio in the last column change?

Applications of Similar Right Triangles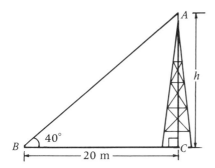

Rick must determine the height of a tower. He observes that the tower casts a shadow 20 m long on the ground and that the sun's rays make an angle of 40° with the ground.

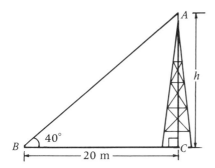

Let h metres represent the height of the tower. To find the height of the tower, Rick can use his knowledge of similar triangles.

From a table like the one you completed on page 403, the value for $\frac{OPP}{ADJ}$ for a 40° angle in a right-angled triangle is 0.84.

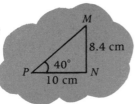

For $\triangle ABC$, $\angle B = 40°$

$\frac{h}{2000} = 0.84$ 20 m = 2000 cm

$h = 2000 \times 0.84$

$h = 1680$

The tower is 16.8 m high.

Exercise

B Use the table you completed for Question 7 on page 404 to answer each of the following questions.

1. Determine the length of side x in each of the following.

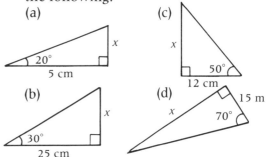

2. A straight tunnel is dug at an angle of 10° with the level surface of the ground. How deep should a vertical shaft be drilled at a point 600 m along the surface from the tunnel entrance in order to meet the tunnel at point K?

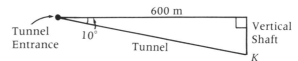

3. Find the width of the river.

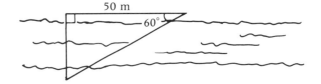

4. Find the height of the building.

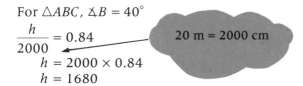

The Tangent Ratio

Trigonometry is concerned with the ratio of lengths of sides of triangles. It is based on the properties of similar triangles.

The results of the activity on pages 402 to 404 indicate the following conclusions.

For all right triangles with a given angle, the ratio below is a constant.

$$\frac{\text{Length of Side Opposite the Angle}}{\text{Length of Side Adjacent to the Angle}}$$

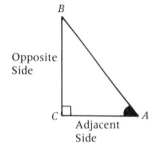

This constant ratio is called the **tangent ratio**.

If $\angle A$ is an acute angle in a right triangle, the tangent ratio of $\angle A$ (tan A) is given by the following ratio.

$$\tan A = \frac{\text{Length of Opposite Side to } \angle A}{\text{Length of Adjacent Side to } \angle A}$$
$$= \frac{OPP}{ADJ}$$

For $\triangle ABC$ above, $\tan A = \frac{BC}{AC}$

In $\triangle MNP$:

$$\tan P = \frac{OPP}{ADJ}$$
$$= \frac{3}{8}$$
$$= 0.375$$

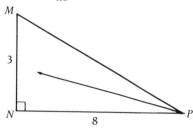

You can use the tangent of an angle to find the length of a side of a right triangle.

Example 1

Find x.

For the 38° angle in the triangle:

$$\frac{x}{21} = \frac{OPP}{ADJ}$$
$$\frac{x}{21} = \tan 38°$$

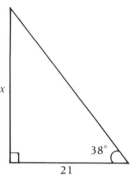

To find tan 38° you could draw a right triangle with an angle of 38°. To make this work easier, mathematicians have calculated the tangent ratios for many angles and arranged these values in tables like the one on page 459.

Here is part of that table.

Angle A	sin A	cos A	tan A
38°	0.616	0.788	0.781
39°	0.629	0.777	0.810
40°	0.643	0.766	0.839
41°	0.656	0.755	0.869

Use tan 38° = 0.781 to solve the equation involving x.

$$\frac{x}{21} \doteq 0.781$$
$$x = 0.781 \times 21$$
$$x = 16.4$$

Example 2

An electrician places a ladder on level ground 2 m from a vertical wall so that the ladder makes a 65° angle with the ground. How far up the wall does the ladder reach?

Let h represent the required distance, in metres.

$$\tan 65° = \frac{h}{2}$$

$$2.145 \doteq \frac{h}{2}$$

$$h = 2 \times 2.145$$
$$h = 4.29$$

The ladder reaches about 4.3 m up the wall.

Exercise

A 1. State the tangent ratio for each angle marked.

(a)

(c)

(b)

(d)

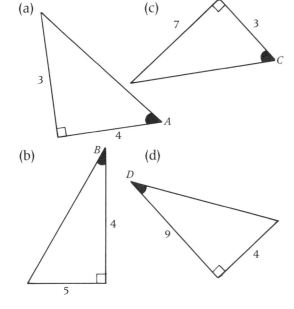

2. Use the table on page 459 to state each value. Compare your answer to the table you completed in the activity on page 404.

(a) tan 10°   (e) tan 50°
(b) tan 20°   (f) tan 60°
(c) tan 30°   (g) tan 70°
(d) tan 40°   (h) tan 80°

3. Use the table on page 459 to determine the measures of angle A.

(a) tan A = 0.649   (d) tan A = 1.000
(b) tan A = 0.141   (e) tan A = 1.664
(c) tan A = 0.754   (f) tan A = 7.115

B 4. Determine y correct to 1 decimal place.

(a) $\dfrac{y}{5} = \tan 30°$ (b) $\dfrac{y}{10} = \tan 85°$

5. Determine x in each of the following, correct to 1 decimal place.

(a)   (d)
(b)   (e)
(c)   (f)
(g)

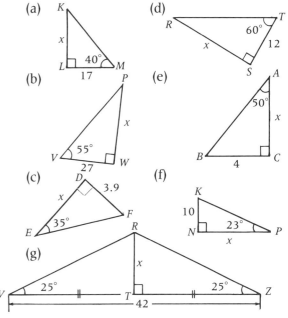

6. Determine the height of a tree casting a 15 m shadow at the same time as the sun's rays make a 33° angle with the ground.

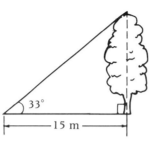

7. Jane must order a new rope for the flagpole. To find out what length of rope is needed, she observes that the flagpole casts a shadow 12.6 m long on the level ground. The sun's rays make a 36° angle with the ground.

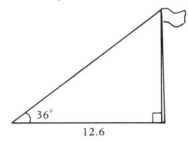

(a) How tall is the pole?
(b) How much rope must she order?

8. Commercial airplanes fly at an altitude of about 10 km. During a landing approach, a pilot wants the plane's path to make an angle of 4° with the ground. How far from the airport must the pilot begin the descent?

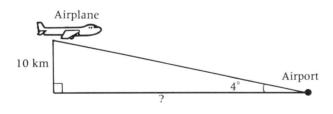

9. From the top of an observation tower, 60 m high, a forest ranger sees a deer at an angle of observation of 32°. How far is the deer from the base of the tower?

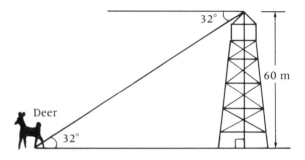

10. Determine the height of a chimney that casts a 45 m shadow at the same time as the sun's rays make an angle of 53° with the ground.

11. A roof is constructed with dimensions as shown below.

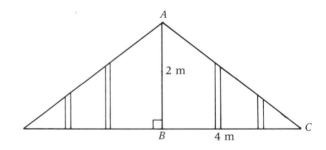

(a) Write the ratio for tan *C* in decimal form.
(b) Find the measure of ∡*C*.

An Activity Involving Hypotenuse of a Right Triangle

1. (a) Draw 4 similar right angles, each one with a 75° angle. (You could use the triangles on page 402.)

   (b) Copy and complete the following table.

Triangle	Measure of Side Opposite 75° Angle	Measure of Side Adjacent to 75° Angle	Measure of Hypotenuse	Opposite Hypotenuse in decimal form (3 places)	Adjacent Hypotenuse in decimal form (3 places)

   (c) How are the ratios related in the second last column? in the last column?

2. Repeat Question 1 for right triangles with one angle in each triangle equal to 30°; 45°.

3. If the measure of one angle of a right triangle is kept the same, then what can be said about the ratio in the second-last column? in the last column?

4. Draw each of the following right triangles.

   (a) △ABC with ∡B = 90°, AC = 10 cm, ∡C = 10°
   (b) △DEF with ∡E = 90°, DF = 10 cm, ∡F = 20°
   (c) △GHK with ∡H = 90°, GK = 10 cm, ∡K = 30°
   (d) △MNP with ∡N = 90°, MP = 10 cm, ∡P = 40°
   (e) △RST with ∡S = 90°, RT = 10 cm, ∡T = 50°
   (f) △UVW with ∡V = 90°, UW = 10 cm, ∡W = 60°
   (g) △XYZ with ∡Y = 90°, XZ = 10 cm, ∡Z = 70°
   (h) △KLM with ∡L = 90°, KL = 10 cm, ∡M = 80°

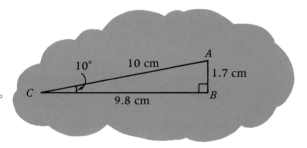

Summary

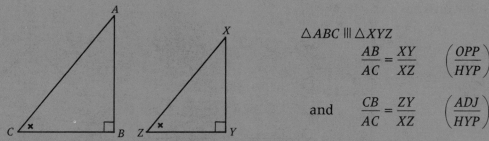

$$\triangle ABC \; ||| \; \triangle XYZ$$

$$\frac{AB}{AC} = \frac{XY}{XZ} \quad \left(\frac{OPP}{HYP}\right)$$

and

$$\frac{CB}{AC} = \frac{ZY}{XZ} \quad \left(\frac{ADJ}{HYP}\right)$$

For a given angle in any right triangle, the ratios $\frac{OPP}{HYP}$ and $\frac{ADJ}{HYP}$ are constants.

5. Use the triangles in Question 4 to obtain the information for each column. Copy and complete the table.

Triangle	Given Angle	Measure of Side Opposite Given Angle	Measure of Side Adjacent to Given Angle	Measure of Hypotenuse	Opposite / Hypotenuse in decimal form (2 places)	Adjacent / Hypotenuse in decimal form (2 places)
$\triangle ABC$	$10°$	1.7 cm	9.8 cm	10 cm	$\frac{1.7}{10} = 0.17$	$\frac{9.8}{10} = 0.98$

6. As the measure of one angle of a right triangle increases, how does the ratio in the last 2 columns change?

Use the table you completed above to answer each of the following questions.

7. Given $\triangle PQR$ as shown in the diagram, answer the following.

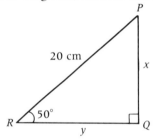

(a) Which angle in the table gives the ratios required?
(b) Use the table to determine the value of x.
(c) Use the table to determine the value of y.

8. Use the table you completed above to determine x and y in each of the following triangles.

(a)   (b)   (c)   (d)

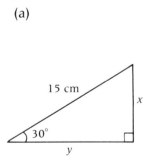

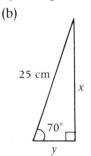

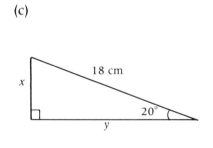

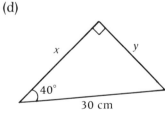

Sine and Cosine

A group of students walks 100 m into a tunnel that slopes downward at a 10° angle from level ground. How far beneath the surface are they?

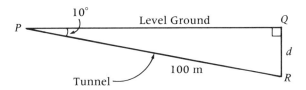

Since the length of the adjacent side is unknown, the tangent ratio cannot be used to solve this problem.

But, from the activity on pages 409 and 410, the ratio below is a constant ratio for an acute angle in a right triangle.

<u>The Opposite Side</u>
The Hypotenuse

This constant ratio is called the **sine ratio** of an angle.

If ∡A is an acute angle in a right triangle:

$$\sin A = \frac{\text{Length of Side Opposite } ∡A}{\text{Length of Hypotenuse}}$$

$$= \frac{OPP}{HYP}$$

sin A is read *sine of angle A*.

To find how far below the ground the students are, first let d metres represent the distance below the surface.

$$\frac{d}{100} = \frac{OPP}{HYP}$$

$$= \sin 10°$$

From the tables you did for pages 409 and 410, you can read that sin 10° = 0.17.

$$\frac{d}{100} = 0.17$$
$$d = 17.5$$

The students are about 17 m below the surface.

To find the sine and cosine of many more acute angles, the table on page 459 can be used.

The activity on page 410 indicates that the ratio below is also a constant ratio for an acute angle in a right triangle.

<u>The Adjacent Side</u>
The Hypotenuse

This constant ratio is called the **cosine ratio** of an angle.

$$\cos A = \frac{\text{Length of Side Adjacent to } A}{\text{Length of Hypotenuse}}$$

$$= \frac{ADJ}{HYP}$$

cos A is read *cosine of angle A*.

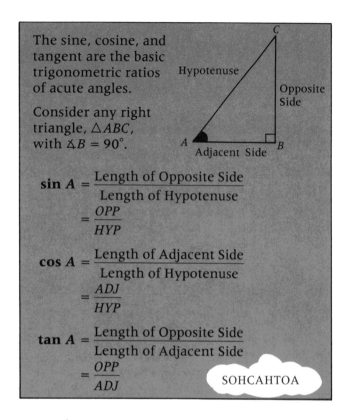

The sine, cosine, and tangent are the basic trigonometric ratios of acute angles.

Consider any right triangle, $\triangle ABC$, with $\angle B = 90°$.

$$\mathbf{sin\ A} = \frac{\text{Length of Opposite Side}}{\text{Length of Hypotenuse}}$$
$$= \frac{OPP}{HYP}$$

$$\mathbf{cos\ A} = \frac{\text{Length of Adjacent Side}}{\text{Length of Hypotenuse}}$$
$$= \frac{ADJ}{HYP}$$

$$\mathbf{tan\ A} = \frac{\text{Length of Opposite Side}}{\text{Length of Adjacent Side}}$$
$$= \frac{OPP}{ADJ}$$

SOHCAHTOA

$$\tan P = \frac{12}{5} \qquad\qquad \tan M = \frac{5}{12}$$
$$= 2.4 \qquad\qquad\quad \doteq 0.42$$
$$\sin P = \frac{12}{13} \qquad\qquad \sin M = \frac{5}{13}$$
$$\doteq 0.92 \qquad\qquad\quad \doteq 0.38$$
$$\cos P = \frac{5}{13} \qquad\qquad \cos M = \frac{12}{13}$$
$$\doteq 0.38 \qquad\qquad\quad \doteq 0.92$$

Example 2

A tunnel slopes downward at a 7° angle from level ground. A vertical ventilating shaft has its base 150 m from the entrance to the tunnel. How far from the entrance is the upper opening of the shaft if it is on the same level ground?

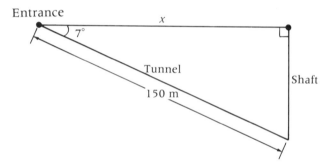

Let x metres represent the distance from the tunnel opening to the shaft opening.

$$\frac{x}{150} = \frac{\text{Side Adjacent to 7° Angle}}{\text{Hypotenuse}}$$
$$= \cos 7°$$
$$\frac{x}{150} \doteq 0.993$$
$$x = 150 \times 0.993$$
$$\doteq 148.9$$

Use the table.

The upper opening of the shaft is about 149 m from the tunnel opening.

Example 1

Calculate the length of the hypotenuse of $\triangle MNP$ and find the 3 basic trigonometric ratios of $\angle P$ and $\angle M$.

$$PM^2 = PN^2 + NM^2$$
$$= 5^2 + 12^2$$
$$PM^2 = 169$$
$$PM = \sqrt{169}$$
$$= 13$$

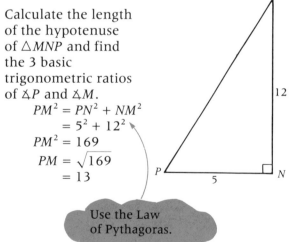

Use the Law of Pythagoras.

Exercise

A 1. State the sine, cosine, and tangent of each marked angle.

(a)

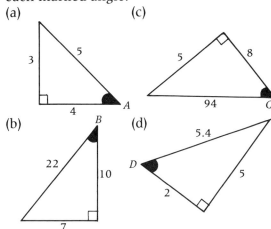

(c)

(b)

(d)

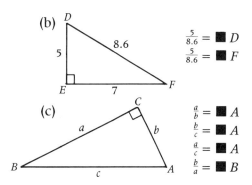

(b)

$\frac{5}{8.6} = \blacksquare D$

$\frac{5}{8.6} = \blacksquare F$

(c)

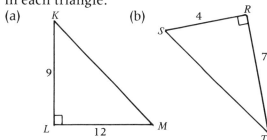

$\frac{a}{b} = \blacksquare A$

$\frac{b}{c} = \blacksquare A$

$\frac{a}{c} = \blacksquare A$

$\frac{b}{a} = \blacksquare B$

2. Use the table on page 459 to state the required values.

(a) sin 42°   (d) cos 24°
(b) cos 53°   (e) sin 75°
(c) tan 22°   (f) tan 60°

3. Use the table on page 459 to determine the value of angle A.

(a) sin A = 0.208   (d) cos A = 0.276
(b) cos A = 0.899   (e) sin A = 0.857
(c) tan A = 1.376   (f) tan A = 0.105

4. State the missing trigonometric ratio for each triangle.

(a)

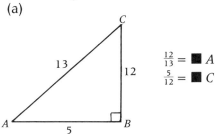

$\frac{12}{13} = \blacksquare A$

$\frac{5}{12} = \blacksquare C$

B 5. Calculate the length of the hypotenuse in each case, then find the 3 basic trigonometric ratios for both acute angles in each triangle.

(a)   (b)

6. Calculate the length of x in each case, then find the 3 basic trigonometric ratios for both angles in each triangle.

(a)   (c)

(b)   (d)

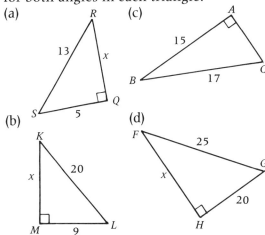

413

7. Determine y in each of the following, correct to one decimal place.

(a) $\dfrac{y}{15} = \cos 30°$ (c) $\dfrac{y}{20} = \sin 65°$

(b) $\dfrac{y}{12} = \cos 70°$ (d) $\dfrac{y}{23} = \sin 22°$

8. Use the sine ratio to find the value of x in each of the following.

(a)
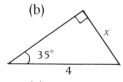

(d)
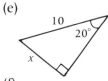

(b)

(e)

(c)

(f)
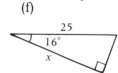

9. Use the cosine ratio to find the value of y in each of the following.

(a)   (d)

(b)   (e)

(c)   (f)

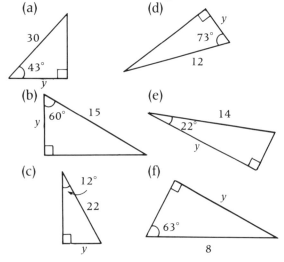

10. A support cable 40 m long runs straight from the top of a tower to the ground. The cable makes an angle of 59° with the ground. Calculate the height of the tower.

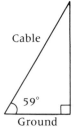

11. How far from a wall must the foot of a 15 m ladder be placed to make a safe angle of 75° with the ground?

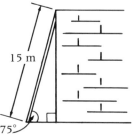

12. Use a trigonometric ratio to determine x in each of the following.

(a)   (b)

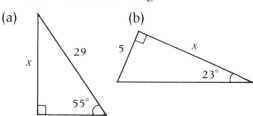

Side Trip

Determine x in each of the following.

1.   2.

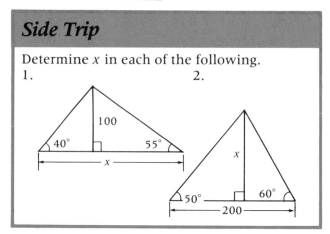

Finding Trigonometric Ratios on a Calculator

Using a calculator is a convenient method of finding the trigonometric ratios of an acute angle.

To determine sin 32°, follow these steps.

$$\boxed{32} \longrightarrow \boxed{\sin} \longrightarrow \boxed{0.5299192} \qquad \sin 32° \doteq 0.5299$$

For cos 54°, enter the following.

$$\boxed{54} \longrightarrow \boxed{\cos} \longrightarrow \boxed{0.5877852} \qquad \cos 54° \doteq 0.5878$$

1. Determine each of the following on a calculator. Check your answer in the tables on page 459.

   (a) sin 30°   (c) tan 45°   (e) tan 22°
   (b) cos 53°   (d) cos 69°   (f) sin 78°

To determine the measure of $\angle A$ if sin A = 0.4789, follow these steps.

$$\boxed{0.4789} \longrightarrow \boxed{\text{INV}} \longrightarrow \boxed{\sin} \longrightarrow \boxed{28.613583} \qquad \angle A = 29°$$

Some calculators have an $\boxed{\text{Arc}}$ or $\boxed{\sin^{-1}}$ key instead of the $\boxed{\text{INV}}$ key.

For cos B = 0.3215, key in the following to find the measure of $\angle B$.

$$\boxed{0.3215} \longrightarrow \boxed{\text{ARC}} \longrightarrow \boxed{\cos} \longrightarrow \boxed{71.246337}$$

$$\boxed{0.3215} \longrightarrow \boxed{\cos^{-1}} \longrightarrow \boxed{71.246337} \qquad \angle B = 71°$$

2. Determine the value of each angle using a calculator. Check your answer in the tables on page 459.

   (a) sin A = 0.4156   (c) tan M = 1.1567   (e) sin K = 0.1356
   (b) cos B = 0.4913   (d) cos C = 0.8931   (f) tan P = 0.3415

Reciprocal Trigonometric Ratios

Michel has a summer job with a company that builds antenna towers. He needs to determine the length of cable needed to stabilize a 30 m tower. The cable must make a 65° angle with the ground.

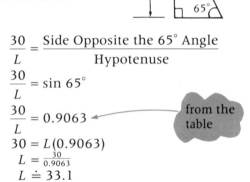

Let L represent the length of the cable in metres.

$$\frac{30}{L} = \frac{\text{Side Opposite the 65° Angle}}{\text{Hypotenuse}}$$

$$\frac{30}{L} = \sin 65°$$

$$\frac{30}{L} = 0.9063 \quad \longleftarrow \text{from the table}$$

$$30 = L(0.9063)$$

$$L = \frac{30}{0.9063}$$

$$L \doteq 33.1$$

A cable about 33.1 m long is required.

The calculation can be simplified using a reciprocal trigonometric ratio.

$$\frac{L}{30} = \frac{\text{Hypotenuse}}{\text{Side Opposite the 65° Angle}}$$

This ratio is the cosecant of 65°, or csc 65°. You could use the cosecant to solve the problem above.

$$\frac{L}{30} = \csc 65°$$

$$\frac{L}{30} = 1.1034$$

$$L = 30(1.1034)$$

$$L \doteq 33.1$$

Consider any right triangle, $\triangle ABC$, with $\angle B = 90°$.

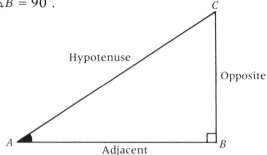

$$\text{cosecant } A \atop (\csc A) = \frac{\text{Length of Hypotenuse}}{\text{Length of Opposite Side}}$$

$$= \frac{HYP}{OPP}$$

$$\text{secant } A \atop (\sec A) = \frac{\text{Length of Hypotenuse}}{\text{Length of Adjacent Side}}$$

$$= \frac{HYP}{ADJ}$$

$$\text{cotangent } A \atop (\cot A) = \frac{\text{Length of Adjacent Side}}{\text{Length of Opposite Side}}$$

$$= \frac{ADJ}{OPP}$$

These are called reciprocal trigonometric ratios because of the following relationships.

$$\csc A = \frac{1}{\sin A}$$

$$\sec A = \frac{1}{\cos A}$$

$$\cot A = \frac{1}{\tan A}$$

To find cot 32° on a calculator, follow the steps below.

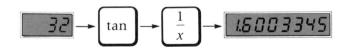

Example 1

Use trigonometric ratios to determine x.

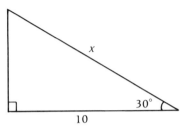

There are 2 different methods possible.

Method 1

Use the basic trigonometric ratios.

$$\cos 30° = \frac{10}{x}$$
$$0.8660 \doteq \frac{10}{x}$$
$$10 = (0.8660)x$$
$$x = \frac{10}{0.8660}$$
$$x \doteq 11.5$$

Method 2

Use the reciprocal trigonometric ratios.
$$\frac{x}{10} = \sec 30°$$
$$\frac{x}{10} \doteq 1.1547$$
$$x = (1.1547)(10)$$
$$x \doteq 11.5$$

Exercise

A **1.** State the cosecant, secant, and cotangent of each marked angle.

(a)   (b)

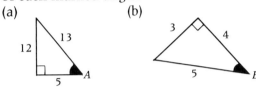

2. State the 3 basic trigonometric ratios for each marked angle in Question 1.

3. State each missing trigonometric ratio.

(a)   (b)

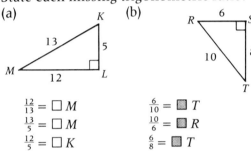

$\frac{12}{13} = \square\, M$ $\frac{6}{10} = \blacksquare\, T$

$\frac{13}{5} = \square\, M$ $\frac{10}{6} = \blacksquare\, R$

$\frac{12}{5} = \square\, K$ $\frac{6}{8} = \blacksquare\, T$

B **4.** Use the trigonometric tables or a calculator to evaluate each of the following.

(a) $\cos 37°$ (f) $\sec 45°$
(b) $\csc 50°$ (g) $\tan 80°$
(c) $\cot 25°$ (h) $\csc 15°$
(d) $\sin 75°$ (i) $\cot 38°$
(e) $\sec 70°$ (j) $\csc 22°$

5. Solve for each variable correct to 1 decimal place.

(a) $\frac{a}{5} = \sin 50°$ (d) $\frac{d}{8} = \sec 65°$

(b) $\frac{b}{10} = \csc 30°$ (e) $\frac{f}{12} = \cot 70°$

(c) $\frac{5}{x} = \tan 25°$ (f) $\frac{9}{y} = \sin 40°$

417

6. Determine the value of each variable.

(a)

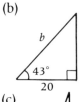

(d)

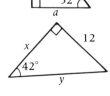

(b)

(e)

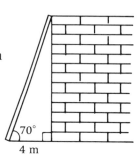

(c)

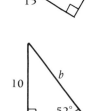

(f)

7. The foot of a ladder is 4 m from a wall. The ladder makes an angle of 70° with the level ground. Determine the length of the ladder.

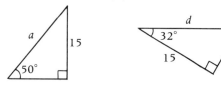

8. The straight support wire of a telephone pole, shown in the diagram, makes an angle of 62° with the ground. The wire is fastened to the ground 5 m from the foot of the pole.

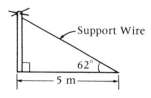

Determine the length of the wire and the height of the telephone pole.

9. A tunnel slopes downward at a 9° angle from level ground. At a point 700 m from the surface entrance to the tunnel a vertical ventilation shaft is drilled to meet the tunnel.

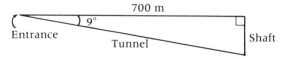

(a) Find the length of the tunnel.
(b) Find the depth of the shaft.

10. An escalator rises 9 m vertically and makes an angle of 22° with the horizontal. What is the length of the escalator?

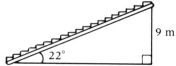

11. (a) Find the length of string attached to the kite shown below.

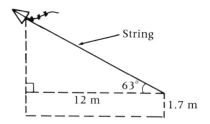

(b) How high is the kite?

12. A train travelling on level tracks encounters a 4° grade, as shown below. At the end of the grade, the train is 250 m above the original level. Calculate the distance the train travelled on the grade.

418

Applications

Trigonometric ratios are used to find unknown sides and angles of right triangles. Many problems in surveying, navigation, and industry involve calculating heights and distances that cannot be measured directly.

Example 1 shows some of the techniques that are useful in solving application problems.

Example 1

Solve $\triangle ABC$.

To **solve** a right triangle means to find the measures of all unknown sides and angles.

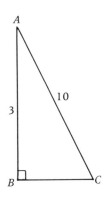

$$AC^2 = AB^2 + BC^2$$
$$10^2 = 3^2 + BC^2$$
$$100 = 9 + BC^2$$
$$BC^2 = 91$$
$$BC = \sqrt{91}$$
$$BC \doteq 9.5$$

Use the sine ratio to find $\angle C$.
$$\tfrac{3}{10} = \sin C$$
$$\sin C = 0.3$$
$$\angle C = 17.4°$$
$$\angle C = 17° \text{ (to the nearest degree)}$$

$$\angle A + \angle B + \angle C = 180°$$
$$\angle A + 90° + 17° = 180°$$
$$\angle A = 73°$$

Why?

Example 2

As part of a shop class project, Sasha needs to find the angle of taper of a 10 cm pin having a small-end diameter of 2.75 cm and a large-end diameter of 3.63 cm.

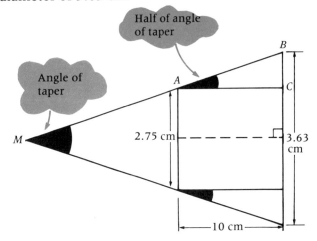

Total taper = $3.63 - 2.75$
= 0.88
$\tfrac{1}{2}$ total taper = 0.44

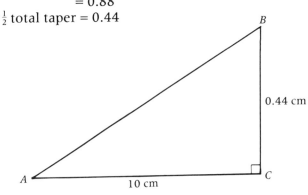

$$\tfrac{0.44}{10} = \tan A$$
$$\tan A = 0.044$$
$$A = 2.5°$$

The angle of taper at M is $2 \times 2.5°$ or $5.0°$.

Two angles that are often used in sighting objects are the *angle of elevation* and the *angle of depression*.

Angle of Elevation

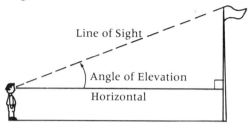

Angle of Depression

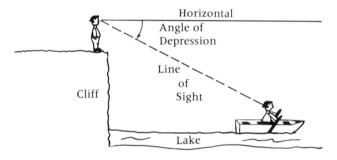

Example 3

A hiker is 500 m from the base of a radio tower. The angle of elevation to the top of the tower is 20°. Determine the height of the tower if the hiker is 1.6 m tall.

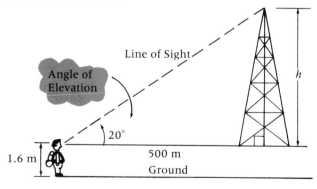

Let h represent the height of the tower shown, in metres.

$$\frac{h}{500} = \tan 20°$$

$$\frac{h}{500} = 0.3640$$

$$h = 500 \times 0.3640$$

$$= 182$$

The tower is 182 + 1.6 or about 183.6 m high.

Example 4

Gregory is standing on top of a cliff 80 m above a lake. The angle of depression to a raft on the lake is 23°. Determine the distance of the raft from the base of the cliff. (Ignore Gregory's height.)

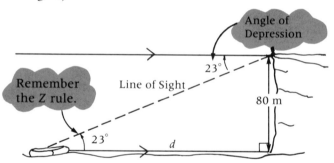

Let d represent the distance from the cliff to the raft in metres.

$$\tan 23° = \frac{80}{d}$$

$$0.4245 \doteq \frac{80}{d}$$

$$80 = (0.4245)d$$

$$d = \frac{80}{0.4245}$$

$$d \doteq 188.5$$

The raft is about 189 m from the base of the cliff.

Exercise

A 1. State the equation that you would use to find each unknown side or angle.

(a)

15

a

43°

(b)

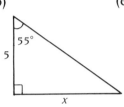

55°

5

x

(c)

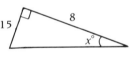

15

8

x°

(d)

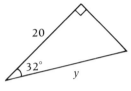

20

32°

y

(e)

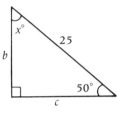

x°

25

b

50°

c

(f)

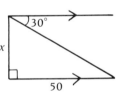

30°

x

50

(b)

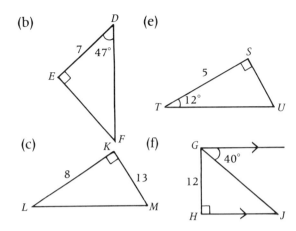

D

7   47°

E

F

(c)

K

8   13

L   M

(e)

S

5

12°

T   U

(f)

G

40°

12

H   J

B 2. Solve for the variables in each part of Question 1.

3. Determine the unknown sides and angles of each triangle. Find sides correct to 1 decimal place and angles to the nearest degree.

(a)

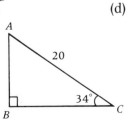

A

20

34°

B   C

(d)

P   Q

6

10

R

4. For each of the following triangles draw a representative diagram and solve each triangle. Find the sides correct to 1 decimal place and angles to the nearest degree.

(a) $\triangle ABC$ with $\angle B = 90°$, $AC = 7$, $\angle A = 42°$

(b) $\triangle KEN$ with $\angle E = 90°$, $KE = 15$, $\angle N = 64$

(c) $\triangle STU$ with $\angle T = 90°$, $ST = 9$, $TU = 5$

(d) $\triangle ENZ$ with $\angle N = 90°$, $EN = 4$, $EZ = 12$

(e) $\triangle JON$ with $\angle O = 90°$, $JN = 9$, $\angle N = 42°$

5. Tracy lets out 50 m of string while flying a kite. She estimates that the string makes an angle of approximately 50° with the ground. Find the height of the kite.

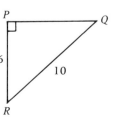

50 m

50°

6. To measure the width of a river, Robert makes the measurements shown on the diagram. Find the width of the river.

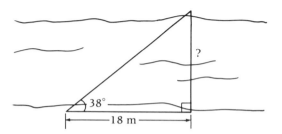

7. Two islands A and B are 2.0 km apart. How far is a third island C from A and from B if $\angle ACB = 90°$?

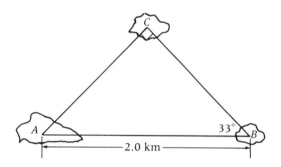

8. At a point 30 m from the base of a tree, the angle of elevation to the top of the tree is 63°. Find the height of the tree to the nearest metre.

9. A helicopter is involved in an air rescue mission. The pilot determines that the angle of depression from the helicopter to the disabled aircraft carrier is 15°. The helicopter is flying at an altitude of 800 m. What is the horizontal distance from the helicopter to the carrier?

10. To determine the height of a cloud, a light is projected from L to the under portion of the cloud at C. At point A, 220 m from the searchlight, the angle of elevation of the light on the cloud is 75°. What is the height of the cloud to the nearest metre?

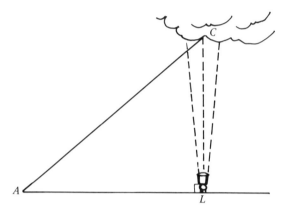

11. A construction engineer determines that a road must rise vertically 35 m over a 200 m distance measured along the road. Calculate the angle of elevation of the road.

12. A triangular field is surveyed by measuring AC, AB, and the angles at A and C.

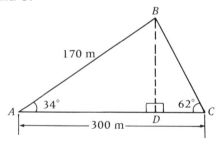

(a) Determine BD.
(b) Determine the length of side BC.
(c) Calculate the perimeter and area of the field.

13. A beam of gamma rays is to be used to treat a tumor that is 4.3 cm beneath a patient's skin. To avoid damaging a vital organ, the radiologist moves the source over 9.3 cm. At what angle must she aim the gamma ray source?

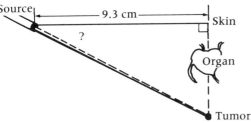

14. A steel bar, as shown in the diagram, has a diameter of 30 mm and is tapered to a point. The distance h is 20 mm.

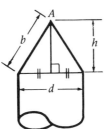

(a) Find the angle of taper at A.
(b) Find the length b.

15. A tapered lampstand with the given dimensions is being cut on a woodworking lathe. Find the angle of taper.

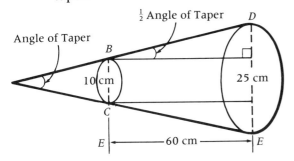

16. A clutch plate has 6 evenly spaced holes drilled for the location of springs on a circle 20 cm in diameter. Calculate the distance between the centres of two adjacent holes, to 1 decimal place.

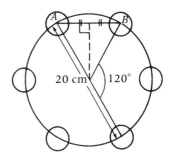

17. The diagram below shows a partial view of a standard V-thread. Calculate the depth, d, when the pitch, p, is 2 cm. ($\triangle ABC$ is equilateral.) Answer correct to 1 decimal place.

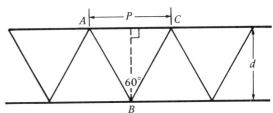

18. The top of a lighthouse is 100 m above sea level. From the top of the lighthouse, the angle of depression of a sailboat at sea is 52°. Find the distance of the boat from the foot of the lighthouse.

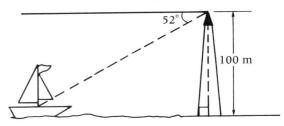

Degrees, Minutes, and Seconds

Historically, surveyors have always expressed angle measures in degrees, minutes, and seconds.

Each degree (1°) is divided into sixty minutes (60′).

Since 1° = 60′ then $(.05)° = 0.5 \times 60′$
$$= 30′$$

Change 43.2° to degrees and minutes.

$43.2° = 43° + 0.2°$ and $0.2° = 0.2 \times 60′$
$$= 12′$$

So $43.2° = 43°12′$

Change 32.73° to degrees and the nearest minute.

$32.73° = 32° + 0.73°$ and $0.73° = 0.73 \times 60′$
$$= 43.8′$$
$$\doteq 44′$$

So $32.73° = 32°44′$

1. Change each of the following to degrees and the nearest minute.

   (a) 0.25°   (e) 47.35°
   (b) 0.75°   (f) 38.65°
   (c) 12.5°   (g) 73.38°
   (d) 23.7°   (h) 54.72°

Change 50°43′ to degrees, to 1 decimal place.

Since $50°43′ = 50° + 43′$, change 43′ to degrees.

$43′ = 43 \times \left(\frac{1}{60}\right)°$
$$\doteq 0.716°$$
$$\doteq 0.7°$$

Since 60′ = 1°
then $1′ = \left(\frac{1}{60}\right)°$

So $50°43′ = 50.7°$, to 1 decimal place

Find the value of sin 36°45′.

First change 36°45′ to degrees.

$36°45′ = 36° + 45′$ and $45′ = 45 \times \left(\frac{1}{60}\right)°$
$$= 0.75°$$

So $36°45′ = 36.75°$

Now use a calculator to evaluate the sine of this angle measure.

$$\sin 36.75° \doteq 0.5983$$

If cos A = 0.3925, find ∡A to the nearest minute.

$$\cos A = 0.3925$$
$$∡A \doteq 66.9°$$

$66.9° = 66° + 0.9°$ and $0.9° = 0.9 \times 60′$
$$= 54′$$

So $∡A = 66°54′$

2. Change each of the following to degrees, correct to 1 decimal place.

   (a) 43°30′   (d) 75°47′
   (b) 32°20′   (e) 23°10′
   (c) 5°45′   (f) 54°24′

3. Use a calculator to determine each of the following. Write your answers correct to 4 decimal places.

   (a) sin 35°30′   (f) tan 48°7′
   (b) cos 22°45′   (g) cos 24°12′
   (c) tan 9°20′   (h) sin 53°34′
   (d) cos 47°50′   (i) cos 6°54′
   (e) sin 57°25′   (j) tan 24°39′

4. Determine the value of the required angle, correct to the nearest minute.

(a) $\cos A = 0.4789$
(e) $\sin M = 0.1349$
(b) $\tan B = 1.3842$
(f) $\tan N = 0.4391$
(c) $\sin C = 0.8542$
(g) $\cos P = 0.8934$
(d) $\cos D = 0.2432$
(h) $\sin R = 0.5325$

Changing to Degrees, Minutes, Seconds

Each minute ($1'$) is divided into sixty seconds ($60''$).

Change $48.34°$ to degrees, minutes, and seconds.

$48.34° = 48° + 0.34°$ and $0.34° = 0.34 \times 60'$
$= 20.4'$
$= 20' + 0.4'$

$0.4' = 0.4 \times 60''$
$= 24''$

So $48.34° = 48°20'24''$

Since $1' = 60''$

Example 1

If $\tan A = 1.4589$, find $\angle A$ to the nearest second.

$\tan A = 1.4589$
$\angle A = 55.5714°$

$0.5714° = 0.5714 \times 60'$
$\doteq 34.284'$

$0.284' = 0.284 \times 60''$
$\doteq 17.04''$

So $\angle A = 55°34'17''$, to the nearest second

Example 2

Express $\sin 43°15'23''$ in degrees.

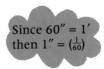

Since $60'' = 1'$
then $1'' = \left(\frac{1}{60}\right)$

$23'' = \frac{23}{60}$
$\doteq 0.3833'$

Then $15'23'' = 15.3833'$
$15.3833' = \frac{15.3833}{60}$
$\doteq 0.2564°$
$\doteq 0.26°$

So $\sin 43°15'23'' \doteq \sin 43.25°$
$\sin 43.26° \doteq 0.6853$

5. Change each of the following to degrees, minutes, and seconds.

(a) $38.42°$
(c) $55.35°$
(b) $2.38°$
(d) $25.18°$

6. Determine the value of the required angle, to the nearest second.

(a) $\sin A = 0.4532$
(c) $\tan A = 0.5432$
(b) $\cos A = 0.3429$
(d) $\sin A = 0.8931$

7. Determine each of the following.

(a) $\sin 24°30'22''$
(c) $\tan 42°21'50''$
(b) $\cos 75°20'35''$
(d) $\sin 78°43'20''$

425

Surveyor

John is a surveyor for a large construction company. Part of John's job involves measuring land sites and checking building construction.

In his work, John frequently uses trigonometry.

In order to find the height of a building, for instance, John uses his surveyor's instrument, called a transit, to measure the angle of elevation, as shown in the diagram below.

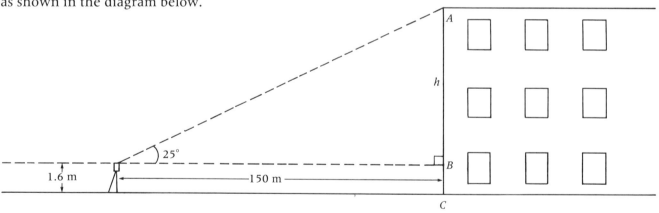

Let h metres represent the distance AB.

$$\frac{h}{150} = \tan 25°$$
$$h = 150 \times \tan 25°$$
$$\doteq 150 \times 0.4663$$
$$\doteq 69.9$$

Since the transit is 1.6 m high, the height of the building, AC, is about $(69.9 + 1.6)$ m or 71.5 m.

Use trigonometry to find the height of the object in each of the following situations.

	Angle of Elevation	Distance from Transit to Object	Height of Transit
1.	65°	70 m	1.65 m
2.	40°	120 m	1.7 m
3.	15°	300 m	1.55 m
4.	8°	500 m	1.6 m

John also uses a transit to measure the following plots of land.

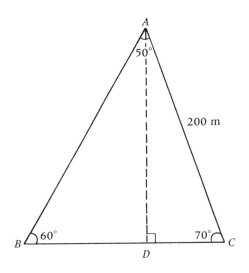

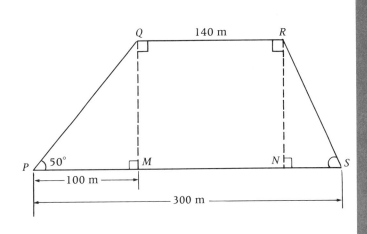

Use trigonometry to help you find the following:
• the length of the sides of each plot of land;
• the area of each plot of land.

Hint in △ABC:
• use △ADC to find AD and DC;
• use △ABD to find BD and AB.

Unit 21 Review

1. Calculate the unknown side and then find the sine, cosine, and tangent of each marked angle.

(a)   (b)

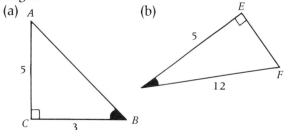

2. Find the lengths of the unknown sides in each of the following to 1 decimal place.

(a)   (c)

(b)   (d)

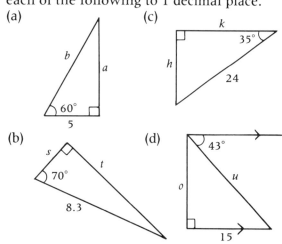

3. Determine the value of the marked angle in each of the following to the nearest degree.

(a)   (b)

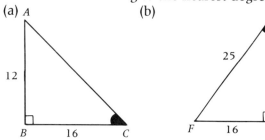

4. For each of the following triangles, draw a representative diagram. Solve each triangle and find the sides correct to 1 decimal place and angles to the nearest degree.

(a) $\triangle ABC$ with $\angle B = 90°$, $AB = 8$, $\angle A = 32°$
(b) $\triangle DEF$ with $\angle E = 90°$, $DE = 7$, $EF = 12$
(c) $\triangle PQR$ with $\angle Q = 90°$, $\angle P = 42°$, $PR = 15$
(d) $\triangle LMN$ with $\angle M = 90°$, $LN = 20$, $NM = 5$

5. How far up a wall does a 12 m ladder reach if the ladder makes an angle of $68°$ with the level ground? Answer correct to 1 decimal place.

6. A flagpole casts a shadow 15 m long when the sun's rays make an angle of $70°$ with the level ground. What is the height of the flagpole? Give your answer correct to 1 decimal place.

7. A 14 m ladder rests against the wall of a house. The foot of the ladder rests on level ground 2 m from the wall. What angle does the ladder make with the ground?

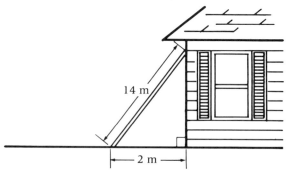

8. An observer, standing 25 m from the base of a tree, notes that the angle of elevation to the top of the tree is $55°$. If the observer's eye level is 1.8 m from the ground, calculate the height of the tree, correct to 1 decimal place.

9. From the top of a 90 m firetower, a forest ranger spots a forest fire. The angle of depression from the top of the tower to the fire is 3°. How far away is the fire?

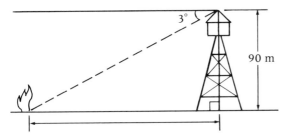

10. From a helicopter, a traffic accident is observed at a 20° angle of depression. If the helicopter is 700 m above the highway, how far along the highway is the accident? Answer correct to 1 decimal place.

11. An overhead sign hangs 2.2 m out from a wall and is suspended as shown.

Calculate the length of the cable.

12. A sailboat has a 12 m mast. The supporting lines for the mast make angles of 62° and 54° as shown on the diagram. Calculate the length of each supporting line.

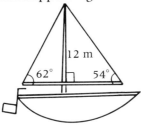

13. The tallest free-standing structure in the world is the 553 m CN Tower in Toronto. Suppose that at a certain time of day it casts a 1200 m shadow. What is the angle that the sun's rays make with the level ground?

14. A bridge across a river makes an angle of 60° with the river bank. If the distance along the bridge from bank to bank is 750 m, what is the width of the river?

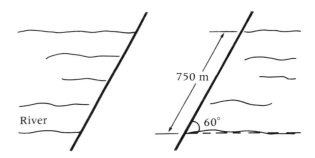

15. A tunnel is to be made through a hill from A to C as shown. The angles of elevation to the top of the hill from points on opposite sides of the hill but on the same level are 29° and 44°. The top of the hill is 500 m above the tunnel. Find the length of the tunnel joining points A and C.

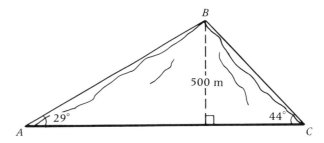

16. A roof has a run of 3.5 m and a rise of 2 m.

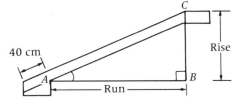

    (a) Find the length of the rafter.
    (b) Find the angle at A.

17. Find the taper angle A for the taper drawn below.

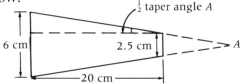

18. The diagram shows a sectional view of a dovetail. Determine the length of BC.

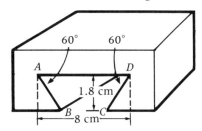

19. The carpenter's square is a convenient instrument for laying out angles. The length on the tongue is 4 cm and the length on the blade is 6.5 cm.

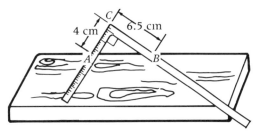

Calculate the measure of the angles at A and B in $\triangle ABC$.

20. For the casting shown in the diagram, calculate the length, x, correct to 1 decimal place.

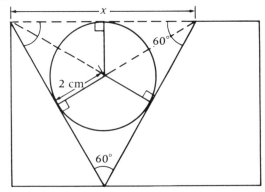

21. In the diagram below, determine the dimension m correct to 1 decimal place.

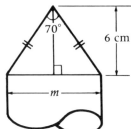

22. Determine the length of the rafter for the roof shown below.

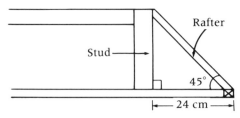

23. Calculate the size of $\angle A$.

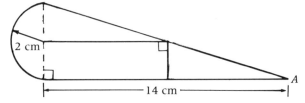

Summary of Units 16 to 21

Unit 16   Statistics

What you have learned to do	For review, see page...
• Identify various methods of collecting data	294-295
• Recognize a biased or unbiased sample	295
• Apply ratio to solve problems involving population size	296
• Apply relative frequency from a sample to make predictions about the total population	297
• Select appropriate intervals for a given list of data	298
• Make frequency tables and histograms from given lists of data	298-299
• Make tables of cumulative frequency and make cumulative frequency histograms to represent data	299
• Make tables of relative frequency and make relative frequency histograms to represent data	299
• Calculate mean, median, or mode of a set of data	303-304
• Indicate the appropriateness of mean, median, or mode to represent a given set of data	303-304
• Calculate mean, median, or mode of large sets of data by extending the frequency table	306
• Calculate mean, median, or mode from grouped data	308
• Read information from statistical graphs	310-311
• Find the curve of best fit for a given graph	313
• Calculate cumulative and moving average, and represent in an appropriate graph	316

Unit 17   Geometric Figures and Their Properties

What you have learned to do	For review, see page...
• Identify types of angles, triangles, and quadrilaterals	322-323
• Identify the parts of a circle	323
• Solve for unknown angles by applying the basic angle properties, including the properties of the transversal of a pair of parallel lines	324-325
• Solve for unknown angles by applying the angle properties of circles	327
• Solve for unknown sides in right-angled triangles by applying the Law of Pythagoras	329
• Apply the Law of Pythagoras to solve for unknown lengths and distances in real-life applications	329
• Identify corresponding angles and sides in a pair of congruent triangles	333
• Identify the 3 sets of conditions for congruent triangles	333-334
• Prove triangles congruent using 1 of the 3 sets of conditions	336-337
• Solve for unknown sides and angles by first proving 2 triangles congruent	336-337

Unit 18   Perimeter, Area, and Volume

What you have learned to do	For review, see page...
• Calculate the perimeter of standard or non-standard plane figures	344-345
• Calculate the area of standard or non-standard plane figures	347-348
• Apply the formulas for surface area to solve for the surface area of a given 3-dimensional figure	350-351
• Apply the formulas for volume to solve for the volume of a given 3-dimensional figure	353-354
• Solve problems involving measurement of perimeter or area	344-345, 347-348, 357-358
• Solve problems involving measurement of surface area	350-351, 357-358
• Solve problems involving volume	353-354, 357-358
• Solve non-standard geometry problems	361-362

Unit 19   Ratio, Proportion, and Rate

What you have learned to do	For review, see page...
• Write proportions involving 2-term ratios	368
• Identify equal ratios	368
• Identify ratios that form a proportion	368
• Solve problems involving 2-term ratios	368, 376
• Write proportions involving 3-term ratios	370
• Rewrite proportions involving 3-term ratios as 3 proportions involving 2-term ratios	370
• Solve problems involving 3-term ratios	370-371
• Solve for unknown terms in proportions	370-371
• Solve problems involving rate	373-374

Unit 20   Variation

What you have learned to do	For review, see page...
• Make tables of values and graphs representing given relationships	380, 385, 388
• Find the constant value in a situation involving direct variation	380-381
• Solve problems involving direct variation	380-382
• Identify the constant value in situations involving partial variation	385-386
• Write equations to represent situations involving partial variation	385-386
• Solve problems involving partial variation	385-386
• Find the constant value in situations involving inverse variation	388-389
• Solve problems involving inverse variation	388-389
• Solve problems involving combined variation	391
• Differentiate between the different types of variation	380, 385, 388, 391
• Make a list to assist in solving problems	393

Unit 21   Trigonometry

What you have learned to do	For review, see page...
• Identify corresponding sides and angles in similar figures	398
• Write equations representing corresponding, proportional sides in similar figures	398
• Solve problems involving unknown sides of similar right triangles	398-399
• Solve problems involving unknown sides in right triangles by referring to established tables	405
• Calculate the tangent ratio for a given angle	406
• Find the tangent ratio for a given angle by using a calculator or tables	406
• Apply the tangent ratio to solve for an unknown side in a right-angled triangle	406-407
• Find the sine or cosine ratio for a given angle by using a calculator or tables	411-412
• Apply the sine and cosine ratios to solve for unknown sides in right-angled triangles	411-412
• Find the value of reciprocal trigonometric ratios	416-417
• Apply the trigonometric ratios and reciprocal trigonometric ratios to solve problems	417-420, 426-427
• Express angle measures in degrees, minutes, and seconds	424-425
• Rewrite angle measures in degrees, minutes, and seconds as degrees, correct to a given number of decimal places	424-425

Units 16 to 21 Review

Unit 16 *Statistics*

1. A survey was taken of individuals at a fast-food restaurant. Each person was asked how much they spent on their meal. The data are listed below.

$2.60	$2.25	$3.05	$2.80	$2.75
$1.90	$2.90	$2.20	$1.40	$4.40
$3.00	$2.40	$2.80	$4.45	$2.30
$1.65	$2.60	$1.75	$4.80	$4.90
$2.05	$1.60	$3.10	$3.95	$1.70
$2.65	$2.70	$1.10	$2.40	$3.30
$2.45	$2.45	$3.75	$2.15	$2.70
$1.35	$2.10	$1.60	$3.80	$3.40
$2.80	$2.95	$2.55	$1.80	$3.90
$2.10	$1.90	$2.50	$3.70	$2.25

(a) What is the range of the data?
(b) Find the interval that will divide the data into 8 classes.
(c) Tally the data to make a frequency table. Start the first interval at $1.00.
(d) Make a frequency distribution histogram.
(e) Extend the table to include a cumulative frequency column and make a cumulative frequency graph.

2. Find the mean, median, and mode of each set of data.

(a) 56, 75, 42, 61, 81, 71, 53, 40, 80, 64, 61, 74, 59

(b) 12.1, 12.8, 11.6, 12.7, 11.8, 11.6, 12.0, 11.4, 12.8, 12.3, 11.2, 11.9

3. Data was collected on the number of accidents at 200 factories during 1 month.

Number of Accidents	Frequency
0	25
1	40
2	33
3	31
4	29
5	21
6	16
7	4
8	1

Extend the table to include the cumulative frequency and product columns. Use the data to find the mean, median and mode.

4. Fritz surveyed 100 people to find data on the number of books read during the summer.

Number of Books Read	Frequency
0 to 3	36
3 to 6	32
6 to 9	14
9 to 12	8
12 to 15	6
15 to 18	5
18 to 21	3

Make a table that includes columns for class value, cumulative frequency, and product. Calculate the mean, median, and mode.

5. The monthly sales at Tinti's Toys for Tots are indicated in the following chart.

Month	Sales
Apr	$3800
May	$5200
Jun	$2800
Jul	$2100
Aug	$1900
Sep	$2500
Oct	$1700

(a) Find the cumulative average for each month and make a graph to display both the data and cumulative average.
(b) Find the 3 month moving average and graph your results.
(c) Describe any trends in sales.

6. Determine the value of each variable.

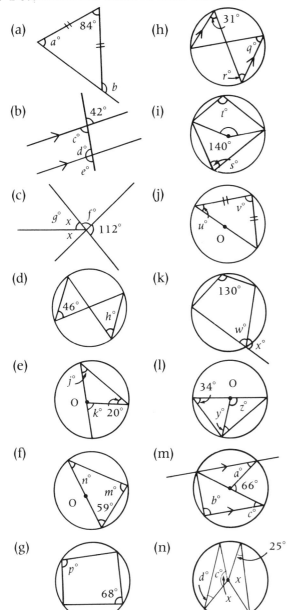

(a)   84° $a°$ b

(b)   42° $c°$ $d°$ $e°$

(c) $g°$ $f°$ x x 112°

(d)   46° $h°$

(e) $j°$ O $k°$ 20°

(f) $n°$ O $m°$ 59°

(g) $p°$ 68°

(h)   31° $q°$ $r°$

(i) $t°$ 140° $s°$

(j) $v°$ $u°$ O

(k)   130° $w°$ $x°$

(l)   34°   O $y°$ $z°$

(m) $a°$ 66° $b°$ $c°$

(n) $d°$ $c°$ x x 25°

7. Calculate the value of each marked angle in the bridge truss shown.

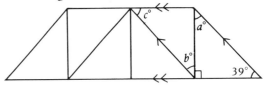

$c°$ $a°$ $b°$ 39°

8. The wheel valve on a gas line has 10 spokes equally spaced around the hub. Determine the angle at the hub between adjacent spokes.

9. Calculate the value of each variable, to the nearest whole number.

(a)

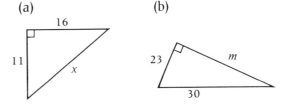

16   11 x

(b)   23 m 30

10. Determine the length of the longest line segment that can be drawn on a rectangular sheet of notepaper measuring 32.7 cm by 20.3 cm. Give your answer correct to 1 decimal place.

11. Determine the dimensions (nearest centimetre) of the largest square beam that can be cut from a log 43 cm in diameter.

12. A hydro pole at the intersection of 2 streets is supported by a cable as shown.

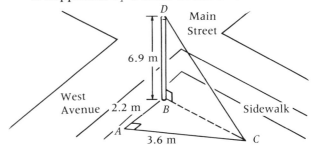

D Main Street   6.9 m   West Avenue   2.2 m B Sidewalk A 3.6 m C

435

(a) Calculate the distance *BC* from the base of the pole to the ground attachment for the cable.

(b) Determine the length *DC* of the support cable.

13. In each diagram:
- prove 2 triangles congruent;
- find values of *x* and *y*.

(a)

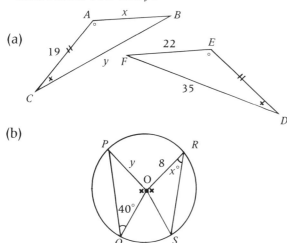

(b)

15. The pulleys on a bandsaw are 25.5 cm in diameter, and the distance between their centres is 52.4 cm.

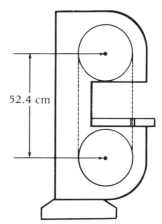

Calculate the length of the bandsaw blade, correct to 1 decimal place.

16. A colander is a metal cone with holes for squeezing juice or pulp from fruit. Calculate the surface area of the colander shown. Give your answer to the nearest whole number.

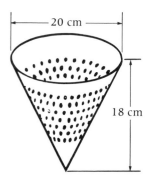

Unit 18   *Perimeter, Area, and Volume*

14. Calculate the perimeter and area of each figure.

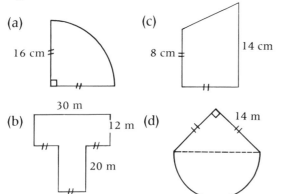

17. A hemispherical punch bowl is 38 cm in diameter. If it is 70% full of punch, how many litres of punch does it hold?

18. A child's play table is made of molded plastic in the form of 3 solid cylinders, with dimensions as shown.

436

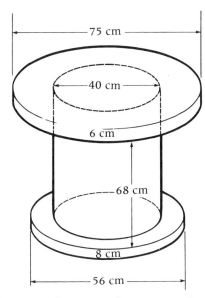

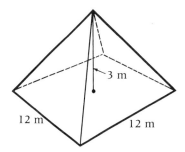

If the manufacturer plans to produce 1200 tables, calculate the number of cubic metres of plastic needed.

19. Styrofoam cones are used to form decorations.

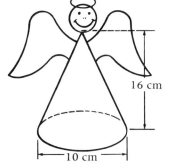

(a) Calculate the area of the side of a cone with the dimensions shown.

16 cm

10 cm

(b) If 45 cones are to be covered with material, and a waste factor of 30% is used, how much material is required? Give your answer in square metres, correct to 2 decimal places.

20. The attic portion of a house is in the form of a pyramid, with the dimensions shown.

(a) In winter, heat is lost through the roof in the form of radiant energy. Calculate the area of the roof from which energy may be lost.

(b) In summer, a fan is used to circulate air through the attic and out vents to keep the living area of the house cool. If the fan can circulate 6 m³ of air each minute, how long will it take to completely change the air in the attic?

21. A metal casting has the dimensions shown. The hole runs completely through the casting.

(a) Calculate the volume of metal in the casting.

(b) If the casting is rust-proofed by dipping it in a paint bath, determine the total area covered by the paint.

22. Determine the value of each variable.

(a) $\frac{5}{9} = \frac{15}{x}$

(b) $7:3 = 28:m$

(c) $\frac{5}{3}:k = \frac{1}{2}:\frac{3}{4}$

(d) $\frac{r}{7.2} = \frac{18}{0.9}$

(e) $5.6:3.6 = m:1.8$

(f) $\frac{t-3}{t} = \frac{5}{6}$

(g) $(k-4):7 = (k-8):3$

(h) $2:5 = (y-1):(y+1)$

(i) $\frac{14}{21} = \frac{8}{n} = \frac{m}{33}$

(j) $4:5:v = 6:w:9$

(k) $1.2:s:3.6 = 4.8:5.2:2t$

23. Solder is an alloy of tin and lead in the ratio $5:3$. Determine the quantity of each metal in 2.8 kg of solder.

24. A hat and a coat together cost $210. If the ratio of the cost of the hat to the cost of the coat is $3:11$, find the cost of each article.

25. In an aerial photograph of a portion of northern Ontario, the ratio of forests to lakes to barren rock is $8:3:1$. In an area of 540 000 ha of the same country, what area might be expected to consist of forests, lakes, and rock?

26. Calculate the unit cost in each case.

Brand	Cost	Quantity	Unit Cost
A	$2.49	150 mL	▨ ¢/mL
B	$16.72	5.3 kg	▨ $/kg
C	$4.19	4.5 L	▨ ¢/L
D	$1.79	205 g	▨ ¢/g

27. Two cones have the dimensions shown.

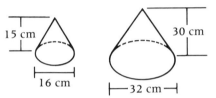

Calculate the ratio of:
- their heights;
- the area of their sides;
- their volumes.

28. Roofing nails are sold in bulk, and 6.5 kg of nails are priced at $8.32.

(a) Find the unit cost of the nails.
(b) What should the price of 10 kg of nails be?
(c) How many kilograms of nails can be purchased for $28.16?

Unit 20 *Variation*

29. For each of the following, write a variation equation using the constant k.

(a) a varies inversely as b.
(b) p varies directly as q and inversely as r.
(c) The interest (i) earned on a loan varies directly with the time (t) of the loan.
(d) The resistance (R) in an electrical circuit varies directly with voltage (V) and inversely with the current (I).

30. For each situation, find the value of k, then determine the values missing from the table.

(a) direct variation

a	16	12	▨
b	40	▨	22.5

(b) inverse variation

m	12	▨	0.625
n	0.125	2	▨

31. Given that $s \propto \frac{1}{w}$, and that $s = 4$ when $w = 10.8$, find s when $w = 14.4$.

32. The time required to travel a fixed distance varies inversely with the speed. Travelling at 60 km/h, the time is 4.8 h.

(a) How long will it take at 96 km/h?
(b) What rate of speed is needed to cover the distance in 6 h?

33. A cooling tower used in the industrial production of sulphuric acid has water drained from it. The height (h) of water in the tower varies inversely with the time (t) of drainage. After 5 min, the height of water is 12 m.

(a) When will the height of water be 6 m?
(b) What is the height of water after 15 min?

34. The mass (m) of metal in a casting varies directly as the volume (v) of the casting. A casting whose volume is 275 cm³ has a mass of 495 g.

(a) Write the variation equation using k as the constant, and determine the value of k.
(b) What will be the mass of a casting with volume 500 cm³?

(c) What will be the volume of a casting with mass 1170 g?
(d) Draw a graph of the relation involving mass and volume of a casting.

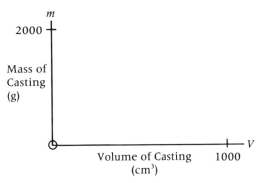

(e) What is the slope of the graph, and what does the slope represent in this situation?

35. The total cost ($$C$) of a wedding reception is the fixed rental cost for the hall ($300) plus a variable cost of $12.50/person.

(a) Write an equation for the total cost of the wedding reception.
(b) What is the total cost if 85 people attend the reception?
(c) If the total cost is limited to $2000, what is the greatest number of people that can attend the reception?

36. If $A \propto B$ and $A \propto \frac{1}{C}$, answer the following.

(a) Write an equation relating A, B, and using the constant k.
(b) Determine the value of k if $A = 5$, $B = 40$, and $C = 12$.
(c) What is the equation relating A, B, and C?
(d) Determine A if $B = 20$ and $C = 7.5$.
(e) Determine B if $A = 36$ and $C = 19.4$.
(f) Determine C if $A = 4.5$ and $B = 27$.

37. Calculate the unknown side (correct to 1 decimal place) and then find the sine, cosine, and tangent of each marked angle.

(a)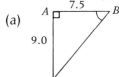

(b)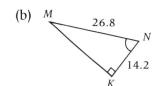

38. Determine the length of each unknown side, correct to 1 decimal place.

(a)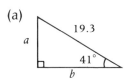

(b)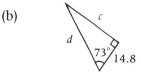

39. Find the value of each marked angle, correct to the nearest degree.

(a)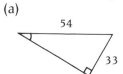

(b)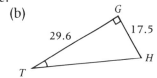

40. Solve each triangle; sides correct to 1 decimal place, and angles correct to the nearest degree.

(a) $\triangle ABC$ with $\angle B = 90°$, $\angle C = 28°$, $AB = 17$
(b) $\triangle KMN$ with $\angle M = 90°$, $\angle K = 55°$, $KN = 36$
(c) $\triangle XYZ$ with $\angle Y = 90°$, $\angle X = 69°$, $XY = 45$

41. A tree makes a shadow 5.8 m long on level ground when the angle of elevation of the sun is 52°.
Determine the height of the tree, to the nearest metre.

42. A radio broadcasting tower AD is supported by cables AB and AC as shown.

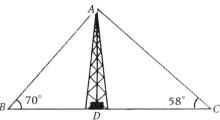

If the height of the tower is 47.6 m, calculate the lengths of cables AB and AC, to the nearest 0.1 m.

43. A pipe is held in a pair of pliers as shown.

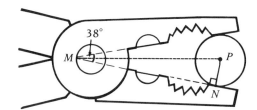

If the angle made by the jaws of the pliers is 38°, and the diameter of the pipe is 3.2 cm, calculate the length MN correct to 1 decimal place.

44. A hydro pole is supported by a cable as shown.

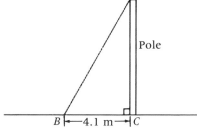

If the length of cable AB is 13.7 m, determine the following.

(a) The size of $\angle B$, correct to the nearest degree
(b) The height AC of the pole, correct to 1 decimal place

45. Two apartment buildings are situated on level ground as shown.

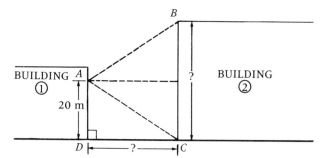

From point A on building ①, the angles of elevation and depression to the top, B, and bottom, C, of building ② are $27°$ and $38°$, respectively. Calculate the following.

(a) The distance DC between the 2 buildings
(b) The height BC of building 2

Give your answers correct to 1 decimal place.

Square Root Table

n	$\sqrt{n}$	n	$\sqrt{n}$	n	$\sqrt{n}$	n	$\sqrt{n}$	n	$\sqrt{n}$	n	$\sqrt{n}$
1	1.00	43	6.56	85	9.22	127	11.27	169	13.00	211	14.53
2	1.41	44	6.63	86	9.27	128	11.31	170	13.04	212	14.56
3	1.73	45	6.71	87	9.33	129	11.36	171	13.08	213	14.59
4	2.00	46	6.78	88	9.38	130	11.40	172	13.11	214	14.63
5	2.24	47	6.86	89	9.43	131	11.45	173	13.15	215	14.66
6	2.45	48	6.93	90	9.49	132	11.49	174	13.19	216	14.70
7	2.65	49	7.00	91	9.54	133	11.53	175	13.23	217	14.73
8	2.83	50	7.07	92	9.59	134	11.58	176	13.27	218	14.76
9	3.00	51	7.14	93	9.64	135	11.62	177	13.30	219	14.80
10	3.16	52	7.21	94	9.70	136	11.66	178	13.34	220	14.83
11	3.32	53	7.28	95	9.75	137	11.70	179	13.38	221	14.87
12	3.46	54	7.35	96	9.80	138	11.75	180	13.42	222	14.90
13	3.61	55	7.42	97	9.85	139	11.79	181	13.45	223	14.93
14	3.74	56	7.48	98	9.90	140	11.83	182	13.49	224	14.97
15	3.87	57	7.55	99	9.95	141	11.87	183	13.53	225	15.00
16	4.00	58	7.62	100	10.00	142	11.92	184	13.56	226	15.03
17	4.12	59	7.68	101	10.05	143	11.96	185	13.60	227	15.07
18	4.24	60	7.75	102	10.10	144	12.00	186	13.64	228	15.10
19	4.36	61	7.81	103	10.15	145	12.04	187	13.67	229	15.13
20	4.47	62	7.87	104	10.20	146	12.08	188	13.71	230	15.17
21	4.58	63	7.94	105	10.25	147	12.12	189	13.75	231	15.20
22	4.69	64	8.00	106	10.30	148	12.17	190	13.78	232	15.23
23	4.80	65	8.06	107	10.34	149	12.21	191	13.82	233	15.26
24	4.90	66	8.12	108	10.39	150	12.25	192	13.86	234	15.30
25	5.00	67	8.19	109	10.44	151	12.29	193	13.89	235	15.33
26	5.10	68	8.25	110	10.49	152	12.33	194	13.93	236	15.36
27	5.20	69	8.31	111	10.54	153	12.37	195	13.96	237	15.39
28	5.29	70	8.37	112	10.58	154	12.41	196	14.00	238	15.43
29	5.39	71	8.43	113	10.63	155	12.45	197	14.04	239	15.46
30	5.48	72	8.49	114	10.68	156	12.49	198	14.07	240	15.49
31	5.57	73	8.54	115	10.72	157	12.53	199	14.11	241	15.52
32	5.66	74	8.60	116	10.77	158	12.57	200	14.14	242	15.56
33	5.74	75	8.66	117	10.82	159	12.61	201	14.18	243	15.59
34	5.83	76	8.72	118	10.86	160	12.65	202	14.21	244	15.62
35	5.92	77	8.77	119	10.91	161	12.69	203	14.25	245	15.65
36	6.00	78	8.83	120	10.95	162	12.73	204	14.28	246	15.68
37	6.08	79	8.89	121	11.00	163	12.77	205	14.32	247	15.72
38	6.16	80	8.94	122	11.05	164	12.81	206	14.35	248	15.75
39	6.24	81	9.00	123	11.09	165	12.85	207	14.39	249	15.78
40	6.32	82	9.06	124	11.14	166	12.88	208	14.42	250	15.81
41	6.40	83	9.11	125	11.18	167	12.92	209	14.46	251	15.84
42	6.48	84	9.17	126	11.22	168	12.96	210	14.49	252	15.87

Square Root Table

n	$\sqrt{n}$	n	$\sqrt{n}$	n	$\sqrt{n}$	n	$\sqrt{n}$	n	$\sqrt{n}$	n	$\sqrt{n}$
253	15.91	295	17.18	337	18.36	379	19.47	421	20.52	463	21.52
254	15.94	296	17.20	338	18.38	380	19.49	422	20.54	464	21.54
255	15.97	297	17.23	339	18.41	381	19.52	423	20.57	465	21.56
256	16.00	298	17.26	340	18.44	382	19.54	424	20.59	466	21.59
257	16.03	299	17.29	341	18.47	383	19.57	425	20.62	467	21.61
258	16.06	300	17.32	342	18.49	384	19.60	426	20.64	468	21.63
259	16.09	301	17.35	343	18.52	385	19.62	427	20.66	469	21.66
260	16.12	302	17.38	344	18.55	386	19.65	428	20.69	470	21.68
261	16.16	303	17.41	345	18.57	387	19.67	429	20.71	471	21.70
262	16.19	304	17.44	346	18.60	388	19.70	430	20.74	472	21.73
263	16.22	305	17.46	347	18.63	389	19.72	431	20.76	473	21.75
264	16.25	306	17.49	348	18.65	390	19.75	432	20.78	474	21.77
265	16.28	307	17.52	349	18.68	391	19.77	433	20.81	475	21.79
266	16.31	308	17.55	350	18.71	392	19.80	434	20.83	476	21.82
267	16.34	309	17.58	351	18.73	393	19.82	435	20.86	477	21.84
268	16.37	310	17.61	352	18.76	394	19.85	436	20.88	478	21.86
269	16.40	311	17.64	353	18.79	395	19.87	437	20.90	479	21.89
270	16.43	312	17.66	354	18.81	396	19.90	438	20.93	480	21.91
271	16.46	313	17.69	355	18.84	397	19.92	439	20.95	481	21.93
272	16.49	314	17.72	356	18.87	398	19.95	440	20.98	482	21.95
273	16.52	315	17.75	357	18.89	399	19.97	441	21.00	483	21.98
274	16.55	316	17.78	358	18.92	400	20.00	442	21.02	484	22.00
275	16.58	317	17.80	359	18.95	401	20.02	443	21.05	485	22.02
276	16.61	318	17.83	360	18.97	402	20.05	444	21.07	486	22.05
277	16.64	319	17.86	361	19.00	403	20.07	445	21.10	487	22.07
278	16.67	320	17.89	362	19.03	404	20.10	446	21.12	488	22.09
279	16.70	321	17.92	363	19.05	405	20.12	447	21.14	489	22.11
280	16.73	322	17.94	364	19.08	406	20.15	448	21.17	490	22.14
281	16.76	323	17.97	365	19.10	407	20.17	449	21.19	491	22.16
282	16.79	324	18.00	366	19.13	408	20.20	450	21.21	492	22.18
283	16.82	325	18.03	367	19.16	409	20.22	451	21.24	493	22.20
284	16.85	326	18.06	368	19.18	410	20.25	452	21.26	494	22.23
285	16.88	327	18.08	369	19.21	411	20.27	453	21.28	495	22.25
286	16.91	328	18.11	370	19.24	412	20.30	454	21.31	496	22.27
287	16.94	329	18.14	371	19.26	413	20.32	455	21.33	497	22.29
288	16.97	330	18.17	372	19.29	414	20.35	456	21.35	498	22.32
289	17.00	331	18.19	373	19.31	415	20.37	457	21.38	499	22.34
290	17.03	332	18.22	374	19.34	416	20.40	458	21.40	500	22.36
291	17.06	333	18.25	375	19.36	417	20.42	459	21.42		
292	17.09	334	18.28	376	19.39	418	20.45	460	21.45		
293	17.12	335	18.30	377	19.42	419	20.47	461	21.47		
294	17.15	336	18.33	378	19.44	420	20.49	462	21.49		

WEEKLY PAY PERIOD—*PÉRIODE HEBDOMADAIRE DE PAIE*

$.00—$134.33

Remuneration *Rémunération*		C.P.P. R.P.C.	Remuneration *Rémunération*		C.P.P. R.P.C.	Remuneration *Rémunération*		C.P.P. R.P.C.	Remuneration *Rémunération*		C.P.P. R.P.C.
From-*de*	To-*à*		From-*de*	To-*à*		From-*de*	To-*à*		From-*de*	To-*à*	
.00 –	34.61	.00	59.34 –	59.88	.45	84.34 –	84.88	.90	109.34 –	109.88	1.35
34.62 –	35.44	.01	59.89 –	60.44	.46	84.89 –	85.44	.91	109.89 –	110.44	1.36
35.45 –	35.99	.02	60.45 –	60.99	.47	85.45 –	85.99	.92	110.45 –	110.99	1.37
36.00 –	36.55	.03	61.00 –	61.55	.48	86.00 –	86.55	.93	111.00 –	111.55	1.38
36.56 –	37.10	.04	61.56 –	62.10	.49	86.56 –	87.10	.94	111.56 –	112.10	1.39
37.11 –	37.66	.05	62.11 –	62.66	.50	87.11 –	87.66	.95	112.11 –	112.66	1.40
37.67 –	38.22	.06	62.67 –	63.22	.51	87.67 –	88.22	.96	112.67 –	113.22	1.41
38.23 –	38.77	.07	63.23 –	63.77	.52	88.23 –	88.77	.97	113.23 –	113.77	1.42
38.78 –	39.33	.08	63.78 –	64.33	.53	88.78 –	89.33	.98	113.78 –	114.33	1.43
39.34 –	39.88	.09	64.34 –	64.88	.54	89.34 –	89.88	.99	114.34 –	114.88	1.44
39.89 –	40.44	.10	64.89 –	65.44	.55	89.89 –	90.44	1.00	114.89 –	115.44	1.45
40.45 –	40.99	.11	65.45 –	65.99	.56	90.45 –	90.99	1.01	115.45 –	115.99	1.46
41.00 –	41.55	.12	66.00 –	66.55	.57	91.00 –	91.55	1.02	116.00 –	116.55	1.47
41.56 –	42.10	.13	66.56 –	67.10	.58	91.56 –	92.10	1.03	116.56 –	117.10	1.48
42.11 –	42.66	.14	67.11 –	67.66	.59	92.11 –	92.66	1.04	117.11 –	117.66	1.49
42.67 –	43.22	.15	67.67 –	68.22	.60	92.67 –	93.22	1.05	117.67 –	118.22	1.50
43.23 –	43.77	.16	68.23 –	68.77	.61	93.23 –	93.77	1.06	118.23 –	118.77	1.51
43.78 –	44.33	.17	68.78 –	69.33	.62	93.78 –	94.33	1.07	118.78 –	119.33	1.52
44.34 –	44.88	.18	69.34 –	69.88	.63	94.34 –	94.88	1.08	119.34 –	119.88	1.53
44.89 –	45.44	.19	69.89 –	70.44	.64	94.89 –	95.44	1.09	119.89 –	120.44	1.54
45.45 –	45.99	.20	70.45 –	70.99	.65	95.45 –	95.99	1.10	120.45 –	120.99	1.55
46.00 –	46.55	.21	71.00 –	71.55	.66	96.00 –	96.55	1.11	121.00 –	121.55	1.56
46.56 –	47.10	.22	71.56 –	72.10	.67	96.56 –	97.10	1.12	121.56 –	122.10	1.57
47.11 –	47.66	.23	72.11 –	72.66	.68	97.11 –	97.66	1.13	122.11 –	122.66	1.58
47.67 –	48.22	.24	72.67 –	73.22	.69	97.67 –	98.22	1.14	122.67 –	123.22	1.59
48.23 –	48.77	.25	73.23 –	73.77	.70	98.23 –	98.77	1.15	123.23 –	123.77	1.60
48.78 –	49.33	.26	73.78 –	74.33	.71	98.78 –	99.33	1.16	123.78 –	124.33	1.61
49.34 –	49.88	.27	74.34 –	74.88	.72	99.34 –	99.88	1.17	124.34 –	124.88	1.62
49.89 –	50.44	.28	74.89 –	75.44	.73	99.89 –	100.44	1.18	124.89 –	125.44	1.63
50.45 –	50.99	.29	75.45 –	75.99	.74	100.45 –	100.99	1.19	125.45 –	125.99	1.64
51.00 –	51.55	.30	76.00 –	76.55	.75	101.00 –	101.55	1.20	126.00 –	126.55	1.65
51.56 –	52.10	.31	76.56 –	77.10	.76	101.56 –	102.10	1.21	126.56 –	127.10	1.66
52.11 –	52.66	.32	77.11 –	77.66	.77	102.11 –	102.66	1.22	127.11 –	127.66	1.67
52.67 –	53.22	.33	77.67 –	78.22	.78	102.67 –	103.22	1.23	127.67 –	128.22	1.68
53.23 –	53.77	.34	78.23 –	78.77	.79	103.23 –	103.77	1.24	128.23 –	128.77	1.69
53.78 –	54.33	.35	78.78 –	79.33	.80	103.78 –	104.33	1.25	128.78 –	129.33	1.70
54.34 –	54.88	.36	79.34 –	79.88	.81	104.34 –	104.88	1.26	129.34 –	129.88	1.71
54.89 –	55.44	.37	79.89 –	80.44	.82	104.89 –	105.44	1.27	129.89 –	130.44	1.72
55.45 –	55.99	.38	80.45 –	80.99	.83	105.45 –	105.99	1.28	130.45 –	130.99	1.73
56.00 –	56.55	.39	81.00 –	81.55	.84	106.00 –	106.55	1.29	131.00 –	131.55	1.74
56.56 –	57.10	.40	81.56 –	82.10	.85	106.56 –	107.10	1.30	131.56 –	132.10	1.75
57.11 –	57.66	.41	82.11 –	82.66	.86	107.11 –	107.66	1.31	132.11 –	132.66	1.76
57.67 –	58.22	.42	82.67 –	83.22	.87	107.67 –	108.22	1.32	132.67 –	133.22	1.77
58.23 –	58.77	.43	83.23 –	83.77	.88	108.23 –	108.77	1.33	133.23 –	133.77	1.78
58.78 –	59.33	.44	83.78 –	84.33	.89	108.78 –	109.33	1.34	133.78 –	134.33	1.79

WEEKLY PAY PERIOD—*PÉRIODE HEBDOMADAIRE DE PAIE*
$134.34—$234.33

Remuneration *Rémunération* From-*de*	To-*à*	C.P.P. R.P.C.	Remuneration *Rémunération* From-*de*	To-*à*	C.P.P. R.P.C.	Remuneration *Rémunération* From-*de*	To-*à*	C.P.P. R.P.C.	Remuneration *Rémunération* From-*de*	To-*à*	C.P.P. R.P.C.
134.34 –	134.88	1.80	159.34 –	159.88	2.25	184.34 –	184.88	2.70	209.34 –	209.88	3.15
134.89 –	135.44	1.81	159.89 –	160.44	2.26	184.89 –	185.44	2.71	209.89 –	210.44	3.16
135.45 –	135.99	1.82	160.45 –	160.99	2.27	185.45 –	185.99	2.72	210.45 –	210.99	3.17
136.00 –	136.55	1.83	161.00 –	161.55	2.28	186.00 –	186.55	2.73	211.00 –	211.55	3.18
136.56 –	137.10	1.84	161.56 –	162.10	2.29	186.56 –	187.10	2.74	211.56 –	212.10	3.19
137.11 –	137.66	1.85	162.11 –	162.66	2.30	187.11 –	187.66	2.75	212.11 –	212.66	3.20
137.67 –	138.22	1.86	162.67 –	163.22	2.31	187.67 –	188.22	2.76	212.67 –	213.22	3.21
138.23 –	138.77	1.87	163.23 –	163.77	2.32	188.23 –	188.77	2.77	213.23 –	213.77	3.22
138.78 –	139.33	1.88	163.78 –	164.33	2.33	188.78 –	189.33	2.78	213.78 –	214.33	3.23
139.34 –	139.88	1.89	164.34 –	164.88	2.34	189.34 –	189.88	2.79	214.34 –	214.88	3.24
139.89 –	140.44	1.90	164.89 –	165.44	2.35	189.89 –	190.44	2.80	214.89 –	215.44	3.25
140.45 –	140.99	1.91	165.45 –	165.99	2.36	190.45 –	190.99	2.81	215.45 –	215.99	3.26
141.00 –	141.55	1.92	166.00 –	166.55	2.37	191.00 –	191.55	2.82	216.00 –	216.55	3.27
141.56 –	142.10	1.93	166.56 –	167.10	2.38	191.56 –	192.10	2.83	216.56 –	217.10	3.28
142.11 –	142.66	1.94	167.11 –	167.66	2.39	192.11 –	192.66	2.84	217.11 –	217.66	3.29
142.67 –	143.22	1.95	167.67 –	168.22	2.40	192.67 –	193.22	2.85	217.67 –	218.22	3.30
143.23 –	143.77	1.96	168.23 –	168.77	2.41	193.23 –	193.77	2.86	218.23 –	218.77	3.31
143.78 –	144.33	1.97	168.78 –	169.33	2.42	193.78 –	194.33	2.87	218.78 –	219.33	3.32
144.34 –	144.88	1.98	169.34 –	169.88	2.43	194.34 –	194.88	2.88	219.34 –	219.88	3.33
144.89 –	145.44	1.99	169.89 –	170.44	2.44	194.89 –	195.44	2.89	219.89 –	220.44	3.34
145.45 –	145.99	2.00	170.45 –	170.99	2.45	195.45 –	195.99	2.90	220.45 –	220.99	3.35
146.00 –	146.55	2.01	171.00 –	171.55	2.46	196.00 –	196.55	2.91	221.00 –	221.55	3.36
146.56 –	147.10	2.02	171.56 –	172.10	2.47	196.56 –	197.10	2.92	221.56 –	222.10	3.37
147.11 –	147.66	2.03	172.11 –	172.66	2.48	197.11 –	197.66	2.93	222.11 –	222.66	3.38
147.67 –	148.22	2.04	172.67 –	173.22	2.49	197.67 –	198.22	2.94	222.67 –	223.22	3.39
148.23 –	148.77	2.05	173.23 –	173.77	2.50	198.23 –	198.77	2.95	223.23 –	223.77	3.40
148.78 –	149.33	2.06	173.78 –	174.33	2.51	198.78 –	199.33	2.96	223.78 –	224.33	3.41
149.34 –	149.88	2.07	174.34 –	174.88	2.52	199.34 –	199.88	2.97	224.34 –	224.88	3.42
149.89 –	150.44	2.08	174.89 –	175.44	2.53	199.89 –	200.44	2.98	224.89 –	225.44	3.43
150.45 –	150.99	2.09	175.45 –	175.99	2.54	200.45 –	200.99	2.99	225.45 –	225.99	3.44
151.00 –	151.55	2.10	176.00 –	176.55	2.55	201.00 –	201.55	3.00	226.00 –	226.55	3.45
151.56 –	152.10	2.11	176.56 –	177.10	2.56	201.56 –	202.10	3.01	226.56 –	227.10	3.46
152.11 –	152.66	2.12	177.11 –	177.66	2.57	202.11 –	202.66	3.02	227.11 –	227.66	3.47
152.67 –	153.22	2.13	177.67 –	178.22	2.58	202.67 –	203.22	3.03	227.67 –	228.22	3.48
153.23 –	153.77	2.14	178.23 –	178.77	2.59	203.23 –	203.77	3.04	228.23 –	228.77	3.49
153.78 –	154.33	2.15	178.78 –	179.33	2.60	203.78 –	204.33	3.05	228.78 –	229.33	3.50
154.34 –	154.88	2.16	179.34 –	179.88	2.61	204.34 –	204.88	3.06	229.34 –	229.88	3.51
154.89 –	155.44	2.17	179.89 –	180.44	2.62	204.89 –	205.44	3.07	229.89 –	230.44	3.52
155.45 –	155.59	2.18	180.45 –	180.99	2.63	205.45 –	205.99	3.08	230.45 –	230.99	3.53
156.00 –	156.55	2.19	181.00 –	181.55	2.64	206.00 –	206.55	3.09	231.00 –	231.55	3.54
156.56 –	157.10	2.20	181.56 –	182.10	2.65	206.56 –	207.10	3.10	231.56 –	232.10	3.55
157.11 –	157.66	2.21	182.11 –	182.66	2.66	207.11 –	207.66	3.11	232.11 –	232.66	3.56
157.67 –	158.22	2.22	182.67 –	183.22	2.67	207.67 –	208.22	3.12	232.67 –	233.22	3.57
158.23 –	158.77	2.23	183.23 –	183.77	2.68	208.23 –	208.77	3.13	233.23 –	233.77	3.58
158.78 –	159.33	2.24	183.78 –	184.33	2.69	208.78 –	209.33	3.14	233.78 –	234.33	3.59

WEEKLY PAY PERIOD—*PÉRIODE HEBDOMADAIRE DE PAIE*

$234.34—$334.33

Remuneration *Rémunération*		C.P.P. *R.P.C.*	Remuneration *Rémunération*		C.P.P. *R.P.C.*	Remuneration *Rémunération*		C.P.P. *R.P.C.*	Remuneration *Rémunération*		C.P.P. *R.P.C.*
From-*de*	To-*à*		From-*de*	To-*à*		From-*de*	To-*à*		From-*de*	To-*à*	
234.34 –	234.88	3.60	259.34 –	259.88	4.05	284.34 –	284.88	4.50	309.34 –	309.88	4.95
234.89 –	235.44	3.61	259.89 –	260.44	4.06	284.89 –	285.44	4.51	309.89 –	310.44	4.96
235.45 –	235.99	3.62	260.45 –	260.99	4.07	285.45 –	285.99	4.52	310.45 –	310.99	4.97
236.00 –	236.55	3.63	261.00 –	261.55	4.08	286.00 –	286.55	4.53	311.00 –	311.55	4.98
236.56 –	237.10	3.64	261.56 –	262.10	4.09	286.56 –	287.10	4.54	311.56 –	312.10	4.99
237.11 –	237.66	3.65	262.11 –	262.66	4.10	287.11 –	287.66	4.55	312.11 –	312.66	5.00
237.67 –	238.22	3.66	262.67 –	263.22	4.11	287.67 –	288.22	4.56	312.67 –	313.22	5.01
238.23 –	238.77	3.67	263.23 –	263.77	4.12	288.23 –	288.77	4.57	313.23 –	313.77	5.02
238.78 –	239.33	3.68	263.78 –	264.33	4.13	288.78 –	289.33	4.58	313.78 –	314.33	5.03
239.34 –	239.88	3.69	264.34 –	264.88	4.14	289.34 –	289.88	4.59	314.34 –	314.88	5.04
239.89 –	240.44	3.70	264.89 –	265.44	4.15	289.89 –	290.44	4.60	314.89 –	315.44	5.05
240.45 –	240.99	3.71	265.45 –	265.99	4.16	290.45 –	290.99	4.61	315.45 –	315.99	5.06
241.00 –	241.55	3.72	266.00 –	266.55	4.17	291.00 –	291.55	4.62	316.00 –	316.55	5.07
241.56 –	242.10	3.73	266.56 –	267.10	4.18	291.56 –	292.10	4.63	316.56 –	317.10	5.08
242.11 –	242.66	3.74	267.11 –	267.66	4.19	292.11 –	292.66	4.64	317.11 –	317.66	5.09
242.67 –	243.22	3.75	267.67 –	268.22	4.20	292.67 –	293.22	4.65	317.67 –	318.22	5.10
243.23 –	243.77	3.76	268.23 –	268.77	4.21	293.23 –	293.77	4.66	318.23 –	318.77	5.11
243.78 –	244.33	3.77	268.78 –	269.33	4.22	293.78 –	294.33	4.67	318.78 –	319.33	5.12
244.34 –	244.88	3.78	269.34 –	269.88	4.23	294.34 –	294.88	4.68	319.34 –	319.88	5.13
244.89 –	245.44	3.79	269.89 –	270.44	4.24	294.89 –	295.44	4.69	319.89 –	320.44	5.14
245.45 –	245.99	3.80	270.45 –	270.99	4.25	295.45 –	295.99	4.70	320.45 –	320.99	5.15
246.00 –	246.55	3.81	271.00 –	271.55	4.26	296.00 –	296.55	4.71	321.00 –	321.55	5.16
246.56 –	247.10	3.82	271.56 –	272.10	4.27	296.56 –	297.10	4.72	321.56 –	322.10	5.17
247.11 –	247.66	3.83	272.11 –	272.66	4.28	297.11 –	297.66	4.73	322.11 –	322.66	5.18
247.67 –	248.22	3.84	272.67 –	273.22	4.29	297.67 –	298.22	4.74	322.67 –	323.22	5.19
248.23 –	248.77	3.85	273.23 –	273.77	4.30	298.23 –	298.77	4.75	323.23 –	323.77	5.20
248.78 –	249.33	3.86	273.78 –	274.33	4.31	298.78 –	299.33	4.76	323.78 –	324.33	5.21
249.34 –	249.88	3.87	274.34 –	274.88	4.32	299.34 –	299.88	4.77	324.34 –	324.88	5.22
249.89 –	250.44	3.88	274.89 –	275.44	4.33	299.89 –	300.44	4.78	324.89 –	325.44	5.23
250.45 –	250.99	3.89	275.45 –	275.99	4.34	300.45 –	300.99	4.79	325.45 –	325.99	5.24
251.00 –	251.55	3.90	276.00 –	276.55	4.35	301.00 –	301.55	4.80	326.00 –	326.55	5.25
251.56 –	252.10	3.91	276.56 –	277.10	4.36	301.56 –	302.10	4.81	326.56 –	327.10	5.26
252.11 –	252.66	3.92	277.11 –	277.66	4.37	302.11 –	302.66	4.82	327.11 –	327.66	5.27
252.67 –	253.22	3.93	277.67 –	278.22	4.38	302.67 –	303.22	4.83	327.67 –	328.22	5.28
253.23 –	253.77	3.94	278.23 –	278.77	4.39	303.23 –	303.77	4.84	328.23 –	328.77	5.29
253.78 –	254.33	3.95	278.78 –	279.33	4.40	303.78 –	304.33	4.85	328.78 –	329.33	5.30
254.34 –	254.88	3.96	279.34 –	279.88	4.41	304.34 –	304.88	4.86	329.34 –	329.88	5.31
254.89 –	255.44	3.97	279.89 –	280.44	4.42	304.89 –	305.44	4.87	329.89 –	330.44	5.32
255.45 –	255.99	3.98	280.45 –	280.99	4.43	305.45 –	305.99	4.88	330.45 –	330.99	5.33
256.00 –	256.55	3.99	281.00 –	281.55	4.44	306.00 –	306.55	4.89	331.00 –	331.55	5.34
256.56 –	257.10	4.00	281.56 –	282.10	4.45	306.56 –	307.10	4.90	331.56 –	332.10	5.35
257.11 –	257.66	4.01	282.11 –	282.66	4.46	307.11 –	307.66	4.91	332.11 –	332.66	5.36
257.67 –	258.22	4.02	282.67 –	283.22	4.47	307.67 –	308.22	4.92	332.67 –	333.22	5.37
258.23 –	258.77	4.03	283.23 –	283.77	4.48	308.23 –	308.77	4.93	333.23 –	333.77	5.38
258.78 –	259.33	4.04	283.78 –	284.33	4.49	308.78 –	309.33	4.94	333.78 –	334.33	5.39

WEEKLY PAY PERIOD—*PÉRIODE HEBDOMADAIRE DE PAIE*

$334.34—$1056.55

Remuneration *Rémunération* From-*de*	To-*à*	C.P.P. *R.P.C.*	Remuneration *Rémunération* From-*de*	To-*à*	C.P.P. *R.P.C.*	Remuneration *Rémunération* From-*de*	To-*à*	C.P.P. *R.P.C.*	Remuneration *Rémunération* From-*de*	To-*à*	C.P.P. *R.P.C.*
334.34 –	334.88	5.40	381.56 –	386.55	6.29	606.56 –	611.55	10.34	831.56 –	836.55	14.39
334.89 –	335.44	5.41	386.56 –	391.55	6.38	611.56 –	616.55	10.43	836.56 –	841.55	14.48
335.45 –	335.99	5.42	391.56 –	396.55	6.47	616.56 –	621.55	10.52	841.56 –	846.55	14.57
336.00 –	336.55	5.43	396.56 –	401.55	6.56	621.56 –	626.55	10.61	846.56 –	851.55	14.66
336.56 –	337.10	5.44	401.56 –	406.55	6.65	626.56 –	631.55	10.70	851.56 –	856.55	14.75
337.11 –	337.66	5.45	406.56 –	411.55	6.74	631.56 –	636.55	10.79	856.56 –	861.55	14.84
337.67 –	338.22	5.46	411.56 –	416.55	6.83	636.56 –	641.55	10.88	861.56 –	866.55	14.93
338.23 –	338.77	5.47	416.56 –	421.55	6.92	641.56 –	646.55	10.97	866.56 –	871.55	15.02
338.78 –	339.33	5.48	421.56 –	426.55	7.01	646.56 –	651.55	11.06	871.56 –	876.55	15.11
339.34 –	339.88	5.49	426.56 –	431.55	7.10	651.56 –	656.55	11.15	876.56 –	881.55	15.20
339.89 –	340.44	5.50	431.56 –	436.55	7.19	656.56 –	661.55	11.24	881.56 –	886.55	15.29
340.45 –	340.99	5.51	436.56 –	441.55	7.28	661.56 –	666.55	11.33	886.56 –	891.55	15.38
341.00 –	341.55	5.52	441.56 –	446.55	7.37	666.56 –	671.55	11.42	891.56 –	896.55	15.47
341.56 –	342.10	5.53	446.56 –	451.55	7.46	671.56 –	676.55	11.51	896.56 –	901.55	15.56
342.11 –	342.66	5.54	451.56 –	456.55	7.55	676.56 –	681.55	11.60	901.56 –	906.55	15.65
342.67 –	343.22	5.55	456.56 –	461.55	7.64	681.56 –	686.55	11.69	906.56 –	911.55	15.74
343.23 –	343.77	5.56	461.56 –	466.55	7.73	686.56 –	691.55	11.78	911.56 –	916.55	15.83
343.78 –	344.33	5.57	466.56 –	471.55	7.82	691.56 –	696.55	11.87	916.56 –	921.55	15.92
344.34 –	344.88	5.58	471.56 –	476.55	7.91	696.56 –	701.55	11.96	921.56 –	926.55	16.01
344.89 –	345.44	5.59	476.56 –	481.55	8.00	701.56 –	706.55	12.05	926.56 –	931.55	16.10
345.45 –	345.99	5.60	481.56 –	486.55	8.09	706.56 –	711.55	12.14	931.56 –	936.55	16.19
346.00 –	346.55	5.61	486.56 –	491.55	8.18	711.56 –	716.55	12.23	936.56 –	941.55	16.28
346.56 –	347.10	5.62	491.56 –	496.55	8.27	716.56 –	721.55	12.32	941.56 –	946.55	16.37
347.11 –	347.66	5.63	496.56 –	501.55	8.36	721.56 –	726.55	12.41	946.56 –	951.55	16.46
347.67 –	348.22	5.64	501.56 –	506.55	8.45	726.56 –	731.55	12.50	951.56 –	956.55	16.55
348.23 –	348.77	5.65	506.56 –	511.55	8.54	731.56 –	736.55	12.59	956.56 –	961.55	16.64
348.78 –	349.33	5.66	511.56 –	516.55	8.63	736.56 –	741.55	12.68	961.56 –	966.55	16.73
349.34 –	349.88	5.67	516.56 –	521.55	8.72	741.56 –	746.55	12.77	966.56 –	971.55	16.82
349.89 –	350.44	5.68	521.56 –	526.55	8.81	746.56 –	751.55	12.86	971.56 –	976.55	16.91
350.45 –	350.99	5.69	526.56 –	531.55	8.90	751.56 –	756.55	12.95	976.56 –	981.55	17.00
351.00 –	351.55	5.70	531.56 –	536.55	8.99	756.56 –	761.55	13.04	981.56 –	986.55	17.09
351.56 –	352.10	5.71	536.56 –	541.55	9.08	761.56 –	766.55	13.13	986.56 –	991.55	17.18
352.11 –	352.66	5.72	541.56 –	546.55	9.17	766.56 –	771.55	13.22	991.56 –	996.55	17.27
352.67 –	353.22	5.73	546.56 –	551.55	9.26	771.56 –	776.55	13.31	996.56 –	1001.55	17.36
353.23 –	353.77	5.74	551.56 –	556.55	9.35	776.56 –	781.55	13.40	1001.56 –	1006.55	17.45
353.78 –	354.33	5.75	556.56 –	561.55	9.44	781.56 –	786.55	13.49	1006.56 –	1011.55	17.54
354.34 –	354.88	5.76	561.56 –	566.55	9.53	786.56 –	791.55	13.58	1011.56 –	1016.55	17.63
354.89 –	355.44	5.77	566.56 –	571.55	9.62	791.56 –	796.55	13.67	1016.56 –	1021.55	17.72
355.45 –	355.99	5.78	571.56 –	576.55	9.71	796.56 –	801.55	13.76	1021.56 –	1026.55	17.81
356.00 –	356.55	5.79	576.56 –	581.55	9.80	801.56 –	806.55	13.85	1026.56 –	1031.55	17.90
356.56 –	361.55	5.84	581.56 –	586.55	9.89	806.56 –	811.55	13.94	1031.56 –	1036.55	17.99
361.56 –	366.55	5.93	586.56 –	591.55	9.98	811.56 –	816.55	14.03	1036.56 –	1041.55	18.08
366.56 –	371.55	6.02	591.56 –	596.55	10.07	816.56 –	821.55	14.12	1041.56 –	1046.55	18.17
371.56 –	376.55	6.11	596.56 –	601.55	10.16	821.56 –	826.55	14.21	1046.56 –	1051.55	18.26
376.56 –	381.55	6.20	601.56 –	606.55	10.25	826.56 –	831.55	14.30	1051.56 –	1056.55	18.35

WEEKLY PAY PERIOD—*PÉRIODE HEBDOMADAIRE DE PAIE*

$1056.56—$1956.55

Remuneration *Rémunération* From-*de*	To-*à*	C.P.P. *R.P.C.*	Remuneration *Rémunération* From-*de*	To-*à*	C.P.P. *R.P.C.*	Remuneration *Rémunération* From-*de*	To-*à*	C.P.P. *R.P.C.*	Remuneration *Rémunération* From-*de*	To-*à*	C.P.P. *R.P.C.*
1056.56 –	1061.55	18.44	1281.56 –	1286.55	22.49	1506.56 –	1511.55	26.54	1731.56 –	1736.55	30.59
1061.56 –	1066.55	18.53	1286.56 –	1291.55	22.58	1511.56 –	1516.55	26.63	1736.56 –	1741.55	30.68
1066.56 –	1071.55	18.62	1291.56 –	1296.55	22.67	1516.56 –	1521.55	26.72	1741.56 –	1746.55	30.77
1071.56 –	1076.55	18.71	1296.56 –	1301.55	22.76	1521.56 –	1526.55	26.81	1746.56 –	1751.55	30.86
1076.56 –	1081.55	18.80	1301.56 –	1306.55	22.85	1526.56 –	1531.55	26.90	1751.56 –	1756.55	30.95
1081.56 –	1086.55	18.89	1306.56 –	1311.55	22.94	1531.56 –	1536.55	26.99	1756.56 –	1761.55	31.04
1086.56 –	1091.55	18.98	1311.56 –	1316.55	23.03	1536.56 –	1541.55	27.08	1761.56 –	1766.55	31.13
1091.56 –	1096.55	19.07	1316.56 –	1321.55	23.12	1541.56 –	1546.55	27.17	1766.56 –	1771.55	31.22
1096.56 –	1101.55	19.16	1321.56 –	1326.55	23.21	1546.56 –	1551.55	27.26	1771.56 –	1776.55	31.31
1101.56 –	1106.55	19.25	1326.56 –	1331.55	23.30	1551.56 –	1556.55	27.35	1776.56 –	1781.55	31.40
1106.56 –	1111.55	19.34	1331.56 –	1336.55	23.39	1556.56 –	1561.55	27.44	1781.56 –	1786.55	31.49
1111.56 –	1116.55	19.43	1336.56 –	1341.55	23.48	1561.56 –	1566.55	27.53	1786.56 –	1791.55	31.58
1116.56 –	1121.55	19.52	1341.56 –	1346.55	23.57	1566.56 –	1571.55	27.62	1791.56 –	1796.55	31.67
1121.56 –	1126.55	19.61	1346.56 –	1351.55	23.66	1571.56 –	1576.55	27.71	1796.56 –	1801.55	31.76
1126.56 –	1131.55	19.70	1351.56 –	1356.55	23.75	1576.56 –	1581.55	27.80	1801.56 –	1806.55	31.85
1131.56 –	1136.55	19.79	1356.56 –	1361.55	23.84	1581.56 –	1586.55	27.89	1806.56 –	1811.55	31.94
1136.56 –	1141.55	19.88	1361.56 –	1366.55	23.93	1586.56 –	1591.55	27.98	1811.56 –	1816.55	32.03
1141.56 –	1146.55	19.97	1366.56 –	1371.55	24.02	1591.56 –	1596.55	28.07	1816.56 –	1821.55	32.12
1146.56 –	1151.55	20.06	1371.56 –	1376.55	24.11	1596.56 –	1601.55	28.16	1821.56 –	1826.55	32.21
1151.56 –	1156.55	20.15	1376.56 –	1381.55	24.20	1601.56 –	1606.55	28.25	1826.56 –	1831.55	32.30
1156.56 –	1161.55	20.24	1381.56 –	1386.55	24.29	1606.56 –	1611.55	28.34	1831.56 –	1836.55	32.39
1161.56 –	1166.55	20.33	1386.56 –	1391.55	24.38	1611.56 –	1616.55	28.43	1836.56 –	1841.55	32.48
1166.56 –	1171.55	20.42	1391.56 –	1396.55	24.47	1616.56 –	1621.55	28.52	1841.56 –	1846.55	32.57
1171.56 –	1176.55	20.51	1396.56 –	1401.55	24.56	1621.56 –	1626.55	28.61	1846.56 –	1851.55	32.66
1176.56 –	1181.55	20.60	1401.56 –	1406.55	24.65	1626.56 –	1631.55	28.70	1851.56 –	1856.55	32.75
1181.56 –	1186.55	20.69	1406.56 –	1411.55	24.74	1631.56 –	1636.55	28.79	1856.56 –	1861.55	32.84
1186.56 –	1191.55	20.78	1411.56 –	1416.55	24.83	1636.56 –	1641.55	28.88	1861.56 –	1866.55	32.93
1191.56 –	1196.55	20.87	1416.56 –	1421.55	24.92	1641.56 –	1646.55	28.97	1866.56 –	1871.55	33.02
1196.56 –	1201.55	20.96	1421.56 –	1426.55	25.01	1646.56 –	1651.55	29.06	1871.56 –	1876.55	33.11
1201.56 –	1206.55	21.05	1426.56 –	1431.55	25.10	1651.56 –	1656.55	29.15	1876.56 –	1881.55	33.20
1206.56 –	1211.55	21.14	1431.56 –	1436.55	25.19	1656.56 –	1661.55	29.24	1881.56 –	1886.55	33.29
1211.56 –	1216.55	21.23	1436.56 –	1441.55	25.28	1661.56 –	1666.55	29.33	1886.56 –	1891.55	33.38
1216.56 –	1221.55	21.32	1441.56 –	1446.55	25.37	1666.56 –	1671.55	29.42	1891.56 –	1896.55	33.47
1221.56 –	1226.55	21.41	1446.56 –	1451.55	25.46	1671.56 –	1676.55	29.51	1896.56 –	1901.55	33.56
1226.56 –	1231.55	21.50	1451.56 –	1456.55	25.55	1676.56 –	1681.55	29.60	1901.56 –	1906.55	33.65
1231.56 –	1236.55	21.59	1456.56 –	1461.55	25.64	1681.56 –	1686.55	29.69	1906.56 –	1911.55	33.74
1236.56 –	1241.55	21.68	1461.56 –	1466.55	25.73	1686.56 –	1691.55	29.78	1911.56 –	1916.55	33.83
1241.56 –	1246.55	21.77	1466.56 –	1471.55	25.82	1691.56 –	1696.55	29.87	1916.56 –	1921.55	33.92
1246.56 –	1251.55	21.86	1471.56 –	1476.55	25.91	1696.56 –	1701.55	29.96	1921.56 –	1926.55	34.01
1251.56 –	1256.55	21.95	1476.56 –	1481.55	26.00	1701.56 –	1706.55	30.05	1926.56 –	1931.55	34.10
1256.56 –	1261.55	22.04	1481.56 –	1486.55	26.09	1706.56 –	1711.55	30.14	1931.56 –	1936.55	34.19
1261.56 –	1266.55	22.13	1486.56 –	1491.55	26.18	1711.56 –	1716.55	30.23	1936.56 –	1941.55	34.28
1266.56 –	1271.55	22.22	1491.56 –	1496.55	26.27	1716.56 –	1721.55	30.32	1941.56 –	1946.55	34.37
1271.56 –	1276.55	22.31	1496.56 –	1501.55	26.36	1721.56 –	1726.55	30.41	1946.56 –	1951.55	34.46
1276.56 –	1281.55	22.40	1501.56 –	1506.55	26.45	1726.56 –	1731.55	30.50	1951.56 –	1956.55	34.55

Remuneration / Rémunération		U.I. Premium / Prime d'a.-c.	Remuneration / Rémunération		U.I. Premium / Prime d'a.-c.	Remuneration / Rémunération		U.I. Premium / Prime d'a.-c.	Remuneration / Rémunération		U.I. Premium / Prime d'a.-c.
From-de	To-à		From-de	To-à		From-de	To-à		From-de	To-à	
159.35 –	159.77	3.67	178.91 –	179.34	4.12	198.48 –	198.90	4.57	218.04 –	218.47	5.02
159.78 –	160.21	3.68	179.35 –	179.77	4.13	198.91 –	199.34	4.58	218.48 –	218.90	5.03
160.22 –	160.64	3.69	179.78 –	180.21	4.14	199.35 –	199.77	4.59	218.91 –	219.34	5.04
160.65 –	161.08	3.70	180.22 –	180.64	4.15	199.78 –	200.21	4.60	219.35 –	219.77	5.05
161.09 –	161.51	3.71	180.65 –	181.08	4.16	200.22 –	200.64	4.61	219.78 –	220.21	5.06
161.52 –	161.95	3.72	181.09 –	181.51	4.17	200.65 –	201.08	4.62	220.22 –	220.64	5.07
161.96 –	162.38	3.73	181.52 –	181.95	4.18	201.09 –	201.51	4.63	220.65 –	221.08	5.08
162.39 –	162.82	3.74	181.96 –	182.38	4.19	201.52 –	201.95	4.64	221.09 –	221.51	5.09
162.83 –	163.25	3.75	182.39 –	182.82	4.20	201.96 –	202.38	4.65	221.52 –	221.95	5.10
163.26 –	163.69	3.76	182.83 –	183.25	4.21	202.39 –	202.82	4.66	221.96 –	222.38	5.11
163.70 –	164.12	3.77	183.26 –	183.69	4.22	202.83 –	203.25	4.67	222.39 –	222.82	5.12
164.13 –	164.56	3.78	183.70 –	184.12	4.23	203.26 –	203.69	4.68	222.83 –	223.25	5.13
164.57 –	164.99	3.79	184.13 –	184.56	4.24	203.70 –	204.12	4.69	223.26 –	223.69	5.14
165.00 –	165.43	3.80	184.57 –	184.99	4.25	204.13 –	204.56	4.70	223.70 –	224.12	5.15
165.44 –	165.86	3.81	185.00 –	185.43	4.26	204.57 –	204.99	4.71	224.13 –	224.56	5.16
165.87 –	166.30	3.82	185.44 –	185.86	4.27	205.00 –	205.43	4.72	224.57 –	224.99	5.17
166.31 –	166.73	3.83	185.87 –	186.30	4.28	205.44 –	205.86	4.73	225.00 –	225.43	5.18
166.74	167.16	3.84	186.31 –	186.73	4.29	205.87 –	206.30	4.74	225.44 –	225.86	5.19
167.17 –	167.60	3.85	186.74 –	187.16	4.30	206.31 –	206.73	4.75	225.87 –	226.30	5.20
167.61 –	168.03	3.86	187.17 –	187.60	4.31	206.74 –	207.16	4.76	226.31 –	226.73	5.21
168.04 –	168.47	3.87	187.61 –	188.03	4.32	207.17 –	207.60	4.77	226.74 –	227.16	5.22
168.48 –	168.90	3.88	188.04 –	188.47	4.33	207.61 –	208.03	4.78	227.17 –	227.60	5.23
168.91 –	169.34	3.89	188.48 –	188.90	4.34	208.04 –	208.47	4.79	227.61 –	228.03	5.24
169.35 –	169.77	3.90	188.91 –	189.34	4.35	208.48 –	208.90	4.80	228.04 –	228.47	5.25
169.78 –	170.21	3.91	189.35 –	189.77	4.36	208.91 –	209.34	4.81	228.48 –	228.90	5.26
170.22 –	170.64	3.92	189.78 –	190.21	4.37	209.35 –	209.77	4.82	228.91 –	229.34	5.27
170.65 –	171.08	3.93	190.22 –	190.64	4.38	209.78 –	210.21	4.83	229.35 –	229.77	5.28
171.09 –	171.51	3.94	190.65 –	191.08	4.39	210.22 –	210.64	4.84	229.78 –	230.21	5.29
171.52 –	171.95	3.95	191.09 –	191.51	4.40	210.65 –	211.08	4.85	230.22 –	230.64	5.30
171.96 –	172.38	3.96	191.52 –	191.95	4.41	211.09 –	211.51	4.86	230.65 –	231.08	5.31
172.39 –	172.82	3.97	191.96 –	192.38	4.42	211.52 –	211.95	4.87	231.09 –	231.51	5.32
172.83 –	173.25	3.98	192.39 –	192.82	4.43	211.96 –	212.38	4.88	231.52 –	231.95	5.33
173.26 –	173.69	3.99	192.83 –	193.25	4.44	212.39 –	212.82	4.89	231.96 –	232.38	5.34
173.70 –	174.12	4.00	193.26 –	193.69	4.45	212.83 –	213.25	4.90	232.39 –	232.82	5.35
174.13 –	174.56	4.01	193.70 –	194.12	4.46	213.26 –	213.69	4.91	232.83 –	233.25	5.36
174.57 –	174.99	4.02	194.13 –	194.56	4.47	213.70 –	214.12	4.92	233.26 –	233.69	5.37
175.00 –	175.43	4.03	194.57 –	194.99	4.48	214.13 –	214.56	4.93	233.70 –	234.12	5.38
175.44 –	175.86	4.04	195.00 –	195.43	4.49	214.57 –	214.99	4.94	234.13 –	234.56	5.39
175.87 –	176.30	4.05	195.44 –	195.86	4.50	215.00 –	215.43	4.95	234.57 –	234.99	5.40
176.31 –	176.73	4.06	195.87 –	196.30	4.51	215.44 –	215.86	4.96	235.00 –	235.43	5.41
176.74 –	177.16	4.07	196.31 –	196.73	4.52	215.87 –	216.30	4.97	235.44 –	235.86	5.42
177.17 –	177.60	4.08	196.74 –	197.16	4.53	216.31 –	216.73	4.98	235.87 –	236.30	5.43
177.61 –	178.03	4.09	197.17 –	197.60	4.54	216.74 –	217.16	4.99	236.31 –	236.73	5.44
178.04 –	178.47	4.10	197.61 –	198.03	4.55	217.17 –	217.60	5.00	236.74 –	237.16	5.45
178.48 –	178.90	4.11	198.04 –	198.47	4.56	217.61 –	218.03	5.01	237.17 –	237.60	5.46

WEEKLY PAY PERIOD—*PÉRIODE HEBDOMADAIRE DE PAIE*

$237.61—$315.86

Remuneration / *Rémunération* From-*de* — To-*à*	U.I. Premium *Prime d'a.-c.*	Remuneration / *Rémunération* From-*de* — To-*à*	U.I. Premium *Prime d'a.-c.*	Remuneration / *Rémunération* From-*de* — To-*à*	U.I. Premium *Prime d'a.-c.*	Remuneration / *Rémunération* From-*de* — To-*à*	U.I. Premium *Prime d'a.-c.*
237.61 – 238.03	5.47	257.17 – 257.60	5.92	276.74 – 277.16	6.37	296.31 – 296.73	6.82
238.04 – 238.47	5.48	257.61 – 258.03	5.93	277.17 – 277.60	6.38	296.74 – 297.16	6.83
238.48 – 238.90	5.49	258.04 – 258.47	5.94	277.61 – 278.03	6.39	297.17 – 297.60	6.84
238.91 – 239.34	5.50	258.48 – 258.90	5.95	278.04 – 278.47	6.40	297.61 – 298.03	6.85
239.35 – 239.77	5.51	258.91 – 259.34	5.96	278.48 – 278.90	6.41	298.04 – 298.47	6.86
239.78 – 240.21	5.52	259.35 – 259.77	5.97	278.91 – 279.34	6.42	298.48 – 298.90	6.87
240.22 – 240.64	5.53	259.78 – 260.21	5.98	279.35 – 279.77	6.43	298.91 – 299.34	6.88
240.65 – 241.08	5.54	260.22 – 260.64	5.99	279.78 – 280.21	6.44	299.35 – 299.77	6.89
241.09 – 241.51	5.55	260.65 – 261.08	6.00	280.22 – 280.64	6.45	299.78 – 300.21	6.90
241.52 – 241.95	5.56	261.09 – 261.51	6.01	280.65 – 281.08	6.46	300.22 – 300.64	6.91
241.96 – 242.38	5.57	261.52 – 261.95	6.02	281.09 – 281.51	6.47	300.65 – 301.08	6.92
242.39 – 242.82	5.58	261.96 – 262.38	6.03	281.52 – 281.95	6.48	301.09 – 301.51	6.93
242.83 – 243.25	5.59	262.39 – 262.82	6.04	281.96 – 282.38	6.49	301.52 – 301.95	6.94
243.26 – 243.69	5.60	262.83 – 263.25	6.05	282.39 – 282.82	6.50	301.96 – 302.38	6.95
243.70 – 244.12	5.61	263.26 – 263.69	6.06	282.83 – 283.25	6.51	302.39 – 302.82	6.96
244.13 – 244.56	5.62	263.70 – 264.12	6.07	283.26 – 283.69	6.52	302.83 – 303.25	6.97
244.57 – 244.99	5.63	264.13 – 264.56	6.08	283.70 – 284.12	6.53	303.26 – 303.69	6.98
245.00 – 245.43	5.64	264.57 – 264.99	6.09	284.13 – 284.56	6.54	303.70 – 304.12	6.99
245.44 – 245.86	5.65	265.00 – 265.43	6.10	284.57 – 284.99	6.55	304.13 – 304.56	7.00
245.87 – 246.30	5.66	265.44 – 265.86	6.11	285.00 – 285.43	6.56	304.57 – 304.99	7.01
246.31 – 246.73	5.67	265.87 – 266.30	6.12	285.44 – 285.86	6.57	305.00 – 305.43	7.02
246.74 – 247.16	5.68	266.31 – 266.73	6.13	285.87 – 286.30	6.58	305.44 – 305.86	7.03
247.17 – 247.60	5.69	266.74 – 267.16	6.14	286.31 – 286.73	6.59	305.87 – 306.30	7.04
247.61 – 248.03	5.70	267.17 – 267.60	6.15	286.74 – 287.16	6.60	306.31 – 306.73	7.05
248.04 – 248.47	5.71	267.61 – 268.03	6.16	287.17 – 287.60	6.61	306.74 – 307.16	7.06
248.48 – 248.90	5.72	268.04 – 268.47	6.17	287.61 – 288.03	6.62	307.17 – 307.60	7.07
248.91 – 249.34	5.73	268.48 – 268.90	6.18	288.04 – 288.47	6.63	307.61 – 308.03	7.08
249.35 – 249.77	5.74	268.91 – 269.34	6.19	288.48 – 288.90	6.64	308.04 – 308.47	7.09
249.78 – 250.21	5.75	269.35 – 269.77	6.20	288.91 – 289.34	6.65	308.48 – 308.90	7.10
250.22 – 250.64	5.76	269.78 – 270.21	6.21	289.35 – 289.77	6.66	308.91 – 309.34	7.11
250.65 – 251.08	5.77	270.22 – 270.64	6.22	289.76 – 290.21	6.67	309.35 – 309.77	7.12
251.09 – 251.51	5.78	270.65 – 271.08	6.23	290.22 – 290.64	6.68	309.78 – 310.21	7.13
251.52 – 251.95	5.79	271.09 – 271.51	6.24	290.65 – 291.08	6.69	310.22 – 310.64	7.14
251.96 – 252.38	5.80	271.52 – 271.95	6.25	291.09 – 291.51	6.70	310.65 – 311.08	7.15
252.39 – 252.82	5.81	271.96 – 272.38	6.26	291.52 – 291.95	6.71	311.09 – 311.51	7.16
252.83 – 253.25	5.82	272.39 – 272.82	6.27	291.96 – 292.38	6.72	311.52 – 311.95	7.17
253.26 – 253.69	5.83	272.83 – 273.25	6.28	292.39 – 292.82	6.73	311.96 – 312.38	7.18
253.70 – 254.12	5.84	273.26 – 273.69	6.29	292.83 – 293.25	6.74	312.39 – 312.82	7.19
254.13 – 254.56	5.85	273.70 – 274.12	6.30	293.26 – 293.69	6.75	312.83 – 313.25	7.20
254.57 – 254.99	5.86	274.13 – 274.56	6.31	293.70 – 294.12	6.76	313.26 – 313.69	7.21
255.00 – 255.43	5.87	274.57 – 274.99	6.32	294.13 – 294.56	6.77	313.70 – 314.12	7.22
255.44 – 255.86	5.88	275.00 – 275.43	6.33	294.57 – 294.99	6.78	314.13 – 314.56	7.23
255.87 – 256.30	5.89	275.44 – 275.86	6.34	295.00 – 295.43	6.79	314.57 – 314.99	7.24
256.31 – 256.73	5.90	275.87 – 276.30	6.35	295.44 – 295.86	6.80	315.00 – 315.43	7.25
256.74 – 257.16	5.91	276.31 – 276.73	6.36	295.87 – 296.30	6.81	315.44 – 315.86	7.26

WEEKLY PAY PERIOD—*PÉRIODE HEBDOMADAIRE DE PAIE*

$315.87—$385.00 AND UP/ET PLUS

Remuneration *Rémunération* From-*de* To-*à*	U.I. Premium *Prime d'a.-c.*	Remuneration *Rémunération* From-*de* To-*à*	U.I. Premium *Prime d'a.-c.*	Remuneration *Rémunération* From-*de* To-*à*	U.I. Premium *Prime d'a.-c.*	Remuneration *Rémunération* From-*de* To-*à*	U.I. Premium *Prime d'a.-c.*
315.87 – 316.30	7.27	335.44 – 335.86	7.72	355.00 – 355.43	8.17	374.57 – 374.99	8.62
316.31 – 316.73	7.28	335.87 – 336.30	7.73	355.44 – 355.86	8.18	375.00 – 375.43	8.63
316.74 – 317.16	7.29	336.31 – 336.73	7.74	355.87 – 356.30	8.19	375.44 – 375.86	8.64
317.17 – 317.60	7.30	336.74 – 337.16	7.75	356.31 – 356.73	8.20	375.87 – 376.30	8.65
317.61 – 318.03	7.31	337.17 – 337.60	7.76	356.74 – 357.16	8.21	376.31 – 376.73	8.66
318.04 – 318.47	7.32	337.61 – 338.03	7.77	357.17 – 357.60	8.22	376.74 – 377.16	8.67
318.48 – 318.90	7.33	338.04 – 338.47	7.78	357.61 – 358.03	8.23	377.17 – 377.60	8.68
318.91 – 319.34	7.34	338.48 – 338.90	7.79	358.04 – 358.47	8.24	377.61 – 378.03	8.69
319.35 – 319.77	7.35	338.91 – 339.34	7.80	358.48 – 358.90	8.25	378.04 – 378.47	8.70
319.78 – 320.21	7.36	339.35 – 339.77	7.81	358.91 – 359.34	8.26	378.48 – 378.90	8.71
320.22 – 320.64	7.37	339.78 – 340.21	7.82	359.35 – 359.77	8.27	378.91 – 379.34	8.72
320.65 – 321.08	7.38	340.22 – 340.64	7.83	359.78 – 360.21	8.28	379.35 – 379.77	8.73
321.09 – 321.51	7.39	340.65 – 341.08	7.84	360.22 – 360.64	8.29	379.78 – 380.21	8.74
321.52 – 321.95	7.40	341.09 – 341.51	7.85	360.65 – 361.08	8.30	380.22 – 380.64	8.75
321.96 – 322.38	7.41	341.52 – 341.95	7.86	361.09 – 361.51	8.31	380.65 – 381.08	8.76
322.39 – 322.82	7.42	341.96 – 342.38	7.87	361.52 – 361.95	8.32	381.09 – 381.51	8.77
322.83 – 323.25	7.43	342.39 – 342.82	7.88	361.96 – 362.38	8.33	381.52 – 381.95	8.78
323.26 – 323.69	7.44	342.83 – 343.25	7.89	362.39 – 362.82	8.34	381.96 – 382.38	8.79
323.70 – 324.12	7.45	343.26 – 343.69	7.90	362.83 – 363.25	8.35	382.39 – 382.82	8.80
324.13 – 324.56	7.46	343.70 – 344.12	7.91	363.26 – 363.69	8.36	382.83 – 383.25	8.81
324.57 – 324.99	7.47	344.13 – 344.56	7.92	363.70 – 364.12	8.37	383.26 – 383.69	8.82
325.00 – 325.43	7.48	344.57 – 344.99	7.93	364.13 – 364.56	8.38	383.70 – 384.12	8.83
325.44 – 325.86	7.49	345.00 – 345.43	7.94	364.57 – 364.99	8.39	384.13 – 384.56	8.84
325.87 – 326.30	7.50	345.44 – 345.86	7.95	365.00 – 365.43	8.40	384.57 – 384.99	8.85
326.31 – 326.73	7.51	345.87 – 346.30	7.96	365.44 – 365.86	8.41	385.00 – AND UP *ET PLUS*	8.86
326.74 – 327.16	7.52	346.31 – 346.73	7.97	365.87 – 366.30	8.42		
327.17 – 327.60	7.53	346.74 – 347.16	7.98	366.31 – 366.73	8.43		
327.61 – 328.03	7.54	347.17 – 347.60	7.99	366.74 – 367.16	8.44		
328.04 – 328.47	7.55	347.61 – 348.03	8.00	367.17 – 367.60	8.45		
328.48 – 328.90	7.56	348.04 – 348.47	8.01	367.61 – 368.03	8.46		
328.91 – 329.34	7.57	348.48 – 348.90	8.02	368.04 – 368.47	8.47		
329.35 – 329.77	7.58	348.91 – 349.34	8.03	368.48 – 368.90	8.48		
329.78 – 330.21	7.59	349.35 – 349.77	8.04	368.91 – 369.34	8.49		
330.22 – 330.64	7.60	349.78 – 350.21	8.05	369.35 – 369.77	8.50		
330.65 – 331.08	7.61	350.22 – 350.64	8.06	369.78 – 370.21	8.51		
331.09 – 331.51	7.62	350.65 – 351.08	8.07	370.22 – 370.64	8.52		
331.52 – 331.95	7.63	351.09 – 351.51	8.08	370.65 – 371.08	8.53		
331.96 – 332.38	7.64	351.52 – 351.95	8.09	371.09 – 371.51	8.54		
332.39 – 332.82	7.65	351.96 – 352.38	8.10	371.52 – 371.95	8.55		
332.83 – 333.25	7.66	352.39 – 352.82	8.11	371.96 – 372.38	8.56		
333.26 – 333.69	7.67	352.83 – 353.25	8.12	372.39 – 372.82	8.57		
333.70 – 334.12	7.68	353.26 – 353.69	8.13	372.83 – 373.25	8.58		
334.13 – 334.56	7.69	353.70 – 354.12	8.14	373.26 – 373.69	8.59		
334.57 – 334.99	7.70	354.13 – 354.56	8.15	373.70 – 374.12	8.60		
335.00 – 335.43	7.71	354.57 – 354.99	8.16	374.13 – 374.56	8.61		

ONTARIO
WEEKLY TAX DEDUCTIONS
Basis—52 Pay Periods per Year

TABLE 2

ONTARIO
DÉDUCTIONS D'IMPÔT PAR SEMAINE
Base—52 périodes de paie par année

WEEKLY PAY Use appropriate bracket — PAIE PAR SEMAINE Utilisez le palier approprié	IF THE EMPLOYEE'S "NET CLAIM CODE" ON FORM TD1 IS—SI LE «CODE DE RÉCLAMATION NETTE» EMPLOYÉ SELON LA FORMULE TD1 EST DE												
	1	2	3	4	5	6	7	8	9	10	11	12	13
	DEDUCT FROM EACH PAY—DÉDUISEZ SUR CHAQUE PAIE												
Under-Moins de 130.00	.00												
$ 130.00 – 131.99	.85												
132.00 – 133.99	2.35												
134.00 – 135.99	3.10												
136.00 – 137.99	3.60	.40											
138.00 – 139.99	4.10	1.95											
140.00 – 141.99	4.65	2.95											
142.00 – 143.99	5.15	3.45											
144.00 – 145.99	5.70	3.95											
146.00 – 147.99	6.20	4.50											
148.00 – 149.99	6.75	5.00	.65										
150.00 – 151.99	7.25	5.55	2.20										
152.00 – 153.99	7.80	6.05	3.05										
154.00 – 155.99	8.30	6.60	3.55										
156.00 – 157.99	8.85	7.15	4.05										
158.00 – 159.99	9.35	7.65	4.60										
160.00 – 161.99	9.90	8.20	5.10	1.15									
162.00 – 163.99	10.45	8.70	5.65	2.65									
164.00 – 165.99	10.95	9.25	6.15	3.20									
166.00 – $167.99	11.50	9.75	6.70	3.70									
168.00 – 169.99	12.00	10.30	7.20	4.20									
170.00 – 171.99	12.55	10.80	7.75	4.75									
172.00 – 173.99	13.05	11.35	8.25	5.25	1.05								
174.00 – 175.99	13.60	11.85	8.80	5.80	2.55								
176.00 – 177.99	14.10	12.40	9.30	6.30	3.15								
178.00 – 179.99	14.65	12.90	9.85	6.85	3.65								
180.00 – 181.99	15.20	13.45	10.35	7.35	4.20								
182.00 – 183.99	15.75	13.95	10.90	7.90	4.70	1.05							
184.00 – 185.99	16.30	14.50	11.45	8.45	5.25	2.55							
186.00 – 187.99	16.85	15.05	11.95	8.95	5.75	3.15							
188.00 – 189.99	17.40	15.60	12.50	9.50	6.30	3.65	.70						
190.00 – 191.99	17.95	16.15	13.00	10.00	6.80	4.20	2.20						
192.00 – 193.99	18.50	16.70	13.55	10.55	7.35	4.70	3.05						
194.00 – 195.99	19.10	17.25	14.05	11.05	7.85	5.25	3.55						
196.00 – 197.99	19.65	17.80	14.60	11.60	8.40	5.75	4.05						
198.00 – 199.99	20.20	18.35	15.10	12.10	8.90	6.30	4.60	1.00					
200.00 – 201.99	20.75	18.95	15.70	12.65	9.45	6.80	5.10	2.50					
202.00 – 203.99	21.30	19.50	16.25	13.15	9.95	7.35	5.65	3.15					
204.00 – 205.99	21.85	20.05	16.80	13.70	10.50	7.85	6.15	3.65					
206.00 – 207.99	22.45	20.60	17.35	14.20	11.05	8.40	6.70	4.15					

ONTARIO
WEEKLY TAX DEDUCTIONS
Basis—52 Pay Periods per Year

TABLE 2

ONTARIO
DÉDUCTIONS D'IMPÔT PAR SEMAINE
Base—52 périodes de paie par année

WEEKLY PAY Use appropriate bracket / PAIE PAR SEMAINE Utilisez le palier approprié	1	2	3	4	5	6	7	8	9	10	11	12	13
	IF THE EMPLOYEE'S "NET CLAIM CODE" ON FORM TD1 IS—SI LE «CODE DE RÉCLAMATION NETTE» EMPLOYÉ SELON LA FORMULE TD1 EST DE												
	DEDUCT FROM EACH PAY—DÉDUISEZ SUR CHAQUE PAIE												
208.00 – 209.99	23.00	21.15	17.90	14.75	11.55	8.90	7.25	4.70					
210.00 – 211.99	23.55	21.70	18.45	15.30	12.10	9.45	7.75	5.20	.10				
212.00 – 213.99	24.10	22.30	19.00	15.85	12.60	10.00	8.30	5.75	1.65				
214.00 – 215.99	24.65	22.85	19.60	16.40	13.15	10.50	8.80	6.25	2.85				
216.00 – 217.99	25.20	23.40	20.15	16.95	13.65	11.05	9.35	6.80	3.35				
218.00 – 219.99	25.75	23.95	20.70	17.50	14.20	11.55	9.85	7.35	3.85				
220.00 – 221.99	26.35	24.50	21.25	18.10	14.70	12.10	10.40	7.85	4.40				
222.00 – 223.99	26.90	25.05	21.80	18.65	15.25	12.60	10.90	8.40	4.90				
224.00 – 225.99	27.45	25.60	22.35	19.20	15.80	13.15	11.45	8.90	5.45				
226.00 – 227.99	28.05	26.20	22.95	19.75	16.35	13.65	11.95	9.45	5.95	1.50			
228.00 – 229.99	28.65	26.75	23.50	20.30	16.90	14.20	12.50	9.95	6.50	2.80			
230.00 – 231.99	29.25	27.30	24.05	20.85	17.50	14.70	13.00	10.50	7.00	3.30			
232.00 – 233.99	29.80	27.90	24.60	21.40	18.05	15.25	13.55	11.00	7.55	3.80			
234.00 – 235.99	30.40	28.50	25.15	22.00	18.60	15.80	14.05	11.55	8.05	4.35			
236.00 – 237.99	31.00	29.10	25.70	22.55	19.15	16.35	14.60	12.05	8.60	4.85			
238.00 – 239.99	31.60	29.65	26.25	23.10	19.70	16.95	15.15	12.60	9.15	5.40			
240.00 – 241.99	32.20	30.25	26.85	23.65	20.25	17.50	15.70	13.10	9.65	5.90	1.00		
242.00 – 243.99	32.75	30.85	27.40	24.20	20.85	18.05	16.25	13.65	10.20	6.45	2.50		
244.00 – 245.99	33.35	31.45	28.00	24.75	21.40	18.60	16.80	14.15	10.70	6.95	3.15		
246.00 – 247.99	33.95	32.00	28.50	25.35	21.95	19.15	17.35	14.70	11.25	7.50	3.65		
248.00 – 249.99	34.55	32.60	29.15	25.90	22.50	19.70	17.90	15.25	11.75	8.00	4.15		
250.00 – 251.99	35.10	33.20	29.75	26.45	23.05	20.25	18.50	15.80	12.30	8.55	4.70		
252.00 – 253.99	35.70	33.80	30.35	27.00	23.60	20.85	19.05	16.35	12.80	9.10	5.20		
254.00 – 255.99	36.30	34.35	30.95	27.60	24.15	21.40	19.60	16.90	13.35	9.60	5.75	.85	
256.00 – 257.99	36.90	34.95	31.55	28.20	24.75	21.95	20.15	17.45	13.85	10.15	6.25	2.35	
258.00 – 262.99	37.90	36.00	32.55	29.20	25.70	22.90	21.15	18.45	14.80	11.05	7.20	3.45	
263.00 – 267.99	39.40	37.45	34.05	30.70	27.10	24.30	22.50	19.85	16.15	12.35	8.50	4.75	
268.00 – 272.99	40.85	38.95	35.50	32.15	28.60	25.70	23.90	21.25	17.55	13.70	9.85	6.10	2.85
273.00 – 277.99	42.35	40.40	36.95	33.60	30.05	27.10	25.30	22.65	18.95	15.00	11.15	7.40	4.10
278.00 – 282.99	43.80	41.90	38.45	35.10	31.50	28.60	26.70	24.00	20.35	16.40	12.45	8.70	5.45
283.00 – 287.99	45.25	43.35	39.90	36.55	33.00	30.05	28.15	25.40	21.75	17.80	13.80	10.05	6.75
288.00 – 292.99	46.75	44.80	41.40	38.05	34.45	31.50	29.65	26.80	23.15	19.20	15.10	11.35	8.05
293.00 – 297.99	48.20	46.30	42.85	39.50	35.95	33.00	31.10	28.25	24.55	20.60	16.50	12.65	9.40
298.00 – 302.99	49.70	47.75	44.35	41.00	37.40	34.45	32.55	29.75	25.95	21.95	17.90	14.00	10.70
303.00 – 307.99	51.15	49.25	45.80	42.45	38.90	35.95	34.05	31.20	27.30	23.35	19.30	15.30	12.00
308.00 – 312.99	52.65	50.70	47.30	43.90	40.35	37.40	35.50	32.70	28.80	24.75	20.65	16.70	13.35
313.00 – 317.99	54.15	52.20	48.75	45.40	41.80	38.90	37.00	34.15	30.30	26.15	22.05	18.10	14.65
318.00 – 322.99	55.70	53.65	50.20	46.85	43.30	40.35	38.45	35.65	31.75	27.60	23.45	19.50	16.00
323.00 – 327.99	57.20	55.15	51.65	48.30	44.70	41.80	39.90	37.05	33.20	29.00	24.80	20.85	17.35
328.00 – 332.99	58.70	56.65	53.10	49.70	46.15	43.20	41.30	38.50	34.60	30.45	26.15	22.20	18.70

ONTARIO
WEEKLY TAX DEDUCTIONS
Basis—52 Pay Periods per Year

TABLE 2

ONTARIO
DÉDUCTIONS D'IMPÔT PAR SEMAINE
Base—52 périodes de paie par année

WEEKLY PAY Use appropriate bracket — PAIE PAR SEMAINE Utilisez le palier approprié	IF THE EMPLOYEE'S "NET CLAIM CODE" ON FORM TD1 IS—SI LE «CODE DE RÉCLAMATION NETTE» EMPLOYÉ SELON LA FORMULE TD1 EST DE												
	1	2	3	4	5	6	7	8	9	10	11	12	13
	DEDUCT FROM EACH PAY—DÉDUISEZ SUR CHAQUE PAIE												
$333.00 – 337.99	60.20	58.20	54.55	51.15	47.60	44.65	42.75	39.90	36.05	31.85	27.55	23.55	20.10
338.00 – 342.99	61.70	59.70	56.05	52.60	49.00	46.05	44.15	41.35	37.45	33.30	29.00	24.90	21.45
343.00 – 347.99	63.20	61.20	57.55	54.05	50.45	47.50	45.60	42.75	38.90	34.70	30.40	26.25	22.80
348.00 – 352.99	64.70	62.70	59.05	55.55	51.85	48.95	47.05	44.20	40.35	36.15	31.85	27.65	24.15
353.00 – 357.99	66.20	64.20	60.60	57.05	53.30	50.35	48.45	45.65	41.75	37.60	33.25	29.10	25.50
358.00 – 362.99	67.70	65.70	62.10	58.55	54.80	51.80	49.90	47.05	43.20	39.00	34.70	30.50	26.85
363.00 – 367.99	69.25	67.20	63.60	60.05	56.30	53.20	51.30	48.50	44.60	40.45	36.10	31.95	28.25
368.00 – 372.99	70.75	68.70	65.10	61.55	57.80	54.70	52.75	49.90	46.05	41.85	37.55	33.40	29.70
373.00 – 377.99	72.25	70.20	66.60	63.05	59.30	56.20	54.20	51.35	47.45	43.30	39.00	34.80	31.10
378.00 – 382.99	73.75	71.70	68.10	64.55	60.80	57.70	55.70	52.75	48.90	44.70	40.40	36.25	32.55
383.00 – 387.99	75.25	73.20	69.60	66.05	62.30	59.20	57.20	54.25	50.35	46.15	41.85	37.65	34.00
388.00 – 392.99	76.75	74.70	71.10	67.60	63.80	60.70	58.75	55.75	51.75	47.60	43.25	39.10	35.40
393.00 – 397.99	78.25	76.25	72.60	69.10	65.30	62.25	60.25	57.25	53.20	49.00	44.70	40.50	36.85
398.00 – 402.99	79.75	77.75	74.10	70.60	66.85	63.75	61.75	58.75	54.70	50.45	46.10	41.95	38.25
403.00 – 407.99	81.35	79.25	75.60	72.10	68.35	65.25	63.25	60.25	56.20	51.85	47.55	43.40	39.70
408.00 – 412.99	83.10	80.75	77.10	73.60	69.85	66.75	64.75	61.75	57.70	53.30	49.00	44.80	41.10
413.00 – 417.99	84.80	82.50	78.65	75.10	71.35	68.25	66.25	63.25	59.20	54.80	50.40	46.25	42.55
418.00 – 422.99	86.55	84.20	80.15	76.60	72.85	69.75	67.75	64.75	60.70	56.30	51.85	47.65	44.00
423.00 – 427.99	88.30	85.95	81.80	78.10	74.35	71.25	69.25	66.30	62.20	57.80	53.25	49.10	45.40
428.00 – 432.99	90.00	87.70	83.50	79.60	75.85	72.75	70.75	67.80	63.70	59.30	54.75	50.50	46.85
433.00 – 437.99	91.75	89.40	85.25	81.20	77.35	74.25	72.25	69.30	65.20	60.80	56.25	51.95	48.25
438.00 – 442.99	93.45	91.15	87.00	82.90	78.85	75.75	73.75	70.80	66.70	62.30	57.75	53.40	49.70
443.00 – 447.99	95.20	92.85	88.70	84.65	80.35	77.25	75.25	72.30	68.20	63.80	59.30	54.90	51.15
448.00 – 452.99	96.95	94.60	90.45	86.40	82.05	78.75	76.80	73.80	69.70	65.30	60.80	56.40	52.55
453.00 – 457.99	98.65	96.35	92.15	88.10	83.80	80.30	78.30	75.30	71.20	66.85	62.30	57.90	54.00
458.00 – 462.99	100.40	98.05	93.90	89.85	85.50	81.95	79.80	76.80	72.75	68.35	63.80	59.40	55.50
463.00 – 467.99	102.10	99.80	95.65	91.55	87.25	83.70	81.40	78.30	74.25	69.85	65.30	60.90	57.00
468.00 – 472.99	103.85	101.50	97.35	93.30	89.00	85.40	83.10	79.80	75.75	71.35	66.80	62.40	58.55
473.00 – 477.99	105.55	103.25	99.10	95.05	90.70	87.15	84.85	81.45	77.25	72.85	68.30	63.90	60.05
478.00 – 482.99	107.30	105.00	100.80	96.75	92.45	88.90	86.60	83.15	78.75	74.35	69.80	65.40	61.55
483.00 – 487.99	109.05	106.70	102.55	98.50	94.15	90.60	88.30	84.90	80.25	75.85	71.30	66.90	63.05
488.00 – 492.99	110.75	108.45	104.30	100.20	95.90	92.35	90.05	86.60	81.90	77.35	72.80	68.40	64.55
493.00 – 497.99	112.50	110.15	106.00	101.95	97.60	94.05	91.75	88.35	83.65	78.85	74.30	69.90	66.05
498.00 – 502.99	114.40	111.90	107.75	103.70	99.35	95.80	93.50	90.05	85.40	80.35	75.80	71.45	67.55
503.00 – 507.99	116.30	113.75	109.45	105.40	101.10	97.50	95.25	91.80	87.10	82.05	77.35	72.95	69.05
508.00 – 517.99	119.10	116.55	112.05	108.00	103.70	100.10	97.80	94.40	89.70	84.65	79.60	75.20	71.30
518.00 – 527.99	122.85	120.35	115.80	111.45	107.15	103.60	101.30	97.85	93.15	88.10	82.90	78.20	74.30
528.00 – 537.99	126.60	124.10	119.55	115.15	110.60	107.05	104.75	101.30	96.65	91.55	86.35	81.30	77.35
538.00 – 547.99	130.40	127.85	123.35	118.90	114.20	110.50	108.20	104.80	100.10	95.05	89.80	84.75	80.35
548.00 – 557.99	134.15	131.60	127.10	122.70	118.00	114.10	111.65	108.25	103.55	98.50	93.25	88.20	83.75

ONTARIO
WEEKLY TAX DEDUCTIONS
Basis—52 Pay Periods per Year

TABLE 2

ONTARIO
DÉDUCTIONS D'IMPÔT PAR SEMAINE
Base—52 périodes de paie par année

WEEKLY PAY Use appropriate bracket — PAIE PAR SEMAINE Utilisez le palier approprié	IF THE EMPLOYEE'S "NET CLAIM CODE" ON FORM TD1 IS—SI LE «CODE DE RÉCLAMATION NETTE» EMPLOYÉ SELON LA FORMULE TD1 EST DE												
	1	2	3	4	5	6	7	8	9	10	11	12	13
	DEDUCT FROM EACH PAY—DÉDUISEZ SUR CHAQUE PAIE												
$558.00 – 567.99	137.90	135.35	130.85	126.45	121.75	117.85	115.35	111.70	107.00	101.95	96.75	91.65	87.20
568.00 – 577.99	141.65	139.15	134.60	130.20	125.50	121.65	119.15	115.40	110.45	105.40	100.20	95.15	90.65
578.00 – 587.99	145.40	142.90	138.35	133.95	129.25	125.40	122.90	119.15	114.05	108.85	103.65	98.60	94.15
588.00 – 597.99	149.20	146.65	142.15	137.70	133.00	129.15	126.65	122.95	117.85	112.35	107.10	102.05	97.60
598.00 – 607.99	152.95	150.40	145.90	141.50	136.80	132.90	130.40	126.70	121.60	116.10	110.55	105.50	101.05
608.00 – 617.99	156.70	154.15	149.65	145.25	140.55	136.65	134.15	130.45	125.35	119.85	114.20	108.95	104.50
618.00 – 627.99	160.45	157.95	153.40	149.00	144.30	140.45	137.95	134.20	129.10	123.60	117.95	112.45	107.95
628.00 – 637.99	164.20	161.70	157.15	152.75	148.05	144.20	141.70	137.95	132.85	127.40	121.70	116.20	111.45
638.00 – 647.99	168.00	165.45	160.95	156.50	151.80	147.95	145.45	141.75	136.65	131.15	125.45	119.95	115.10
648.00 – 657.99	171.75	169.20	164.70	160.30	155.60	151.70	149.20	145.50	140.40	134.90	129.20	123.75	118.90
658.00 – 667.99	175.50	172.95	168.45	164.05	159.35	155.45	152.95	149.25	144.15	138.65	133.00	127.50	122.65
668.00 – 677.99	179.25	176.75	172.20	167.80	163.10	159.25	156.75	153.00	147.90	142.40	136.75	131.25	126.40
678.00 – 687.99	183.00	180.50	175.95	171.55	166.85	163.00	160.50	156.75	151.65	146.20	140.50	135.00	130.15
688.00 – 697.99	186.80	184.25	179.75	175.30	170.60	166.75	164.25	160.55	155.45	149.95	144.25	138.75	133.90
698.00 – 707.99	190.55	188.00	183.50	179.10	174.40	170.50	168.00	164.30	159.20	153.70	148.00	142.55	137.70
708.00 – 717.99	194.30	191.75	187.25	182.85	178.15	174.25	171.75	168.05	162.95	157.45	151.80	146.30	141.45
718.00 – 727.99	198.20	195.55	191.00	186.60	181.90	178.05	175.55	171.80	166.70	161.20	155.55	150.05	145.20
728.00 – 737.99	202.70	199.70	194.75	190.35	185.65	181.80	179.30	175.55	170.45	165.00	159.30	153.80	148.95
738.00 – 747.99	207.25	204.20	198.80	194.10	189.40	185.55	183.05	179.35	174.25	168.75	166.80	157.55	152.70
748.00 – 757.99	211.75	208.70	203.30	198.00	193.20	189.30	186.80	183.10	178.00	172.50		161.35	156.50
758.00 – 767.99	216.25	213.20	207.80	202.50	196.95	193.05	190.55	186.85	181.75	176.25	170.60	165.10	160.25
768.00 – 777.99	220.75	217.75	212.30	207.00	201.40	196.85	194.35	190.60	185.50	180.00	174.35	168.85	164.00
778.00 – 787.99	225.30	222.25	216.80	211.55	205.90	201.25	198.25	194.35	189.25	183.80	178.10	172.60	167.75
788.00 – 797.99	229.80	226.75	221.35	216.05	210.40	205.75	202.75	198.30	193.05	187.55	181.85	176.35	171.50
798.00 – 807.99	234.30	231.25	225.85	220.55	214.90	210.25	207.30	202.80	196.80	191.30	185.60	180.15	175.30
808.00 – 817.99	238.80	235.80	230.35	225.05	219.45	214.80	211.80	207.30	201.20	195.05	189.40	183.90	179.05
818.00 – 827.99	243.35	240.30	234.85	229.60	223.95	219.30	216.30	211.85	205.70	199.10	193.15	187.65	182.80
828.00 – 837.99	247.85	244.80	239.40	234.10	228.45	223.80	220.80	216.35	210.25	203.65	196.90	191.40	186.55
838.00 – 847.99	252.35	249.30	243.90	238.60	232.95	228.30	225.35	220.85	214.75	108.15	201.35	195.15	190.30
848.00 – 857.99	256.85	253.85	248.40	243.10	237.45	232.85	229.85	225.35	219.25	212.65	205.85	199.25	194.10
858.00 – 867.99	261.40	258.35	252.90	247.65	242.00	237.35	234.35	229.90	223.75	217.15	210.35	203.75	197.95
868.00 – 877.99	265.90	262.85	257.45	252.15	246.50	241.85	238.85	234.40	228.30	221.70	214.85	208.30	202.45
878.00 – 887.99	270.40	267.35	261.95	256.65	251.00	246.35	243.35	238.90	232.80	226.20	219.40	212.80	207.00
888.00 – 897.99	274.90	271.90	266.45	261.15	255.50	250.90	247.90	243.40	237.30	230.70	223.90	217.30	211.50
898.00 – 907.99	279.45	276.40	270.95	265.65	260.05	255.40	252.40	247.95	241.80	235.20	228.40	221.80	216.00
908.00 – 917.99	283.95	280.90	275.50	270.20	264.55	259.90	256.90	252.45	246.35	239.75	232.90	226.30	220.50
918.00 – 927.99	288.45	285.40	280.00	274.70	269.05	264.40	261.40	256.95	250.85	244.25	237.45	230.85	225.00
928.00 – 937.99	292.95	289.95	284.50	279.20	273.55	268.95	265.95	261.45	255.35	248.75	241.95	235.35	229.55
938.00 – 947.99	297.50	294.45	289.00	283.70	278.10	273.45	270.45	266.00	259.85	253.25	246.45	239.85	234.05
948.00 – 957.99	302.00	298.95	293.55	288.25	282.60	277.95	274.95	270.50	264.35	257.80	250.95	244.35	238.55

Table of Number of Days in a Year

Day of Month	Jan.	Feb.	Mar.	Apr.	May	June	July	Aug.	Sept.	Oct.	Nov.	Dec.	Day of Month
1	1	32	60	91	121	152	182	213	244	274	305	335	1
2	2	33	61	92	122	153	183	214	245	275	306	336	2
3	3	34	62	93	123	154	184	215	246	276	307	337	3
4	4	35	63	94	124	155	185	216	247	277	308	338	4
5	5	36	64	95	125	156	186	217	248	278	309	339	5
6	6	37	65	96	126	157	187	218	249	279	310	340	6
7	7	38	66	97	127	158	188	219	250	280	311	341	7
8	8	39	67	98	128	159	189	220	251	281	312	342	8
9	9	40	68	99	129	160	190	221	252	282	313	343	9
10	10	41	69	100	130	161	191	222	253	283	314	344	10
11	11	42	70	101	131	162	192	223	254	284	315	345	11
12	12	43	71	102	132	163	193	224	255	285	316	346	12
13	13	44	72	103	133	164	194	225	256	286	317	347	13
14	14	45	73	104	134	165	195	226	257	287	318	348	14
15	15	46	74	105	135	166	196	227	258	288	319	349	15
16	16	47	75	106	136	167	197	228	259	289	320	250	16
17	17	48	76	107	137	168	198	229	260	290	321	351	17
18	18	49	77	108	138	169	199	230	261	291	322	352	18
19	19	50	78	109	139	170	200	231	262	292	323	353	19
20	20	51	79	110	140	171	201	232	263	293	324	354	20
21	21	52	80	111	141	172	202	233	264	294	325	355	21
22	22	53	81	112	142	173	203	234	265	295	326	356	22
23	23	54	82	113	143	174	204	235	266	296	327	357	23
24	24	55	83	114	144	175	205	236	267	297	328	358	24
25	25	56	84	115	145	176	206	237	268	298	329	359	25
26	26	57	85	116	146	177	207	238	269	299	330	360	26
27	27	58	86	117	147	178	208	239	270	300	331	361	27
28	28	59	87	118	148	179	209	240	271	301	332	362	28
29	29	*	88	119	149	180	210	241	272	302	333	363	29
30	30		89	120	150	181	211	242	273	303	334	364	30
31	31		90		151		212	243		304		365	31

*For leap years, February has 29 d, and the number of each day from March 1 is one greater than the number given in the table.

Compound Interest Table

n	½%	1%	1½%	2%	2½%	3%	3½%	n
1	1.00500	1.01000	1.01500	1.02000	1.02500	1.03000	1.03500	1
2	1.01003	1.02010	1.03023	1.04040	1.05063	1.06090	1.07123	2
3	1.01508	1.03030	1.04568	1.06121	1.07689	1.09273	1.10872	3
4	1.02015	1.04060	1.06136	1.08243	1.10381	1.12551	1.14752	4
5	1.02525	1.05101	1.07728	1.10408	1.13141	1.15927	1.18769	5
6	1.03038	1.06152	1.09344	1.12616	1.15969	1.19405	1.22926	6
7	1.03553	1.07214	1.10985	1.14869	1.18869	1.22987	1.27228	7
8	1.04071	1.08286	1.12649	1.17166	1.21840	1.26677	1.31681	8
9	1.04591	1.09369	1.14339	1.19509	1.24886	1.30477	1.36290	9
10	1.05114	1.10462	1.16054	1.21899	1.28008	1.34392	1.41060	10
11	1.05640	1.11567	1.17795	1.24337	1.31209	1.38423	1.45997	11
12	1.06168	1.12683	1.19562	1.26824	1.34489	1.42576	1.51107	12
13	1.06699	1.13809	1.21355	1.29361	1.37851	1.46853	1.56396	13
14	1.07232	1.14947	1.23176	1.31948	1.41297	1.51259	1.61869	14
15	1.07768	1.16097	1.25023	1.34587	1.44830	1.55797	1.67535	15
16	1.08307	1.17258	1.26899	1.37279	1.48451	1.60471	1.73399	16
17	1.08849	1.18430	1.28802	1.40024	1.52162	1.65285	1.79468	17
18	1.09393	1.19615	1.30734	1.42825	1.55966	1.70243	1.85749	18
19	1.09940	1.20811	1.32695	1.45681	1.59865	1.75351	1.92250	19
20	1.10490	1.22019	1.34686	1.48595	1.63862	1.80611	1.98979	20
21	1.11042	1.23239	1.36706	1.51567	1.67958	1.86029	2.05943	21
22	1.11597	1.24472	1.38756	1.54598	1.72157	1.91610	2.13151	22
23	1.12155	1.25716	1.40838	1.57690	1.76461	1.97359	2.20611	23
24	1.12716	1.26973	1.42950	1.60844	1.80873	2.03279	2.28333	24
25	1.13280	1.28243	1.45095	1.64061	1.85394	2.09378	2.36324	25
26	1.13846	1.29526	1.47271	1.67342	1.90029	2.15659	2.44596	26
27	1.14415	1.30821	1.49480	1.70689	1.94780	2.22129	2.53157	27
28	1.14987	1.32129	1.51722	1.74102	1.99650	2.28793	2.62017	28
29	1.15562	1.33450	1.53998	1.77584	2.04641	2.35657	2.71188	29
30	1.16140	1.34785	1.56308	1.77584	2.09757	2.42726	2.80679	30
31	1.16721	1.36133	1.58653	1.84759	2.15001	2.50008	2.90503	31
32	1.17304	1.37494	1.61032	1.88454	2.20376	2.57508	3.00671	32
33	1.17891	1.38869	1.63448	1.92223	2.25885	2.65234	3.11194	33
34	1.18480	1.40258	1.65900	1.96068	2.31532	2.73191	3.22086	34
35	1.19073	1.41660	1.68388	1.99989	2.37321	2.81386	3.33359	35
36	1.19668	1.43077	1.70914	2.03989	2.43254	2.89828	3.45027	36
37	1.20266	1.44508	1.73478	2.08069	2.49335	2.98523	3.57103	37
38	1.20868	1.45953	1.76080	2.12230	2.55568	3.07478	3.69601	38
39	1.21472	1.47412	1.78721	2.16474	2.61957	3.16703	3.82537	39
40	1.22079	1.48886	1.81402	2.20804	2.68506	3.26204	2.95926	40
41	1.22690	1.50375	1.84123	2.25220	2.75219	3.35990	4.09783	41
42	1.23303	1.51879	1.86885	2.29724	2.82100	3.46070	4.24126	42
43	1.23920	1.53398	1.89688	2.34319	2.89152	3.56452	4.38970	43
44	1.24539	1.54932	1.92533	2.39005	2.96381	3.67145	4.54334	44
45	1.25162	1.56481	1.95424	2.43785	3.03790	3.78160	4.70236	45
46	1.25788	1.58046	1.98353	2.48661	3.11385	3.89504	4.86694	46
47	1.26417	1.59626	2.01328	2.53634	3.19170	4.01190	5.03728	47
48	1.27049	1.61223	2.04348	2.58707	3.27149	4.13225	5.21359	48
49	1.27684	1.62835	2.07413	2.63881	3.35328	4.25622	5.39606	49
50	1.28323	1.64463	2.10524	2.69159	3.43711	4.38391	5.58493	50
n	½%	1%	1½%	2%	2½%	3%	3½%	n

Compound Interest Table

n	4%	5%	6%	7%	8%	9%	10%	n
1	1.04000	1.05000	1.06000	1.07000	1.08000	1.09000	1.10000	1
2	1.08160	1.10250	1.12360	1.14490	1.16640	1.18810	1.21000	2
3	1.12486	1.15763	1.19102	1.22504	1.25971	1.25903	1.33100	3
4	1.16986	1.21551	1.26248	1.31080	1.36049	1.41158	1.46410	4
5	1.21665	1.27628	1.33823	1.40255	1.46933	1.53862	1.61051	5
6	1.26532	1.34010	1.41852	1.50073	1.58687	1.67710	1.77156	6
7	1.31593	1.40710	1.50363	1.60578	1.71382	1.82804	1.94872	7
8	1.36857	1.47746	1.59385	1.71819	1.85093	1.99256	2.14359	8
9	1.42331	1.55133	1.68948	1.83846	1.99900	2.17189	2.35795	9
10	1.48024	1.62889	1.79085	1.96715	2.15892	2.36736	2.59374	10
11	1.53945	1.71034	1.89830	2.10485	2.33164	2.58043	2.85312	11
12	1.60103	1.79586	2.01220	2.25219	2.51817	2.81266	3.13843	12
13	1.66507	1.88565	2.13293	2.40985	2.71962	3.06580	3.45227	13
14	1.73168	1.97993	2.26090	2.57853	2.93719	3.34173	3.79750	14
15	1.80094	2.07893	2.39656	2.75903	3.17217	3.64248	4.17725	15
16	1.87298	2.18287	2.54035	2.95216	3.42594	3.97031	4.59497	16
17	1.94790	2.29202	2.69277	3.15882	3.70002	4.32763	5.05447	17
18	2.02582	2.40662	2.85434	3.37993	3.99602	4.71712	5.55992	18
19	2.10685	2.52695	3.02560	3.61653	4.31570	5.14166	6.11591	19
20	2.19112	2.65330	3.20714	3.86968	4.66096	5.60441	6.72750	20
21	2.27877	2.78596	3.39956	4.14056	5.03383	6.10881	7.40025	21
22	2.36992	2.92526	3.60354	4.43040	5.43654	6.65860	8.14027	22
23	2.46472	3.07152	3.81975	4.74053	5.87146	7.25787	8.95430	23
24	2.56330	3.22510	4.04893	5.07237	6.34118	7.91108	9.84973	24
25	2.66584	3.38635	4.29187	5.42743	6.84848	8.62308	10.83471	25
26	2.77247	3.55567	4.54938	5.80735	7.39635	9.39916	11.91818	26
27	2.88337	3.73346	4.82235	6.21387	7.98806	10.24508	13.10999	27
28	2.99870	3.92013	5.11169	6.64884	8.62711	11.16714	14.42099	28
29	3.11865	4.11614	5.41839	7.11426	9.31727	12.17218	15.86309	29
30	3.24340	4.32194	5.74349	7.61226	10.06266	13.26768	17.44940	30
31	3.37313	4.53804	6.08810	8.14511	10.86767	14.46177	19.19434	31
32	3.50806	4.76494	6.45339	8.71527	11.73708	15.76333	21.11378	32
33	3.64838	5.00319	6.84059	9.32534	12.67605	17.18203	23.22515	33
34	3.79432	5.25335	7.25103	9.97811	13.69013	18.72841	25.54767	34
35	3.94609	5.51602	7.68609	10.67658	14.78534	20.41397	28.10244	35
36	4.10393	5.79182	8.14725	11.42394	15.96817	22.25123	30.91268	36
37	4.26809	6.08141	8.63609	12.22362	17.24563	24.25384	34.00395	37
38	4.43881	6.38548	9.15425	13.07927	18.62528	26.43668	37.40434	38
39	4.61637	6.70475	9.70351	13.99482	20.11530	28.81598	41.14478	39
40	4.80102	7.03999	10.28572	14.97446	21.72452	31.40942	45.25926	40
41	4.99306	7.39199	10.90286	16.02267	23.46248	34.23627	49.78518	41
42	5.19278	7.76159	11.55703	17.14426	25.33948	37.31753	54.76370	42
43	5.40050	8.14967	12.25045	18.34435	27.36664	40.67611	60.24007	43
44	5.61652	8.55715	12.98548	19.62846	29.55597	44.33696	66.26408	44
45	5.84118	8.98501	13.76461	21.00245	31.92045	48.32729	72.89048	45
46	6.07482	9.43426	14.59049	22.47262	34.47409	52.67674	80.17953	46
47	6.31782	9.90597	15.46592	24.04571	37.23201	57.41765	88.19749	47
48	6.57053	10.40127	16.39387	25.72891	40.21057	62.58524	97.01723	48
49	6.83335	10.92133	17.37750	27.52993	43.42742	68.21791	106.71896	49
50	7.10668	11.46740	18.42015	29.45703	46.90161	74.35752	117.39085	50
n	4%	5%	6%	7%	8%	9%	10%	n

Table of Trigonometric Ratios

Angle A	sin A	cos A	tan A
0	0.000	1.000	0.000
1	0.017	1.000	0.017
2	0.035	0.999	0.035
3	0.052	0.999	0.052
4	0.070	0.998	0.070
5	0.087	0.996	0.087
6	0.105	0.995	0.105
7	0.122	0.993	0.123
8	0.139	0.990	0.141
9	0.156	0.988	0.158
10	0.174	0.985	0.176
11	0.191	0.982	0.194
12	0.208	0.978	0.213
13	0.225	0.974	0.231
14	0.242	0.970	0.249
15	0.259	0.966	0.268
16	0.276	0.961	0.287
17	0.292	0.956	0.306
18	0.309	0.951	0.325
19	0.326	0.946	0.344
20	0.342	0.940	0.364
21	0.358	0.934	0.384
22	0.375	0.927	0.404
23	0.391	0.921	0.424
24	0.407	0.914	0.445
25	0.423	0.906	0.466
26	0.438	0.899	0.488
27	0.454	0.891	0.510
28	0.469	0.883	0.532
29	0.485	0.875	0.554

Angle A	sin A	cos A	tan A
30	0.500	0.866	0.577
31	0.515	0.857	0.601
32	0.530	0.848	0.625
33	0.545	0.839	0.649
34	0.559	0.829	0.675
35	0.574	0.819	0.700
36	0.588	0.809	0.727
37	0.602	0.799	0.754
38	0.616	0.788	0.781
39	0.629	0.777	0.810
40	0.643	0.766	0.839
41	0.656	0.755	0.869
42	0.669	0.743	0.900
43	0.682	0.731	0.933
44	0.695	0.719	0.966
45	0.707	0.707	1.000
46	0.719	0.695	1.036
47	0.731	0.682	1.072
48	0.743	0.669	1.111
49	0.755	0.656	1.150
50	0.766	0.643	1.192
51	0.777	0.629	1.235
52	0.788	0.616	1.280
53	0.799	0.602	1.327
54	0.809	0.588	1.376
55	0.819	0.574	1.428
56	0.829	0.559	1.483
57	0.839	0.545	1.540
58	0.848	0.530	1.600
59	0.857	0.515	1.664

Angle A	sin A	cos A	tan A
60	0.866	0.500	1.732
61	0.875	0.485	1.804
62	0.883	0.469	1.881
63	0.891	0.454	1.963
64	0.899	0.438	2.050
65	0.906	0.423	2.145
66	0.914	0.407	2.246
67	0.921	0.391	2.356
68	0.927	0.375	2.475
69	0.934	0.358	2.605
70	0.940	0.342	2.747
71	0.946	0.326	2.904
72	0.951	0.309	3.078
73	0.956	0.292	3.271
74	0.961	0.276	3.487
75	0.966	0.259	3.732
76	0.970	0.242	4.011
77	0.974	0.225	4.331
78	0.978	0.208	4.705
79	0.982	0.191	5.145
80	0.985	0.174	5.671
81	0.988	0.156	6.314
82	0.990	0.139	7.115
83	0.993	0.122	8.144
84	0.995	0.105	9.514
85	0.996	0.087	11.430
86	0.998	0.070	14.301
87	0.999	0.052	19.081
88	0.999	0.035	28.636
89	1.000	0.017	57.290
90	1.000	0.000	

Table of Inverse Trigonometric Ratios

A	csc A	sec A	cot A
0		1.0000	
1	57.299	1.0002	57.290
2	28.654	1.0006	28.636
3	19.107	1.0014	19.081
4	14.336	1.0024	14.301
5	11.474	1.0038	11.4301
6	9.5668	1.0055	9.5144
7	8.2055	1.0075	8.1443
8	7.1853	1.0098	7.1154
9	6.3925	1.0125	6.3138
10	5.7588	1.0154	5.6713
11	5.2408	1.0187	5.1446
12	4.8097	1.0223	4.7046
13	4.4454	1.0263	4.3315
14	4.1336	1.0306	4.0108
15	3.8637	1.0353	3.7321
16	3.6280	1.0403	3.4874
17	3.4203	1.0457	3.2709
18	3.2361	1.0515	3.0777
19	3.0716	1.0576	2.9042
20	2.9238	1.0642	2.7475
21	2.7904	1.0711	2.6051
22	2.6695	1.0785	2.4751
23	2.5593	1.0864	2.3559
24	2.4586	1.0946	2.2460
25	2.3662	1.1034	2.1445
26	2.2812	1.1126	2.0503
27	2.2027	1.1223	1.9626
28	2.1301	1.1326	1.8807
29	2.0627	1.1434	1.8041

A	csc A	sec A	cot A
30	2.0000	1.1547	1.7321
31	1.9416	1.1666	1.6643
32	1.8871	1.1792	1.6003
33	1.8361	1.1924	1.5399
34	1.7883	1.2062	1.4826
35	1.7434	1.2208	1.4281
36	1.7013	1.2361	1.3764
37	1.6616	1.2521	1.3270
38	1.6243	1.2690	1.2799
39	1.5890	1.2868	1.2349
40	1.5557	1.3054	1.1918
41	1.5243	1.3250	1.1504
42	1.4945	1.3456	1.1106
43	1.4663	1.3673	1.0724
44	1.4396	1.3902	1.0355
45	1.4142	1.4142	1.0000
46	1.3902	1.4396	0.9657
47	1.3673	1.4663	0.9325
48	1.3456	1.4945	0.9004
49	1.3250	1.5243	0.8693
50	1.3054	1.5557	0.8391
51	1.2868	1.5890	0.8098
52	1.2690	1.6243	0.7813
53	1.2521	1.6616	0.7536
54	1.2361	1.7013	0.7265
55	1.2208	1.7434	0.7002
56	1.2062	1.7883	0.6745
57	1.1924	1.8361	0.6494
58	1.1792	1.8871	0.6249
59	1.1666	1.9416	0.6009

A	csc A	sec A	cot A
60	1.1547	2.0000	0.5774
61	1.1434	2.0627	0.5543
62	1.1326	2.1301	0.5317
63	1.1223	2.2027	0.5095
64	1.1126	2.2812	0.4877
65	1.1034	2.3662	0.4663
66	1.0946	2.4586	0.4452
67	1.0864	2.5593	0.4245
68	1.0785	2.6695	0.4040
69	1.0711	2.7904	0.3839
70	1.0642	2.9238	0.3640
71	1.0576	3.0716	0.3443
72	1.0515	3.2361	0.3249
73	1.0457	3.4203	0.3057
74	1.0403	3.6280	0.2867
75	1.0353	3.8637	0.2679
76	1.0306	4.1336	0.2493
77	1.0263	4.4454	0.2309
78	1.0223	4.8097	0.2126
79	1.0187	5.2408	0.1944
80	1.0154	5.7588	0.1763
81	1.0125	6.3925	0.1584
82	1.0098	7.1853	0.1405
83	1.0075	8.2055	0.1228
84	1.0055	9.5668	0.1051
85	1.0038	11.474	0.0875
86	1.0024	14.336	0.0699
87	1.0014	19.107	0.0524
88	1.0006	28.654	0.0349
89	1.0002	57.299	0.0175
90	1.0000		0.0000

Answer Key

Unit 1

Page 3

2. (a) 6 h 8 min (c) 3 h 18 min
(b) 2 h 55 min (d) 4 h 12 min

3. (a) $167
(b) $139.50
(c) $669
(d) 4 h 52 min
(e) 6 h 32 min
(f) stop-over in Toronto

4. (a) 2 h 40 min
(b) AC 247
(c) 1 h 50 min
(d) 3 h

5. (a) 10:00
(b) 23:20

6. (a) 4 h 10 min
(b) 4 h 50 min
(c) Answers will vary.

Page 5

4. (a) 38.85 (f) 2.4
(b) 22.33 (g) 0.24
(c) 0.01345 (h) 0.06
(d) 3470 (i) 60
(e) 7500 (j) 0.6

5. (a) 4 (g) 480
(b) 16 (h) 66
(c) 28 (i) 24
(d) 5 (j) 6
(e) 47 (k) 25
(f) 5

6. (a) -6 (h) 21
(b) -12 (i) 14
(c) -160 (j) -2
(d) 47 (k) -5
(e) -30 (l) -390
(f) -39 (m) -136
(g) -6

7. Andy is the winner.
His score is 9.4

8. (a) 24.29 (d) 105
(b) 12.1 (e) 0.27
(c) 0.06

Page 8

4. (a) -1 (d) $\frac{19}{24}$
(b) -5 (e) $\frac{17}{24}$
(c) $-\frac{161}{36}$

5. (a) -4 (d) $\frac{8}{27}$
(b) 5 (e) $\frac{9}{49}$
(c) $-\frac{5}{6}$ (f) $-\frac{1}{3}$

6. (a) $10\frac{1}{8}$, $12\frac{5}{8}$
(b) Loss of $812.50
(c) Profit of $2220.00
(d) $450.00 could be saved

7. (a) $\frac{38}{29}$ (f) $\frac{32}{27}$
(b) $\frac{7}{36}$ (g) $-\frac{23}{10}$
(c) $-\frac{35}{36}$ (h) $-\frac{9}{40}$
(d) $-\frac{5}{6}$ (i) $-\frac{39}{10}$
(e) $-\frac{6}{5}$ (j) $\frac{13}{10}$

Page 10

4. (a) 38% (h) 37.5%
(b) 12.5% (i) 93.75%
(c) 5.7% (j) 88.9%
(d) 0.5% (k) 41.7%
(e) 120% (l) 125%
(f) 307.5% (m) 962.5%
(g) 1.25% (n) 1155.6%

5. (a) 0.06 (i) 0.005
(b) 0.098 (j) 0.0075
(c) 0.7223 (k) 0.1225
(d) 0.355 (l) 0.0675
(e) 0.0125 (m) 0.157
(f) 0.1005 (n) 0.0175
(g) 0.006 (o) 0.168
(h) 1.482

6. (a) $\frac{1}{4}$ (d) $\frac{1}{3}$
(b) $\frac{11}{20}$ (e) $\frac{1}{16}$
(c) $1\frac{1}{5}$ (f) $\frac{1}{12}$

7. (a) $10 (f) $128
(b) $30 (g) $3.75
(c) $24 (h) $0.30
(d) $1.80 (i) $243.60
(e) $3 (j) $1.17

8. (a) 40% (d) 250%
(b) 7.5% (e) 5.25%
(c) 75%

9. $25 800

10. (a) $3.36
(b) $16\frac{2}{3}$%

11. 22.2%

12. (a) $119
(b) $128.52

13. No

14. 15.05

Page 12

1. (a) -16 (g) -1.97
(b) 130 (h) 0.2
(c) 104 (i) $\frac{13}{7}$
(d) -8 (j) $-\frac{17}{16}$
(e) 315 (k) $\frac{21}{22}$
(f) 80

2. (a) 40 wpm
(b) 65 wpm

3. (a) 20 Ω
(b) 8 Ω
(c) 6.1 Ω

4. (a) 77 cm^2
(b) 103.74 cm^2

5. (a) 210
(b) 5050

6. (a) 6 L/100 km
(b) 3.3 L/100 km
(c) 3.2 L/100 km

7. (a) 34.76 cm^2
(b) 1.738 cm^2

8. (a) 12.8°C
(b) 3.3°C
(c) -34.44°C

9. (a) 90%
(b) 93.125%

10. (a) $100
(b) $4285.72
(c) $333.33

11. Sue

12. (a) 6 cm
(b) 4 cm
(c) 3.43 cm

1. (a) 477.792 383
   (b) 99.262 023
   (c) 52.834 92
   (d) 486.459 506

2. (a) 17; 18.32
   (b) 34; 20.521
   (c) 160; 187.45
   (d) 30; 41.26
   (e) 7; 13.00
   (f) 34; 23.59

3. 911 760

4. (a) 400; 338.64
   (b) 800; 694.54
   (c) 1; 0.29
   (d) 1.2; 1.69

5. (a) 4290; 442 890; 44 428 890; 4 444 288 890
   (b) 1088; 110 888; 11 108 888; 111 110 888 888
   (c) 8649; 986 049; 99 860 049; 99 999 860 000 049
   (d) 444 440 808 887

1. (a) 6
   (b) 15
   (c) 2
   (d) 8
   (e) 180

2. (a) $I = P*R*T*$
   (b) $a = M*V \uparrow 2$
   (c) $b = (3*x - 2*y)/5$
   (d) $k = ((a + b)*(a - b))/(a \uparrow 2 + 1)$

3. (a) $5x + x^2$
   (b) $4xy + \frac{3}{z}$
   (c) $\frac{4xy + 3}{z^2}$
   (d) $3x^2 + 5x + 7 = 0$
   (e) $x = \frac{3}{(y + 1)^2}$

4. $50\ C = 23.50*D + 0.09*K$

5. (a) 10 PRINT ''HOW MANY KILOMETRES DID THE CUSTOMER DRIVE?''
   20 INPUT K
   30 C = 49 + 0.19K
   40 PRINT ''THE CAR

RENTAL COST IS $'';C
50 GOTO 10

   (b) Renting at the regular rates is cheaper for all the distances except for 100 km.

6. 10 PRINT ''HOW MANY DAYS HAVE THE CASSETTES BEEN RENTED?''
   20 INPUT D
   3O PRINT ''HOW MANY CASSETTES DID THE CUSTOMER RENT?''
   40 INPUT K
   50 C = 15.90*D + 7.98*K
   60 PRINT ''THE CAR RENTAL COST IS $'';C
   70 GOTO 10

7. 10 PRINT ''HOW MUCH MONEY IS INVESTED (IN DOLLARS)?''
   20 INPUT P
   30 PRINT ''WHAT IS THE RATE OF INTEREST (EXPRESS AS A DECIMAL)?''
   40 INPUT R
   50 PRINT ''FOR HOW MANY MONTHS WAS THE MONEY INVESTED (EXPRESS AS A FRACTION OF A YEAR)?''
   60 INPUT T
   70 I = PRT
   80 PRINT ''THE INTEREST EARNED ON THIS INVESTMENT IS '';I
   90 GOTO 10

1. 1.65 cm
2. 208 kPa
3. (a) 879 kg
   (b) 586 kg

4. 87.50 cm

1. (a) 71.4   (d) 43.47
   (b) 68.25   (e) 72.27
   (c) 63.0

1. (a) 75   (g) 0
   (b) 4   (h) −7
   (c) 7   (i) 116
   (d) 4   (j) 2.75
   (e) 15   (k) 600
   (f) 5

2. (a) $-\frac{29}{24}$ (d) $\frac{19}{2}$
   (b) 98   (e) $\frac{26}{15}$
   (c) $-\frac{1}{15}$ (f) $-\frac{11}{6}$

3. (a) 27%   (f) 45%
   (b) 75.5%   (g) 44%
   (c) 200%   (h) 62.5%
   (d) 0.5%   (i) 121%
   (e) 150%   (j) 4.05%

4. (a) 0.65   (d) 0.022
   (b) 1.20   (e) 0.935
   (c) 0.064   (f) 0.0075

5. (a) 77%
   (b) 73%
   (c) 70%

6. (a) 3.02%
   (b) 278.8 kg copper, 30.6 kg iron, 18.7 kg tin, 1.36 kg lead, 0.272 kg magnesium, 10.268 kg zinc

7. $607.50

8. 17%

9. (a) 41   (e) 68
   (b) 48   (f) 26
   (c) 1   (g) 62.8
   (d) −45

10. (a) 48%/a
    (b) 30%/a

11. (a) 92.8 cm
    (b) 116.2 cm

12. (a) 10; 10.79
    (b) 18; 17.92
    (c) 3; 2.92
    (d) 180; 164.76
    (e) 13; 13.62

Side Trip

1. 527

2. 1056

3. 2236

4. 9250

Unit 2

Page 25

3. (a) 16   (n) 1
    (b) 16   (o) −1
    (c) −16   (p) 6
    (d) 0   (q) 0
    (e) 7   (r) 512
    (f) 45   (s) 512
    (g) 81   (t) 7
    (h) 64   (u) 5
    (i) $\frac{8}{125}$ (v) 36
    (j) $-\frac{27}{8}$ (w) 12
    (k) 80   (x) 6
    (l) 10 000   (y) −2
    (m) −80   (z) −49

4. (a) 120   (g) 240
    (b) 10   (h) −28
    (c) 11   (i) 5
    (d) −120   (j) 24
    (e) −48   (k) 9
    (f) 16   (l) −64

5. (a) $(1.2)^5$; 2.49
    (b) $600(1.8)^6$; 20 407.33
    (c) $(1.3)^4 (1.5)^3$; 9.64
    (d) $(2.31)^4(90)$; 2562.66

6. (a) 1.86
    (b) 1077.51
    (c) 166.82
    (d) 7.66

Side Trip

1. Decimals: 0.1428..., 0.2857..., 0.4285..., 0.5714...,0.7142..., 0.8571....

3.

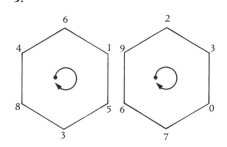

Page 27

3. (a) a^{20} (i) $9x^{120}$
    (b) a^{36} (j) $8x^{21}$
    (c) a^{144} (k) 10^{38}
    (d) a^4 (l) 7^{18}
    (e) $49x^{10}$ (m) $16x^{240}$
    (f) $7x^{10}$ (n) 3^{24}
    (g) $24y^{10}$ (o) $81a^{24}$
    (h) 3^{120}

4. (a) x^4 (h) 2^{60}
    (b) a^{60} (i) 3^{66}
    (c) a^{120} (j) 10^{55}
    (d) $125a^{24}$ (k) $4x^6$
    (e) $-36x^{18}$ (l) $8ab^5$
    (f) a^{14} (m) a
    (g) a^{16}

5. (a) a^{30} (d) $2x^8y^{23}$
    (b) $\frac{-8}{3}a^7b$ (e) c^{24}
    (c) $4x^6y^8$

6. (a) 16   (d) 25
    (b) 81   (e) 10 000
    (c) 64

Page 29

4. (a) 14   (h) −28
    (b) 10   (i) 6
    (c) 48   (j) 2
    (d) 40   (k) 22
    (e) 30   (l) −19
    (f) 7000   (m) 65
    (g) −40

5. (a) 7.81   (c) 55.68
    (b) 8.77   (d) 2.26

6. (a) 6   (e) 6.48
    (b) 10   (f) 5.20
    (c) 5.74   (g) 5.66
    (d) 8.66   (h) 3.16

7. (a) x^7y (e) x^6
    (b) $3x^{10}y^3$ (f) $8x^{15}$
    (c) $10x^8$ (g) $6a^6b^3$
    (d) $12a^4b^5$

8. (a) 6   (f) 3
    (b) 30   (g) 120
    (c) 5   (h) 6.32
    (d) 2   (i) 1.60
    (e) 6

9. (a) 2.24 A
    (b) 1.41 A

10. 5.11 cm

11. 8.6 cm

12. (a) 10.95 m
    (b) 14.14 m

Page 31

2. (a) repeating
    (b) terminating
    (c) terminating
    (d) terminating
    (e) repeating
    (f) repeating

Side Trip

1. (a) $0.\dot{7}$ (e) $0.0\dot{5}\dot{3}$
    (b) $0.\dot{4}$ (f) $0.00\dot{2}$
    (c) $0.\dot{2}\dot{3}$ (g) $0.423\dot{5}$
    (d) $0.11\dot{9}$

2. (a) $\frac{8}{9}$ (e) $\frac{352}{999}$
    (b) $\frac{9}{9}$ (f) $\frac{5}{999}$
    (c) $\frac{71}{99}$ (g) $\frac{1234}{9999}$
    (d) $\frac{24}{99}$ (h) $-2\frac{52}{99}$

Page 34

3. (a) 7   (h) 10
    (b) 5   (i) −10
    (c) 12   (j) 3
    (d) 512   (k) 10
    (e) 2   (l) −2
    (f) 9   (m) $\frac{3}{2}$
    (g) 8

4. (a) 49   (g) 6
    (b) 4   (h) 2
    (c) $\frac{2}{3}$ (i) 2
    (d) $\frac{2}{5}$ (j) $\frac{5}{4}$
    (e) $\frac{4}{3}$ (k) −2
    (f) $\frac{1}{2}$

5. (a) c^{10} (f) c^5
    (b) $x^{10} y^3$ (g) a^3b^{10}
    (c) a^5b (h) $3x^4$
    (d) $2a^4$ (i) $10a^8$
    (e) $6x^3$ (j) $5x^6y$

6. (a) 2   (d) 2
    (b) 9   (e) 2
    (c) 10   (f) 5

7. (a) 2.24   (e) 2.37
   (b) 1.91   (f) 3.43
   (c) 1.82   (g) 6.03
   (d) 2.51   (h) 1.91

Side Trip

1. 4   **6.** 8
2. 8   **7.** 4
3. 125   **8.** 100 000
4. 81   **9.** 27
5. 32   **10.** −1024

Page 35

4. (a) $\frac{1}{16}$ (g) $2\frac{1}{4}$
   (b) 16   (h) $\frac{125}{64}$
   (c) $\frac{1}{125}$ (i) $\frac{1}{10\,000}$
   (d) $\frac{1}{9}$ (j) $1\frac{1}{100}$
   (e) $-\frac{1}{27}$ (k) $\frac{9}{25}$
   (f) $\frac{4}{3}$

5. (a) $\frac{1}{2}$ (g) $\frac{1}{2}$
   (b) $\frac{1}{3}$ (h) $1\frac{1}{5}$
   (c) $\frac{1}{2}$ (i) 2
   (d) $\frac{1}{5}$ (j) $-\frac{1}{2}$
   (e) $\frac{1}{16}$ (k) −2
   (f) $\frac{3}{2}$ (l) 2

6. (a) $\frac{3}{2}$ (g) $\frac{3}{2}$
   (b) $\frac{5}{6}$ (h) $\frac{19}{8}$
   (c) $\frac{3}{4}$ (i) $\frac{5}{24}$
   (d) 5   (j) −1
   (e) 16   (k) 4
   (f) $4\frac{1}{4}$

7. (a) $45a^{-3}$ (f) $36a^{-2}\,b^{-8}$
   (b) $63x^{-10}$ (g) $x^{12}y^{-10}$
   (c) $a^{-15}b^3$ (h) $\frac{1}{9}x^6$
   (d) $3a^{-4}$ (i) $\frac{1}{8x^{15}}$
   (e) $9x^9y^3$ (j) a^{26}

8. (a) $\frac{1}{49}$ (f) $\frac{1}{64}$
   (b) $\frac{1}{225}$ (g) $\frac{1}{6}$
   (c) $\frac{1}{64}$ (h) 16
   (d) 1   (i) $\frac{3}{2}$
   (e) $\frac{1}{9}$ (j) 12

9. (a) 0.06   (d) 0.55
   (b) 0.08   (e) 0.98
   (c) 0.86   (f) 0.97

10. (a) 0.0002   (c) 128.79
    (b) 0.55   (d) 0.63

Page 37

1. (a) $1007.54
   (b) $2113.11

2. (a) $262.16
   (b) $12 136.67
   (c) $5031.33

3. (a) 10 m
   (b) 10.20 m
   (c) 10.21 m

4. (a) 54 cm
   (b) 150 cm
   (c) 81.43 cm

5. (a) 9.1%
   (b) 20.1%

6. (a) 9.04 cm
   (b) 56.5 cm
   (c) 7.15 cm

7. (a) 64 km/h
   (b) 40 km/h
   (c) 80 km/h
   (d) 32 km/h
   (e) 64 km/h
   The car, having a skid mark 4 times longer, is going twice as fast.

8. (a) 60 cm
   (b) 180 cm
   (c) 67 cm

9. (a) $1.20
   (b) $24.67

10. 1.8 s

11. (a) 2.88 cm
   (b) 1.81 m
   (c) 10.61 m

12. (a) $108.95
   (b) $125.92
   Increase in the monthly payment is 16%.

Page 42

2. (a) 9.5×10^8
   (b) 1.4×10^{-8}
   (c) 1.274×10^9 cm
   (d) 5.983×10^{24} kg
   (e) 7.6×10^{-5} cm
   (f) 1.4×10^{12} km^3
   (g) 3.0×10^8 m/s
   (h) 4.8×10^9 operations per minute

3. (a) 5.74×10^{10}
   (b) 4.30×10^{-5}
   (c) 1.00×10^{-2}
   (d) 6.43×10^6
   (e) 4.48×10^9

4. (a) 74 000 000
   (b) 0.000 0031
   (c) 8000
   (d) 0.18
   (e) 0.000 030

5. (a) 2 800 000 000
   (b) 0.000 60
   (c) 0.000 000 20
   (d) 2000
   (e) 0.000 32
   (f) 0.000 000 000 50
   (g) 40 000
   (h) 41 000 000
   (i) 240 000

6. (a) 18 000
   (b) 30
   (c) 0.2
   (d) 350 000 000
   (e) 0.009
   (f) 0.0025
   (g) 0.000 0004

7. 5.0×10^2 s

8. 4×10^{11} L

9. 3.3×10^5

10. 8×10^4 t

11. 7.6%

12. 2×10^{11}

Page 44

1. (a) 3.54 cm   (b) 13.42 cm

2. (a) 9   (c) 4.02 cm
   (b) 4

1. (a) F   (f) F
   (b) T   (g) F
   (c) F   (h) T
   (d) T   (i) T
   (e) F   (j) T

2. (a) 81   (k) $\frac{5}{4}$
   (b) 81   (l) $1\frac{9}{16}$
   (c) -81 (m) $\frac{4}{9}$
   (d) $\frac{1}{81}$ (n) $-\frac{1}{64}$
   (e) 3   (o) 3
   (f) $\frac{1}{3}$ (p) 1
   (g) 27   (q) $4\frac{2}{3}$
   (h) $\frac{1}{3}$ (r) $\frac{3}{5}$
   (i) not   (s) 3
      possible   (t) $\frac{1}{3}$
   (j) -3 (u) -3
              (v) $-\frac{1}{3}$

3. (a) c^{15} (j) $12a^{25}b^5$
   (b) c^{26} (k) $25a^8b^{10}$
   (c) c^{72} (l) $-64m^{27}$
   (d) m^{18} (m) x^{18}
   (e) m^{32} (n) $4x^8$
   (f) $16x^{12}$ (o) $2x^2y$
   (g) $4x^{12}$ (p) c^{10}
   (h) 4^{12} (q) $-6a^{10}$
   (i) $12x^{13}y^{15}$

4. (a) 8   (d) $\frac{1}{25}$
   (b) 9   (e) $\frac{1}{1000}$
   (c) 1

5. (a) x^4 (f) $-48x^2$
   (b) c^{-16} (g) $20x^{-6}y^{-8}$
   (c) c^{60} (h) $a^{20}b^{-15}$
   (d) c^4 (i) $-2a^7b^{-5}$
   (e) $7a^{-20}$ (j) $24a^2$

6. (a) 1000   (h) $1\frac{1}{25}$
   (b) 100 000   (i) $\frac{3}{8}$
   (c) $\frac{1}{9}$ (j) $-\frac{1}{3}$
   (d) 3   (k) 2
   (e) $\frac{2}{5}$ (l) 110
   (f) $\frac{81}{16}$ (m) 18
   (g) $\frac{3}{2}$ (n) $-\frac{3}{4}$

7. (a) 6   (e) $\frac{1}{5}$
   (b) 7   (f) 10
   (c) 1   (g) 4
   (d) 24   (h) 28

8. (a) 8.92   (f) 3.49
   (b) 288.38   (g) 0.08
   (c) 256.58   (h) 0.002
   (d) 3.46   (i) 0.54
   (e) 4.80   (j) 0.13

9. (a) 1.87
   (b) 0.79
   (c) 6.76

10. (a) 8.09 m

11. (a) \$630.81
   (b) \$12 049.26

12. (a) 8.4 cm; 11.9 cm
   (b) No

13. (a) 75 300; 75 000
   (b) 9.30×10^{40}; 9.3×10^{40}
   (c) 0.000 0600; 0.000 060
   (d) 4.75×10^{-7}; 4.7×10^{-7}

14. (a) 8.7×10^{10}
   (b) 2.5×10^{-6}
   (c) 9.3×10^{14}
   (d) 5.4×10^{-11}

15. (a) 5890
   (b) 0.000 0729
   (c) 0.000 000 042 5
   (d) 928
   (e) 0.000 001 25
   (f) 419

16. (a) 9   (d) $\frac{1}{81}$
   (b) 1   (e) 80
   (c) 12   (f) $-\frac{1}{9}$

Unit 3

7. (a) $39k - 2p$
   (b) $6a + 12b$
   (c) $-x - 19y$
   (d) $14a^2 - 25a$
   (e) 9
   (f) $19x^2 - 26x - 14$
   (g) $-12a^2b^3 - 10a^3b^2$
   (h) $-8c^2 + 23cy - 5y^2$
   (i) $-17t^3 + 13t^2$
   (j) 0

8. (a) $4a + 3b + 3c$
   (b) $4x - 14y - 4z$
   (c) $-7x$
   (d) $2p + 2q - 10r$
   (e) $-2w^2 + 4w + 9$
   (f) $6ab - 2ac - 5a$

9. (a) $90abc$ (f) $-9x^{12}$
   (b) $17a^2$ (g) $47qr$
   (c) $-35x^3$ (h) $-15y$
   (d) $-9ac$ (i) $-5x$
   (e) $-26y$ (j) $60x^2$

10. (a) $8x + 14$
   (b) $12x + 4y$
   (c) $20a + 6b$

3. (a) $3ac - 5ab$
   (b) $10xz + 120zy$
   (c) $-6gr + 27r$
   (d) $-5w^2 - 3aw$
   (e) $28t^6 - 36t^2$
   (f) $48m - 120m^2 + 6am$
   (g) $-r^3 - 2r^2$
   (h) $18y^2 - 54y$
   (i) $3x^3 - 18x^2 + 48x$
   (j) $-6a^2b + 48a^2b^2$

4. (a) $19x + 36$
   (b) $21x - 21y$
   (c) $58c - 53$
   (d) $26a - 30$
   (e) $13x + 37y$
   (f) $4k + 17m$
   (g) $5t - 14$
   (h) $6a - 58b - 78c$
   (i) -3
   (j) $15y - 12a$

5. (a) $15x - 51y$
   (b) $-14a - 14b + 21c$
   (c) $22m^2 - 36m - 10$
   (d) $26ax - 5xy$
   (e) $4x^2 - 32x$
   (f) $-3a^2 + 2a$
   (g) $10w^2 + 17tw - 22t^2$
   (h) $-20c^3 + 11c^2 + c$
   (i) $-3w^2$
   (j) $30x^2y - 52x^2y^2 - 8xy^2$

6. (a) $96 - 32a$
(b) $12x - 24$
(c) $-52a^2 + 12a$
(d) $21y^2 - 57y$
(e) $-9t - 5$
(f) $3c - 32$
(g) $39x + 27$
(h) $32a^3 - 4a^2$
(i) $3z - 45$
(j) $-9w^3 + 17w^2$

7. (a) $48x^2 - 40x$
(b) $11x^2 + 11x$
(c) $11x^2 - 10x$

8. (a) $26a + 6;\ 14a^2 + 4a$
(b) $12a + 8;\ 6a^2 + 12a$

9. (a) $20x^2 - 24x$
(b) $9y^2 + 18y + 18$

Page 55

2. (a) $t^2 + 14t + 48$
(b) $6a^2 + 23a + 20$
(c) $x^2 + 3x - 70$
(d) $d^2 + 2d - 99$
(e) $y^2 - 9y + 18$
(f) $2p^2 + 3p - 20$
(g) $6r^2 + 15r - 9$
(h) $12c^2 - 34c + 20$
(i) $-4c + 20$
(j) $16s^2 - 9$
(k) $25x^2 + 30x + 9$
(l) $16r^2 - 56r + 49$
(m) $9a^2 - 48a + 64$
(n) $9a^2 - 64$

3. (a) $a^2 + 5ac + 6c^2$
(b) $6x^2 + 7xy + 2y^2$
(c) $6w^2 + 7tw - 3t^2$
(d) $30x^2 + 19xy - 4y^2$
(e) $21m^2 - 52mn + 32n^2$
(f) $20b^2 - 23bq + 6q^2$
(g) $a^2 + 10ax + 25x^2$
(h) $9c^2 - 24cb + 16b^2$
(i) $100y^2 - 49t^2$
(j) $3a^2 + 2aq - 16q^2$
(k) $12x^4 + 11x^3 + 2x^2$
(l) $14a^2b^2 - 29ab + 12$

4. (a) $a^2 + 5a + 14$
(b) $2w^2 - 3w - 11$
(c) $2x^2 - 23$
(d) $3y^2 - 16y - 65$
(e) $5a^2 - 11a - 25$

5. (a) $4x^2 + 8x - 96$
(b) $6a^2 - 15a - 54$
(c) $-4w^2 + 22w - 24$
(d) $-15a^2 - 20a + 20$
(e) $12x^2 + 42xy - 24y^2$

6. (a) $4a^2 + 17a - 36$
(b) $6x^2 - 6x - 12$
(c) $2a^2 + 2a + 41$
(d) $2y^2 - 10y + 73$
(e) $7s^2 - 18s - 15$
(f) $5x^2 - 8x + 14$
(g) $5a^2 - 6a + 52$

7. (a) $-a^2 - 18a - 60$
(b) $-9x - 43$
(c) $x^2 - 13x + 69$
(d) $2c + 7$
(e) $-y^2 - 29y + 60$
(f) $-2a^2 + 35a + 24$
(g) $w^2 + 12w + 24$
(h) $x^3 + 7x^2 + 17x + 14$
(i) $x^3 - 7x^2 + 21x - 27$

8. $x^2 + 23x + 24$

Page 57

3. (a) $x + 2n$
(b) $2a - 1$
(c) $-3x - 4p$
(d) $-4a + 5p$
(e) $4x + 7$
(f) $2a - b + 8c$
(g) $s + 2$
(h) $y - 2 + x$
(i) $-5w + 4q - 9r$
(j) $-x^2 - 3x + 4$

4. (a) $4t$
(b) $-9s - 6$
(c) $-3r + 4s$
(d) $2x + 10 - 3y$
(e) $8y - 10$

5. (a) $6(2w - 3)$
(b) $10(5x + 2)$
(c) $8(8a - 3)$

(d) $5(1 - 6p)$
(e) $3(2s - 3t + 4)$
(f) $4(5x + 8y)$
(g) $8(5w - 3 + t)$
(h) $6(5s + 2q - 1)$
(i) $8(2p - 7q)$
(j) $15(6 + p)$
(k) $x(a + 6)$
(l) $y(21x - 5)$
(m) $t(t - 8)$
(n) $x(4 - x)$
(o) $p(a + t - 1)$
(p) $r(9 - s + r^2)$
(q) $y^2(y^2 + 3y - 2)$
(r) $a(1 - a^2 + 3a^4)$
(s) $3r^3(2r^3 + 1)$
(t) $2s(2 + 5t)$

6. (a) $3x(5 + 4y)$
(b) $4x(8x - 7)$
(c) $8t^2(5t^2 + 1)$
(d) $3a(4a - 3b)$
(e) $15y(4 - 3y)$
(f) $25w^2(3w^4 + 2)$
(g) $3n^2(3n^3 - 1)$
(h) $2x^2(1 + 5x^2 - 4x^4)$
(i) $5s(7r - 11t + 1)$
(j) $ab(c + d - e)$
(k) $bc(2 - 7a)$
(l) $3m^3(1 + 3m^6 - 2m^3)$
(m) $3w^2(4q - 5w)$
(n) $12x^4(10 + 3x^2y)$

7. (a) $2qr(5p - 9t + 11s)$
(b) $6mn(2 + 7m)$
(c) $rt(5t - 8r - rt)$
(d) $16z(5z^3 - 2z + 4)$
(e) $(x + 6)\,(x + 9)$
(f) $(3a + 7)\,(a - 4)$
(g) $(5r - 3s)\,(r + s)$
(h) $3(m + 6)\,(a - 2x)$
(i) $(p + 1)\,(p + 8)$
(j) $(4x - 1)\,(x - 6)$

Page 59

3. (a) $(x + 3)\,(x + 4)$
(b) $(x + 2)\,(x + 6)$
(c) $(x + 1)\,(x + 12)$
(d) $(x + 2)\,(x + 11)$

466

(e) $(a + 3) (a + 10)$
(f) $(y + 4) (y + 5)$
(g) $(s + 4) (s + 10)$
(h) $(f + 1) (f + 1)$
(i) $(w + 1) (w + 5)$
(j) $(m + 2) (m + 3)$
(k) $(y - 2) (y - 7)$
(l) $(v - 1) (v - 4)$
(m) $(a - 5) (a - 10)$
(n) $(b - 2) (b - 25)$
(o) $(c - 6) (c - 10)$
(p) $(d - 4) (d - 15)$
(q) $(q - 1) (q - 2)$
(r) $(x - 2) (x - 12)$
(s) $(p - 10) (p - 10)$
(t) $(6 - s) (4 - s)$

4. (a) $(x - 5) (x + 2)$
(b) $(y - 5) (y + 3)$
(c) $(a - 3) (a + 5)$
(d) $(b - 3) (b + 10)$
(e) $(c - 5) (c + 4)$
(f) $(z - 9) (z + 3)$
(g) $(q + 12) (q - 1)$
(h) $(k - 8) (k + 5)$
(i) $(t + 7) (t - 6)$
(j) $(n + 12) (n - 4)$
(k) $(s - 12) (s - 2)$
(l) $(t - 6) (t + 4)$
(m) $(v + 24) (v - 1)$
(n) $(q + 3) (q + 8)$
(o) $(w - 6) (w - 6)$
(p) $(y - 9) (y + 4)$
(q) $(h + 8) (h - 7)$
(r) $(p + 4) (p + 8)$
(s) $(z - 20) (z + 3)$
(t) $(m - 4) (m - 15)$

5. (a) $(x + 2y) (x + 4y)$
(b) $(a - 2b) (a - 8b)$
(c) $(c - 5d) (c + 4d)$
(d) $(x - 5y) (x + 9y)$
(e) $(p - q) (p - q)$
(f) $(r + 8s) (r - 6s)$
(g) $(q + 4r) (q + 12r)$
(h) $(t - 9v) (t - v)$
(i) $(q - 10w) (q + 3w)$
(j) $(xy - 4) (xy + 9)$

6. (a) $2(a + 3)^2$
(b) $3(x - 2) (x - 5)$
(c) $5(z - 3) (z + 2)$
(d) $2(b - 3) (b + 8)$
(e) $6(c - 3) (c + 1)$
(f) $3(q + 7) (q - 2)$
(g) $12(m - 1) (m - 6)$
(h) $x(x - 3) (x + 7)$
(i) $2a(a + 1) (a + 3)$
(j) $x(y - 8) (y + 9)$
(k) $4t(t - 5) (t + 3)$
(l) $2(x + 2y) (x + 3y)$
(m) $4(a - 3b) (a + 4b)$
(n) $s(s - 3t) (s - 11t)$
(o) $3b(a - 2) (a + 5)$

7. (a) 9500
(b) $(x - 5) (x - 10); 9500$

8. (a) $11\ 000$
(b) $996\ 000$
(c) 1.6864
(d) 400
(e) 1.41

Side Trip

1. 520

2. 3256

3. 1344

4. 7799

5. 7245

6. 6335

7. 665

8. 4180

9. $10\ 872$

10. $64\ 480$

Page 63

3. (a) $(2x + 5) (x + 2)$
(b) $(2x - 1) (8x - 1)$
(c) $(2x + 3) (2x - 1)$
(d) $(2x - 3) (3x + 1)$
(e) $(7a - 2) (3a + 1)$
(f) $(3z - 4) (4z - 1)$

4. (a) $(2a + 1) (a + 3)$
(b) $(3x + 1) (x + 5)$
(c) $(3x + 5) (x + 1)$
(d) $(5x + 3) (x + 1)$
(e) $(3x - 7) (x - 1)$
(f) $(5y - 1) (y - 7)$
(g) $(2t - 1) (2t - 3)$
(h) $(3a + 7) (a - 1)$
(i) $(3x + 2) (x - 2)$
(j) $(2y - 1) (2y + 5)$
(k) $(3t + 1) (2t - 5)$
(l) $(2x - 1) (5x - 3)$

5. (a) $(3a + 2)(a + 2)$
(b) $(4x - 1)(x - 3)$
(c) $(2x - 1)(3x - 5)$
(d) $(2y + 5) (3y + 1)$
(e) $(x - 3)(5x - 2)$
(f) $(5t - 1)(t + 6)$
(g) $(4x + 1)(2x + 5)$
(h) $(10a + 1)(a - 2)$
(i) $(3w + 2)(4w + 1)$
(j) $(5a - 2)(5a + 1)$
(k) $(2c + 1)(6c + 5)$
(l) $(12c + 5)(c + 1)$

6. (a) $(3t - 4)(t + 1)$
(b) $(4t - 3)(t + 1)$
(c) $(3x + 4)(2x + 1)$
(d) $(16y - 1)(y - 2)$
(e) $(5t - 1)(t + 4)$
(f) $(5t + 4)(t - 1)$
(g) $(5a + 1)(3a + 2)$
(h) $(3s + 1)(3s - 4)$
(i) $(3s - 1)(3s - 4)$
(j) $(3s - 2)(3s - 2)$
(k) $(2w - 3)(w - 5)$
(l) $(2w - 15)(w + 1)$
(m) $(2v - 5)(v - 3)$
(n) $(10a + 1)(a + 6)$
(o) $(6s - 1)(s + 10)$
(p) $(2k - 11)(k + 1)$
(q) $(8x + 9)(x - 1)$
(r) $(8x - 9)(x - 1)$
(s) $(4x + 3)(2x - 3)$
(t) $(2y + 5)(5y - 2)$

7. (a) $(2x + 3)(3x + 2)$
(b) $(9x + 2)(2x + 1)$
(c) $(9x + 1)(4x + 1)$
(d) $(2x - 1)(9x + 2)$
(e) $(2x + 3)(3x - 2)$

467

(f) $(2t - 1)(10t - 5)$
(g) $(5t - 1)(4t + 5)$
(h) $(3s - 1)(7s - 2)$
(i) $(12r - 5)(2r + 1)$
(j) $(8w + 1)(w - 8)$

8. (a) $x(4x + 3)(x + 2)$
   (b) $y(9y - 2)(y - 1)$
   (c) $c^3(5c + 3)(c - 1)$
   (d) $a(2b - 1)(4b + 5)$
   (e) $100(3x - 1)(2x - 3)$

Page 64
2. (a) $(b + 6)(b - 6)$
   (b) $(5x + 7)(5x - 7)$
   (c) $(3xz - 2)(3xz + 2)$
   (d) $5(a + 1)(a - 1)$
   (e) $3(3 - 5c)(3 + 5c)$
   (f) $z(z - 10)(z + 10)$
   (g) $b(a + 8)(a - 8)$
   (h) $p(q + 1)(q - 1)$
   (i) $20(z - 5y)(z + 5y)$
   (j) $8(4x^2 + 1)$
   (k) $3(xy - 4)(xy + 4)$
   (l) $2w(2 - 3w)(2 + 3w)$
   (m) $t(ts - 1)(ts + 1)$
   (n) $(x^2 - 3)(x^2 + 3)$
   (o) $(y^3 - 10)(y^3 + 10)$
   (p) $(3z^3 + 11c)(3z^3 - 11c)$
   (q) $x(x^3 - 12)(x^3 + 12)$
   (r) $10(s - 5t)(s + 5t)$
   (s) $3z(z - 5)(z + 5)$
   (t) $4t(7s^{10} - 1)$

3. (a) $(y^2 + 9)(y + 3)(y - 3)$
   (b) $(x^2 + 4)(x + 2)(x - 2)$
   (c) $(4s^2 + 1)(2s + 1)(2s - 1)$
   (d) $(9q^2 + 25)(3q + 5)(3q - 5)$
   (e) $(a^2 + b^2)(a + b)(a - b)$
   (f) $(x^2 + 16y^2)(x + 4y)(x - 4y)$
   (g) $(a^2 - 2)(a^2 + 9)$
   (h) $(x^2 - 2)(x + 4)(x - 4)$
   (i) $(y^2 + 1)(y + 2)(y - 2)$
   (j) $(s + 1)(s - 1)(s^2 - 10)$
   (k) $(x + 1)(x - 1)(x + 3)(x - 3)$
   (l) $(p + 2)(p - 2)(p + 3)(p - 3)$

Page 65
1. (a) $q(p - r + 5)$
   (b) $2a(8a - 7b)$
   (c) $2(x - 3)(x + 7)$
   (d) $(q - 6)(q - 8)$

(e) $(x + 4)(x + 10)$
(f) $(y - 1)(y - 2)$
(g) $(h - 12)(h + 12)$
(h) $(3x - 7)(x - 1)$
(i) $(3y - 1)(2y + 3)$
(j) $9(w - 2b)(w + 2b)$
(k) $x(x - 2)(x + 2)$
(l) $(p - 11q)(p + 6q)$
(m) $x(x - 7)(x + 8)$
(n) $6x(x - 1)(x + 1)$
(o) $4x(x + 5)$
(p) $(2x - 1)(2x + 11)$
(q) $4(x - 1)(x + 6)$
(r) $3(x - 1)(x - 4)$
(s) $3x(x - 2)(x + 2)$
(t) $3x(x - 4)$
(u) $5(w + 2r)(w + 4r)$
(v) $(3z - 2)(z + 5)$
(w) $(3z - 10)(z - 1)$
(x) $3(z - 10)(z + 5)$

2. (a) $w(w - 16)$
   (b) $w(w - 4)(w + 4)$
   (c) $w(w - 2)(w + 2)(w^2 + 4)$
   (d) $(w - 2)(w - 14)$
   (e) $(w - 18)(w + 2)$
   (f) $w(w - 20)(w + 4)$
   (g) $2(w - 10)(w + 2)$
   (h) $(3w + 2)(w - 6)$
   (i) $w(3w - 4)(w - 4)$
   (j) $3(w - 4)(w + 3)$

Page 66
1. (a) 26   (c) 45
   (b) 96   (d) 67

2. (a) $23(8x - 5y)$
   (b) $34(13a - 7b)$
   (c) $51x(23x - 62)$

Page 67
1. (a) $-5a - 6b$
   (b) $8x^2 + 4x$
   (c) $12xy - 8xz + 6yz$
   (d) $-14st$
   (e) $18pqr$
   (f) $-30a^2bc$
   (g) $-48x^{16}$
   (h) $-3x^8$
   (i) $-12x^{12} + 4x^4$
   (j) $100x^{12}y^8$
   (k) 4

(l) $-25x^6y^4$
(m) $12x^2$
(n) $-33t^2$
(o) $-10r$
(p) $50w^3$
(q) $100w^4$
(r) $49w^2$
(s) $8x - 7y - 5z$
(t) $-3x + 5t - 12$
(u) $3x^2 - 16x$
(v) $4a - 4ab + b$
(w) $2x - 5y + z$
(x) $-2a + 7b - 1$
(y) $-2x^2 + 8x - 5$
(z) $-2t^3 + s^4$

2. (a) $20a - 30b + 45$
   (b) $-24x + 32y - 8z$
   (c) $8x^2 - 40xy$
   (d) $20t^3 - 15t^2$
   (e) $-6x^2 + 24x - 66$
   (f) $10a^2b + 15ab^2 - 5abc$
   (g) $-45x^2 + 54xy$
   (h) $4x + 6y$
   (i) $11b - 13$
   (j) $-19a + 20w$
   (k) $15z^2 - 86z$
   (l) $9a^2b^2 + 25a^2b$

3. (a) $y^2 + 16y + 63$
   (b) $x^2 - 16x + 48$
   (c) $a^2 + 9a - 70$
   (d) $x^2 - 4xy + 3y^2$
   (e) $40 - 3x - x^2$
   (f) $31a - 8$
   (g) $42a^2 + 10a - 8$
   (h) $14b^2 - 60pb + 16p^2$
   (i) $6x^2 + 28xy - 10y^2$
   (j) $25t^2 - 40t + 16$
   (k) $12x^2y^2 + 23xy + 5$
   (l) $36q^4 - 64t^2$

4. (a) $2k^2 - 5k - 52$
   (b) $28s^2 - 61s + 6$
   (c) $-3t^2 - 26t - 6$
   (d) $23 + 4y$
   (e) $7r^2 + 48r - 7$
   (f) $r^2 + 14r + 49$
   (g) $-3a^2 - 3ab + 18b^2$
   (h) $6w^2 + 24w + 20$
   (i) $a^2 - 43a + 54$
   (j) $12x^3 - 25x^2 - 9x + 28$

5. (a) $-44xy$
   (b) $-40x + 30$
   (c) -2
   (d) $-x - 4$
   (e) $-30x^2 + 96x$
   (f) $18x^2 - 30x + 50$
   (g) $-10x - 4$
   (h) $-2t + 4$

6. (a) $a(a + 5)$
   (b) $3a(4b - 5a + 1)$
   (c) $2xz(y - 3w + 2)$
   (d) $(3w + 7)(w - 5)$
   (e) $3xy(5x + 9)$
   (f) $(3a - 1)(4a - 3b)$

7. (a) $(c - 8)(c - 1)$
   (b) $(y + 4)(y - 12)$
   (c) $(z + 9)(z - 10)$
   (d) $(s + 2)(s + 45)$
   (e) $(q + 5)(q - 11)$
   (f) $(x - 2)(x + 35)$
   (g) $(a - 10)(a - 7)$
   (h) $(2a + 3)(a + 1)$
   (i) $(3a + 1)(a + 2)$
   (j) $(5a + 2)(a - 5)$
   (k) $(3y + 5)(y + 2)$
   (l) $(8s - 9)(s + 1)$
   (m) $(4s - 9)(2s - 1)$
   (n) $(6w + 5)(2w - 1)$
   (o) $(5a + 1)(4a - 5)$
   (p) $(6r - 1)(r - 11)$
   (q) $(4y - 3)(y + 3)$
   (r) $(10t + 3)(3t - 1)$

8. (a) $(q + 5)(q - 5)$
   (b) $t(t - 25)$
   (c) $(t - 5)(t - 20)$
   (d) $(t + 1)(t - 26)$
   (e) $2(a + 2)(a + 5)$
   (f) $2a(a - 10)(a + 3)$
   (g) $(3w + 11)(w + 1)$
   (h) $(8q - 1)(q + 4)$
   (i) $(2a - 5)(a + 4)$
   (j) $30(t - 2)(t + 2)$
   (k) $30t(t - 2)(t + 2)$
   (l) $30(t - 5)(t + 1)$
   (m) $(5t + 1)(6t + 1)$
   (n) $(r - 9t)(r + 7t)$
   (o) $(3y - x)(4y + 5x)$
   (p) $(xy + 9)(xy + 3)$
   (q) $2(m - 7n)(m + 4n)$

   (r) $(2r + 3s)(r - 3s)$
   (s) $2(5t - 7s)(5t + 7s)$
   (t) $(w^2 + 5)(w + 2)(w - 2)$

Side Trip

1. $(y + 7)(y - 3)$ **5.** $8(t + 4)$

2. $x(x - 6)$ **6.** $-11(2s + 3)$

3. $a(a + 2b)$ **7.** $-5(2w - 11)$

4. $(x - 1)(x + 11)$ **8.** $3(w + 1)(w + 3)$

Unit 4

Page 71

4. (a) -5 (e) 20
   (b) 8 (f) 4
   (c) -14 (g) $-\frac{15}{4}$
   (d) -6 (h) $\frac{23}{40}$

5. (a) 10 (d) 7
   (b) 1 (e) 2
   (c) 11 (f) $\frac{1}{2}$

6. (a) $-\frac{9}{2}$ (e) 5
   (b) -4 (f) 1
   (c) 12 (g) 8
   (d) $\frac{1}{2}$

7. (a) 0
   (b) $\frac{46}{7}$
   (c) 4

8. (a) A; B
   (b) 4 h

9. 4

10. 2

Page 73

3. (a) 24 (d) 6
   (b) 14 (e) 3
   (c) 11 (f) -1

4. (a) no   (b) yes

5. (a) 15 (d) 5
   (b) 20 (e) -2
   (c) 1 (f) -9

6. (a) $-\frac{20}{3}$ (c) 8
   (b) $\frac{9}{7}$ (d) 13

7. (a) 28
   (b) $\frac{4}{13}$
   (c) $\frac{8}{5}$

Page 75

3. (a) $0; -3$
   (b) $1; 2$
   (c) $0; -5$
   (d) $7; -2$
   (e) ± 7
   (f) $0; \frac{1}{3}$
   (g) $-\frac{3}{2}; 8$
   (h) $\frac{3}{5}; -\frac{1}{4}$

4. (a) $(m + 5)(m + 3)$
   (b) $(y + 2)(y + 7)$
   (c) $(x - 3)(x - 2)$
   (d) $4a(a - 2)$
   (e) $(3k - 4)(3k + 4)$
   (f) $3x(1 + 3x)$
   (g) $(6n - 1)(6n + 1)$
   (h) $(2s + 1)(s - 3)$

5. (a) $-2; -3$ (f) $2; 6$
   (b) $-1; -3$ (g) $3; 5$
   (c) $-4; -5$ (h) $2; -9$
   (d) $-3; -6$ (i) $-3; 5$
   (e) $-5; -7$

6. (a) $1; 7$ (d) $\frac{1}{3}; -3$
   (b) $5; -3$ (e) $0; \frac{7}{5}$
   (c) $4; -7$

7. (a) $-2; -10$ (d) $7; -8$
   (b) $8; -3$ (e) $5; -\frac{3}{2}$
   (c) $3; 4$

8. (a) $1; 6$ (d) $3; 8$
   (b) $7; -5$ (e) $-\frac{7}{2}; -4$
   (c) ± 3

9. 11 by 9

10. 8

11. $5, 9$

Page 77

1. (a) $w = 7$ m
   (b) $h = 9$ cm
   (c) $r = 10$ m
   (d) $b = 5$ cm
   (e) $a = 29.2$ m
   (f) $s = 17.5$ m

2. (a) 3.28 m
   (b) 1.42 kg/m
3. (a) 1500 W
   (b) 120 V
4. (a) $1999.72
   (b) $2433.07
5. 8 Ω

Page 79

2. (a) $d = \frac{C}{\pi}$
   (b) $h = \frac{V}{\pi r^2}$; $r = \sqrt{\frac{V}{\pi h}}$; $h = \frac{A - 2\pi r^2}{2\pi r}$
   (c) $a = \frac{2A}{h} - b$
   (d) $R_2 = \frac{L}{\pi S} - R_1$
   (e) $b = \sqrt{\frac{2p^2}{\pi^2} - a^2}$

3. (a) $D = \sqrt{\frac{A}{0.7854}}$
   (b) 84.44 cm

4. (a) 7.64 Ω
   (b) 21.30 Ω

5. (a) 30 cm
   (b) 11 cm

Page 81

1. (a) 0.0380   (c) 0.0127
   (b) 0.0978   (d) 0.0129

2. (a) 27.93 cm   (c) 25 cm
   (b) 91.35 cm   (d) 38.38 cm

3. (a) 5.72 cm   (c) 5.82 cm
   (b) 3.70 cm   (d) 9.50 cm

4. (a) 4.09 cm   (c) 4.17 cm
   (b) 3.20 cm   (d) 4.90 cm

Page 83

1. (a) 12
   (b) 9.5
   (c) 11

2. (a) 7
   (b) 3

3. (a) $u = \frac{s + 5t^2}{t}$
   (b) 48.3

4. (a) $d = \sqrt{l^2 - h^2}$
   (b) 4.2 m

5. (a) 3.7 m
   (b) 3.7 m
   (c) The answers are the same.

Page 84

1. (a) $5a - 15 = 4a + 4$
   (b) $7x + 3 = 19$
   (c) $30\left[\frac{4k-3}{2}\right] - 30\left(\frac{1}{3}\right) = 30\left(\frac{2+k}{5}\right)$

2. (a) 32   (d) 104
   (b) 5   (e) −5
   (c) 1.2   (f) 3

3. (a) yes   (d) yes
   (b) yes   (e) no
   (c) no   (f) yes

4. (a) $m = 0$; $2m + 1 = 0$
   (b) $2k = 0$; $k - 5 = 0$
   (c) $a + 3 = 0$; $a - 3 = 0$
   (d) $2y - 5 = 0$; $3y + 7 = 0$

5. (a) $t = \frac{I}{Pr}$
   (b) $u = v - at$
   (c) $m = \frac{E}{c^2}$
   (d) $r = \sqrt{\frac{A}{\pi}}$

6. (a) yes   (d) yes
   (b) yes   (e) no
   (c) no   (f) yes

7. (a) 1   (d) 9
   (b) 6   (e) −2
   (c) 3   (f) 3; −2

8. (a) 0; 3   (d) −4
   (b) 0; 7   (e) 4; −3
   (c) $\pm\frac{5}{2}$ (f) $-\frac{1}{2}$; −1

9. (a) −2   (d) $\frac{120}{7}$
   (b) 3   (e) $3, -\frac{1}{2}$
   (c) 8   (f) $\frac{22}{3}, -2$

10. 23 weeks

11. 1.5 m

12. (a) 3.54 m   (d) 17 m
    (b) 11 cm   (e) 20.5 cm
    (c) 16.4 cm

13. 5

14. $-\frac{7}{3}$; −2

15. (a) 40.8 cm²
    (b) 1.5 cm
    (c) 5.3 cm

16. (a) 3461.64 r/min
    (b) 100 040.4 cm/min
    (c) 22.82 cm

17. 24

18. 1.80 cm

19. 25.20 Ω

20. 223.4 cm

21. (a) 2550 r/min
    (b) 22 cm

22. (a) 14.69 W
    (b) 281.25 Ω
    (c) 60.79 V

Unit 5

Page 88

3. (a) $2a$ (e) $\frac{5}{7}$
   (b) x^2y^2 (f) $(a + b)^2$
   (c) m^4n^7 (g) $\frac{3}{y + 2}$
   (d) $\frac{x - 1}{2}$ (h) 2

Page 89

1. (a) $2a^2$ (c) $\frac{2r}{3}$
   (b) $\frac{k}{3(k - 2)}$ (d) $\frac{2}{y}$

2. (a) $\frac{22}{3m}$ (e) $\frac{y^5}{4x}$
   (b) $\frac{4y}{x}$ (f) $\frac{2}{a + b}$
   (c) $\frac{12g}{f}$ (g) $\frac{1}{2w^2}$
   (d) $\frac{9a^5}{16b^4}$ (h) $\frac{(m + 3)^3}{5m}$

3. (a) $\frac{8}{75a^2b}$ (c) $\frac{8a^3}{5}$
   (b) $\frac{5}{3r}$ (d) $\frac{(a + 1)^2}{10a^3}$

Page 91

3. (a) $(2k - 9)(2k + 9)$
   (b) $(m - 16)(m + 3)$
   (c) $(u - 18)(u + 4)$
   (d) $(x - 3)(x - 7)$
   (e) $(c - 2)(c - 1)$
   (f) $2(3x + 2)(x - 5)$
   (g) $5a(a - 3)(a + 3)$

4. (a) $\frac{2}{3}$ (e) $4w$
   (b) $\frac{1}{2}$ (f) $\frac{5}{x}$
   (c) $\frac{3k}{4}$ (g) $\frac{r}{2}$
   (d) $\frac{1}{m}$ (h) $\frac{3(a + b + 1)}{2(a - b - 1)}$

5. (a) $\frac{k + 1}{k - 1}$ (e) $\frac{a - 2}{a + 4}$
   (b) $\frac{m + 3}{m + 1}$ (f) $\frac{n + 3}{n - 1}$
   (c) $\frac{y + 4}{y + 2}$ (g) $\frac{y + 1}{y + 3}$
   (d) $\frac{x + 2}{x + 3}$ (h) $\frac{(a + 1)(a - 3)}{(a + 4)(a + 2)}$

6. (a) $\frac{a}{4}$ (c) k
    (b) $\frac{m+1}{6}$ (d) $\frac{x-8}{x+10}$

7. (a) $\frac{3}{4}$ (c) $\frac{1}{2c}$
    (b) $\frac{n+3}{2}$ (d) $\frac{y-2}{4y}$

8. (a) $\frac{y-2}{y+6}$ (d) $\frac{1}{2}$
    (b) $\frac{d-2}{d+3}$ (e) $\frac{5}{m}$
    (c) $\frac{k+6}{k+1}$

9. $\frac{2(x+2)}{(x-1)}$

10. (a) $3k-5$
    (b) $3y$
    (c) $a+5$

Side Trip
1. $4b$ **5.** $y-2$
2. $3n^3$ **6.** 2
3. 1 **7.** $x+3$
4. $9a^3$

Page 95
3. (a) x (c) $\frac{18t-13}{12}$
    (b) $2m$ (d) $\frac{13y-14}{24}$

4. (a) $-\frac{c}{4}$ (d) $\frac{a+7}{30}$
    (b) $\frac{7k}{12}$ (e) $\frac{-3y-29}{28}$
    (c) $-\frac{3n}{8}$ (f) $\frac{22-9x}{15}$

5. (a) $\frac{15}{m}$ (c) $\frac{2}{r^2}$
    (b) $\frac{8}{y}$ (d) $\frac{4}{xy}$

6. (a) $-\frac{4}{3a}$ (c) $\frac{6}{k}$
    (b) $\frac{1}{m}$ (d) $-\frac{2}{ab}$

7. (a) $\frac{23}{12y}$ (d) $\frac{10+3s}{5s^2}$
    (b) $-\frac{1}{30xy}$ (e) $\frac{3a-b}{14}$
    (c) $\frac{6-5b}{12ab}$ (f) $\frac{7xy-3y^2-2x^2}{6xy}$

8. (a) $\frac{2x^2-4}{x(x+4)}$ (c) $\frac{3(2k+1)}{(k-1)(k+2)}$
    (b) $\frac{2r^2+4r+10}{(r-3)(r+2)}$ (d) $\frac{7y^2-2y-12}{y^2(y-2)}$

9. (a) $\frac{15b+8a+42}{12ab}$
    (b) $\frac{6y+8}{xy}$

Page 96
1. 0.375

2. (a) -2 (c) 0
    (b) -2.5

3. (a) 3.63 (c) 3.6
    (b) 12.4

4. 5.92
5. 2.88

Page 97
1. (a) 2 (c) $\frac{a}{2b}$
    (b) $\frac{9}{5}$ (d) $\frac{3n}{4m}$

2. (a) $\frac{y}{2}$ (d) $(y-1)^3$
    (b) $\frac{5}{2}$ (e) $\frac{5(w-1)}{4}$
    (c) k^3n (f) 2

3. (a) $\frac{8b}{5a}$
    (b) $\frac{4n^3}{3m}$
    (c) $\frac{-12a}{5}$
    (d) $\frac{2}{3}$

4. (a) $\frac{3y(y-2)}{y+5}$
    (b) $\frac{6(a+2)}{a}$
    (c) $\frac{3m(m+1)}{4(m-1)}$
    (d) $\frac{12x}{x-5}$

5. (a) $\frac{2}{3}$ (d) $\frac{c-2}{c+3}$
    (b) $\frac{m}{m+3}$ (e) $\frac{y+1}{5}$
    (c) $\frac{a^2b}{a+1}$ (f) $\frac{x-5}{x-7}$

6. (a) 15
    (b) 6
    (c) $12m$
    (d) $4a^2$

7. (a) $3k$ (f) $\frac{13}{10a}$
    (b) $\frac{3m}{7}$ (g) $\frac{4x-3}{x^2y}$
    (c) $\frac{4}{y}$ (h) $\frac{5+3r}{r^2s}$
    (d) $\frac{27k}{4m}$ (i) $\frac{x-2xy}{y^2}$
    (e) $\frac{7y}{6x}$ (j) $\frac{6m^2+5mn-3n^2}{6mn}$

8. $-\frac{1}{5}$

9. (a) 4.5 (c) -5
    (b) 0 (d) 6

10. (a) $\frac{5y+4}{2}$ (d) $\frac{18k+26}{(k+1)(k+2)}$
    (b) $\frac{39}{2x}$ (e) $\frac{52n-3}{15}$
    (c) $\frac{17a+7b}{20}$

11. 2

12. (a) $2m-5$
    (b) $2y-5$

13. 1.2

14. $\frac{14k+12}{k(k+1)}$; 3.4

Unit 6

Page 100
2. (c) $(1,1)$; $(2.5, 2.5)$

3. (b) $(2,4)$; $(-0.5,1.5)$

4. (b) $(3,4)$; $(-4,4)$
    (c) $(1,3)$; $(0,3)$; $(-2,3)$; $(3,3)$; $(-3,3)$

5. $(-1,0)$; $(-1,2)$; $(-1,4)$; $(-1,-1)$; $(-1,-3)$
Answers will vary.

6. (b) $D(5,2)$

7. (b) $R(5,-2)$; $S(5,3)$

8. (a) Points lie on line $x = 2$, parallel to y-axis
    (b) Points lie on line $y = 3$, parallel to x-axis

12. (b) $(2,4)$; no

Page 103
4. (a)
$y = 3x - 2$

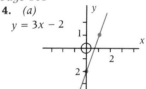

(b) $y = \frac{2}{3}x + 2$

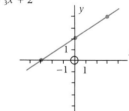

(c) $y = -2x + 1$

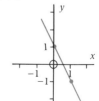

(d) $y = x + 3$

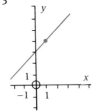

(e) $y = 3x$

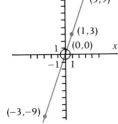

(3,9)
(1,3)
(0,0)
(-3,-9)

(f) $y = 4$

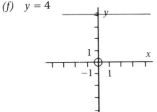

(g) $x = 3$

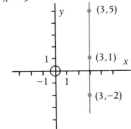

(3,5)
(3,1)
(3,-2)

5. *(a)* $y = 2x - 3$

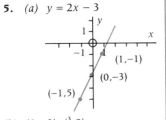

(1,-1)
(0,-3)
(-1,5)

(b) $(0,-3); \left(\frac{3}{2},0\right)$
(c) $(-2,-7); (2,1); (3,3); (-3,-9)$

---

6. *(a)* $y = x - 3$

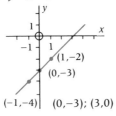

(1,-2)
(0,-3)
(-1,-4) $(0,-3); (3,0)$

(b) $y = 2x - 4$

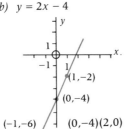

(1,-2)
(0,-4)
(-1,-6) $(0,-4)(2,0)$

(c) $y = -x + 2$

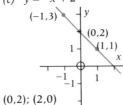

(-1,3)
(0,2)
(1,1)
$(0,2); (2,0)$

(d) $y = 3x - 1$

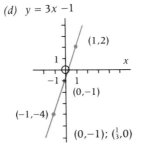

(1,2)
(0,-1)
(-1,-4)
$(0,-1); \left(\frac{1}{3},0\right)$

(e) $y = -2x + 3$

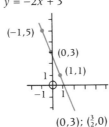

(-1,5)
(0,3)
(1,1)
$(0,3); \left(\frac{3}{2},0\right)$

(f) $y = \frac{1}{2}x + 2$

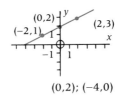

(0,2)
(-2,1)
(2,3)
$(0,2); (-4,0)$

(g) $y = -\frac{1}{3}x + 4$

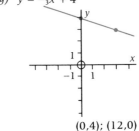

$(0,4); (12,0)$

(h) $y = \frac{3}{4}x - 2$

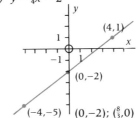

(4,1)
(0,-2)
(-4,-5) $(0,-2); \left(\frac{8}{3},0\right)$

(i) $y = -\frac{2}{3}x + 2$

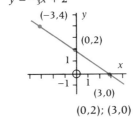

(-3,4)
(0,2)
(3,0)
$(0,2); (3,0)$

(j) $y = \frac{2}{3}x + 2$

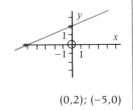

$(0,2); (-5,0)$

---

7. *(a)* $y = x^2$

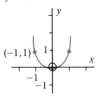

(-1,1)

(b) $y = x^2 + 2$

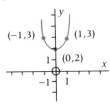

(-1,3)
(1,3)
(0,2)

(c) $y = x^2 - 4$

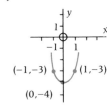

(-1,-3)
(1,-3)
(0,-4)

(d) $y = 2x^2$

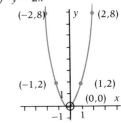

(-2,8)
(2,8)
(-1,2)
(1,2)
(0,0)

(e) $y = 2x^2 + 1$

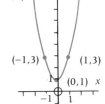

(-2,9)
(2,9)
(-1,3)
(1,3)
(0,1)

472

(f) $y = 2x^2 - 3$

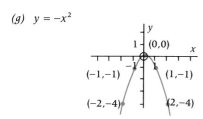

(g) $y = -x^2$

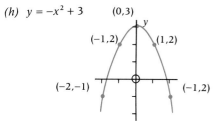

(h) $y = -x^2 + 3$

Page 104

2. *(b)* $9600; $16 000; $20 000
   (c) The point of intersection represents the basic charge.

3. *(b)* 500 L   *(d)* 300 L
   (c) 50 s

4. *(a)* $C = 3.5t + 4$ *(c)* $21.50
   (b) $4   *(d)* $3.50

5. *(a)* $N = -0.105b + 63$ *(d)* 42 L
   (b) 63 L   *(e)* 10.5 L
   (c) 600 km

6. *(a)* $d = -5t^2 + 20t + 1$ *(c)* 4 s
   (b) 21 m   *(d)* 1 m

7. *(a)* $D = -800t + 4000$ *(c)* 5 h
   (b) 2400 km   *(d)* 2.5 h

Page 107

4. *(a)* 5   *(f)* $\sqrt{65}$
   (b) $\sqrt{10}$ *(g)* $\sqrt{34}$
   (c) $\sqrt{13}$ *(h)* $\sqrt{106}$
   (d) $\sqrt{113}$ *(i)* $\sqrt{50}$
   (e) $\sqrt{65}$ *(j)* $\sqrt{194}$

5.

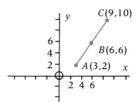

Since $DE = EF = 5$, then $\triangle DEF$ is isosceles.

6. *(a)* $D(-2,-2)$
   (b) $AC = \sqrt{61}$; $BD = \sqrt{61}$
   (c) The lengths of the diagonals are equal.
   (d) 22

7. *(a)* 10
   (b) 5
   (c) 78.5; 31.4

8. *(a)* $AB = 114$ km;
       $AC = 103$ km;
       $BC = 134$ km
   (b) 3.43 h

9. *(a)* $AB = 5$; $AC = 10$; $BC = 5$
   (b)

Page 109

2. *(a)* $m(5,7)$ *(f)* $m(-3,-6)$
   (b) $m(4.5,6)$ *(g)* $m(0.5,3)$
   (c) $m(1,6)$ *(h)* $m(2,-4)$
   (d) $m(1,2)$ *(i)* $m(-2.5,1.5)$
   (e) $m(7,6)$ *(j)* $m(-3,0)$

3. *(b)* $M(0,2)$; $N(8,2)$
   (c) $MN = 8$
   (d) $BC = 16$
   (e) BC is twice the length of MN.

4. *(b)* $(1,0)$; $(1,0)$
   (c) The diagonals bisect each other.

5. *(b)* M of $AB = (0,6)$; M of $BC = (1,-1)$; M of $AC = (5,3)$
   (c) See above.
   (d) They intersect at one point.
   (e) median

6. *(a)* $M(5,4)$
   (b) $\sqrt{26}$ or 5.10 units
   (c) 81.6 square units

7. $(6,8)$

8. *(a)*

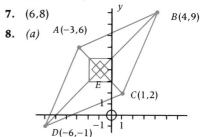

   (b) Since M of $DB = (-1,4)$ and M of $AC = (-1,4)$, then the diagonals of the rhombus bisect one another.

Page 111

1.

Time (years)	Amount
0	$1000.00
1	$1100.00
2	$1210.00
3	$1331.00
4	$1464.10
5	$1610.50
6	$1771.56
7	$1948.72
8	$2143.59
9	$2357.95
10	$2593.75

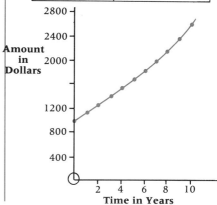

2. *(a)*

Population in millions (y-axis), years (x-axis)

(b) exponential curve
(c) no
(d) From 1901 to 1941, Canada's population increased exponentially. Then the rate of growth changed and decreased during World War II.
(e) 26.88 million; 30.11 million

Page 112

1. *(a)* $y = x + 3$
$(0,-3)(-3,0)$

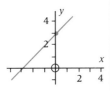

(b) $y = 2x - 2$
$(0,-2)(1,0)$

(c) $y = -3x + 4$
$(0,4)(\frac{4}{3},0)$

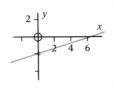

(d) $y = \frac{1}{3}x - 2$
$(0,-2)(6,0)$

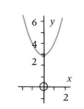

(e) $y = -2x - 3y$
$(0,-3)$ $(-\frac{3}{2},0)$

(f) $y = -\frac{1}{2}x + 2$
$(0,2)$ $(4,0)$

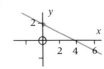

(g) $y = \frac{2}{3}x - 5$
$(0,-5)(\frac{15}{2},0)$

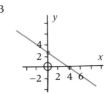

(h) $y = -\frac{3}{4}x + 3$
$(0,3)(4,0)$

2. *(a)* $y = x^2 - 1$

(b) $y = x^2 + 3$

(c) $y = x^2 - 2$

(d) $y = 2x^2 + 2$

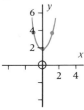

(e) $y = -x^2 + 1$

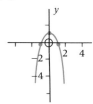

(f) $y = -2x^2 + 3$

3. *(b)* 116 cm
(c) 5 kg
(d) The actual length of the spring is 60 cm.

4. *(b)* 20°C   *(d)* 200 min
(c) 150 min

5. *(a)* $AB = 4.47$ *(d)* $AB = 8.54$
(b) $AB = 6.40$ *(e)* $AB = 5.83$
(c) $AB = 4.47$ *(f)* $AB = 13.93$

6. *(a)* $M(7,6)$ *(d)* $M(3,3)$
    (b) $M(6,1)$ *(e)* $M(-4,2)$
    (c) $M(-6,-3)$ *(f)* $M(\frac{3}{2},-\frac{5}{2})$

Unit 7

Page 115

2. *(a)* $\frac{3}{4}$; slants to the right
    (b) $-\frac{5}{9}$; slants to the left
    (c) $-\frac{7}{10}$; slants to the left
    (d) undefined; vertical
    (e) $\frac{1}{4}$; slants to the right
    (f) 0; horizontal
    (g) $-\frac{3}{4}$; slants to the left
    (h) $\frac{5}{13}$; slants to the right
    (i) $\frac{5}{8}$; slants to the right
    (j) -3; slants to the left

3. *(a)* $(0,3)$, $(-3,1)$

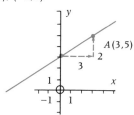

    (b) $(3,0)$, $(8,-4)$ (answers will vary)

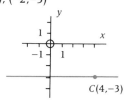

    (c) $(0,-3)$, $(-2,-3)$

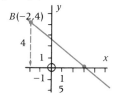

(d) $(-5,7)$, $(-1,-3)$
    (answers will vary)

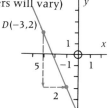

(e) $(3,-3)$, $(10,-1)$
    (answers will vary)

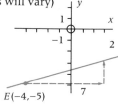

(f) $(2,4)$, $(2,-1)$

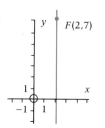

(g) $(3,4)$, $(0,8)$

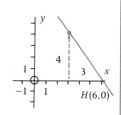

(h) $(6,1)$, $(4,-5)$
    (answers will vary)

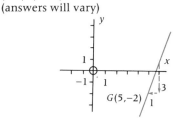

4. *(b)* All points are on the same straight line.
    (c) $\frac{1}{3}$
    (d) The slopes of all segments of the same straight line are equal.

5. *(a)* $\frac{3}{10}$
    (b) $\frac{1}{3}$

6. $\frac{1}{20}$

7. $\frac{1}{4}$

8. $\frac{1}{12}$

9. $\frac{1}{2}$

10. *(a)* 2
    (b) 11; -1; -3; 19

Page 118

3. *(a)* $m = 2$; $b = 1$

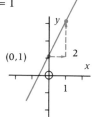

    (b) $m = \frac{3}{4}$
       $b = -2$

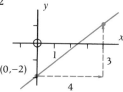

    (c) $m = \frac{5}{3}$; $b = 3$

475

(d) $m = 1$; $b = 4$

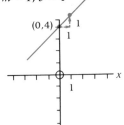

(e) $m = -1$; $b = 2$

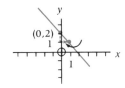

(f) $m = -2$; $b = -3$

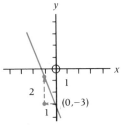

(g) $m = -\frac{3}{7}$; $b = 1$

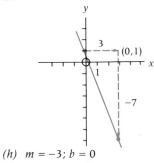

(h) $m = -3$; $b = 0$

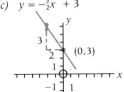

(i) m is undefined; no b

(j) $m = 0$; $b = 4$

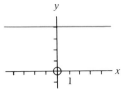

4. *(a)* $y = 3x + 1$
(b) $y = \frac{4}{3}x - 2$
(c) $y = -\frac{4}{5}x + 3$
(d) $y = -2x$
(e) $y = -\frac{2}{3}x - 4$

5. *(a)*

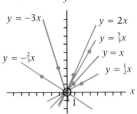

(b) $2, 0$; $\frac{1}{2}, 0$; $1, 0$;
$-3, 0$; $-\frac{2}{3}, 0$; $\frac{5}{3}, 0$
(c) All lines meet at the origin.

6. *(a)*

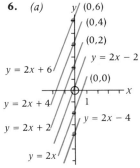

(b) $2, 6$; $2, 4$; $2, 2$;
$2, 0$; $2, -2$; $2, -4$
(c) The lines are parallel.

7. *(a)*

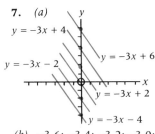

(b) $-3, 6$; $-3, 4$; $-3, 2$; $-3, 0$;
$-3, -2$; $-3, -4$
(c) The lines are parallel.

8. The slopes of parallel lines are equal.

Page 119

1. *(a)* $y = -2x + 3$; -2; 3
(b) $y = -3x + 4$; -3; 4
(c) $y = 4x - 2$; 4; -2
(d) $y = -x + 3$; -1; 3
(e) $y = -\frac{2}{3}x + 2$; $-\frac{2}{3}$; 2
(f) $y = \frac{3}{5}x - 3$; $\frac{3}{5}$; -3
(g) $y = -\frac{4}{3}x + 4$; $-\frac{4}{3}$; 4
(h) $y = -\frac{1}{2}x + 2$; $-\frac{1}{2}$; 2
(i) $y = \frac{1}{3}x - 3$; $\frac{1}{3}$; -3
(j) $y = -\frac{3}{2}x + \frac{5}{2}$; $-\frac{3}{2}$; $\frac{5}{2}$

2. *(a)* $y = -3x + 2$

(b) $y = 2x - 4$

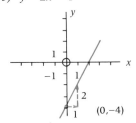

(c) $y = -\frac{3}{2}x + 3$

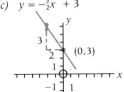

(d) $y = \frac{4}{3}x - 4$

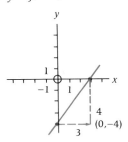

Side Trip

(a) $y = -\frac{A}{B}x - \frac{C}{B}$

(b) $m = -\frac{A}{B}$

(c) $\frac{1}{2}$; $-\frac{3}{5}$; $\frac{9}{2}$; -2

Page 120

1. *(a)* 3; 2
(b) 8; 2
(c) 2; 6
(d) 2; -4
(e) 6; -2
(f) 3; -4
(g) 7; 2
(h) 3; -5
(i) 5; 2
(j) 2; -5
(k) 4; 3
(l) 6; 2.4
(m) 7; -3
(n) 3; 3.6

Page 122

3. *(a)* -2
(b) 15
(c) 11

4. *(a)* $y = 3x - 1$
(b) $y = 2x + 2$
(c) $y = -4x + 17$
(d) $y = -x + 3$
(e) $y = 5x - 2$
(f) $y = \frac{1}{2}x$
(g) $y = \frac{3}{4}x + 4$
(h) $y = -\frac{2}{5}x + 3$
(i) $y = \frac{5}{3}x - \frac{29}{3}$
(j) $y = -\frac{4}{7}x - \frac{57}{7}$

5. (a)

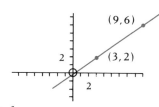

(b) $\frac{2}{3}$

(c) $y = \frac{2}{3}x$

6. (a) $y = 3x - 3$ (e) $y = \frac{9}{8}x + \frac{1}{2}$

   (b) $y = 2x - 10$ (f) $y = -\frac{3}{4}x + 3$

   (c) $y = -2x + 6$ (g) $y = -\frac{3}{4}x$

   (d) $y = \frac{8}{5}x - \frac{1}{5}$ (h) $y = \frac{2}{3}x + \frac{13}{3}$

7. (a) $y = \frac{3}{4}x + \frac{3}{2}$

(b)

LS	RS
9	$\frac{3}{4}(10) + \frac{3}{2}$
	$= \frac{15}{2} + \frac{3}{2}$
	$= \frac{18}{2}$
	$= 9$

(c) All points satisfy the equation $y = \frac{3}{4}x + \frac{3}{2}$.

8. (a) $\frac{3}{4}; \frac{3}{4}$

(b) The slope of a line is constant, or equal, for all parts of a line.

9. $m(PQ) = m(PR) = m(QR) = -\frac{3}{2}$

10. $m(MN) = m(MP) = m(NP) = \frac{3}{5}$

Page 123

1. (a) 178; 418

   (b) 9 a; 24 a; 34.4 a

2. (b) $C = 0.15d + 2000$

   (c) The slope represents the cost per kilometre. The C-intercept represents the fixed cost.

   (d) $5000

   (e) 22 000 km

3. (b) $C = 2L + 7$

   (c) 2; 7

   (d) The slope represents the cost per metre; the C-intercept represents the initial cost.

   (e) $307

   (f) 157 m

4. (b) $T = 0.18A$

   (c) 0.18; 0

   (d) tax/$ assessment; minimum tax payable

   (e) $2160; $1530

   (f) $5000; $8333.33

5. (b) The quantity of water is decreasing.

   (c) $N = -120t + 20\,000$

   (d) -120; 20 000

   (e) The slope represents the number of litres that drain in a minute. The N-intercept represents the amount of water in the pool before it is drained.

   (f) 167 min

Page 126

5. $AB \| CD$, $GH \| IJ \| MN$;
$AB \perp EF$, $CD \perp EF$, $GH \perp PQ$,
$IJ \perp PQ$, $MN \perp PQ$

6. (a) $\triangle ABC$ is not a right-angled triangle.

   (b) $m(KL) \perp m(LM)$ and $\triangle KLM$ is a right-angled triangle.

   (c) PQR is not a right-angled triangle.

7. (b) $m(AB) \times m(AC)$
$= 1 \times -1$
$= -1$
$m(AB) \times m(AC)$
$= \frac{4}{3} \times -\frac{3}{4}$
$= -1$
$m(AB) \times m(AC)$
$= \frac{3}{2} \times -\frac{2}{3}$
$= -1$

   (c) The slopes of AB and AC are negative reciprocals.

Page 127

1. 161.56 m²

2. 152.7 m²

3. 247.8 m²

4. 395.29 m²

Page 128

1. (a) $\frac{9}{5}$ (c) 0

   (b) $-\frac{3}{2}$ (d) $-\frac{3}{13}$

2. (a)

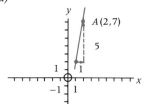

(b)

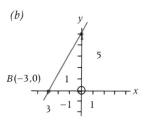

(c)

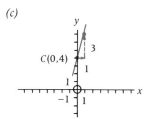

(d)

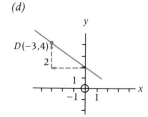

(e)

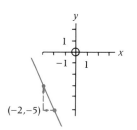

477

3. (a) $\frac{1}{5}$
　　(b) $\frac{2}{5}$

4. $\frac{39}{140}$

5. (a) 18 m
　　(b) 20.6 m

6. (a) 3; 2; (0,2)

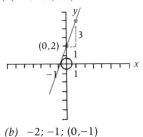

　　(b) -2; -1; $(0,-1)$

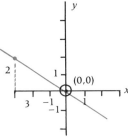

　　(c) $\frac{1}{3}$; 2; (0,2)

　　(d) $\frac{5}{2}$; 1; (0,1)

　　(e) $-\frac{3}{5}$; -4; $(0,-4)$

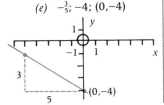

(f) $-\frac{2}{3}$; 0; (0,0)

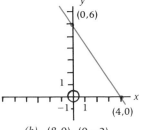

(g) 0; -2, $(0,-2)$

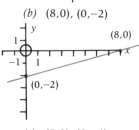

y = -2

(h) undefined; no y-intercept

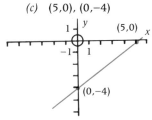

x = -4

7. (a) $y = 2x - 1$
　　(b) $y = \frac{5}{3}x + 2$
　　(c) $y = -x - 3$
　　(d) $y = x$
　　(e) $y = -\frac{4}{3}x + 2$
　　(f) $y = -\frac{3}{5}x - 4$

8. (a) $y = -3x + 2$; -3; 2
　　(b) $y = 4x - 4$; 4; -4
　　(c) $y = -\frac{3}{2}x + 4$; $-\frac{3}{2}$; 4
　　(d) $y = \frac{4}{3}x - 4$; $\frac{4}{3}$; -4
　　(e) $y = -\frac{3}{5}x + 3$; $-\frac{3}{5}$; 3
　　(f) $y = -\frac{1}{4}x + 3$; $-\frac{1}{4}$; 3
　　(g) $y = \frac{4}{5}x - \frac{9}{5}$; $\frac{4}{5}$; $-\frac{9}{5}$

9. (a) (4,0), (0,6)

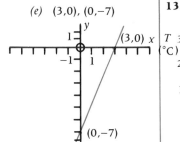

　　(b) (8,0), (0,-2)

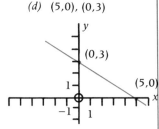

　　(c) (5,0), (0,-4)

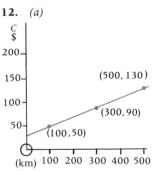

　　(d) (5,0), (0,3)

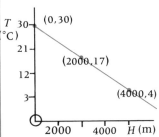

　　(e) (3,0), (0,-7)

10. (a) $y = 2x - 1$
　　(b) $y = -3x - 5$
　　(c) $y = \frac{1}{4}x + \frac{17}{4}$
　　(d) $y = \frac{3}{5}x - \frac{12}{5}$
　　(e) $y = -\frac{1}{2}x + 3$
　　(f) $y = -\frac{4}{3}x - 9$
　　(g) $y = \frac{7}{2}x - \frac{25}{2}$
　　(h) $y = -\frac{4}{5}x - \frac{53}{5}$

11. (a) $y = \frac{1}{3}x + 1$
　　(b) $y = \frac{9}{2}x + 15$
　　(c) $y = -\frac{1}{6}x + \frac{11}{3}$
　　(d) $y = \frac{4}{3}x + 4$
　　(e) $y = -\frac{1}{2}x$
　　(f) $y = \frac{3}{2}x - \frac{13}{2}$

12. (a)

　　(b) $C = 0.2D + 30$
　　(c) The slope represents the cost per km driven.
　　(d) The C-intercept represents the basic rental.
　　(e) $80; $230
　　(f) 700 km; 325 km

13. (a)

478

(b) The temperature decreases.
(c) $T = -\frac{13}{2000}H + 30$
(d) $-\frac{13}{2000}$; 30
(e) The slope represents the rate of decrease of temperature per metre. The T-intercept represents the temperature at sea level.
(f) 10.5°C; −9°C
(g) 1000 m; 7385 m; 4615 m

14. (a)

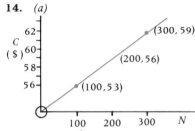

(b) $C = \frac{3}{100}N + 50$
(c) $\frac{3}{100}$; 50
(d) $50
(e) $0.03
(f) $80; $155
(g) 2000

15. (a)

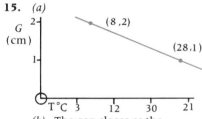

(b) The gap closes as the temperature rises.
(c) $G = -0.05T + 2.4$
(d) −0.05; 2.4
(e) The slope represents the rate of decrease in the width of the gap as the temperature increases. The G-intercept represents the width of the gap at 0°C.
(f) 2.4 cm; 1.9 cm; 0.9 cm; 2.9 cm
(g) 18°C

16. (a) $\frac{3}{4}$ (b) $\frac{3}{4}$
    (c) $-\frac{4}{3}$

(d) $-\frac{4}{3}$
$AB\|CD$; $EF\|GH$; $AB\perp EF$; $AB\perp GH$; $CD\perp EF$; $CD\perp GH$

17. $\triangle ABC$ is a right-angled triangle if $m(AB) \times m(AC) = -1$.
$m(AB) \times m(AC)$
$= 4 \times -\frac{1}{4}$
$= -1$

Unit 8

Page 133
3. (a) (−3,−2)   (g) (0,−3)
   (b) (−3,−3)   (h) $(\frac{7}{3}, -\frac{10}{9})$
   (c) (3,4)   (i) (6,4)
   (d) (3,4)   (j) (4,3)
   (e) (1,2)
   (f) (4,−3)

4. (a) (280,840)
   (b) (600,2400)

5. (a) S = $15 000; P = $1550
   (b) The intersection point represents that, for both Mary and John, they will earn $1550 for sales of $15 000.
   (c) sales of more than $15 000
   (d) sales of less than $15 000

6. (a) $t = 50$ s; $d = 160$ m
   (b) The point of intersection represents the time and place where the daughter catches up to the father.
   (c) daughter; by 30 s; by 74 m

7. (a) (400,3400)
   (b) The point of intersection represents the situation when costs are equal for both machines, i.e. when 400 hockey sticks are manufactured.
   (c) more than 400
   (d) $150; $900

8. (a) (4,6600)
   (b) The point of intersection represents the cost after 4 a, which is the same for both companies.

(c) B; by $700
(d) The slope of each line represents the cost per year. The C-intercept represents the cost of installing the heating systems.

9. (a) (50 000,12 500)
   (b) The point of intersection represents that the cost of driving the two cars is equal when the distance is 50 000 km.
   (c) gasoline, by $1200; diesel, by $1200
   (d) The slope of each line represents the cost per kilometre. The C-intercept of each line represents the initial cost of operating each car.

10. (a) 9 a after installation
    (b) $2800

11. (a) (16,1120)
    (b) It represents the time when A and B have travelled the same distance.

Side Trip
    (b) $50   (c) 120

Page 137
4. (a) (6,3)   (e) (0,3)
   (b) (3,4)   (f) (2,−1)
   (c) (1,1)   (g) $(-\frac{4}{3},6)$
   (d) (7,−8)   (h) $(\frac{11}{2},-3)$

5. (a) (2,2)   (c) (2,2)
   (b) (1,1)   (d) (2,−3)

6. (a) (3,−5)   (g) (−2,−6)
   (b) (1,2)   (h) (4,−2)
   (c) (2,−3)   (i) (3,−3)
   (d) (4,−2)   (j) $(-\frac{1}{2},1)$
   (e) $(-\frac{1}{2},1)$ (k) $(3,\frac{5}{2})$
   (f) $(\frac{17}{4},2)$ (l) $(\frac{7}{9},-\frac{13}{9})$

7. (a) (7,10)   (c) (5,−1)
   (b) (3,1)   (d) $(-\frac{25}{4},\frac{15}{2})$

8. (a) 350 adults; 650 students
   (b) Equation ② represents the amount received in ticket sales.

9. (a) $x = 60$, $y = 20$
(b) The equation represents the total number of tapes and albums sold.
(c) The equation represents the sales of these two items for one day.

10. (a) $(9,9)$
(b) The first equation represents the total number of bills received. The second equation represents the value of the cheque.

Page 139
1. (a) $(4,13)$ (e) $(-1,3)$
(b) $(7,23)$ (f) $(10,17)$
(c) $(\frac{1}{2},-2)$ (g) $(7,1)$
(d) $(3,2)$ (h) $(1,2)$

2. (a) $(3,13)$ (c) $(-\frac{43}{11},\frac{74}{11})$
(b) $(2,1)$ (d) $(1,5)$

3. 300 km

Page 141
2. (a) 150 km
(b) $48
(c) distance less than 150 km

3. (a) 5d
(b) $100
(c) $10

4. (a) 6 weeks
(b) $110

5. (a) 10 000
(b) $1300
(c) $300

6. 100

7. $3000 at 8%; $7000 at 10%

8. $1000 at 6%; $2000 at 9%

9. (a) $x + y = 700$
(b) $3x$
(c) $4y$
(d) $3x + 4y = 2300$
(e) 500

10. 52

11. 25

12. 10 m³; 7 m³

13. 35, 35

14. (a) $2x$, $3x$
(b) $3y$, $4y$
(c) $2x + 3y = 15.50$; $3x + 4y = 21.50$
(d) peanuts: $2.50; almonds: $3.50

15. leaded: 43.5¢; unleaded: 45.5¢

16. $2.50 when babysitting; $4 when at the variety store

17. spikes: $1.50/kg; finishing nails: $1.25/kg

18. $(7, 4)$

19. (a) 30 m by 25 m
(b) 750 m²

20. 2-mark questions: 35; 3-mark questions: 10

Page 144
1. no

2. 11; 19

3. 8; 12; 6; 1

4. (a) 36
(b) 120

Page 145
1. (a) $(3,2)$ (d) $(3,4)$
(b) $(-1,4)$ (e) $(0,0)$
(c) $(2,-2)$ (f) $(4,\frac{2}{5})$

2. (a) $(4,360)$
(b) The solution represents that both companies charge the same amount to rent the machine for 4 weeks.
(c) $30

3. (a) $(140,81)$
(b) over 140
(c) X cheaper by $93

4. (a) $(7,-2)$ (f) $(2,-1)$
(b) $(5,0)$ (g) $(\frac{5}{2},-\frac{7}{4})$
(c) $(3,0)$ (h) $(\frac{7}{2},-\frac{1}{2})$
(d) $(-1,3)$ (i) $(-1,2)$
(e) $(3,1)$ (j) $(-5,-4)$

5. (a) $(-3,-13)$
(b) $(-3,-6)$
(c) $(\frac{27}{17},\frac{64}{17})$
(d) $(3,-4)$

6. $t = 2$

7. (a) It represents the total value of the coins in cents.
(b) 10 dimes; 25 quarters

8. 60 h

9. $2000 at 8% and $4000 at 11%

10. car: $5; person: $1.50

11. apples: $5; oranges: $12

12. 10 touchdowns; 17 field goals

Side Trip

Page 150
1. (a) 27   (c) 0.0086
(b) -4.5 (d) 5

2. (a) $\frac{7}{12}$
(b) $\frac{7}{3}$
(c) -13

3. (a) $18
(b) $1.6

4. 2835

5. 85%

6. (a) 19
(b) 27
(c) 2

7. (a) 1320 W
(b) 6600 W
(c) 137.5 W

8. (a) 9   (f) 1
(b) 9   (g) 5
(c) -9 (h) -2
(d) $\frac{1}{9}$ (i) $\frac{2}{3}$
(e) $\frac{9}{16}$ (j) -8

9. (a) a^{10} (e) $6a^{14}$
(b) $12m^6$ (f) $5a^{-2}$
(c) $9x^6$ (g) $12x^{-2}y^{-9}$
(d) a^{12} (h) $6t^2$

10. (a) 5   (e) 17
    (b) 63   (f) 30
    (c) 11   (g) −12
    (d) 2   (h) 8

11. (a) 1000   (d) 5
    (b) 1   (e) $3\frac{1}{2}$
    (c) 25

12. (a) 20
    (b) 12
    (c) 141

13. (a) 8.5×10^{-2}
    (b) 3.2×10^{10}
    (c) 2.0×10^{3}

14. 120 cm

15. (a) 77 km
    (b) 4.76 km

16. (a) $12x - 6y$
    (b) $11b$
    (c) $-5w^2 - w + 20$
    (d) $40ab$
    (e) $3x - 5y + 8w$
    (f) $-3c^2 + 2$
    (g) $-30a^3b^3$

17. (a) $-8y + 3$
    (b) $2p^2 + 4p$
    (c) $a^2 + 8a + 15$
    (d) $2x^2 - 11x + 15$
    (e) $8x^2 + 2x - 21$
    (f) $6x^2 + 25xy - 25y^2$
    (g) $9t^2 - 12t + 4$
    (h) $2x^2 - 4x + 42$
    (i) $3a^2 + 2ab - 6b^2$
    (j) $24w^2 - 69w - 55$
    (k) $5x^2 + 44x - 9$
    (l) $3x^3 - 11x^2 + 27x - 14$

18. (a) $2q(4q - 1)$
    (b) $5b(5a - 2b + 1)$
    (c) $(x - 5)(4x + 3)$
    (d) $(x - 5)(x - 3)$
    (e) $(y - 6)(y + 1)$
    (f) $(a + 4)^2$
    (g) $(p + 11)(p - 4)$
    (h) $(3x + 2)(x + 5)$
    (i) $(3a - 5)(a - 2)$
    (j) $(3q - 10)(2q + 1)$
    (k) $(2y - 7)(5y + 2)$
    (l) $(x - 5)(x + 5)$

    (m) $(3x - 5)(3x + 5)$
    (n) $3(x - 4)(x + 4)$
    (o) $2(3y - 5)(y - 1)$
    (p) $2w(6w - 5)(w + 7)$

19. (a) 5   (g) $\frac{13}{6}$
    (b) 4   (h) $-\frac{35}{2}$
    (c) −11   (i) $-\frac{23}{8}$
    (d) 3   (j) $\frac{2}{9}$
    (e) 5
    (f) −1

20. (a) ±5   (d) 11,−2
    (b) 0,2   (e) $\frac{5}{2}$,−3
    (c) 2,3

21. (a) 25
    (b) 18
    (c) 19

22. (a) $d = \frac{C}{\pi}$
    (b) $a = \frac{V - u}{t}$
    (c) $r = \frac{-2R}{V} + R$

23. 3

24. (a) $\frac{1}{2}$ (f) ab^2c^2
    (b) $\frac{5}{2}$ (g) $\frac{3(w - 4)}{(w + 4)}$
    (c) 2   (h) $\frac{10}{7}$
    (d) $\frac{25xy^2}{8w^2}$ (i) $\frac{x}{x + 2}$
    (e) $6b^{-7}c^3$

25. (a) 2   (d) $\frac{x - 3}{3}$
    (b) $\frac{y + 3}{y + 4}$ (e) $\frac{5(x + 2)}{4(x + 3)}$
    (c) $\frac{a - 5}{a}$ (f) $\frac{21}{(c - 3)(c + 3)}$

26. (a) $\frac{11a}{20}$ (e) $\frac{13}{6x}$
    (b) $\frac{-x - 9}{12}$ (f) $\frac{7m}{6x}$
    (c) $\frac{x + 6}{6}$ (g) $\frac{7x + 1}{(x + 1)(x - 1)}$
    (d) $\frac{a + 12b}{6}$ (h) $\frac{-2y + 6}{y^2 - 3y + 2}$

27. (a)

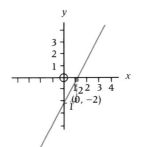

(b)

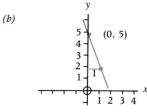

(c)

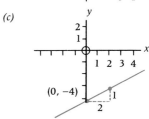

(d)

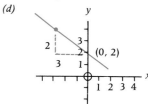

28. (a)

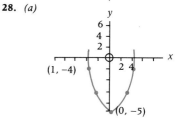

(b)

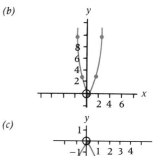

(c)

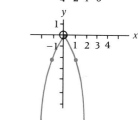

(d)

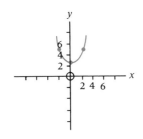

(c) $-\frac{5}{2}$; $(0,-2)$

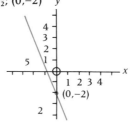

(c)

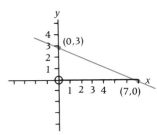

29. *(b)* 25°C; 65°C; 81°C
    (c) 3 min, 5 min, 13 min, 17 min

30. *(b)* $1300; $2200
    (c) The initial cost is $100.

31. *(b)* 10°C
    (c) 2°C; −10°C
    (d) 6000 m

32. *(a)* 8.6
    (b) 12.2

33. *(a)* $\left(5, 10\frac{1}{2}\right)$
    (b) $(1,-4)$

34. *(a)* $\frac{5}{4}$
    (b) $-\frac{4}{3}$
    (c) 0

35. *(a)* 5%
    (b) 75 m

36. $\frac{2}{5}$; $\frac{1}{4}$

37. *(a)* 2; $(0,-3)$

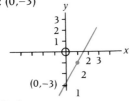

    (b) $\frac{2}{3}$; $(0,4)$

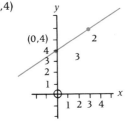

(d) -2; $(0,4)$

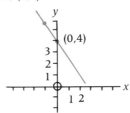

(e) $\frac{5}{2}$; $(0,-5)$

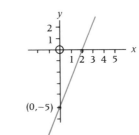

38. *(a)*

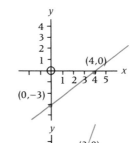

    (b)

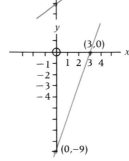

(d)

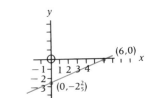

(e)

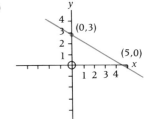

(f)

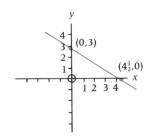

39. *(a)* $y = 3x - 2$ *(d)* $y = -\frac{7}{2}x - 11$
    (b) $y = -\frac{1}{3}x + 4$ *(e)* $y = \frac{4}{3}x - \frac{13}{3}$
    (c) $y = \frac{2}{5}x + 5$ *(f)* $y = -\frac{7}{5}x + 5$

40. *(b)* $C = 30t + 28$
    (c) The slope represents the charge per hour. The C-intercept represents the initial or service charge.

(d) $193
(e) 8 h

41. (b) $L = \frac{3}{20}m + 30$
(c) It represents the original length of the spring.
(d) 37.5 cm
(e) 70 g

42. (a) $\frac{5}{4}$
(b) $-\frac{11}{6}$
(c) $\frac{5}{4}$
(d) $\frac{6}{11}$

43. (a) (2,5)
(b) (−5,5)

44. (a) (240,960) (b) (200,660)

45. (a) (12,500,1050)
(b) The monthly pay for Ivan and Michelle is equal for sales of $12 500.
(c) sales of more than $12 500

46. (a) (2,−5) (f) $(-1,-\frac{7}{2})$
(b) $(\frac{1}{2},\frac{3}{2})$ (g) $(\frac{1}{2},\frac{1}{4})$
(c) (−1,−6) (h) (3,13)
(d) (−2,6) (i) (1,1)
(e) (−5,−4) (j) $(\frac{1}{7},\frac{5}{7})$

47. (a) $C = 2d + 5$; $C = 3.50d + 2$
(b) 2 d
(c) $9

48. $2000 at 7%; 3000 at 10%

49. $6/h for one job, and $4/h for the other

Unit 9

Page 159
4. $403.75; $532.80; $401.48; $460.53; $309.60

5. $690

6. $480

7. $434.50

8. $187.42

9. $450.20

Page 161
2. (a) $217.95

(b) $180.41
(c) $161.68
(d) $335.18
(e) $216.14

3. $2158.80

4. (a) $373.56
(b) $9.96/h
(c) $2760.33

5. (a) $66.93 (d) 8.5%
(b) $380.30 (e) $1156.22
(c) $1526.63 (f) 42%

6. • $597.90; $640; $660.65; $611.75; TOTAL: $2510.30
• $16.74

7. (a) $77.60 (f) $463.20
(b) $50.63 (g) $241.40
(c) $140 (h) $865.73
(d) $291.25 (i) $33.02
(e) $107.48 (j) $632.76

Page 165
3. (a) $252.89; $27.00
(b) $314.98; $54.15
(c) $228.06; $23.50
(d) $466.80; $83.70
(e) $377.35; $70.20

4. $301.90

5. $254.79

6. $228.45

7. $344.58

8. $299.79

9. $322.66

Page 167
1. (a) 25%
(b) $75; $150; $367.50
(c) $400; $700; $1264

2. (a) $150; $500
(b) $1000; $2000
(c) 0.30; 30%
(d) 0.40; 40%
(e) $1044

3. (a) $200
(b) $250; $350; $450
(c) $0; $4000

(d) 5%
(e) $441.15

4. (a) $50; $300; $450
(b) $1000; $1500; $3000
(c) 10%; 20%; 30%
(d) $138.60; $86.50; $545.70

5. (a) $1000
(b) $1500; $2000; $3000
(c) 0; $40 000
(d) 5%; 10%
(e) $1928.10; $3126.35

6. (a) $300
(b) $400; $500; $600; $750
(c) 0; $1250; $3000
(d) 10%; 20%; 30%;
(e) $1556.30
Side Trip
Unit 9

Side Trip

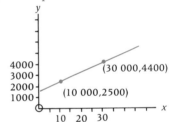

Page 171
4. (a) $700
(b) 30 h to 60 h
(c) When each works 40 h/week
(d) $17.50/h
(e) $175
(f) $350

5. (a) $400 (d) $2000
(b) 5% (e) $200
(c) 25% (f) $300

6. (a) $8000
(b) 40%
(c) 20% for sales up to $4000; 60% for sales above $4000;
(d) $800
(e) $400

Page 172
1. (a) $462 (d) $460.20
(b) $362.60 (e) $406.55
(c) $417.81

2. $794.38

3. $1419.08

4. $268

5. $516.40

6. *(a)* $243.25   *(d)* $231.25
   (b) $106.58   *(e)* $585
   (c) $89.70

7. *(a)* $473.91
   (b) $12.64/h
   (c) $3329.45

8. *(a)* $88.50   *(d)* 8.5%
   (b) $120.36   *(e)* $4017
   (c) $419.67

9. *(a)* $93.75   *(f)* $117.28
   (b) $176   *(g)* $400
   (c) $229,12   *(h)* $197.55
   (d) $307.21   *(i)* $329.84
   (e) $63.42   *(j)* $528.66

10. $615; $784.50; $488.70; $1620;
   $3508.20

11. *(a)* $254.78; $34.35
   (b) $229.05; $28.65
   (c) $315.75; $48.75
   (d) $461.46; $85.50
   (e) $374.67; $70.20

12. $313.69

13. $304.80

14. $374.31

15. $231.37

16. $317.79

17. $351.82

18. *(a)* $300
   (b) $500; $800; $1000
   (c) $500; $1200; $1800
   (d) 0.20, 20%; 0.50, 50%

19. *(a)* Ed: $100; *(f)* $50
      Sam: $200 *(g)* $200
   (b) Ed   *(h)* Ed: $580.90;
   (c) $500   Sam: $393.63
   (d) 20%
   (e) 40%, 60%

Unit 11

Page 195

4. *(a)* $185.32; $10.32
   (b) $260.56; $20.56
   (c) $496.90; $46.90

5. *(a)* $13.80
   (b) 7.3%

6. *(a)* $35   *(c)* $16
   (b) 5   *(d)* 12

7. *(a)* $205.20
   (b) 13.68%

8. 20 months

9. $34.50

Page 197

2. *(a)* $69; $14
   (b) $76.16; $63.92
   (c) $35.88; $70.84
   (d) $14.51; $53.24
   (e) $12.27; $73.10
   (f) $62.13; $241.12

Page 198

1. *(a)* 16.11%   *(c)* 35.37%
   (b) 34.77%   *(d)* 20.4%

2. *(a)* $132.40
   (b) 19.80%

3. 15.05%

4. 26.25%

Page 200

3. *(a)* 20%
   (b) $213.95

4. *(a)* $27.97
   (b) $30.48

5. *(a)* $31.50
   (b) $93.59

6. *(a)* $403.75
   (b) $36.62

7. *(a)* 22%
   (b) 20%
   (c) 27%

8. 64%

9. *(a)* 20%
   (b) 27%

10. 16.4%

11. *(a)* $9.25
   (b) 18.50%

12. The store that offers 30% off has
   the better deal ($122.50).

13. *(a)* A ($728.20)
   (b) A (18%)
   (c) Answers will vary.

14. *(a)* A ($528.80)
   (b) B (21%)
   (c) Answers will vary.

15. *(a)* X ($1413.60)
   (b) Y (16.96%)
   (c) Answers will vary.

16. $47.41

Page 203

1. *(a)* 45
   (b) 40
   (c) 12

2. $10

3. *(a)* $49
   (b) 9.16%

4. *(a)* $772.30; $87.30
   (b) $1161.30; $171.30

5. 18 months

6. $29.50

7. *(a)* $56.16; $110.88
   (b) $77.94; $17.64
   (c) $56.25; $50
   (d) $59.88; $237.12

8. *(a)* 19.2%
   (b) 17.9%

9. 17.37%

10. *(a)* 12%
   (b) $1199
   (c) $1050
   (d) $58.75

11. 19%

12. 6%

13. *(a)* A ($2007.20)
   (b) A (20%)
   (c) Answers will vary.

Unit 12

Page 207

4. (a) $16   (f) $124.66
    (b) $91.20   (g) $108.38
    (c) $82.50   (h) $1.33
    (d) $21   (i) $4687.50
    (e) $12.75   (j) $32.51

5. $254.79

6. (a) $32.40
    (b) $27.60

7. $8565.48

Page 210

2. (a) $685   (c) $467.74
    (b) $45   (d) $14 531.51

3. (a) 115 d   (d) 231 d
    (b) 314 d   (e) 283 d
    (c) 175 d

4. $688.72

5. $2259.11

6. $7410.45; January 8

7. (a) September 16
    (b) $1432.62
    (c) $673.44

8. (a) $919.54   (c) $94.49
    (b) $624.74   (d) $4780.53

9. $629.33

10. (a) November 30
     (b) $347.46

Page 212

1. (a) $70.88   (e) $755.24
    (b) 12%   (f) 114 d
    (c) 16.73%   (g) 90 d
    (d) $714.29

2. $794.12

3. 162 d

4. 10.6%

5. 3 a 209 d

6. 76%

7. (a) 102 d
    (b) June 22

8. 22.33%

9. November 16

10. 17 more days

Page 213

1. 1 a 237 d; 35 d; 261 d; 199 d; 19 d; 193 d

2. $1586.96; $844.13; $632.25

Page 215

2. (a) $656
    (b) $724.26

3. (a) $12 320
    (b) $13 416.80

4. (a) $1440   (c) $1458.61
    (b) $1452   (d) $1462.08

5. (a) $830
    (b) $830.46

6. (a) $716.43   (d) $1442.42
    (b) $109.49   (e) $794.94
    (c) $317.32

7. (a) $424   (c) $424.54
    (b) $424.36   (d) $424.67

Page 217

3. (a) $30(1 + \frac{0.08}{4})^{24}$
    (b) $200(1 + \frac{0.24}{12})^{48}$
    (c) $3000(1 + \frac{0.09}{2})^{22}$
    (d) $5(1 + \frac{0.13}{4})^{7}$
    (e) $90\,000(1 + \frac{0.09}{12})^{20}$

4. (a) 36.02   (c) 664.43
    (b) 4570.69   (d) 261.75

5. (a) $983.58   (c) $2370.87
    (b) $95 734.44   (d) $65.76

6. (a) $301.54   (c) $49 959.89
    (b) $21.17   (d) $17.61

7. (a) $8815.03
    (b) $4815.03

8. $3224.45; $1224.45

9. (a) $17 958.56
    (b) $19 799.32
    (c) $1840.76

10. first bank; $1.04

11. $1582.74

12. $1789.71

13. (a)

14. $937.51

15. $441.15

Page 221

3. (a) 8 a   (d) 6 a
    (b) 7 a 6 months   (e) 3 a
    (c) 6 a   (f) 3 a

4. (a) 19 a
    (b) 9 a 6 months
    (c) 6 a 6 months

5. 5 a

6. (a) 5.1%   (c) 3.4%
    (b) 6.8%   (d) 5.7%

7. 7.2%

8. 8.7%

9. 13.4%

Page 222

1. (a) 49
    (b) 242
    (c) 192
    (d) 358

2. (a) 0.07; 10   (d) 0.015; 15
    (b) 0.075; 32   (e) 0.01; 108
    (c) 0.025; 72

3. (a) $17.50   (d) $7590
    (b) $88.99   (e) $3.29
    (c) $0.86

4. $6.66

5. (a) 196 d
    (b) 237 d
    (c) 307 d

6. (a) $32.29
    (b) $7.71

7. (a) $799.75   (c) $314.67
    (b) $1410.27   (d) $963.76

8. $373.19

9. April 12; $3854.55

10. (a) $619.05
     (b) $5261.89
     (c) $1524.22

11. $1729.41

12. *(a)* $21.45   *(e)* 16.6%
     (b) $19.77   *(f)* 6.4%
     (c) $177.78   *(g)* 6 months
     (d) $3164.09   *(h)* 254 d

13. $1350

14. 3.9%

15. December 27

16. *(a)* $A = 50 (1 + 0.05)^{16}$
     (b) $A = 85 (1 + 0.015)^{36}$
     (c) $A = 3000 (1 + 0.0125)^{60}$
     (d) $A = 20 (1 + 0.175)^{19}$
     (e) $A = 5400 (1 + 0.035)^{8}$
     (f) $A = 250 (1 + 0.057)^{9}$
     (g) $A = 90\,000 (1 + 0.0075)^{240}$

17. *(a)* $1326.65; $826.65
     (b) $1342.53; $842.53
     (c) $1296.87; $796.87
     (d) $11 979.87; $4979.87
     (e) $116.47; $41.47

18. *(c)* $3525

19. $5.22

20. *(a)* $2436.81
     (b) $1095.94
     (c) $159.13

21. *(a)* 12   *(c)* 32
     (b) 12   *(d)* 17

22. *(a)* 10 a
     (b) 9 a
     (c) 9 a

23. 2 a 4 months

24. *(a)* $2\frac{1}{2}$%   *(c)* $2\frac{1}{2}$%
     (b) 5%   *(d)* 6%

25. *(a)* 4.2%
     (b) 4.5%
     (c) 5.1%

Side Trip
1. *(a)* $820   *(c)* $129 237.67
     (b) $89 759.69

2. *(a)* $124   *(d)* $127.12
     (b) $126.82   *(e)* $127.12
     (c) $127.11

Unit 13

Page 228
1. *(a)* $0.06   *(d)* $4.73
     (b) $0.20   *(e)* $41.86
     (c) $7.73   *(f)* $14.78

2. *(a)* $26.03
     (b) $333.90
     (c) $6510.18

3. *(a)* $23.29   *(f)* $6416.26
     (b) $51.78   *(g)* $23.42
     (c) $7357.68   *(h)* $4212.18
     (d) $106.03   *(i)* $234.74
     (e) $4049.28   *(j)* $2239.26

Page 231

1. $1803.49

2. 6 a

3. 12 a

4. 25 a

5. 18 a

6. The (simple interest) amounts at at the end of each consecutive year are: $1100, $1200, $1300, $1400, $1500, $1600, $1700, $1800, $1900, $2000, $2100, $2200.
The (compound interest) amounts at the end of each consecutive year are: $1100, $1210, $1331, $1464.10, $1610.51, $1771.56, $1948.72, $2143.59, $2357.95, $2593.74, $2853.12, $3138.42.

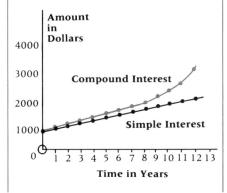

7. $938.42

8. 10 a; 7.5 a

9. 15 a

10. 30 a

Side Trip
9a; 8 a; 7 a and 3 months;
6 a; About the same.

Page 234
1. *(a)* $400 + 400 (1.08) + $400
       $(1.08)^2 + 400 (1.08)^3 + $400
       $(1.08)^4 + $400 (1.08)^5$;
       $2934.37; $534.37
     (b) $200 + 200(1.05)^1 +\ldots+$
       $200(1.05)^9$; $2515.58;
       $515.58
     (c) $50 + 50 (1.01) + $50 (1.01)^2$
       $+ $50 (1.01)^3$; $203.02; $3.02

2. *(a)* 6 a; $400; 1 a
     (b) 5 a; $200; 6 months
     (c) 4 months; $50; 1 month

3. *(a)*

     (b)

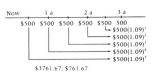

     (c)

4. $1909.82; $309.82

Page 236
1. *(a)* 0.7130   *(d)* 3.77
   (b) 0.7089   *(e)* 106.66
   (c) 630.48   *(f)* 102.70

2. *(a)* 1   *(d)* 10
   (b) 1   *(e)* 300
   (c) .2000   *(f)* 455

3. *(a)* $231.66   *(c)* $1220.54
   (b) $3384.20   *(d)* $2795.70

4. *(a)* $735.03
   (b) $730.69
   (c) $728.45
   (d) $726.92
   As the compounding period increases, the present value decreases.

5. *(a)* $1693.42   *(c)* $403.78
   (b) $250.96   *(d)* $702.11

6. $3104.61

7. $762.90

8. $1578.82

Page 239
1. *(a)* $\frac{\$500}{(1.10)^1} + \frac{\$500}{(1.10)^2} + \frac{\$500}{(1.10)^3} + \frac{\$500}{(1.10)^4}$
   (b) $\frac{\$200}{(1.05)^1} + \frac{\$200}{(1.05)^2} + \ldots + \frac{\$200}{(1.05)^8}$
   (c) $\frac{\$1000}{(1.03)^1} + \frac{\$1000}{(1.03)^2} + \ldots + \frac{\$1000}{(1.03)^8}$
   (d) $\frac{\$50}{(1.015)^1} + \frac{\$50}{(1.015)^2} + \ldots + \frac{\$50}{(1.015)^5}$

2. *(a)* $PV = \frac{\$300}{(1.09)^1} + \frac{\$300}{(1.09)^2} + .. + \frac{\$300}{(1.09)^5}$;
     $1166.90
   (b) $PV = \frac{\$500}{(1.06)^1} + \frac{\$500}{(1.06)^2} + .. + \frac{\$500}{(1.06)^6}$;
     $2458.66
   (c) $PV = \frac{\$1000}{(1.01)^1} + \frac{\$1000}{(1.01)^2} + .. + \frac{\$1000}{(1.01)^6}$;
     $5795.48

3. *(b)* $18 181.82; $16 528.93;
     $15 026.30; $13 660.27;
     $12 418.43; $11 289.48
   (c) $87 105.20
   (d) $12 894.80

4. $2391.33

Page 241
1. *(a)* $0.06
   (b) $3.50

---

2. *(a)* $10.60   *(c)* $1017.60
   (b) $74.18   *(d)* $8835.59

3. *(a)* Amounts at simple interest:
     $2180, 2360, 2540, 2720,
     2900, 3080, 3260, 3440,
     3620, 3800, 3980, 4160.
     Amounts at compound
     interest: $2180, 2376.20,
     2590.06, 2823.16, 3077.25,
     3354.20, 3656.08, 3985.13,
     4343.79, 4734.73, 5160.85,
     5625.33

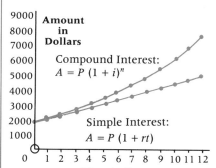

Amount in Dollars

Compound Interest:
$A = P(1 + i)^n$

Simple Interest:
$A = P(1 + rt)$

Time in Years

   (b) $1465.33
   (c) 11 a at simple interest; 8 a at compound interest

4. *(a)* $914.63; $114.63
   (b) $2720.77; $320.77

5. *(a)*

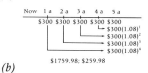

     $1759.98; $259.98
   (b)

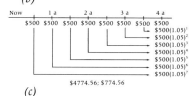

     $4774.56; $774.56
   (c)

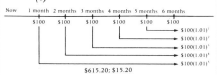

     $615.20; $15.20

---

6. $1543.12

7. $51.01

8. *(a)* 68.06   *(c)* 164.11
   (b) 167.28   *(d)* 4.17

9. *(a)* $735.03
   (b) $373.11

10. *(a)* $1299.86
   (b) $704.96
   (c) $3150.26

11. $3203.01

12. *(a)* $1288.55
   (b) $578.16

13. *(a)* $3889.65
   (b) $2897.74

14. *(a)* $7581.57
   (b) $2418.43

Unit 14

Page 245
4. $3581

5. $2728.15

6. *(a)* $2369.94
   (b) $369.94

7. $222.78

Page 247
3. *(a)* $10 708
   (b) $12 402.97
   (c) $10 858.79

4. *(a)* $11 564.64
   (b) $13 395.21
   (c) $11 727.49

5. car *(b)*

6. Answers will vary.

7. $14 086.44 (Answers may vary according to provincial sales tax.)

Page 249
1. *(a)* $3916.70; $4770.80; $854.10
   (b) $5298.94; $6651.80;
     $1352.86
   (c) $2968; $3447.12; $479.12
   (d) $6625; $9746.92; $3121.92

2. (a) 24.0%   (c) 29.8%
   (b) 19.5%   (d) 36.0%

3. (a) $815.78
   (b) 28.5%

4. (a) $1006.32
   (b) 14.8%

5. (a) $11 711.06
   (b) 15%

Page 251

6. (a) $5936
   (b) $1484
   (c) $4452; $3498; $2650
   (d) $954

7. (a) $194.95; $18.45
   (b) $286.43; $20.52
   (c) $262.78; $23.41
   (d) $266.26; $21.96

8. (a) $561.93
   (b) $45.68

9. $21.89

10. $19.32

11. $14.32

Page 253

1. $25.27

2. $42.68

3. $91.15

Page 255

2. $212.30

3. $56.23

4. $51.96

5. $249.12

Page 257

2. (a) $12.11
   (b) $14.78
   (c) $16.92

3. $11.60

4. car (Save $23.81)

5. $270

Page 259

1. (a) $1351
   (b) $552
   (c) $185

2. (a) $991
   (b) -0-
   (c) $729

Page 260

1. $4305

2. $3642.95

3. (a) $10 667.05
   (b) $11 496.20
   (c) $10 660.65

4. (a) set (a) more expensive by
    $515.65

5. $14 403.86

6. (a) $5826.60; $7120; $1293.40;
    25.7%
   (b) $6750; $10 440; $3690;
    35.5%

7. (a) $4611.38
   (b) 35.6%

8. (a) $366.33; $29.21
   (b) $271.40; $18.49
   (c) $513.54; $31.44
   (d) $380.41; $31.96

9. $19.42

10. $74.15

11. $38.15

12. (a) $67.77
   (b) $60.92

13. $112.52

14. $1215.60

15. Answers will vary.

Unit 15

Page 266

3. (a) 20%; $90
   (b) 40%; $168
   (c) $14; 20%
   (d) $22.30; 63.4%
   (e) $16; $96
   (f) $4.50; $8.10
   (g) $255; 17.6%
   (h) $71.30; 32.5%
   (i) $37.50; $52.50
   (j) $96.15; $158.65
   (k) $7.69; $2.31
   (l) $112.68; $47.32
   (m) $145.60; $665.60
   (n) $41.49; 52.9%
   (o) $180.45; $59.55

4. $1.30; 35.6%

5. 249%

6. $202.50

7. $11.37; $38.12

8. $13.30

9. $13.11; $25.56

10. $19.56

11. $18.00; $21.95

Page 269

3. (a) 25%; $30
   (b) 20%; $272
   (c) $28.80; $35.20
   (d) $91; $39
   (e) $30; 38%
   (f) $1.40; 58%
   (g) $466.67; $396.67
   (h) $413.75; $248.25
   (i) $126; 29%
   (j) $10.50; 62%
   (k) $588.24; $188.24
   (l) $15.63; $3.13
   (m) 40%; $45
   (n) $300; $1700
   (o) $3.25; 35%
   (p) $1.42; $0.57
   (q) $1280; 28%
   (r) $52.84; $23.25

4. $14; 40%

5. 47.4%

6. $23.58; $41.92

7. $366.60

8. $102.32; $126.32

9. $158.33

10. $57.92

11. *(a)* 35%; 53%
    (b) 55%; 122%

12. $101.81

Page 271

4. *(a)* 20%; $320
    (b) 55%; $7.50
    (c) $16; $48
    (d) $4.80; $35.15
    (e) $37.60; 40%
    (f) $0.56; 16%
    (g) $26.67; $18.67
    (h) $625; $475
    (i) $120.50; 38%
    (j) $1150; 55%
    (k) $545.45; $245.45
    (l) $146.91; $96.96
    (m) $1200; $1200
    (n) $12.30; 29%
    (o) $2589.29; $1864.29
    (p) $135.90; $81.54

5. $3; 27%

6. $1140.10

7. yes

8. *(a)* 34%
    (b) 44%
    (c) 34%

9. 41%

10. $23.10; $33

11. *(a)* $13.43
    (b) $3.83

Page 273

4. *(a)* $243   *(d)* $81.56
    (b) $162   *(e)* $33.09
    (c) $40.91   *(f)* $234.36

5. *(a)* $3.64
    (b) $4.81

6. supplier Y

7. *(a)* $26.93
    (b) $26.33
    (c) $24.75
    (d) no; (c); (a)
    (e) first supplier

8. *(a)* $25.17
    (b) $25.17
    (c) no

9. first supplier

10. *(a)* A: $136.32; B: $136.34; A
    (b) A: $137.70; B: $143.51; A
    (c) A: $153; B: $143.51; B
    (d) A: $153; B: $170.85; A

Page 277

2. *(a)* $52.80   *(e)* $226.73
    (b) $37.31   *(f)* $47.65
    (c) $104.50   *(g)* $208.48
    (d) $29.92   *(h)* $936.31

3. *(a)* 35.6%   *(d)* 61%
    (b) 51.8%   *(e)* 65.7%
    (c) 23.7%   *(f)* 41.9%

4. *(a)* B (33.5%)
    (b) B (52.2%)
    (c) A (36.3%)
    (d) A (31.6%)
    (e) A (33.1%)
    (f) B (45.1%)

5. *(a)* 45.8%
    (b) $276.42; $793.49; $156.10

6. 7.4%

7. *(a)* 4.7%
    (b) 18.3%
    (c) 2%

Page 279

1. *(a)* $3900
    (b) $5280
    (c) $1979.94

2. *(a)* $46 808.51
    (b) $71 204.19

3. *(a)* $66 666.67
    (b) $47 166.67

4. $66 021

Page 280

1. *(a)* $85   *(f)* $50
    (b) $80   *(g)* $620
    (c) $2   *(h)* $0.40
    (d) $85   *(i)* $28
    (e) $18

2. *(a)* 85%   *(c)* 38%
    (b) 55%   *(d)* 1%

3. *(a)* 27.5%; $102
    (b) $30; $180
    (c) $3; 33%
    (d) $370; $416.25
    (e) $99.48; $44.77
    (f) $395; 132%
    (g) 38%; $38
    (h) $113.40; $306.60
    (i) $490; 35%
    (j) $7.50; $5.10
    (k) $239.48; 30.4%
    (l) $59.64; $9.69
    (m) 7.7%; $86.80
    (n) $68.64; $243.36
    (o) $552.73; 39%
    (p) $994; $894.60
    (q) $53.62; $24.13
    (r) $6.23; 52%

4. *(a)* $0.25   *(c)* $0.25
    (b) 62.5%   *(d)* 38.5%

5. *(a)* 126.1%
    (b) 55.8%

6. $0.50; 14.3%

7. $23.24; $89.64

8. $11.12; $41.83

9. *(a)* 25.8%
    (b) 17.6%

10. 33.7%

11. $9.91; $14.17

12. $21.12; $28.54

13. $9.66

14. $52.81

15. *(a)* $27.97   *(d)* $4.11
     (b) $9.05   *(e)* $255.68
     (c) $60.54   *(f)* $747.61

16. *(a)* 34.7%
     (b) 55.9%
     (c) 71.4%

17. *(b)*

18. *(a)* $128.60
     (b) $215.42
     (c) $175.66

19. 2.8%

20. *(a)* $36; 42.9%; 30%
     (b) $32.50; 30%; 23%
     (c) $320; 37.5%; 27.3%
     (d) $18.70; 51.2%; 33.9%; 9.4%; $50
     (e) $1561.40; 90.1%; 47.4% 14.4%; $1336.40
     (f) $1.89; 190.5%; 65.6%; $1.10; $4.39
     (g) $145; 58%; 36.7%; $59.25; $335.75
     (h) $510; $170; 33.3%; $127.50; $382.50
     (i) $56.25; $18.75; 33.3%; $5; 6.7%
     (j) $2380; $980; 41.2%; $380; 16%
     (k) $140; $200; 42.9%; $24; $176
     (l) $9.53; $13.82; 31%; $4.56; $9.26
     (m) $115.50; $23.10; 25%; 4.3%; $110.50

Units 9 to 15 Review

Page 286

1. *(a)* $373.50   *(c)* $513.56
     (b) $328.35   *(d)* $285.30

2. $210.39

3. $477.38

4. *(a)* $189.90   *(c)* $880
     (b) $52.67   *(d)* 4.8%

5. *(a)* $49.80   *(d)* $267.69
     (b) $165.60   *(e)* $349.51
     (c) $242.46   *(f)* $606.81

6. $367.12

7. $318.14

8. *(a)* $100
     (b) $1600; $2400; $2800
     (c) 6.25%; 25%

Page 288

11. *(a)* $164
     (b) 13%

12. *(a)* $1030; $135
     (b) $1522; $212

13. 16

14. *(a)* $74.10; $278.40
     (b) $45.75; $73.50
     (c) $335.07; $1612.10

15. *(a)* 38.85%
     (b) 12.90%

16. *(a)* 19.4%
     (b) $39.58

17. 35.75%

18. *(a)* $51.33
     (b) $70.31
     (c) $1092

19. $22.22

20. *(a)* $909.50
     (b) $1155.66
     (c) $211.26

21. *(a)* $16.88
     (b) $843.07
     (c) $666.67
     (d) 10.7%
     (e) 15.4%
     (f) 2 a 103 d
     (g) 1 a 65 d

22. 15.1%

23. *(a)* $379.60; $79.60
     (b) $1185.23; $305.23

     (c) $5890.88; $1390.88

24. *(b)* $1834.99

25. *(a)* 11
     (b) 28

26. *(a)* 13 a
     (b) 9 a 3 months

27. *(a)* 0.055
     (b) 2.0% (0.020)

28. *(a)* $575.07; $75.07
     (b) $1497.37; $97.37

29. *(a)* $1261.63; $61.63
     (b) $204.03; $4.03

30. $213.18; $3.18

31. *(a)* $705.17
     (b) $2606.40

32. $2468.11; $2507.49

33. *(a)* $1039.53
     (b) $246.29

34. *(a)* $3909.95
     (b) $3996.42

35. $3771.55

36. *(a)* $11 228.90
     (b) $10 513

37. *(b)* by $253.85

38. $12 826.40

39. $4681.55; $5420; $738.45; 19.79%

40. *(a)* $361.03
     (b) $234.18

41. $16.92

42. $39

43. $42.27

44. *(a)* $3.60   *(c)* $3.60
     (b) 90%   *(d)* 47.4%

45. $22.92; $72.57

46. $407.14; $692.14

47. $123.53

48. 35.3%

49. *(a)* $28.17
   (b) $23.60
   (c) $307.79

50. *(a)* 31.8%
   (b) 37.2%
   (c) 53.4%

51. $176.70

Unit 16

Page 297

1. *(a)* 3.75%; 338
   (b) Answers will vary.

2. *(a)* 224 000; 188 000
   (b) Answers will vary.

3. 875

Page 301

6. *(a)* Cumulative Frequency: 4, 15, 39, 55, 58, 60 Relative Frequency: 7%, 18%, 40%, 27%, 5%, 3%

(b)

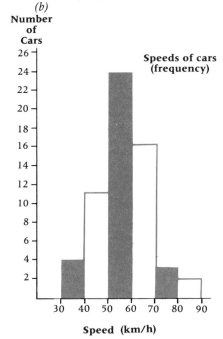

(c)

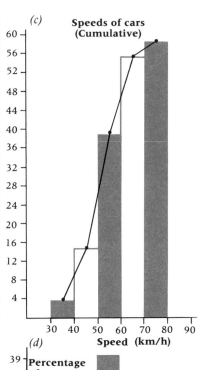

(d)

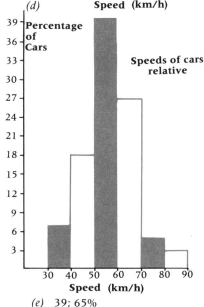

(e) 39; 65%

7. *(a)* 30 to 96   *(b)* 10
   (c) The frequencies are: 2, 6, 12, 24, 19, 12, 5.

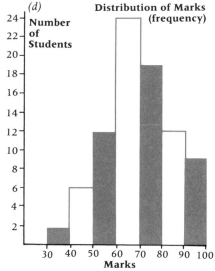

(e) The cumulative frequencies are: 2, 8, 20, 44, 63, 75, 80.

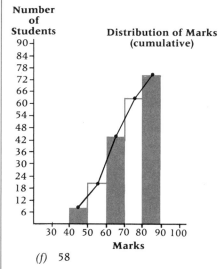

(f) 58

8. *(a)* The frequencies are: 1, 19, 9, 12, 9, 1, 5, 4.

(b)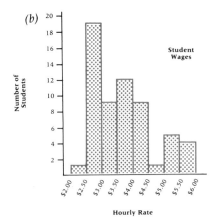

(c) Relative frequency: 2%, 32%, 15%, 20%, 15%, 2%, 8%, 7%

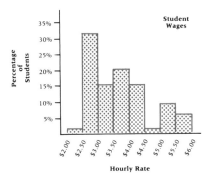

9. *(a)* The intervals for hourly wages are: $2.00 to $3.00, $3.00 to $4.00, $4.00 to $5.00, $5.00 to $6.00. The frequencies are 20, 21, 10, 9.

(b)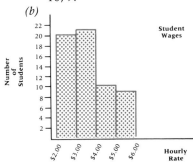

(c) What number of students earn a minimum wage; the average hourly age; etc.

Page 305

5. *(a)* 12; 8.5; 5
(b) mode; answers will vary.
(c) Answers will vary.
(d) median

6. *(a)* 27.3; 25.5; 19
(b) 6.3; 6.6; 4.9
(c) 74.9; 75; 75 and 82

7. *(a)* 188.8; 192.5
(b) 183.9; 186.5
(c) 221

8. 66.3

9. *(a)* 364.3, 380, 500; 500, 450,—; 348.6, 500,—
(b) mode; mean; median
(c) Answers will vary.

Page 307

3. 4.6; 5; 4

Page 309

2. 68; 60 to 70; 70 to 80

3. *(a)* 12.9; 15 to 18; 21 to 24
(b)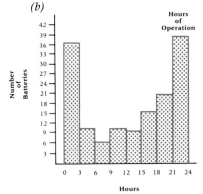

4. The table should contain this information as follows. Time (s): 32 to 35, 35 to 38, 38 to 41, 41 to 44, 44 to 47, 47 to 50, 50 to 53, 53 to 56; Class Value: 33.5, 36.5, 39.5, 42.5, 45.5, 48.5, 51.5, 54.5; Frequency: 5, 10, 6, 6, 4, 2, 6, 6; Cumulative Frequency: 5, 15, 21, 27, 31, 33, 39, 45; Product (Class Value x Frequency): 167.5, 365, 237, 255, 182, 97, 309, 327. 35 to 38; 43.1; 41 to 44

Page 312

3.

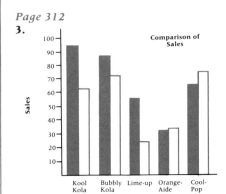

4. *(a)*

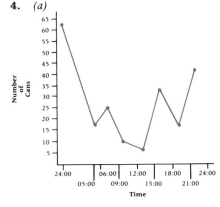

(b) Answers will vary.

Page 314

1. *(a)* A; A; C
(b) 16 000 units
(c) April
(d) C
(e) B
(f) A: 7000; B: 65 000; C: 54 000

492

2. *(a)*

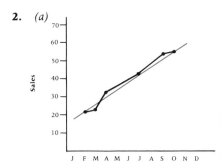

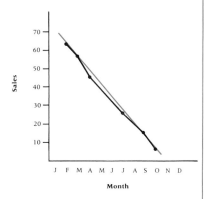

(b) See *(a)*.
(c) Paper A: 37, 41, 49, 60, 65;
Paper Z: 43, 35, 22, 0 ,—
(d) Circumstances will influence shape of the line.

3. *(a)*

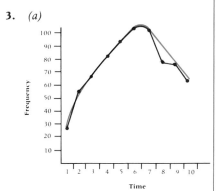

(b) See *(a)*.
(c) 50; 30

4. *(a)* Frequency: 25, 30, 20, 15, 5, 10, 5
(b) Cumulative Frequency: 25, 55, 75, 90, 95, 105, 110;
Product: 25, 60, 60, 60, 25, 60, 35
(c) 3; 3; 2
(d) Answers will vary.

5. *(a)* 8; 8; 9
(b) 11; 10 to 12; 12 to 14

Page 317

1. *(a)*

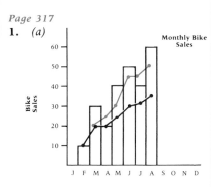

(b) Cumulative frequency: 10, 40, 60, 100, 150, 190, 250;
Cumulative Average: 10, 20, 20, 25, 30, 31.7, 35.7
(c) See part *(a)*.
(d) The graph indicates an upward trend; 40 bikes
(e) 2-month moving average: 20, 25, 30, 45, 45, 50
(f) See part *(e)*.

2. *(a)*

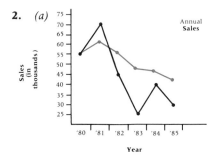

(b) The table should contain this information as follows.
Year: 1980, 1981, 1982, 1983, 1984, 1985; Sales: $55 000, $45 000, $25 000, $40 000, $30 000;
Cumulative Frequency: $55 000, $125 000, $170 000, $195 000, $235 000,$265 000;
Cumulative Average: $55 000, $62 500, $56 667, $48 750, $47 000, $44 167.
(c) See part *(a)*.
(d) About $42 000

3. *(a)*

(b) The 2-month averages are: 107.5, 55.5, 62, 118, 148.5, 170.5, 187.5, 194.5
(c) The 3-month averages are:—, 87.7, 62.3, 94.7, 124.3, 167, 170.7, 197.7.
(d) See part *(a)*.

493

4. *(b)* The table should contain
this information as follows.
Month: Jan, Feb, Mar, Apr,
May, Jun, Jul, Aug, Sep,
Oct; Sales: 30, 10, 20, 50,
40, 80, 60, 70, 40, 20;
Cumulative Frequency: 30,
40, 60, 110, 150, 230, 290,
360, 400, 420; Cumulative
Average: 30, 20, 20, 27.5,
30, 38.3, 41.4, 45, 44.4, 42;
3 Month Moving Average:—,
—, 20, 26.7, 36.7, 56.7, 60, 70,
56.7, 43.3.

(c)

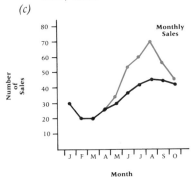

Page 318

1. Answers will vary.

2. *(a)* 1979
 (b) 12 billion
 (c) 1970 to 1972

3. *(a)* 57 to 94
 (b) 102 to 211
 (c) 2.8 to 8.9

4. *(a)* 6; 5; 10
 (b) 4; 2; 1 and 8
 (c) 7; 6.5;—

5. *(a)* Ontario, British Columbia
 (b) $7000
 (c) Answers will vary.

6. 1096

7. *(a)* $305 to $645
 (b) $50

(c) The table should contain
this information as follows:
Interval: $300 to $350, $350
to $400, $400 to $450,
$450 to $500, $500 to $550,
$550 to $600, $600 to $650;
Frequency: 10, 3, 1, 14, 9, 5,
8; Gumulative Frequency:
10, 13, 14, 28, 37, 42, 50;
Relative Frequency: 20%, 6%,
2%, 28%, 18%, 10%, 16%.

(d)

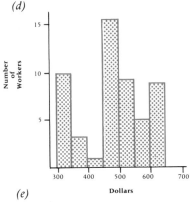

(e)

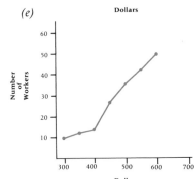

(f)

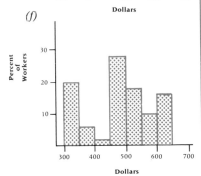

8. *(a)* 28.3; 27;—
 (b) 74.4; 79; 56, 85
 (c) 5.6; 6; 2

9. *(a)* 82.6; 80; 79
 (b) 80.6; 80; 79
 (c) 70

10. The cumulative frequencies are:
20, 44, 84, 119, 149, 159, 164,
168, 170.
The products are: 20, 48, 120,
140, 150, 60, 35, 32, 18; 3.7;
4 d; 3 d

11. The class values are: 1.5, 4.5,
7.5, 10.5, 13.5, 16.5, 19.5, 22.5.
The cumulative frequencies are:
24, 29, 41, 57, 76, 84, 88, 90.
The products are: 36, 22.5, 90,
168, 256.5, 132, 78, 45; 9.2; 9 to
12; 0 to 3

12.

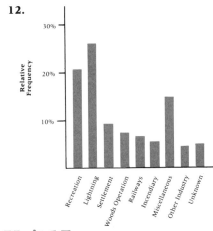

Unit 17

Page 325

3. 62°

4. 30°

5. *(a)* $a = 71°; b = 71°; c = 109°$
 (b) $e = 127°; f = 53°; g = 127°$
 (c) $d = 42°$
 (d) $h = 72°; k = 36°$

6. 135°

7. 150°

8. (a) $a = 29°$; $b = 122°$
   (b) $c = 71°$; $d = 38°$; $e = 71°$;
      $f = 38°$
   (c) $g = 45°$; $h = 33°$; $k = 57°$
   (d) $m = 25°$; $n = 25°$; $p = 25°$
   (e) $q = 49°$; $r = 41°$; $s = 90°$
   (f) $t = 66°$; $u = 66°$
   (g) $v = 42°$; $x = 24°$; $y = 48°$
   (h) $z = 52°$

Side Trip
1. 12
2. 47

Page 328
3. (a) $a = 21°$; $b = 69°$; $c = 69°$
   (b) $d = 32°$; $e = 32°$; $f = 32°$
   (c) $g = 31°$; $h = 59°$
   (d) $x = 64°$; $y = 90°$; $z = 28°$
   (e) $a = 50°$; $b = 130°$; $c = 25°$
   (f) $p = 70°$; $q = 29°$
   (g) $r = 40°$; $s = 25°$
   (h) $t = 120°$; $w = 120°$
   (i) $k = 42°$; $m = 48°$; $n = 21°$
   (j) $k = 50°$; $m = 80°$; $n = 40°$;
      $p = 40°$; $q = 40°$; $r = 80°$

Page 330
3. (a) 30   (c) 56
   (b) 16   (d) insufficient
                 information

4. (a) 15.5   (c) 36.8
   (b) 20.7   (d) 13.8

5. 66.7 cm

6. 3.8 m

7. 308 cm

8. (a) 7.6 m
   (b) 41.0 cm
   (c) 5.4 m
   (d) 125.1 cm

9. Diagonal measure is 135 cm
   ($135 > 122$).

10. 152.6 cm

11. 208.2 cm

12. 537 cm

13. 26.2 cm
14. 22 cm by 22 cm
15. (a) 273 cm
   (b) 280 cm

Page 332
1. 187 cm
2. $AB = 20$; $AD = 48$; no

Page 335
9. (a) $\triangle KLM \equiv \triangle PNM$, SSS
   (b) $\triangle EOF \equiv \triangle HOG$, SSS
   (c) $\triangle MNK \equiv \triangle PNQ$, SAS
   (d) $\triangle ABC \equiv \triangle EDC$, ASA

10. (a) SAS
   (b) Sides: $GH = GK$, $GJ = GJ$,
      $HJ = KJ$;
      Angles: $\angle HGJ = \angle KGJ$, $\angle GHJ$
      $= \angle GKJ$, $\angle GJH = \angle GJK$

11. (a) ASA
   (b) Sides: $MP = MP$, $MQ = PN$,
      $QP = NM$
      Angles: $\angle QMP = \angle NPM$,
      $\angle Q = \angle N$, $\angle MPQ = \angle PMN$

Page 337
2. SAS

3. (a) SAS; $x = 79°$; $y = 38$
   (b) ASA; $x = 20°$; $y = 28$
   (c) SAS; $x = 82°$; $y = 14$
   (d) ASA; $x = 48°$; $y = 18$
   (e) SAS; $x = 44°$; $y = 23$
   (f) SSS; $x = 80°$; $y = 30$

4. SAS
5. ASA
6. SSS; $x = 48$

Page 339
1. (a) rectangle
   (b) trapezoid
   (c) rhombus
   (d) parallelogram

2. (a) chord
   (b) radius
   (c) sector
   (d) segment
   (e) arc
   (f) semi-circle

3. (a) $48°$
   (b) $50°$
   (c) $m = 50°$; $n = 80°$
   (d) $p = q = 40°$; $r = 140°$
   (e) $k = 50°$
   (f) $w = 45°$
   (g) $u = 90°$; $v = 30°$
   (h) $t = 105°$

4. (a) m; $m^2 = k^2 + n^2$
   (b) y; $y^2 = x^2 + w^2$

5. (a) $\triangle ABC \equiv \triangle ADC$; SSS; Sides:
      $AB = AD$, $BC = DC$; $AC = AC$;
      Angles: $\angle B = \angle D$, $\angle BAC =$
      $\angle DAC$; $\angle ACB = \angle ACD$
   (b) $\triangle EFG = \triangle KHJ$: ASA; Sides:
      $EF = KH$, $EG = KJ$, $FG = HJ$;
      Angles: $\angle E = \angle K$, $\angle F = \angle H$,
      $\angle G = \angle J$
   (c) $\triangle MNP \equiv \triangle RQP$; SAS; Sides:
      $MP = RP$, $MN = RQ$, $NP = QP$,
      Angles: $\angle M = \angle R$, $\angle N = \angle Q$,
      $\angle MPN = \angle RPQ$
   (d) $\triangle TSV \equiv \triangle WSV$; SSS; Sides:
      $TS = WS$, $TV = WV$, $VS = VS$;
      Angles: $\angle T = \angle W$;
      $\angle TSV = \angle WSV$,
      $\angle TVS = \angle WVS$

6. (a) $a = 60°$; $b = 60°$
   (b) $c = 36°$
   (c) $d = 68°$; $e = 124°$; $f = 56°$
   (d) $g = 61°$; $h = 61°$; $k = 58°$
   (e) $m = 32°$; $n = 29°$
   (f) $p = 23°$

7. $56°$

8. $40°$

9. 156

10. (a) $a = b = 41°$
   (b) $c = d = 45°$
   (c) $e = 48°$; $f = 66°$; $g = 24°$
   (d) $h = 50°$; $k = 130°$
   (e) $m = 144°$; $n = 54°$
   (f) $p = 41°$; $q = 98°$

11. (a) 24
   (b) 34
   (c) 27
   (d) 49

12. 529.8 m

13. (a) 25.7 cm
(b) 25.4 m
(c) 13.3 cm

14. 58.1 cm

15. (a) 1826 cm
(b) 2065 cm

16. 117 cm

17. 66.3 cm

18. 3.3 m

19. (a) 52 cm
(b) 52 cm

20. 43 cm

21. SAS

22. (a) ASA: $y = 108°$
(b) SSS; $x = 84°$; $y = 61°$
(c) SAS; $x = 45°$; $y = 45°$
(d) SAS; $x = 58°$

23. ASA

Unit 18

Page 345

2. (a) 53.8 cm
(b) 23.3 m
(c) 30.9 cm
(d) 46.8 cm

3. (a) 38 m
(b) 21.6 m
(c) 55. 2 cm
(d) 53.6 cm
(e) 91.4 m
(f) 104 cm

4. $828.80

5. 1442 cm

6. (a) 47 m
(b) $211.50

7. 3.77 km

8. 102 cm

9. $344.50

10. 60.85

11. 638 cm

12. 8.7 m by 11.7 m

Page 348

2. (a) 157 m²
(b) 177 cm²
(c) 96 m²
(d) 557 cm²
(e) 178 m²
(f) 302 cm²

3. (a) 628 cm²
(b) 714 m²
(c) 672 cm²
(d) 243 cm²

4. 19.6 km²

5. 268 cm²

6. 13

7. 976 cm²

8. 8602 cm²

9. (a) 99.5 m²
(b) 16.6 kg
(c) $24.70

10. (a) 12.18 m²
(b) 22.14 m²
(c) 9.96 m²

11. 16.5 cm

12. 6.5 cm

13. (a) 92.3 m²
(b) $119.70

14. 435.6 cm²

Page 351

2. (a) 3217 cm²
(b) 980 cm²
(c) 136 cm²
(d) 13 m²

3. 778 cm²

4. 131.9 cm²

5. 2463 cm²

6. 3.35 m²

7. 94.2 cm²

8. $1428.90

9. 1863 cm²

10. 47.5 m²

11. 33 cm²

12. $2118.69

13. (a) $869.35 cm²
(b) $60.85

14. 18 530 cm²

Page 355

3. (a) 2787 cm³
(b) 195 cm³
(c) 3136 cm³
(d) 11 m³
(e) 107 cm³
(f) 309 cm³

4. (a) 7.5 cm
(b) 3.82 cm
(c) 4.15 cm
(d) 13.8 cm

5. 284 L

6. 47

7. $1224.50

8. 402 L

9. (a) 532 cm³
(b) 93 cm³

10. 0.024 m³

11. 222 cm³

12. (a) 40.23 m³
(b) 242.2 m³

13. 0.36 m³

14. 7854 m³

Page 359

1. 16.6 m

2. 23 km²

3. 80 min

4. (a) 3360
    (b) 70 h

5. 272 cm

6. 5027 cm²

7. 2597 cm²

8. 85.2 m

9. 2.26 m

10. (a) 750 m
    (b) 9375 m²

11. 175 kL

12. (a) 68 m³
    (b) 49.24 m³
    (c) $3545.28

13. (a) 191 cm³
    (b) 687.6 g

14. (a) 348.5 cm³
    (b) 557 cm²

15. 83 907 cm³

Page 361

1. 118 cm²

2. (a) right-angled triangles
    (b) 35.3 cm
    (d) spiral

3. 41 cm

4. 135 m

5. 8 cm

6. 30

7. $12

8. (c) 65 kg/cm²

9. sphere: 4189 cm³
cylinder: 6284 cm³
cone: 2093 cm³

10.

11. (a) $400
    (b) 82.2 kL
    (c) about 86.5 h
    (d) 95.8 m²

Page 363

1. (a) 60 cm; 92 cm²
    (b) 67.1 cm; 235.6 cm²
    (c) 44 m; 60 m²
    (d) 60.9 cm; 230.5 cm²
    (e) 30.1 m; 26.7 m²
    (f) 112 cm; 600 cm²

2. 8.1 m

3. 213 m

4. 53.54 m²

5. (a) 1036 cm²
    (b) 3284 cm²
    (c) 176 cm
    (d) 92 cm

6. (a) 33.18 m²
    (b) 53.4 m²
    (c) $1800

7. 2.43 cm²

8. 1716 cm²

9. 703.7 cm²

10. (a) 24 m²
    (b) 6 m³

11. 27 cm

12. (a) 1256.6 m²
    (b) 51
    (c) $966.45
    (d) 4188.8 kL

13. (a) 96.5 m²
    (b) 87.2 m³
    (c) 104.6 t

14. (a) 4524 kL
    (b) $1750

15. (a) 1344 cm³
    (b) 1200 cm³
    (c) 366 cm³
    (d) 34 m³

16. (a) 10 m
    (b) 6 m
    (c) 7 cm
    (d) 13.5 cm
    (e) 9.2 m
    (f) 11 cm

17. 9668 L

18. yes (V = 2.6 L)

19. 14

20. 276 m³

21. 84.75 kL

22. (a) $2537
    (b) $14 176
    (c) $26 332
    (d) $21 544

23. (a) 96.17 m³
    (b) 11.23 m³

Unit 19

Page 369

4. (a) 13.125
    (b) 19.25
    (c) 6
    (d) 11.6
    (e) 1.37
    (f) 2.375
    (g) 11.6
    (h) 1.37
    (i) 24.26
    (j) 7.83
    (k) 2.375
    (l) 2.05

5. $60.48

6. 304 r/min

7. 3 : 4; 2 : 3; 7 : 10; 1 : 2

8. 16 : 25

9. A:117; B:52

10. Bat: $22.05; Glove: $28.35

Side Trip
21.1 cm

Page 371

3. (a) $x = 20$; $y = 60$
(b) $m = 5\frac{1}{11}$; $k = 20\frac{3}{7}$
(c) $r = 128$; $s = 11.43$
(d) $a = 8\frac{8}{9}$; $b = 15\frac{3}{4}$
(e) $p = 3\frac{11}{15}$; $q = 25\frac{5}{7}$
(f) $r = 29$; $t = 1.5$
(g) $x = -5.6$; $w = 3.375$

4. 52 cm; 65 cm

5. (a) 7.2 kg; 3.6 kg
(b) 13.5 kg

6. 3300; 495; 1815

7. 76; 114; 95

8. (a) 360 g; 240 g
(b) 6.52 kg; 4.35 kg; 1.63 kg

9. 18.36 t; 12.24 t; 16.2 t

10. $25 548; $17 032

11. (a) 6.25 kg; 8.75 kg
(b) 21 kg; 8.75 kg; 12.25 kg

12. 2800; 10 200; 5000

Page 374

2. (a) 4¢/g
(b) $1.39/g
(c) 5¢/g
(d) 55¢/g
(e) 2¢/g

3. 0.21¢/mL

4. (a) $1.30/kg
(b) $32.48
(c) 30.8 kg

5. Chris earns $0.25 more per hour.

6. (a) 7.9 L/100 km; 5.4 L/100 km; 10.1 L/100 km
(b) 632 L; 432 L; 808 L
(c) $204.61; $139.86; $261.59

7. (a) 102
(b) 734.4 cm
(c) 1938

8. 31.2 a

9. 8 m³/h

10. 730 kg/a; 365 000 000 kg; 18 250 000 000 kg

11. 12 cm³

Page 376

1. (a) f/3.5
(b) f/5.6
(c) f/8
(d) f/11
(e) f/16
(f) f/22

2. 135 mm

3. 12.5 mm

Page 377

1. (a) yes
(b) no
(c) no
(d) yes

2. (a) 5 : 2
(b) $\frac{9}{16}$
(c) 10 : 3
(d) $\frac{3}{4}$

3. (a) 14
(b) 54
(c) 3
(d) $\frac{7}{8}$
(e) 3.4
(f) 3.4
(g) 4
(h) 8
(i) 25.5
(j) $m = 21$; $n = 17$
(k) $k = \frac{6}{7}$; $y = \frac{35}{2}$
(l) $a = 14.7$; $b = 0.4$

4. (a) 4.00 : 1
(b) 4.27 : 1
(c) 3.50 : 1
(d) 3.33 : 1
(e) 4.17 : 1

5. 8.8 : 1

6. $13.30; $38

7. (a) 1 : 2
(b) 1 : 4
(c) 1 : 8

8. $9120; $6080

9. 461; 322; 46

10. (a) Ernie
(b) 25

11. 6.49; 0.72; 1.71; 0.93; 1.46

12. 122 min

13. (a) $7.21/kg
(b) $6.06
(c) 1.66 kg

14. 113 a

Unit 20

Page 382

2. (a) 21
(b) 4
(c) 4.5
(d) 8.6
(e) 1.3
(f) 46.1

3. (a) 3
(b) 0.6
(c) 0.6
(d) 2.1

4. (a) $m \propto w$; $m = kw$
(b) 2.5
(c) $m = 2.5w$
(d) 12.5; 23.75; 4; 14

5. (a) $\frac{s_1}{s_2} = \frac{p_1}{p_2}$
(b)

S	8	16	12	40
P	11	22	16.5	55

6. (a) 18
(b) 10
(c) 20.46

7. (a) $c \propto n$; $c = kn$
(b) 12
(c) $1440
(e) 12
(f) The cost for each guest is $12.

8. (a) $t = kd$
(b) 3
(c) 6 s; 10.2 s; 21 s

9. (a) $C = kd$
(b) 3.14
(c) 28.3 cm
(d) 6 cm

10. (a) $p = kd$
(b) 43.3
(c) 606.2 kPa

11. (a) $V = kI$
(b) 2.25
(c) 27 V

12. (a) $T = ka$ (c) \$1425
(b) 0.15 (d) \$8300

13. (a) $m = kv$ (c) 700 g
(b) 1.18 (d) 504.2 cm^3

14. 850 g

Page 386

4. (a) $C = 10t + 25$
(b) \$95

5. (a) $I = 0.10S + 800$
(b) \$1770

6. (a) $C = kn + F$
(b) 5
(c) $C = 5n + 120$
(d) \$5120

7. (a) $C = kN + F$
(b) $k = 6; F = 50$
(c) $C = 6N + 50$
(d) The value of k represents the cost per guest.
(e) \$3050

8. (a) $C = Kt + F$
(b) $k = 200; F = 50$
(c) $C = 200t + 50$
(d) The value of k represents the cost per day of operating the slide.
(e) \$4050

9. (a) $P = 10d + 100$
(b) 240 kPa

10. (a) $C = kd + F$
(b) $k = 0.07; F = 3100$
(c) $C = 0.07d + 3100$

Page 389

2. (a)

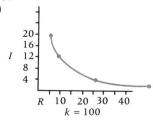

$k = 100$

(b)

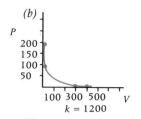

$k = 1200$

(c)

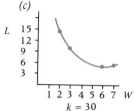

$k = 30$

3. (a)

a	2	5	8	2.2
b	10	4	2.5	9.2

(b)

T	4	8	6	20
S	240	120	160	48

(c)

T	15	3	40	1.05
P	42	210	15600	

4. (a) $IR = k$
(b) 80
(c) $IR = 80$
(d) 16
(e) 0.0016 A

5. (a) $tw = k$
(b) 0.36
(c) $tw = 0.36$
(d) 0.03 cm
(e) 7.2 min

6. (a) $sn = k$
(b) 9720
(c) 27

7. (a) $ts = k$
(b) 320
(c) 3.6 h; 3.2 h
(d) 107 km; 64 km; 71 km

8. (a) $vL = k$
(b) 75 000
(c) 18.75 cm; 12.5 cm

Page 392

2. (a) $x = k\frac{y}{w}$ (d) 2.3
(b) 2 (e) 42
(c) $x = 2\frac{y}{w}$ (f) 4

3. (a) $r = (k\frac{s^2}{t})$ (c) $\frac{8s^2}{t}$
(b) 8 (d) 32

4. 20

5. 1.2 A

6. 346.5

Page 393

1. 3 ways

2. 7 ways

3. 4

Side Trip

1. 9 ways

2. 22 ways

Page 394

1. (a) $x = ky$
(b) $q = k\frac{1}{t}$
(c) $f = k\frac{m}{a}$
(d) $a = kF$
(e) $V = \frac{k}{t}$
(f) $d = ka$

2. (a)

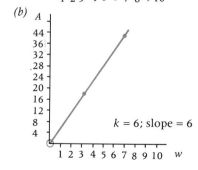

$k = 4$; slope = 4

(b)

$k = 6$; slope = 6

3. (a) $A = kB$
   (b) 5
   (c) $A = 5B$
   (d) 20, 31.5; 9, 2.5

4. 63

5. 30 L

6. 96 kg

7. 75 N

8. (a) 270 km
   (c) 45; the slope represents the number of kilometres driven per hour.

9. (a) $C = 0.15n + 20$
   (b) \$245

10. (a) $C = kn + F$
   (b) 0.20
   (c) \$5800

11. (a) $C = kN + F$
   (b) $k = 25$; $F = 400$
   (c) $C = 25N + 400$
   (d) The value of k represents the cost for each person.
   (e) \$925

12. (a) $C = kV + F$
   (b) $k = 2$; $F = 50$
   (c) \$72

13. (a)

   (b)

14. (a) $t = k\frac{1}{s}$
   (b) 325
   (c) 3.6 *h*

15. 16 min

16. \$1065

17. 56 kPa

18. (a) 1120 Ω
   (b) 1.8 A

19. (a) $A = k\frac{t}{w}$ (c) $A = \frac{15t}{w}$
   (b) 15   (d) 27

20. 6 h

21. 80 mL

Unit 21

Page 400
3. (a) 16.8   (c) 1.4
   (b) 8.9   (d) 20.6

4. 11.25m

5. 8.62 m

6. 8 m

7. 7.2 m

8. 6.25 m

9. 47 m

10. 2.71 m

Side Trip
134 m

Page 405
1. (a) 1.8   (c) 14.3
   (b) 14.4   (d) 41.2

2. 106 m

3. 86.6 m

4. 510 m

Page 407
4. (a) 2.9
   (b) 114.3

5. (a) 14.3   (e) 3.4
   (b) 38.6   (f) 23.6
   (c) 5.6   (g) 9.8
   (d) 20.8

6. 9.7 m

7. (a) 9.2 m
   (b) 18.4 m

8. 143 km

9. 96 km

10. 59.7 m

11. (a) 0.5
   (b) 27°

Page 413
5. (a) $\sin K = \frac{12}{15}$, $\cos K = \frac{9}{15}$, $\tan K = \frac{12}{9}$; $\sin M = \frac{9}{15}$, $\cos M = \frac{12}{15}$, $\tan M = \frac{9}{12}$
   (b) $\sin S = \frac{7}{8.1}$, $\cos S = \frac{4}{8.1}$, $\tan S = \frac{7}{4}$; $\sin T = \frac{4}{8.1}$, $\cos T = \frac{7}{8.1}$, $\tan T = \frac{4}{7}$

6. (a) $\sin S = \frac{12}{13}$, $\cos S = \frac{5}{13}$, $\tan S = \frac{12}{5}$; $\sin R = \frac{5}{13}$, $\cos R = \frac{12}{13}$, $\tan R = \frac{5}{12}$
   (b) $\sin K = \frac{9}{20}$, $\cos K = \frac{17.9}{20}$, $\tan K = \frac{9}{17.9}$; $\sin L = \frac{17.9}{20}$, $\cos L = \frac{9}{20}$, $\tan L = \frac{17.9}{9}$
   (c) $\sin B = \frac{8}{17}$, $\cos B = \frac{15}{17}$, $\tan B = \frac{8}{15}$; $\sin C = \frac{15}{17}$, $\cos C = \frac{8}{17}$, $\tan C = \frac{15}{8}$
   (d) $\sin F = \frac{20}{25}$, $\cos F = \frac{15}{25}$, $\tan F = \frac{20}{15}$; $\sin G = \frac{15}{25}$, $\cos G = \frac{20}{25}$, $\tan G = \frac{15}{20}$

7. (a) 13.0   (c) 18.1
   (b) 4.1   (d) 8.6

8. (a) 12.9   (d) 22.1
   (b) 2.3   (e) 3.4
   (c) 6.3   (f) 24.0

9. (a) 21.9   (d) 3.5
   (b) 7.5   (e) 13.0
   (c) 4.6   (f) 7.1

10. 34.3 m

11. 3.9 m

12. (a) 23.8
   (b) 11.8

Side Trip
1. 189.2

2. 141.2

Page 415
1. (a) 0.500   (d) 0.358
   (b) 0.602   (e) 0.404
   (c) 1.000   (f) 0.978

2. (a) 25° (d) 27°
    (b) 61° (e) 8°
    (c) 49° (f) 19°

Page 417

4. (a) 0.799 (f) 1.414
    (b) 1.305 (g) 5.671
    (c) 2.145 (h) 3.864
    (d) 0.966 (i) 1.280
    (e) 2.924 (j) 2.669

5. (a) 3.8   (d) 18.9
    (b) 20.0 (e) 4.4
    (c) 10.7 (f) 14.0

6. (a) 19.6
    (b) 27.3
    (c) 6.4
    (d) 17.7
    (e) $a = 7.8; b = 12.7$
    (f) $x = 13.3; y = 17.9$

7. 11.7 m

8. 10.6 m; 9.4 m

9. (a) 709 m
    (b) 111 m

10. 24 m

11. (a) 26.4 m
    (b) 25.3 m

12. 3583 m

Page 421

2. (a) 10.2
    (b) 7.1
    (c) 62°
    (d) 23.6
    (e) $b = 19.2; x = 40°; c = 16.1$
    (f) $x = 28.9$

3. (a) $AB = 11.2, BC = 16.6, \angle A = 56°$
    (b) $DF = 10.3, EF = 7.5, \angle F = 43°$
    (c) $LM = 15.3, \angle L = 58°, \angle M = 32°$
    (d) $PQ = 8, \angle R = 53°, \angle Q = 37°$
    (e) $TU = 5.1, SU = 1.06, \angle U = 78°$
    (f) $HJ = 14.3, \angle J = 40°, \angle G = 50°, GJ = 18.7$

4. (a) $\angle C = 48°, AB = 5.2, BC = 4.7$
    (b) $\angle K = 26°, KN = 16.7, EN = 7.3$

(c) $\angle U = 61°, \angle S = 29°, SU = 10.3$
(d) $\angle Z = 19°, \angle E = 71°, NZ = 11.3$
(e) $\angle J = 48°, JO = 6.0, ON = 6.7$

5. 38.3 m

6. 14.1 m

7. from *A*: 1.11 km; from *B*: 1.7 km

8. 59 m

9. 2986 m

10. 821 m

11. 10°

12. (a) 95 m
    (b) 107.6 m
    (c) 577.6 m; 14 250 m²

13. 24.8°

14. (a) 74°
    (b) 25 mm

15. 14°

16. 10 cm

17. 1.7 cm

18. 78.1 m

Page 424

1. (a) 15′ (e) 47°21′
    (b) 45′ (f) 38°39′
    (c) 12°30′ (g) 73°23′
    (d) 23°42′ (h) 54°43′

2. (a) 43.5° (d) 75.8°
    (b) 32.3° (e) 23.2°
    (c) 5.75° (f) 54.4°

3. (a) 0.5807 (f) 1.1152
    (b) 0.9222 (g) 0.9121
    (c) 0.1644 (h) 0.8045
    (d) 0.6713 (i) 0.9928
    (e) 0.8426 (j) 0.4589

Page 425

4. (a) 61°23′ (e) 7°45′
    (b) 54°9′ (f) 23°42′
    (c) 58°40′ (g) 26°42′
    (d) 75°55′ (h) 32°10′

5. (a) 38°25′12″ (c) 55°21′
    (b) 2°22′48″ (d) 25°10′48″

6. (a) 26°56′57″ (c) 28°30′39″
    (b) 69°56′47″ (d) 63°15′55″

7. (a) 0.415 (c) 0.912
    (b) 0.253 (d) 0.981

Page 427

1. 151.8 m
2. 102.4 m
3. 81.9 m
4. 71.9 m

Left plot of land: $AB = 217$ m, $BC = 177$ m, Area = 16 619.8 m² Right plot of land: $PQ = 155.6$ m, $RS = 133.4$ m, area of $PQRS = 26\ 224$

Area = 20 750 m²

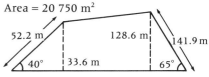

52.2 m   128.6 m   141.9 m
40°   33.6 m   65°

Page 428

1. (a) 5.8; sin B = 0.862, cos B = 0.517, tan B = 1.667
    (b) 10.9; sin D = 0.908, cos D = 0.417, tan D = 2.180

2. (a) $a = 8.7; b = 10$
    (b) $s = 2.8; t = 7.8$
    (c) $h = 13.8; k = 19.7$
    (d) $v = 14.0; u = 20.5$

3. (a) 37° (b) 40°

4. (a) $\angle C = 58°; AC = 9.4; BC = 5.0$
    (b) $\angle D = 30°; \angle F = 60°, DF = 13.9$
    (c) $\angle R = 48°; QR = 10.0; QP = 11.1$
    (d) $\angle N = 76°; \angle L = 14°; LM = 19.4$

5. 11.1 m
6. 41.2 m
7. 82°
8. 37.5 m
9. 1717.3 m
10. 1923.2 m
11. 2.7 m
12. 13.6 m; 14.8 m
13. 25°
14. 650 m
15. 1420 m
16. (a) 4.4 m (b) 30°
17. 10°
18. 5.9 cm
19. $\angle A = 58°; \angle B = 32°$
20. 6.9 cm
21. 8.4 cm
22. 33.9 cm
23. 16°

Units 16 to 21 Review

2. *(a)* 58, 61, 61   *(b)* 12.0, 11.95, 11.6 or 12.8

1. *(a)* $1.10 to $4.90
   (b) $0.48 rounded to $0.50

(c)

Amount Spent	Tally	Frequency	Cumulative Frequency
$1.00 to $1.50	///	3	3
$1.50 to $2.00	⟋⟋⟋⟋ ///	8	11
$2.00 to $2.50	⟋⟋⟋⟋ ⟋⟋⟋⟋ ///	13	24
$2.50 to $3.00	⟋⟋⟋⟋ ⟋⟋⟋⟋ //	12	36
$3.00 to $3.50	⟋⟋⟋⟋	5	41
$3.50 to $4.00	⟋⟋⟋⟋	5	46
$4.00 to $4.50	//	2	48
$4.50 to $5.00	//	2	50

(d)

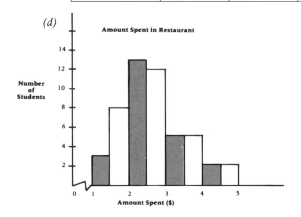

(e)

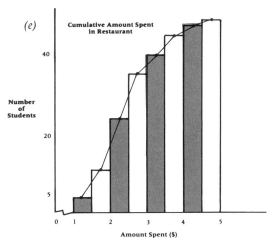

3.

No. of Accidents	Frequency	Cumulative Frequency	Product
0	25	25	0
1	40	65	40
2	33	98	66
3	31	129	93
4	29	158	116
5	21	179	105
6	16	195	96
7	4	199	28
8	1	200	8

mean $\frac{552}{200} \doteq 3$ median 3   mode 1

4.

No. of Books Read	Class Value	Frequency	Cumulative Frequency	Product Class Value × Frequency
0 to 3	1.5	36	36	54
3 to 6	4.5	32	68	144
6 to 9	7.5	14	82	105
9 to 12	10.5	8	90	84
12 to 15	13.5	6	96	81
15 to 18	16.5	5	101	82.5
18 to 21	19.5	3	104	58.5

mean 6   median 3 to 6   mode 0 to 3

5. *(a)*

Month	Sales	Cumulative Frequency	a) Cumulative Average	b) 3-month Moving Average
April	$3800	3 800	3800	—
May	$5200	9 000	4500	—
June	$2800	11 800	$\doteq$3930	3930
July	$2100	13 900	3475	3370
Aug.	$1900	15 800	3160	2270
Sept.	$2500	18 300	$\doteq$2610	2170
Oct.	$1700	20 000	2500	2030

(b)

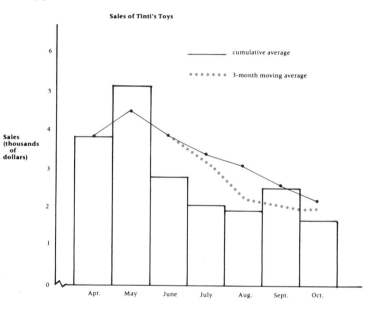

Sales of Tinti's Toys

(c) Answers will vary

6. *(a)* $a = 48°$
   $b = 132°$
   (b) $c = 42°$
   $d = 138°$
   $e = 42°$
   (c) $f = 68°$
   $g = 56°$
   (d) $h = 46°$
   (e) $j = 20°$
   $k = 40°$
   (f) $m = 90°$
   $n = 31°$
   (g) $p = 112°$
   (h) $q = 31°$
   $r = 31°$
   (i) $s = 70°$
   $t = 110°$
   (j) $u = 45°$
   $v = 90°$
   (k) $w = 50°$
   $x = 130°$
   (l) $y = 56°$
   $z = 68°$
   (m) $a = 33°$
   $b = 90°$
   $c = 33°$
   (n) $c = 130°$
   $d = 25°$

7. $a = 51°$, $b = 51°$, $c = 39°$

8. $36°$

9. *(a)* $x \doteq 19$ *(b)* $m \doteq 19$

10. 38.5 cm

11. 30×30 (cm)

12. *(a)* 2.8 m   *(b)* 7.5 m

13. *(a)* ASA congruence.
   $x = 22$, $y = 35$
   (b) SAS congruence.
   $x = 40°$, $y = 8$

14.   Perimeter   Area
   (a) $32 + 8\pi$ cm 64π cm²
   (b) 124 m   560 m²
   (c) 40 cm   88 cm²
   (d) $28 + 10\pi$ cm $98 + 98\pi$ cm²
   (nearest whole numbers)

15. 184.9 cm

16. 647 cm²

17. 10 litres

18. 158 m³

19. *(a)* 263 cm²   *(b)* 15.40 m²

20. *(a)* 161 m²   *(b)* 24 minutes

21. *(a)* 696 cm³   *(b)* 650 cm²

22. *(a)* 27   *(h)* $\frac{7}{3}$
   (b) 12   *(i)* $m = 22$
   (c) $\frac{5}{2}$ $n = 12$
   (d) 144   *(j)* $v = 6$
   (e) 2.8 $w = 7\frac{1}{2}$
   (f) 18   *(k)* $s = 1.3$
   (g) 11 $t = 7.2$

23. tin : 1.75 kg   lead : 1.05 kg

24. hat $45   coat $165

25. 360 000 : 135 000 : 45 000

26. A 1.7¢/mL
   B $3.15/kg
   C 93.1¢/L
   D 0.9¢g

27. 1 : 2; 1 : 4; 1 : 8

28. *(a)* $1.28/kg
   (b) $12.80
   (c) 22 kg

29. (a) $a = \frac{k}{b}$
(b) $p = \frac{kq}{r}$
(c) $i = kt$
(d) $R = \frac{kV}{I}$

30. (a) $a = 9 \quad b = 30$
(b) $m = 0.75 \quad n = 2.4$

31. 3

32. (a) 3 hours (b) 48 km/h

33. (a) after 10 minutes (b) 4 m

34. (a) $m = kv$; $k = 1.8$
(b) 900 g
(c) 650 cm³
(d) slope is 1.8, the value of k

35. (a) $C = 300 + 12.50N$
(b) \$1362.50 (c) 136

36. (a) $A = \frac{kB}{C}$ (b) $k = \frac{3}{2}$
(c) $A = \frac{3B}{2C}$ (d) 4
(e) 465.6 (f) 9

37. (a) $\sin B = 0.769$; $\cos B = 0.641$;
$\tan B = 1.2$
(using 11.7 for hypotenuse BC)
(b) $\sin N = 0.847$;
$\cos N = 0.530$;
$\tan N = 1.599$
(using 22.7 for MK)

38. (a) $a = 12.7$; $b = 14.6$
(b) $c = 48.4$; $d = 50.6$

39. (a) 38° (b) 31°

40. (a) $\angle A = 62°$, $BC = 32.0$,
$AC = 36.2$
(b) $\angle N = 35°$, $MN = 29.5$,
$KM = 20.7$
(c) $\angle Z = 21°$, $YZ = 117.2$,
$XZ = 125.6$

41. 7 m

42. $AB = 50.7$ m; $AC = 56.1$ m

43. 4.6 cm

44. (a) 73° (b) 13.1 m

45. (a) 25.6 m (b) 33.1 m

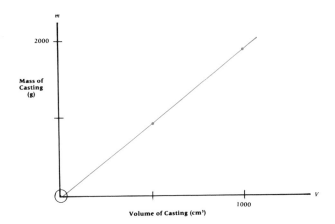

Index